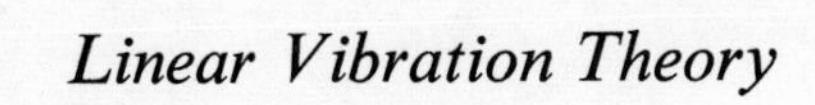

Linear Vibration Theory

Linear Vibration Theory

GENERALIZED PROPERTIES AND
NUMERICAL METHODS

James B. Vernon
University of Southern California
Los Angeles

JOHN WILEY & SONS, INC. New York · London · Sydney

LIBRARY OF CONGRESS CATALOG CARD NUMBER: 66–26760
PRINTED IN THE UNITED STATES OF AMERICA

Preface

This book, with a companion volume, *Linear Vibration and Control System Theory, Computer Applications*, is the outgrowth of notes written to explain the practical uses of "generalized" quantities, numerical methods, and computers in the analysis of complex linear, mechanical systems. As a result of consultation and classroom experience, I became aware of an apparent discontinuity in the level of proficiency required to understand the idealized situations often discussed in the classroom and the complex problems encountered in practice. One objective has been to bridge this gap and, for this reason, both volumes are addressed to the senior undergraduate or first-year graduate student, and to the practicing engineer.

In this text, emphasis is placed on the theory pertaining to linear, mechanical vibration, especially as applied to complex systems, although several early chapters are devoted to an explanation of elementary vibration theory. Extensive use is made of the generalized coordinate concept, and one of my intentions is to make this a familiar and easily used tool in the analysis of complex systems. Numerical methods appropriate to vibration analysis are emphasized and explained in considerable detail.

The subjects selected for discussion are those thought to be consistent with the intended objectives, although a few short topics are included simply because they are often encountered. Certain important aspects of vibration theory are omitted in the interests of economy; notably, random vibration theory, which would require too much space for a thorough treatment, and nonlinear theory, which is outside the scope of the book.

The methods employed in this book are among those commonly used in engineering and applied mathematics, although there are instances where they have been modified or extended to suit a particular purpose. These methods have generally evolved with usage, so that in the form presented they are attributable to numerous anonymous inventors rather than to a single easily identified source. The book, although mathematical in nature, has been written with the purpose of providing explanation and enlightenment, and thus, a reasonable compromise between practical utilization and mathematical rigor has been attempted. I hope that this will be helpful to the reader in achieving a good degree of understanding.

For full comprehension of the mathematics employed, the reader should be familiar with the use of Laplace transforms, complex variables, and matrix algebra. Although these subjects are believed to be in the repertoire of the intended audience, they and several other subjects are reviewed in considerable detail in Appendix 1.

The problems that have been suggested often provide important extensions of the text material. Some are "project-type" problems, requiring perhaps days or weeks to complete. The reader is urged to give his attention to these, as well as to the simpler ones, and at least formulate a method of solution even if he does not actually complete the solution.

This book could be used as a textbook for either a first or second course in vibration theory, or for a two-course sequence. Division of the book for this purpose could logically occur at the end of Chapter 8, 9, or 10, depending on the preparation of the student. Selected parts of Appendix 1 could be included in the first course, if a review of the appropriate mathematics is deemed advisable.

The purpose of the companion volume, *Linear Vibration and Control System Theory, Computer Applications*, is to relate useful topics in control-system theory to the material usually associated with the study of mechanical vibration, and to explain the use of digital and analogue computers in the utilization of the numerical methods of this book. Transparent overlays for frequency-response analysis and FORTRAN programs for solution of commonly occurring problems are furnished in appendices.

Individual acknowledgement of former students who have been of assistance to me was originally intended, but this has become impractical because of the numbers involved. Their criticisms and suggestions are appreciated. Special thanks are extended to Dr C. R. Freberg for his suggestions and encouragement, to Harry Himelblau for his helpful and significant comments, and to Louise Maurer for her assistance with the manuscript.

James B. Vernon

Contents

Recommended General References

The following short list of references is given for those who would like additional explanation of topics related to the ones discussed in the text. The list is deliberately abbreviated to several books in each of the appropriate areas. Although many of these references are cited in the text, the list is intended primarily for general reference.

1. Vernon, James B., *Linear Vibration and Control System Theory, Computer Applications*, John Wiley and Sons, Inc., New York, 1967.
2. Freberg, C. R., and E. N. Kemler, *Elements of Mechanical Vibration*, second edition, John Wiley and Sons, Inc., New York, 1949.
3. Tong, Kin N., *Theory of Mechanical Vibration*, John Wiley and Sons, Inc., New York, 1960.
4. Morrow, Charles T., *Shock and Vibration Engineering*, John Wiley and Sons, Inc., New York, 1963.
5. Tse, Francis S., Ivan E. Morse, and Rolland T. Hinkle, *Mechanical Vibrations*, Allyn and Bacon, Inc., Boston, 1963.
6. Wylie, C. R., Jr., *Advanced Engineering Mathematics*, second edition, McGraw–Hill Book Company, Inc., New York, 1960.
7. Kreyszig, Erwin, *Advanced Engineering Mathematics*, John Wiley and Sons, Inc., New York, 1962.
8. Hildebrand, Francis B., *Methods of Applied Mathematics*, Prentice–Hall, Inc., Englewood Cliffs, 1952.
9. Churchill, Ruel V., *Complex Variables and Applications*, second edition, McGraw–Hill Book Company, Inc., New York, 1960.
10. Pipes, Louis A., *Matrix Methods for Engineering*, Prentice–Hall, Inc., Englewood Cliffs, 1963.
11. Pestel, Edward C., and Frederick A. Leckie, *Matrix Methods in Elastomechanics*, McGraw–Hill Book Company, Inc., New York, 1963.

CHAPTER 1

Equations of Motion for the Single-Degree-of-Freedom System

1.1 Differential Equations of Motion for Single-Degree System

One of the purposes of this text is to explain the use of generalized properties in the analysis of complex systems. This often results in the treatment of a complex system as if it were an equivalent single-degree-of-freedom system. Consequently, a thorough understanding of the single-degree system is an essential preliminary to the investigation of more advanced topics. This chapter explains the origin of the equations which describe the motion. Chapters 2 to 5 investigate other aspects of simple systems.

Assumptions and Definitions. Perhaps the simplest vibration problem which can be proposed is illustrated in Fig. 1-1, which represents a mass, m, attached by a spring to a wall. The mass is supported by frictionless and weightless wheels against the force of

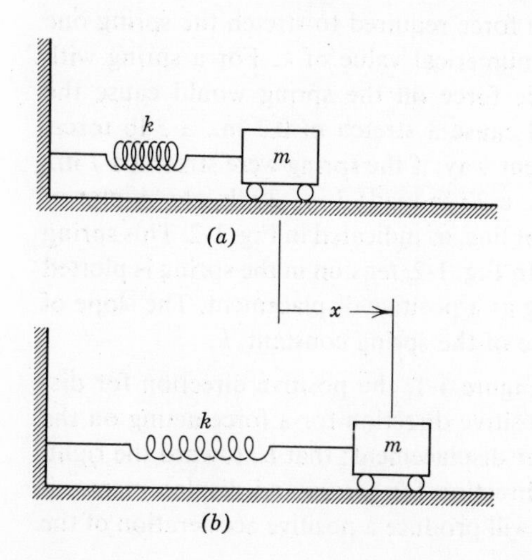

Fig. 1-1 Spring-mass system (a) Mass at rest. (b) Mass displaced

gravity in this idealized problem, so that gravity will have no effect on the motion of the mass to the right and left in the problem proposed, and the wheels are guided so that the mass cannot move in or out of the plane of the figure. Also, the spring is imagined to be supported and guided without friction in a tube (not shown) so that it will not sag under gravity forces or buckle if it is compressed. In addition to this the spring itself is assumed to have negligible mass compared to m. This system is therefore restrained to only one type of motion, to the right and left in the plane of the figure. Figure 1-1*a* shows the mass at rest with the spring unstressed. Figure 1-1*b* shows the mass in a displaced position and the spring stretched. It is possible to define the position of the mass and the stretch of the spring in this system by assigning a number to the distance, x. The coordinate, x, is therefore defined as the distance from the equilibrium position of the mass to the deflected position of the mass, and will have a positive value when the mass is to the right of the equilibrium position. Thus, when $x = 2$, the mass is two units to the right of the equilibrium position and the spring is stretched two units. When $x = -1$, the mass is to the left of the equilibrium position and the spring is compressed one unit. Such a system is an example of a single-degree-of-freedom system.

A system is said to have a single degree of freedom if only one coordinate is required to completely define the configuration of the system at a given instant.

Linear Spring. In the problem under study, the spring is indicated by the symbol, k. This is the symbol usually assigned to represent the "spring constant," "spring rate,"

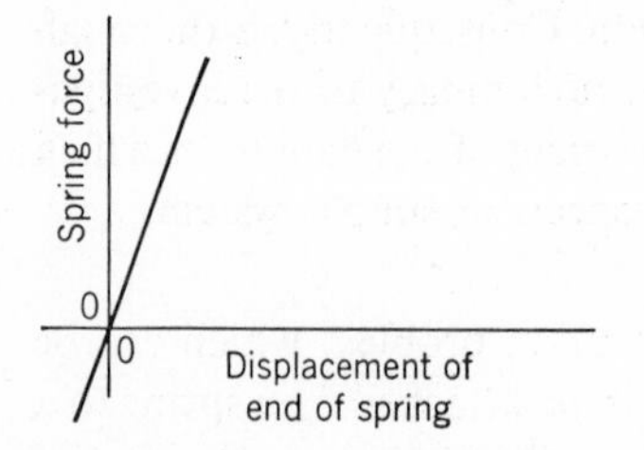

Fig. 1-2 Characteristics of a linear spring

or "spring stiffness," which is defined as the force required to stretch the spring one unit. A positive sign is associated with the numerical value of k. For a spring with spring constant, $k = 10$ lb/in., a 1-lb tensile force on the spring would cause the spring to stretch 0.1 in. A 2-lb force would cause a stretch of 0.2 in., a 3-lb force, 0.3 in., etc. Or, looking at it a slightly different way, if the spring were stretched 1 in., it would exert a 10-lb load; if stretched 2 in., a 20-lb load; 3 in., 30 lb, etc. A plot of the force exerted by the spring shows a straight line, as indicated in Fig. 1-2. This spring is therefore referred to as a "linear" spring. In Fig. 1-2, tension in the spring is plotted as a positive load, and a stretch of the spring as a positive displacement. The slope of the line is determined by the numerical value of the spring constant, k.

Newton's Law and Sign Conventions. In Figure 1-1, the positive direction for displacement, x, is toward the right. Let the positive direction for a force acting on the mass be the same as the positive direction for displacement; that is, toward the right. By virtue of the definition of the positive direction for forces and displacements, it can be said that a positive force on the mass will produce a positive acceleration of the mass, and a negative force on the mass will produce a negative acceleration. The acceleration in this problem is denoted by the second derivative of the displacement with respect to time; that is, d^2x/dt^2, which may take on various numerical values according to the magnitude of the force and depending on whether the force is positive or negative. In this problem, if the mass were considered a free body, there is only one force acting on the mass. This is the force exerted by the spring, and its magnitude is kx. However, since a positive force is defined as toward the right, it is clear that when x is positive the force which the spring exerts on the mass is toward the left and therefore negative. (In order to avoid possible confusion, it should be noted that if the force exerted by the spring on the mass were plotted as a function of x, the slope of the graph would be the negative of that of Fig. 1-2.) Newton's law for this system is mass times acceleration of mass (in the positive x direction) equals force (on mass in the positive x direction) or, at the instant depicted in Fig. 1-1*b*,

$$m\frac{d^2x}{dt^2} = -kx \tag{1-1}$$

Now, as a final check on the signs, Equation 1-1 should be tested to see if it is correct. If the numerical value of x is positive, as in Fig. 1-1, Equation 1-1 says the acceleration of the mass is negative or toward the left. This agrees with the physical fact that when x is positive the spring is in tension and produces a force toward the left on the mass. On the other hand, if the numerical value of x were negative, the spring would be compressed and would exert a force toward the right, which is positive, and agrees with the sign obtained from Equation 1-1 for x negative. Thus, even if the original deflected position had been chosen so that the mass were displaced to the left, the same differential equation would result. The differential equation should be the same regardless of the configuration.

This rather lengthy discussion of signs is necessary because it is one of the most common sources of error in the setting up of differential equations from physical problems. Of course, this simple problem affords only slight opportunity for error, but more complex problems can be quite puzzling. In general, the best way to proceed is to sketch the physical problem in some deflected configuration, preferably with all coordinates positive, and then set up the equation or equations for this configuration. After the differential equations are derived, it is wise to check the signs by imagining various numerical values of the coordinates to see if the equations give "sensible" results in all configurations. Of course, as pointed out previously, the same differential equation should result, regardless of the configuration.

General Single-Degree System. The physical problem has now been expressed mathematically in terms of a differential equation. Instead of solving this differential equation, it is convenient to solve the differential equation for a somewhat more general physical problem (Fig. 1-3). In this problem all the remarks which were made in idealizing the problem represented by Fig. 1-1 are applicable, and the only changes are that a "damper," represented by c, and an external force, represented by $f(t)$, have been added. $f(t)$ means "a function of t," and not f times t. Specific functions for $f(t)$ will be assigned in subsequent chapters. Note that the force is a function of time only, and is in no way dependent on the coordinate x.

The damper is represented as a dashpot, and can be thought of that way if desired. The force which the damper exerts depends on the relative *motion* or velocity with which the plunger moves in the cylinder. That is, the force required to move the plunger is a function of dx/dt. If the force exerted by the damper is a "linear damper" or "viscous damper," then the force exerted by the damper can be calculated from $c(dx/dt)$, where c is the proportionality factor, called "damping constant" or "damping coefficient." The dimensions of c would be consistent with dx/dt, so that if x is in inches c would have dimensions of pounds per inch/second.

If it is imagined that at the instant which Fig. 1-3 represents, the velocity of the mass is toward the right, dx/dt is positive and the force exerted by the damper on the mass is toward the left or in the negative direction. Setting mass times acceleration equal to force results in

$$m\frac{d^2x}{dt^2} = -kx - c\frac{dx}{dt} + f(t) \tag{1-2}$$

Again checking to see if the sign is correct, if dx/dt is positive (or the mass is moving toward the right), the damper exerts a force toward the left which would tend to cause a negative acceleration of the mass, and if the mass were moving toward the left (dx/dt negative) the effect of the damper is to produce a positive force on the mass and a positive acceleration, all of which agrees with intuition.

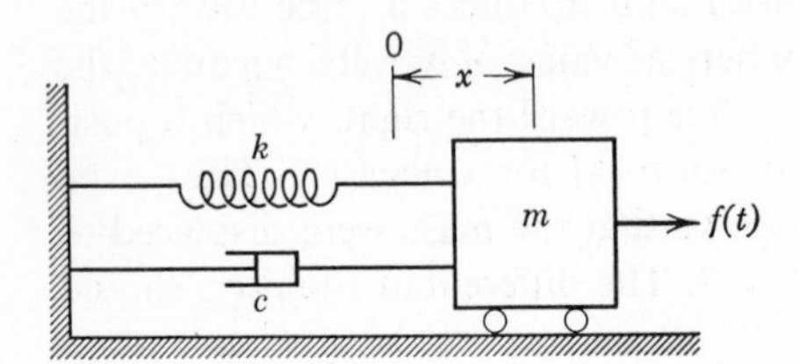

Fig. 1-3 Spring-mass-damper system with forcing function

Equation 1-2 is more general than Equation 1-1, so it is perhaps more convenient to solve Equation 1-2 and then let $c = 0$ and $f(t) = 0$ for the solution of Equation 1-1.

Other examples of physical problems in the category of single-degree-of-freedom systems which lead to an equation similar to Equation 1-2 can be found in the problems for Chapter 5.

The solution of equations similar to Equation 1-2 is discussed in Appendix 1. At this time a discussion of the solution after it has been obtained is of more interest than the method of obtaining the solution. Before proceeding to this discussion, however, it is convenient to rewrite Equation 1-2 in a different form, the utility of which will become evident later. If the terms involving x and its derivatives are transposed to the left side of the equation leaving terms which involve only t on the right side, Equation 1-2 becomes

$$\frac{d^2x}{dt^2} + \frac{c}{m}\frac{dx}{dt} + \frac{k}{m}x = \frac{1}{m}f(t) = \frac{k}{m}\frac{1}{k}f(t) \tag{1-3}$$

This can be written

$$\frac{d^2x}{dt^2} + 2\zeta\beta\frac{dx}{dt} + \beta^2 x = \frac{\beta^2}{k}f(t) \tag{1-4}$$

where

$$\zeta = \frac{c}{2\sqrt{mk}} \equiv \frac{c\beta}{2k} \equiv \frac{c}{2\beta m} \tag{1-5}$$

$$\beta = \sqrt{\frac{k}{m}} \tag{1-6}$$

In this section the formation of the differential equation of motion of a single-degree-of-freedom system from the physical problem has been discussed, using Newton's law: mass times acceleration equals force. In Chapter 7 it is shown that this equation and others representing more complex systems can be derived by use of energy relations.

1.2 Algebraic Equations of Motion for a Free System

Differential equations of the form obtained in the previous section can be solved by techniques discussed in Appendix 1. There is considerable difference in the solution according to whether $f(t)$ is zero. $f(t)$ is an external force on the mass (Fig. 1-3), which varies with time in some manner. Therefore, if $f(t)$ is zero, it is implied that no external force is acting on the system, which is moving "freely" or "naturally." Accordingly, an investigation of the solution when $f(t)$ is zero should lead to an understanding of "free vibration." Intuitively, it is apparent that the mass would not tend to move at all if there is no external force on it, but would merely stay in its position of equilibrium where $x = 0$, unless it were displaced by an external agency and then released. After being released it would move freely. Therefore, the initial displacement, and also the initial velocity, must enter into the equation which describes the motion of the system. If $f(t)$ is zero, Equation 1-4 becomes

$$\frac{d^2x}{dt^2} + 2\zeta\beta\frac{dx}{dt} + \beta^2 x = 0 \tag{1-7}$$

In Appendix 1 it is shown that the solution of this equation is, for $-1 < \zeta < 1$,

$$x = e^{-\zeta\beta t}\left[x_0 \cos(\beta\sqrt{1-\zeta^2}\,t) + \frac{\dot{x}_0 + \zeta\beta x_0}{\beta\sqrt{1-\zeta^2}}\sin(\beta\sqrt{1-\zeta^2}\,t)\right]$$

or

$$x = \sqrt{x_0{}^2 + \frac{(\dot{x}_0 + \zeta\beta x_0)^2}{\beta^2(1-\zeta^2)}}\, e^{-\zeta\beta t}\sin(\beta\sqrt{1-\zeta^2}\,t + \psi) \tag{1-8}$$

where

$$\psi = \tan^{-1}\left(\frac{x_0\beta\sqrt{1-\zeta^2}}{\dot{x}_0 + \zeta\beta x_0}\right)$$

and x_0 and $\dot{x}_0$ are the values of displacement and velocity when $t = 0$.

For $\zeta > 1$, or $\zeta < -1$, the solution becomes

$$x = e^{-\zeta\beta t}\left[x_0 \cosh(\beta\sqrt{\zeta^2-1}\,t) + \frac{\dot{x}_0 + \zeta\beta x_0}{\beta\sqrt{\zeta^2-1}}\sinh(\beta\sqrt{\zeta^2-1}\,t)\right]$$

or

$$x = \left[\frac{\beta(\sqrt{\zeta^2-1}+\zeta)x_0 + \dot{x}_0}{2\beta\sqrt{\zeta^2-1}}\right]e^{-\beta(\zeta-\sqrt{\zeta^2-1})t} + \left[\frac{\beta(\sqrt{\zeta^2-1}-\zeta)x_0 - \dot{x}_0}{2\beta\sqrt{\zeta^2-1}}\right]e^{-\beta(\zeta+\sqrt{\zeta^2-1})t} \tag{1-9}$$

For $\zeta = 1$, the solution is

$$x = [(1 + \beta t)x_0 + \dot{x}_0 t]\, e^{-\beta t} \tag{1-10}$$

For $\zeta = -1$, it is

$$x = [(1 - \beta t)x_0 + \dot{x}_0 t]\, e^{\beta t} \tag{1-11}$$

The condition $\zeta = 1$ corresponds to "critical damping," to be discussed later, and from Equation 1-5 the damping constant for critical damping, c_c, is

$$c_c = 2\sqrt{mk} \equiv \frac{2k}{\beta} \equiv 2m\beta \tag{1-12}$$

CHAPTER 2

Characteristics of Free Vibration of a Single-Degree System

2.1 Free Vibration Without Damping

The equations which describe the free vibration of a single-degree system without damping were developed in Chapter 1. An appreciation of the important parameters which affect the motion of a free system can be gained by an interpretation of these equations. Consider first the free system without damping; that is, let $c = 0$ or $\zeta = 0$ in Equation 1-8. That equation then becomes

$$\left.\begin{aligned} x &= x_0 \cos \beta t + \frac{\dot{x}_0}{\beta} \sin \beta t \\ &\text{or} \\ x &= \sqrt{x_0 + \left(\frac{\dot{x}_0}{\beta}\right)^2} \sin (\beta t + \psi) \\ &\text{where} \\ \psi &= \tan^{-1} \frac{\beta x_0}{\dot{x}_0} \end{aligned}\right\} \qquad (2\text{-}1)$$

Simple Harmonic Motion. It is evident that the motion depends on the initial deflection, x_0, and the initial velocity, $\dot{x}_0$, and that the displacement varies with "simple harmonic motion"; that is, according to a sine or cosine curve when plotted against time. Figure 2-1 shows a plot of the displacement as a function of time.

The dashed curve in this plot shows the variation if there were initial displacement but no initial velocity, and corresponds to the first term of Equation 2-1. The dash-dot curve shows the variation if an initial velocity existed but initial displacement did not, and corresponds to the second term of Equation 2-1. The solid line is the sum of the other two, and corresponds to the motion which would result if the mass had been given both an initial displacement and an initial velocity. The motion is "periodic"; that is, it repeats itself at intervals. When $t = T$ (see Fig. 2-1), the motion starts to repeat itself. The interval T is referred to as the "period" of the oscillation. From the form of Equation 2-1 and from Fig. 2-1, it is clear that $\beta T = 2\pi$, or that the period is given by

$$T = \frac{2\pi}{\beta} = 2\pi\sqrt{\frac{m}{k}} \tag{2-2}$$

Frequency and Amplitude. The "frequency" of a simple harmonic oscillation is the number of times the motion is repeated in one unit of time, often designated in cycles per second. Therefore, since the period is the number of seconds required for the completion of one cycle, the frequency could be obtained from the inverse of the period, or

$$f_n = \frac{1}{T} \equiv \frac{\beta}{2\pi} \equiv \frac{1}{2\pi}\sqrt{\frac{k}{m}} \tag{2-3}$$

where f_n is the "natural frequency," so designated because it is the frequency at which the system would oscillate "naturally," or if allowed to oscillate of its own accord

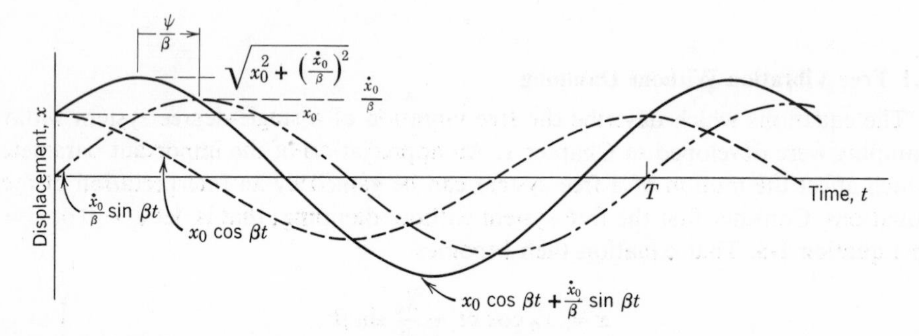

Fig. 2-1 Periodic motion of a vibrating system having initial displacement and velocity

without outside interference. Since the natural frequency is proportional to the quantity, β, it is also customary to refer to β as the "natural frequency," the units of β being radians per second instead of cycles per second. This is because there are 2π radians in one revolution, or cycle. (Actually, the dimension of either f_n or β is 1/sec, since radian or cycle has no length, time, or mass dimension. For clarity, it is preferable to designate these frequencies with "cycles per second" or "radians per second.") Sometimes a frequency, when designated in radians per second, is referred to as "circular frequency."

Figure 2-1 shows that the displacement reaches a maximum value at intervals. This maximum value is referred to as the "amplitude" of the vibration. The amplitude is always a positive number, and represents physically the distance from the point of equilibrium to the point of maximum displacement. Occasionally the phrase "double amplitude" is encountered. This means the total distance between the minimum and maximum values of displacement, or twice the amplitude.

Example 2-1. What is the natural frequency and period of an undamped spring-mass system if the mass weighs 3 lb and the spring constant is 10 lb per inch?

If ft-slug-sec units are to be used, then $k = (10)(12) = 120$ lb per ft and $m = 3/32.2 = 0.0932$ slugs.

$$\beta = \sqrt{\frac{k}{m}} = \sqrt{\frac{120}{0.0932}} = 35.9 \text{ rad/sec}$$

$$f_n = \frac{35.9}{2\pi} = 5.72 \text{ cycles/sec}$$

$$T = \frac{1}{f_n} = 0.175 \text{ sec} = \text{period}$$

Example 2-2. A spring of spring rate 100 lb/in. is used as a stop. A machine part weighing 10 lb slides in such a manner as to hit the spring at a velocity of 5 ft/sec. What is the maximum deflection of the spring under the impact, and what is the maximum load imposed on the spring?

The initial load in the spring is assumed to be zero since information to the contrary is not given. While the mass is in contact with the spring, the system is like that of Fig. 1-1. The second form of Equation 2-1 shows that the maximum deflection of the spring is

$$\sqrt{x_0^2 + \left(\frac{\dot{x}_0}{\beta}\right)^2} = \frac{\dot{x}_0}{\beta}$$

for this case, or since

$$\beta = \sqrt{\frac{k}{m}} = \sqrt{\frac{100 \times 12 \times 32.2}{10}} = 62.1 \text{ rad/sec}, \; x_{\text{max}} = \frac{5}{62.1} = 0.0805 \text{ ft or } 0.965 \text{ in.}$$

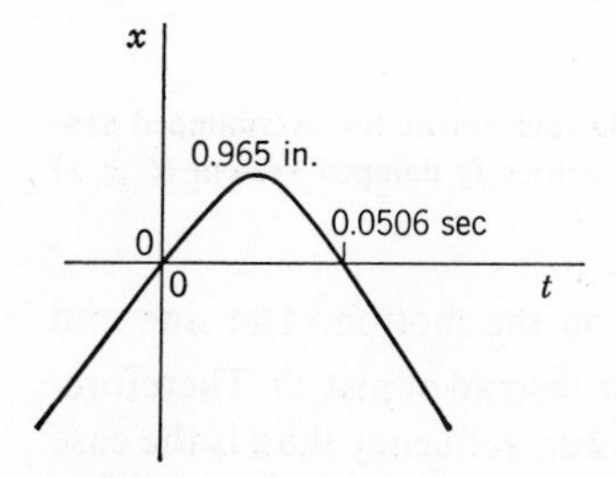

Fig. 2-2

The maximum load in the spring $= kx_{\text{max}} = 100(0.965) = 96.5$ lb.

Notice in the problem analyzed that since $x_{\text{max}} = \dot{x}_0\sqrt{m}/\sqrt{k}$ the more flexible the spring the greater the displacement, but that since the load to which the spring is subjected is kx_{max} or $\dot{x}_0\sqrt{m}\,\sqrt{k}$, the more flexible the spring the less the maximum spring load. In this example the time at which the maximum spring load occurs is calculated from $\sin(\beta t + \psi) = 1$ where $\psi = \tan^{-1}(x_0\beta)/\dot{x}_0 = 0$. $\beta t = \pi/2$ or $t = \pi/2\beta = 0.0253$ sec, and the mass remains in contact with the spring for twice this time (shown in Fig. 2-2).

2.2 Free Vibration with Damping

Critically Damped and Overdamped Systems. Now it is of interest to examine the various solutions of Equation 1-7 if the damping is not zero. First, if $\zeta > 1$, the system is strongly damped, said to be "overdamped," and Equation 1-9 applies. From the form of the solution it is possible to see that an oscillation cannot exist. If the system is displaced and released with zero velocity, it will move toward its equilibrium position;

that is, x will approach zero asymptotically. Such motion is "aperiodic" (not periodic), and is often referred to as a "subsidence." (It subsides.) If the mass is given an initial positive velocity, x will increase positively to some maximum value and then decrease asymptotically to zero. If the mass is given an initial positive displacement and a sufficiently high negative velocity, it is possible for x to pass from positive to negative once, but then x would approach zero asymptotically from the negative side. These possibilities are shown graphically in Fig. 2-3.

Examination of Equation 1-10 for $\zeta = 1$ shows that here too the motion is aperiodic, and the same discussion applies as for the overdamped system; thus, a plot of displacement versus time would have the same general appearance. However, this is the lowest value of damping for which aperiodic motion can exist, and so the amount of damping corresponding to this condition is called "critical" damping. The magnitude of the damping constant for critical damping depends on the mass and spring and can be calculated from Equation 1-12. If the damping constant is less than this, then $\zeta < 1$, and Equation 1-8 applies. This is the condition for oscillatory motion with damping.

Damped Natural Frequency. Since the effect of initial velocity for $\zeta < 1$ is similar to its effect when $\zeta > 1$ or $\zeta = 1$, the initial velocity will be set equal to zero and the

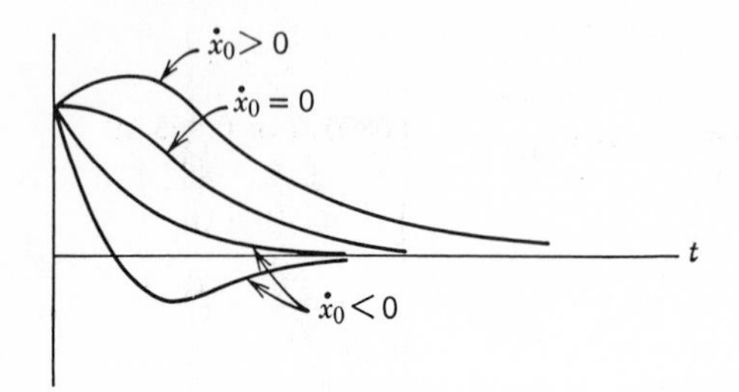

Fig. 2-3 Displacement for overdamped system or for critically damped system ($\zeta \geqq 1$)

investigation will be confined to the effect of damping on the motion. The sine and cosine functions are now seen to be functions of $\beta\sqrt{1-\zeta^2}t$ instead of just βt. Therefore, these functions indicate that the oscillation occurs at a lower frequency than is the case for no damping, or the "damped natural frequency" is less than the "undamped natural frequency" since $\beta\sqrt{1-\zeta^2}$ is less than β. Also, the period of the damped motion is correspondingly greater than the period of the undamped motion. (If the reader is not convinced from the form of Equation 1-8 that the term $\beta\sqrt{1-\zeta^2}$ is the natural frequency of the damped oscillation, he may satisfy himself on this point by differentiating Equation 1-8 and equating to zero to find the time separation between two maximum points, thus determining the period of the damped oscillation.) The form of the solution suggests that there might be some utility in expressing the damped frequency in terms of the undamped frequency and a correction factor. If β_d is the damped frequency and β the undamped frequency, then

$$\beta_d = \beta\sqrt{1-\zeta^2} \tag{2-4}$$

Damping Factor. The ratio ζ is significant. $\zeta = 1$ corresponds to critical damping, or the value of the damping constant is c_c. Therefore, from Equations 1-5 and 1-12,

$\zeta = c/(2\sqrt{mk}) = c/c_c$ and ζ is the ratio of the actual damping constant for the system to the critical damping constant for the system. Thus, if a system has 10% critical damping, $\zeta = 0.10$. Often, ζ is referred to as the "damping factor." Equation 2-4 is plotted in Fig. 2-4. If the same scale is used for the ordinate and abscissa, the plot forms a semicircle.

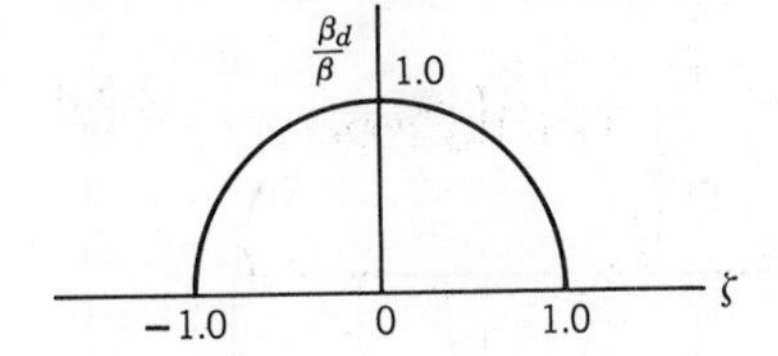

Fig. 2-4 Ratio of damped frequency to undamped frequency as a function of damping factor

The presence of the factor $e^{-\zeta\beta t}$ multiplying the periodic terms in Equation 1-8 means that the oscillation will diminish in amplitude as time goes on. Figure 2-5 illustrates this for a function starting with unit amplitude and zero initial velocity. The dashed line indicates the variation of the term, $e^{-\zeta\beta t}$, which when multiplied by the periodic function describes the damped oscillation.

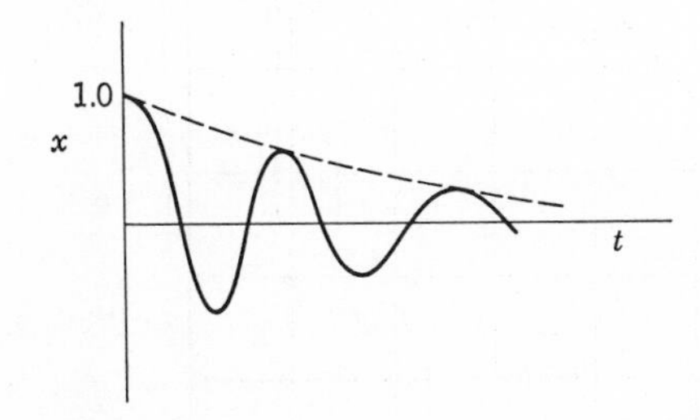

Fig. 2-5 Damped oscillation

Although the point is of minor significance, the dashed line is not the envelope of the solid line in the sense of being tangent to it. The dashed line, representing $e^{-\zeta\beta t}$, intersects the solid line, representing the damped oscillation described by

$$e^{-\zeta\beta t}(\cos \beta\sqrt{1-\zeta^2}\, t + \frac{\zeta}{\sqrt{1-\zeta^2}} \sin \beta\sqrt{1-\zeta^2}\, t)$$

at the points where $\beta\sqrt{1-\zeta^2}\, t = 0, 2\pi, 4\pi$, etc. At these points the solid curve has its maximum values, with zero slopes. Therefore, the slopes of the two curves are not the same where they are coincident.

Other Damping Criteria. It is of interest to determine how rapidly a vibration damps out. One measure of this is the ratio of the amplitudes for successive oscillations. This would be determined by setting $\beta\sqrt{1-\zeta^2}\, T = 2\pi$ to solve for the period, and then substituting this value of T in the factor $e^{-\zeta\beta t}$, giving for this factor $e^{-\zeta\beta(2\pi/\beta\sqrt{1-\zeta^2})}$,

or $e^{-2\pi\zeta/\sqrt{1-\zeta^2}}$. Thus the ratio of any two successive peaks in the displacement curve is a constant depending on the damping factor:

$$\frac{x_{\max_2}}{x_{\max_1}} = e^{-2\pi\zeta/\sqrt{1-\zeta^2}} \tag{2-5}$$

For very low damping ($\zeta < 0.02$), Equation 2-5 may be satisfactorily approximated by

$$\frac{x_{\max_2}}{x_{\max_1}} = 1 - 2\pi\zeta \tag{2-5a}$$

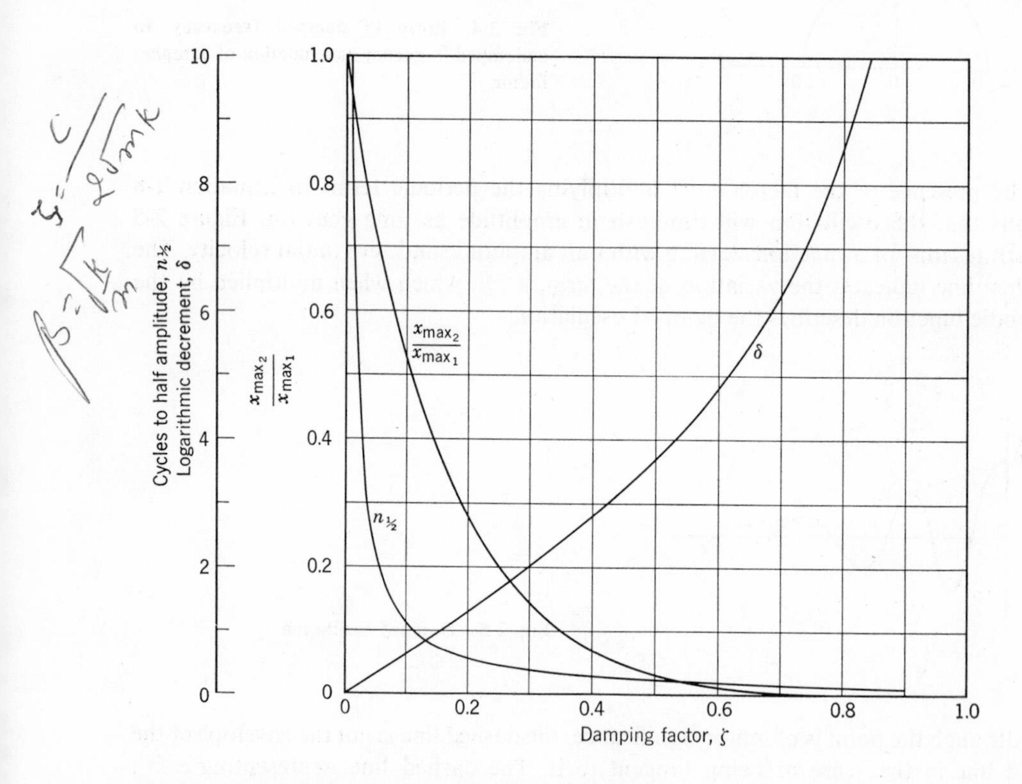

Fig. 2-6 Damping criteria as functions of damping factor

The natural logarithm of the foregoing ratio (disregarding the negative sign) is designated as the "logarithmic decrement," δ, which is therefore

$$\delta = \frac{2\pi\zeta}{\sqrt{1-\zeta^2}} \tag{2-6}$$

For values of $\zeta < 0.2$, this is satisfactorily approximated by

$$\delta = 2\pi\zeta \tag{2-6a}$$

Figure 2-6 shows a plot of Equations 2-5 and 2-6. It can be seen that even for small values of damping factor, the oscillation decreases in amplitude rapidly. For instance, a damping factor of 0.02 is small (2% of critical damping), yet each maximum is only 89% of the previous maximum.

Another measure of the rapidity with which the oscillation will damp out is the number of cycles necessary for the oscillation to reduce to half amplitude. (It would theoretically take an infinite time and an infinite number of cycles to die out completely.) To determine the number of cycles to damp to half amplitude, it is only necessary to determine the time required for the factor $e^{-\zeta\beta t}$ to become 0.5 and then find how many cycles can be completed in this time. Time necessary for this is $\ln 2/\zeta\beta$ and the number of cycles would be determined from time $= \ln 2/\zeta\beta = 2\pi n_{1/2}/\beta_d$, where $n_{1/2}$ is the number of cycles to reduce to half amplitude, or

$$n_{1/2} = \frac{\ln 2}{2\pi}\frac{\sqrt{1-\zeta^2}}{\zeta} = \frac{\ln 2}{\delta} \tag{2-7}$$

Equation 2-7 is also plotted in Fig. 2-6. For 2% critical damping, 5.5 cycles are required before the amplitude reduces to half its initial value.

Negative Damping. If ζ has a negative value, a condition corresponding to a negative damper exists, since $\zeta = c/(2\sqrt{mk})$. Under these circumstances the oscillation builds up. This is called a "divergent oscillation," or a "self-excited oscillation." A plot of the displacement with time appears in Fig. 2-7. A dashpot damper (Fig. 1-3) would not

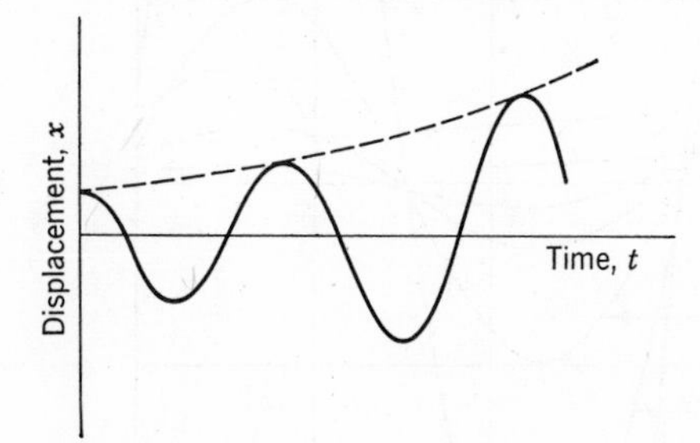

Fig. 2-7 Divergent oscillation

have a negative coefficient, but it is possible for divergent oscillations to occur in some dynamic systems, as is discussed in later chapters. For the system indicated in Fig. 1-3, the "damper" would be a device which would sense the velocity and pump oil into a hydraulic cylinder, pushing the mass in the same direction as the velocity, and having a magnitude proportional to the velocity. For negative damping, Equations 2-5 and 2-6 are valid, with ζ negative, and so Fig. 2-6 can be used as follows: If ζ is negative, the curve labeled $x_{\max_2}/x_{\max_1}$ can be used just as if ζ were positive, but the value obtained from the curve will really be $x_{\max_1}/x_{\max_2}$ instead of $x_{\max_2}/x_{\max_1}$. The logarithmic decrement curve will be exactly the same except it will have a negative value. The curve for $n_{1/2}$ will yield the number of cycles for the amplitude to build up to twice its original value. Also, from Equation 2-4, it is seen that the frequency for negative damping is less than for zero damping, and Fig. 2-4 shows β_d/β for negative value of ζ.

When $\zeta < -1$, the solution given by Equation 1-9 applies, except that ζ is negative. The motion in this case is a "divergence." No oscillation occurs, and the mass moves toward infinity in the positive or negative direction (depending on initial conditions) with ever increasing speed. A system with negative damping is unstable, since the motion does not tend to die out. Figure 2-8 shows how the displacement varies with time for various values of damping factor, ζ, starting with an initial displacement of x_0 and with zero initial velocity. It is evident that a value of ζ which has a considerable

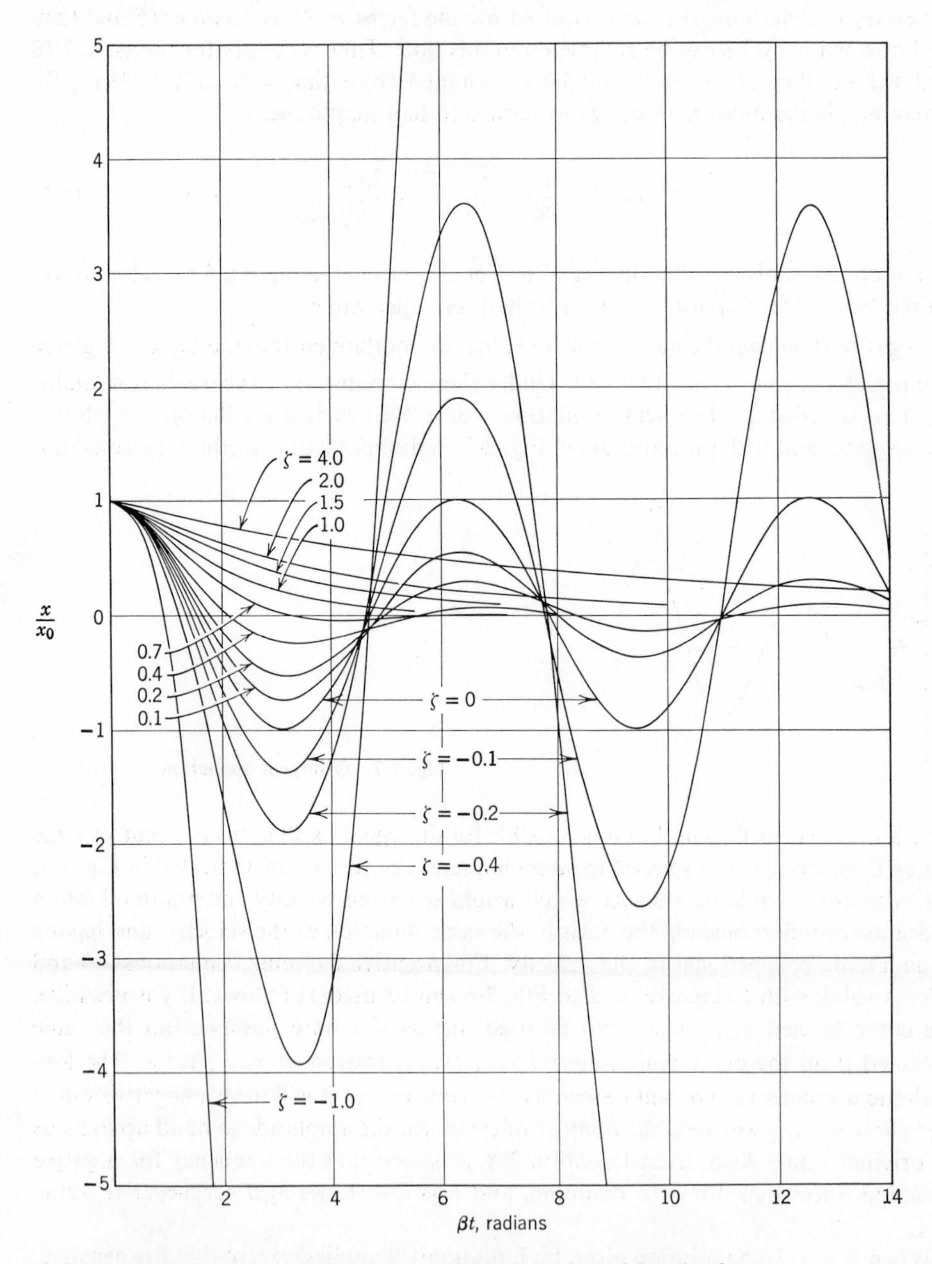

Fig. 2-8 Displacement as a function of time for several values of damping factor

effect on amplitude may have little effect on the frequency. Figure 2-9 shows how the displacement varies for values of ζ which yield aperiodic motion only, again starting from rest with initial displacement x_0.

When $\zeta = -1$, Equation 1-11 applies. This condition has much the same significance as $\zeta = 1$; that is, forming one boundary between oscillatory and nonoscillatory motion, except that the system is unstable instead of stable.

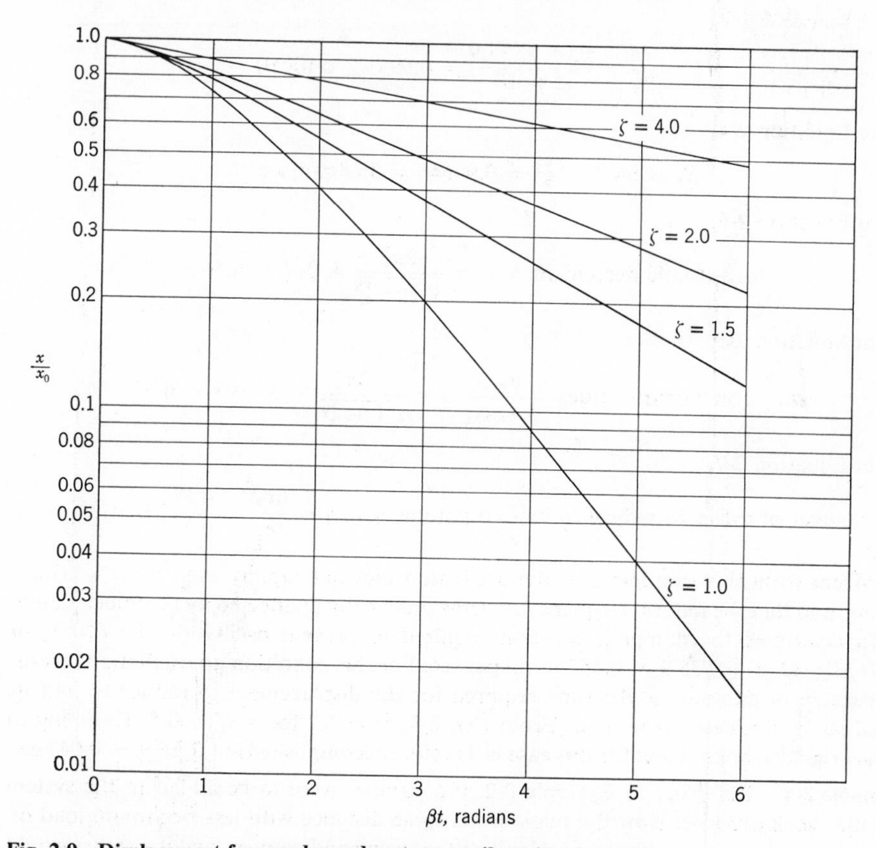

Fig. 2-9 Displacement for overdamped system, semilogarithmic scales

Summary of Damping Effects. Summarizing this discussion of the effect of damping: if ζ is negative the system is unstable; if $\zeta \leqq -1$, the motion is a nonoscillatory divergence; if $-1 < \zeta < 0$, the motion is a divergent oscillation. If ζ is positive the motion decays with time; if $\zeta \geqq 1$, the motion dies out without oscillation, and if $0 < \zeta < 1$, the motion is oscillatory as it dies out. For the special condition, $\zeta = 0$, the oscillation continues forever without either dying out or building up. If there is oscillation (for $-1 < \zeta < 1$), the frequency of the oscillation is greatest for $\zeta = 0$, decreasing for either positive or negative values of ζ. However, the reduction in frequency is not significant until the value of ζ becomes large enough to have a great effect on amplitude (for $\zeta = \pm 0.2$ approximately).

Example 2-3. A mass-spring-damper system is composed of a 3-lb weight, a 10 lb/in. spring, and a 0.05 lb/in. per sec damper. (Example 2-1 with the damper added.) What is the natural frequency and rate of decay of vibration? What damping constant would prevent oscillation, and what rate of decay would result if this damper were used?

From Example 2-1,

$$\beta = \sqrt{\frac{k}{m}} = 35.9 \text{ rad/sec}$$

From Equation 1-5,

$$\zeta = \frac{c\beta}{2k} = \frac{0.05 \times 35.9}{2 \times 10} = 0.09 \text{ (9\% critical)}$$

From Equation 2-4,

$$\beta_d = \beta\sqrt{1 - \zeta^2} = 0.9964\beta = 35.8 \text{ rad/sec}$$

From Equation 2-6,

$$\text{logarithmic decrement} = \delta = \frac{2\pi\zeta}{\sqrt{1 - \zeta^2}} \doteq 2\pi\zeta = 0.565$$

From Equation 2-5,

$$\text{ratio of maximum values} = \frac{x_{\max_2}}{x_{\max_1}} = e^{\frac{-2\pi\zeta}{\sqrt{1-\zeta^2}}} = e^{-0.565} = 0.57$$

From Equation 2-7,

$$\text{number of cycles to reduce to half amplitude} = n_{1/2} = \frac{\ln 2}{\delta} = \frac{0.694}{0.565} = 1.23$$

It is evident from this example that the oscillation dies out rapidly even for 9% critical damping, and that the natural frequency remains practically unaffected by this much damping. To determine the damping constant required to prevent oscillation, let $\zeta = 1$, or $c_c = 2k/\beta = (2 \times 10)/35.9 = 0.557$ lb/in. per sec. For this condition no oscillation results. One measure of damping is the time required for the displacement to reduce to half its original value if released from rest. From Fig. 2-8, $\beta t = 1.7$ for $x/x_0 = 0.5$. Damping to half the original displacement for this case is therefore accomplished in $1.7/35.9 = 0.047$ sec.

Example 2-4. Referring to Example 2-2, if a damper were to be added to the system could the shock absorber slow the mass in the same distance with less maximum load on the spring and also less maximum total load on the spring and damper, and if so what would be the optimum combination of spring and damper, assuming that the initial spring load is zero?

It is immediately evident that a damper is able to limit the maximum deflection to less than that which would exist without a damper, and therefore the load in the spring would be less.

However, even with smaller maximum deflection, whether the total load would be less is not so immediately apparent. The reasoning is as follows. The maximum total load on the spring-damper combination is a function of the maximum acceleration of the mass striking the shock absorbers. With no damper, the load should follow a sine curve, reaching a maximum at the maximum displacement. With damper, it should be possible to have an acceleration more nearly constant, so that if total deflection is the design limitation, the maximum acceleration can be less, resulting in a lower total load. Intuitively, the spring constant may have to be less in order to maintain the same maximum deflection. It is clear that $\zeta > 0$, but not clear whether $\zeta < 1$ or > 1 or $= 1$, so it may be necessary to investigate the several forms of the solution before determining the optimum combination.

First, it is assumed that the spring has no initial load, or that the instant the mass hits the shock absorber ($t = 0$), $x_0 = 0$. Then, from Equation 1-8, for $\zeta < 1$,

$$x = \frac{\dot{x}_0}{\beta\sqrt{1-\zeta^2}} e^{-\zeta\beta t} \sin \beta\sqrt{1-\zeta^2}\, t$$

$$\dot{x} = \dot{x}_0 e^{-\zeta\beta t}\left(-\frac{\zeta}{\sqrt{1-\zeta^2}} \sin \beta\sqrt{1-\zeta^2}\, t + \cos \beta\sqrt{1-\zeta^2}\, t\right)$$

When x is maximum, $\dot{x} = 0$, or $\tan \beta\sqrt{1-\zeta^2}\, t_m = \sqrt{1-\zeta^2}/\zeta$ yields the time corresponding to maximum deflection, t_m, which then gives the maximum deflection from

$$x_{\max} = \frac{\dot{x}_0}{\beta} e^{-\frac{\zeta}{\sqrt{1-\zeta^2}} \tan^{-1} \frac{\sqrt{1-\zeta^2}}{\zeta}}$$

The acceleration is (again differentiating),

$$\ddot{x} = \dot{x}_0 \beta\, e^{-\zeta\beta t}\left[\frac{2\zeta^2 - 1}{\sqrt{1-\zeta^2}} \sin \beta\sqrt{1-\zeta^2}\, t - 2\zeta \cos \beta\sqrt{1-\zeta^2}\, t\right]$$

so it is now possible to express $\ddot{x}$ as a function of $x_{\max}$ and $\dot{x}_0$, giving

$$\ddot{x} = \frac{\dot{x}_0^{\,2}}{x_{\max}} e^{-\frac{\zeta}{\sqrt{1-\zeta^2}} \tan^{-1} \frac{\sqrt{1-\zeta^2}}{\zeta}} e^{-\zeta\beta t}\left[\frac{2\zeta^2 - 1}{\sqrt{1-\zeta^2}} \sin \beta\sqrt{1-\zeta^2}\, t - 2\zeta \cos \beta\sqrt{1-\zeta^2}\, t\right]$$

This will be maximum when the derivative of $\ddot{x}$ is zero or when

$$\tan \beta\sqrt{1-\zeta^2}\, t_{ma} = \frac{(1-4\zeta^2)\sqrt{1-\zeta^2}}{\zeta(3-4\zeta^2)}$$

then

$$\ddot{x}_{\max} = \frac{\dot{x}_0^{\,2}}{x_{\max}} e^{-\frac{\zeta}{\sqrt{1-\zeta^2}} \tan^{-1} \frac{\sqrt{1-\zeta^2}}{\zeta}} e^{-\frac{\zeta}{\sqrt{1-\zeta^2}} \tan^{-1} \frac{(1-4\zeta^2)\sqrt{1-\zeta^2}}{\zeta(1-4\zeta^2)}}$$

$$\times \left[\frac{2\zeta^2 - 1}{\sqrt{1-\zeta^2}} \frac{(1-4\zeta^2)\sqrt{1-\zeta^2}}{\sqrt{(1-4\zeta^2)^2(1-\zeta^2) + \zeta^2(3-4\zeta^2)^2}} - 2\zeta \frac{\zeta(3-4\zeta^2)}{\sqrt{(1-4\zeta^2)^2(1-\zeta^2) + \zeta^2(3-4\zeta^2)^2}}\right].$$

Simplifying,

$$\ddot{x}_{\max} = -\frac{\dot{x}_0^{\,2}}{x_{\max}} \exp\left[-\frac{\zeta}{\sqrt{1-\zeta^2}} \tan^{-1}\left(\frac{4\zeta(1-2\zeta^2)\sqrt{1-\zeta^2}}{-8\zeta^4 + 8\zeta^2 - 1}\right)\right]$$

For the optimum condition it is necessary to set $d\ddot{x}_{\max}/d\zeta = 0$. This is tedious and will not be repeated here, but for optimum conditions the following equation must be satisfied.

$$\tan 4\zeta\sqrt{1-\zeta^2} = \frac{4\zeta(1-2\zeta^2)\sqrt{1-\zeta^2}}{-8\zeta^4 + 8\zeta^2 - 1}$$

The value of ζ which satisfies this equation is approximately 0.4. Thus, to produce the least acceleration and total load with a given maximum stroke, the damper should be about 40% of critical. For this value of damping constant the maximum acceleration is about $0.52(\dot{x}_0^{\,2}/x_{\max})$ compared to $1.0(x_0^{\,2}/x_{\max})$ if no damper is used. These conclusions are valid for a shock absorber composed of linear elements and starting from a condition wherein the initial load in the spring is zero. (There should be an initial spring load, however, in order to return the system to the original position. This would change the optimum damper slightly.)

Example 2-5. The musical note A is struck on the piano and held. If the vibration dies out so that in 5 sec the sound has decreased from 35 to 5 db, determine the effective damping factor, logarithmic decrement, ratio between amplitude of successive oscillations, and number of oscillations to damp to half amplitude.

In subsequent chapters it is shown that such a problem can be treated like the simple problem of Fig. 1-1, but using "effective" masses, springs, and dampers. The definition of the decibel in accoustics is $10 \log_{10} (I/I_0)$, where I is sound intensity and I_0 is the intensity of the faintest sound having a frequency of 1000 cps which can be heard (10^{-16} w/cm^2). The intensity of a sound is proportional to the square of the amplitude of the particle motion (also pressure differential) or proportional to the square of the amplitude of the object generating the sound. If I_1 is initial amplitude, and I_2 is the amplitude at the end of 5 sec, then

$$\frac{I_1}{I_2} = 10^{((35-5)/10)} = 1000$$

$$\frac{\text{amplitude}_2}{\text{amplitude}_1} = \sqrt{\frac{1}{1000}} = 0.0316$$

Since the amplitude decreases according to $e^{-\zeta\beta t}$, and since t is known (5 sec) and β is known (frequency for the the note is 440 cycles per sec or 2760 rad/sec), it is possible to solve for ζ from $0.0316 = e^{-\zeta \times 2760 \times 5}$ or

$$\zeta = 0.00025$$

From Equation 2-6a,

$$\text{logarithmic decrement, } \delta = 2\pi\zeta = 0.00157$$

From Equation 2-5a,

$$\frac{x_{\max_2}}{x_{\max_1}} = e^{-2\pi\zeta} = 1 - 0.00157 = 0.99863$$

From Equation 2-7,

$$n_{1/2} = \frac{\ln 2}{\delta} = 440 \text{ cycles for half amplitude}$$

(The time required to reduce to half amplitude is therefore 1 sec.)

This example indicates that the damping of spring steel wire subjected to small disturbances is very small. The actual damping inherent in any material may be expressed in terms of an equivalent viscous damper, but since the actual damping is not really linear, the equivalent damping constant then depends on the amplitude of the oscillation. The damping computed in this example is not all attributable to material damping in spring steel, which would be less than this. Much of this apparent damping results from the transfer of energy from the vibrating string to the atmosphere.

2.3 Stability

The stability of a system is often of critical importance, and is the subject of considerable discussion in subsequent chapters. Although system instability is more frequently encountered in complex, multiple-degree systems than in the single-degree systems which are the topic of this chapter, the use of the terms "stable" and "unstable" in the previous discussion of negative damping implies the existence of suitable definitions of these terms. A linear system is "stable" if the coordinates which describe its configuration remain finite for any combination of finite initial conditions and forcing functions. (In the language of Section 4.2 and subsequent chapters, this is equivalent to stating that every root of the characteristic equation has a negative real part.) A linear system is "unstable" if the coordinate or coordinates which describe its configuration become infinite for some combination of finite initial conditions and forcing functions. (This is equivalent to stating that at least one root of the characteristic equation has zero or positive real part.) The border between stability and instability is often referred to as "marginal stability," or "neutral stability." (This corresponds to one or more roots of the characteristic equation having real parts exactly zero, which, according to the foregoing definitions, is technically classed as unstable.) of course, "infinity" in the foregoing context is a relative magnitude, because linear systems eventually encounter nonlinearities when deflections become large.

In the light of these definitions it is seen that negative damping is only one cause of instability. A negative spring constant also causes instability of the type previously described as divergence. Sometimes the phrase "static stability" is used to describe the tendency of a system to return to an equilibrium position when displaced (essentially positive spring constants), and the phrase "dynamic stability" is then used to further differentiate the stability or instability of statically stable systems.

CHAPTER 3

Forced Vibration of Elementary Systems

3.1 Steady-State Vibration

In Chapter 2 the system under investigation did not include an external force. The system vibrated naturally or freely. If an external force exists which is independent of displacement, velocity, or other derivatives or integrals of x (and is, therefore, a function of time alone), the motion of the system is said to be "forced," and the physical problem is that proposed by Fig. 1-3.

For linear systems, the motion of the mass under these circumstances is exactly the same as described in Chapter 2, except that an additional motion is superimposed, which depends on how the external force varies with time. The solution of Equation 1-4 depends on the particular form of the function, $f(t)$, which describes how the force varies with time. It is apparent that there are as many possible solutions as there are functions, $f(t)$, but only one of these will be considered at this time.

General Equation of Motion for Sinusoidal Forcing Function. If the force varies sinusoidally, the function, $f(t)$, is described as

$$f(t) = f_0 \sin \omega t \tag{3-1}$$

Then the differential equation is,

$$m\frac{d^2x}{dt^2} + c\frac{dx}{dt} + kx = f_0 \sin \omega t$$

$$\frac{d^2x}{dt^2} + 2\zeta\beta\frac{dx}{dt} + \beta^2 x = \frac{\beta^2}{k} f_0 \sin \omega t \tag{3-2}$$

From Appendix 1 the solution of this equation for $\zeta < 1$, is

$$x = e^{-\zeta\beta t}\left[x_0 \cos \beta\sqrt{1-\zeta^2}\,t + \frac{\dot{x}_0 + \zeta\beta x_0}{\beta\sqrt{1-\zeta^2}} \sin \beta\sqrt{1-\zeta^2}\,t\right]$$

$$+\frac{f_0}{k}\frac{\omega}{\beta}e^{-\zeta\beta t}\left\{\frac{2\zeta\cos\beta\sqrt{1-\zeta^2}\,t+\dfrac{\left(\dfrac{\omega}{\beta}\right)^2-1+2\zeta^2}{\sqrt{1-\zeta^2}}\sin\beta\sqrt{1-\zeta^2}\,t}{\left[1-\left(\dfrac{\omega}{\beta}\right)^2\right]^2+\left(2\zeta\dfrac{\omega}{\beta}\right)^2}\right\} \tag{3-3}$$

$$+\frac{f_0}{k}\left\{\frac{-2\zeta\dfrac{\omega}{\beta}\cos\omega t+\left[1-\left(\dfrac{\omega}{\beta}\right)^2\right]\sin\omega t}{\left[1-\left(\dfrac{\omega}{\beta}\right)^2\right]^2+\left(2\zeta\dfrac{\omega}{\beta}\right)^2}\right\}$$

Although this is a rather formidable looking equation, it can be interpreted in such a way that the results are easily understood. The first term is the same as was obtained in Chapter 2, namely, Equation 1-8. This term is dependent only on the initial displacement and velocity and damps out and effectively disappears after some time because of the presence of the factor $e^{-\zeta\beta t}$. The second term in Equation 3-3, which depends on f_0, or the magnitude of the force, also dies out with time, because of the presence of the factor $e^{-\zeta\beta t}$. Notice that this term describes a motion oscillating at the natural frequency, $\beta\sqrt{1-\zeta^2}$. This means that the force starts an oscillation at the natural frequency of the system, the oscillation decaying at the same rate as that discussed in Section 2.2. After a considerable period of time, the motion described by the first two terms of Equation 3-3 will die out and leave only that described by the third term. This term describes an oscillation having the frequency, ω (rad/sec), which is the same as the frequency of the force. This type of oscillation is a "forced vibration" because it is forced by an external repeating force. The vibration which does not die out may also be referred to as "steady state" vibration. If the forcing function were to change, the steady-state vibration would also change. The motion which occurs during a change from one steady-state condition to another is "transient" motion. This includes all terms that decay with time or, for negative damping, build up with time.

Steady-State Equation. In the third term of Equation 3-3 is the factor, f_0/k. This factor can be interpreted physically as the displacement that occurs if the force were a steady force having a magnitude f_0 instead of a force varying with time. This deflection, which would exist under a static load, is called the "static deflection," and may be designated with the symbol δ_{st}. Then the third term of Equation 3-3, which represents the steady-state vibration caused by the force, $f_0 \sin \omega t$, can be written

$$\frac{x}{\delta_{st}}=\frac{-2\zeta\dfrac{\omega}{\beta}\cos\omega t+\left[1-\left(\dfrac{\omega}{\beta}\right)^2\right]\sin\omega t}{\left[1-\left(\dfrac{\omega}{\beta}\right)^2\right]^2+\left(2\zeta\dfrac{\omega}{\beta}\right)^2}$$

or, by trigonometric manipulation,

$$\frac{x}{\delta_{st}}=\frac{1}{\sqrt{\left[1-\left(\dfrac{\omega}{\beta}\right)^2\right]^2+\left(2\zeta\dfrac{\omega}{\beta}\right)^2}}\sin(\omega t+\phi) \tag{3-4}$$

where

$$\left.\begin{aligned}
\phi &= -\sin^{-1}\frac{2\zeta\dfrac{\omega}{\beta}}{\sqrt{\left[1-\left(\dfrac{\omega}{\beta}\right)^2\right]^2+\left(2\zeta\dfrac{\omega}{\beta}\right)^2}}\\
\phi &= -\cos^{-1}\frac{1-\left(\dfrac{\omega}{\beta}\right)^2}{\sqrt{\left[1-\left(\dfrac{\omega}{\beta}\right)^2\right]^2+\left(2\zeta\dfrac{\omega}{\beta}\right)^2}}\\
\phi &= -\tan^{-1}\frac{2\zeta\dfrac{\omega}{\beta}}{1-\left(\dfrac{\omega}{\beta}\right)^2}
\end{aligned}\right\} \tag{3-5}$$

Displacement Amplitude. It is seen from the second form of Equation 3-4 that the amplitude of the motion, determined by obtaining the value of x when the sine is 1, is

$$\frac{x_{\max}}{\delta_{\mathrm{st}}} = \frac{1}{\sqrt{\left[1-\left(\dfrac{\omega}{\beta}\right)^2\right]^2+\left(2\zeta\dfrac{\omega}{\beta}\right)^2}} \tag{3-6}$$

Equations 3-5 and 3-6 have significance. Equation 3-6 is plotted in Fig. 3-1* for several values of damping factor. For zero damping there is a condition wherein the steady-state vibration would approach infinity. This would occur if the forcing frequency, ω, were equal to the natural frequency of the undamped system, β, or if $\omega/\beta = 1$. This condition is called "resonance." If some damping is present, the peak of the curve is limited to some finite value and occurs at $\omega/\beta < 1$. In fact, it occurs at $\omega/\beta = \sqrt{1-2\zeta^2}$, or forcing frequency equal to damped natural frequency. For this resonance point, the maximum value of the amplitude is given by

$$\left(\frac{x_{\max}}{\delta_{\mathrm{st}}}\right)_{\max} = \frac{1}{2\zeta\sqrt{1-\zeta^2}} \tag{3-7}$$

For $\zeta \geqq \sqrt{2}/2$, $x_{\max}/\delta_{\mathrm{st}} = 1$, which occurs at $\omega/\beta = 0$.

Velocity and Acceleration Amplitude. It is also of interest to determine how the velocity and acceleration felt by the mass are affected by damping and frequency ratio. Differentiating the second form of Equation 3-4 yields for the maximum value of the velocity,

$$\dot{x}_{\max} = \frac{\omega\delta_{\mathrm{st}}}{\sqrt{\left[1-\left(\dfrac{\omega}{\beta}\right)^2\right]^2+\left(2\zeta\dfrac{\omega}{\beta}\right)^2}} \tag{3-8}$$

* Figures 3-1 to 3-15 are to be found on pp. 32–46.

This can be changed to the dimensionless form by multiplying and dividing by β, which gives

$$\frac{\dot{x}_{\max}}{\beta\delta_{st}} = \frac{\left(\frac{\omega}{\beta}\right)}{\sqrt{\left[1-\left(\frac{\omega}{\beta}\right)^2\right]^2+\left(2\zeta\frac{\omega}{\beta}\right)^2}} \tag{3-9}$$

Similarly, the maximum value of the acceleration felt by the mass is given by

$$\frac{\ddot{x}_{\max}}{\beta^2\delta_{st}} = \frac{\left(\frac{\omega}{\beta}\right)^2}{\sqrt{\left[1-\left(\frac{\omega}{\beta}\right)^2\right]^2+\left(2\zeta\frac{\omega}{\beta}\right)^2}} \tag{3-10}$$

Equations 3-9 and 3-10 are plotted in Figs. 3-2 and 3-3.

Transmissibilty. In order to know how much the exciting force is amplified or reduced in passing through the mass-spring-damper system it is necessary to obtain the amount of force exerted by the spring and damper on the wall. From Equation 3-4,

Force on wall = spring force + damper force = $kx + c\dot{x}$

$$= k\delta_{st}\frac{\sin(\omega t+\phi)}{\sqrt{\left[1-\left(\frac{\omega}{\beta}\right)^2\right]^2+\left(2\zeta\frac{\omega}{\beta}\right)^2}} + \frac{c\delta_{st}\omega\cos(\omega t+\phi)}{\sqrt{\left[1-\left(\frac{\omega}{\beta}\right)^2\right]^2+\left(2\zeta\frac{\omega}{\beta}\right)^2}}$$

Usually only the maximum value of the force is of interest. This is

$$\sqrt{\frac{(k\delta_{st})^2+(c\delta_{st}\omega)^2}{\left[1-\left(\frac{\omega}{\beta}\right)^2\right]^2+\left(2\zeta\frac{\omega}{\beta}\right)^2}}$$

which could be manipulated, using $\delta_{st} = f_0/k$ and $c = 2k\zeta/\beta$, into

$$\frac{f_{\text{wall, max}}}{f_0} = \sqrt{\frac{1+\left(2\zeta\frac{\omega}{\beta}\right)^2}{\left[1-\left(\frac{\omega}{\beta}\right)^2\right]^2+\left(2\zeta\frac{\omega}{\beta}\right)^2}} \tag{3-11}$$

The ratio of the maximum force on the wall to the input force is called "transmissibility." The transmissibility as a function of ζ and ω/β is shown in Fig. 3-4.

3.2 Interpretation of Frequency Response Charts

Amplitude. Some interesting conclusions can be drawn from Figs 3-1 to 3-4. Figure 3-1 show that the amplitude of vibration can be reduced by making the natural frequency of the system sufficiently low compared to the forcing frequency (thus making ω/β large). Figures 3-2 and 3-4 show that this would also decrease the velocity and force transmitted to the wall. However, according to Fig. 3-3, the acceleration ratio approaches an asymptote of 1.0 for large values, of ω/β, so that the acceleration of the mass is not necessarily reduced by large values of ω/β. The effect of increased damping at a specified frequency ratio is to decrease the amplitude, velocity, and acceleration (Figs. 3-1 to 3-3), but the force transmitted to the wall is increased if $\omega/\beta > \sqrt{2}$ (see

Fig. 3-4). It is also seen that the force f_0 is amplified in being transmitted to the wall if $\omega/\beta < \sqrt{2}$, the amount of amplification being smaller for larger damping. If $\omega/\beta > \sqrt{2}$, the force felt by the wall would be less than the impressed force, the amount of reduction being greater for less damping.

Phase Angle. Equations 3-4 and 3-5 reveal another item of interest: the "phase angle," ϕ. The force causing the oscillation was described by the expression $f_0 \sin \omega t$. From the second form of Equation 3-4, it is seen that the displacement caused by this force is a constant multiplied by $\sin (\omega t + \phi)$. This means that when the force reaches its maximum value ($\sin \omega t = 1$), the displacement has not yet reached its maximum because $\omega t + \phi$ is less than ωt (since ϕ is negative) and so the $\sin (\omega t + \phi)$ is not yet 1. The displacement is "lagging" the force. The phase angle by which the displacement leads the force is the angle ϕ. From Equations 3-5 it is seen that for ζ positive, $\sin \phi$ must be negative, but $\cos \phi$ is positive or negative according to whether ω/β is greater or less than 1. Therefore, ϕ must be an angle between 0 and $-180°$. A plot of phase angle versus frequency ratio for various damping factors is shown in Fig. 3-12. (It is interesting to note that for negative damping the displacement would lead the force by 0 to 180° and the same graph could be used to determine the magnitude of ϕ.) To further clarify the concept of the phase angle, Fig. 3-15 (p. 46) shows the steady-state variation of the force and displacement with time for a damping factor of 0.5 and $\omega/\beta = 1.5$.

Description of Elementary Systems. One specific forcing function $f = f_0 \sin \omega t$ has been discussed in some detail. There are several other types of sinusoidal forcing functions of interest. Useful information about these systems, as well as the system already discussed, is presented in Table 3-1 and Figs. 3-1 to 3-14 (pp. 32–45). The derivation of the differential equations and the steady-state solutions which apply to these systems are omitted from this discussion, but parallels that already given for System 1 of the table.

Technically, these systems are not single degree of freedom systems, since they require more than one coordinate to completely define the configuration. However, they are discussed in this chapter because of their close similarities to the single-degree system as far as *forced* vibration is concerned. To ensure complete understanding of the physical system depicted a short description of each of the systems shown in Table 3-1 is now presented.

System 1 has already been described in detail. System 2 is similar to System 1 except that a rotating unbalance excites the vibration. This is idealized by imagining a small motor attached to the principal mass. This motor drives a shaft at constant speed, ω, with a small mass, m_e attached eccentrically to the shaft, so that $m_e\epsilon$ is the first moment of the unbalanced weight about the shaft center line. The total mass is m, including the rotating unbalanced mass, so that $(m\text{-}m_e)$ represents the amount of mass which excludes the rotating unbalance. This is indicated on the figure. The motion of the principal mass is again restricted to one dimension by guides, and the x coordinate is measured from the rest position as before.

System 3 is similar to System 1 except that the excitation is produced by a constant amplitude motion of the end of the spring not attached to the mass. It may be imagined that the spring and damper are attached to a weightless platform which is caused to move back and forth around a neutral point with a motion $y = y_0 \sin \omega t$, where y is measured in the same direction as x. (It does not matter whether the platform is weightless as long as its motion is restricted as indicated. Only the external force required to move the platform with the prescribed motion would be affected by the mass of the platform.) The dimension, x_r, is the displacement of the mass from the rest and mean position as previously described (Fig. 1-1) except that the displacement is measured relative to the platform. Therefore, x_r is the amount the spring stretches. Both this relative displacement and the absolute displacement in space are of interest. If the absolute displacement in space is still designated as x, then $x = y + x_r$.

System 4 is similar to System 3 except that the platform is not weightless and the motion is caused by a rotating unbalance attached to the platform. The total mass including the unbalanced part is m_a, so that (m_a-m_e) represents that part which excludes the unbalanced weight.

Although there are many other combinations of spring-mass-damper systems which could be listed (spring and damper in series instead of parallel, damper or spring attached to a fixed surface instead of to a movable platform, etc.), the systems listed are of most interest. Several applications of the use of the graphs are indicated in the problems accompanying this chapter.

Equations are listed in Table 3-2 (p. 27) instead of Table 3-1. From the form of the equations it is evident that one graph may represent more than one dimensionless ratio, so that the same figure number may appear in more that one place in Table 3-1. All equations are given in such a form that amplitude and phase angle can be identified immediately.

Resonance. One point is often misunderstood: if a sinusoidal forcing function is applied to a one-degree system, there is a resonance when the frequency of the forcing function is equal to the natural frequency, as seen in all of the figures. It is often thought that a resonance occurs if the forcing function is one half or double the natural frequency or some other integral multiple or fraction of the natural frequency. This is not true, however, since there is only one peak of the frequency-response curve. The reason for the misunderstanding is that a physical forcing function is often composed of a combination of sinusoidal forcing functions. One of these will have the lowest frequency, and this is called the "fundamental." The rest will have the frequencies which are double, triple, or other integral multiples of the fundamental, and these are termed "harmonics." It may be that the forcing function is composed predominantly of the fundamental or one of the harmonics. If so, the principal resonance will occur when the predominant frequency coincides with the natural frequency. However, there could be a resonance when any of the other harmonics in the forcing function coincides with the natural frequency, but it must be understood that when this happens it is because the forcing function itself is not composed of a single pure sine function. Another possible source of confusion on this point is that the physical system itself may not be a single degree of freedom system as assumed and may have more than one natural frequency.

Table 3–1. Index of Equations and Graphs pertaining to Forced Vibration of Four Frequently Encountered Elementary Systems

System	Differential and Defining Equations	Displacement	Velocity	Acceleration	Combined Force of damper and Spring
1	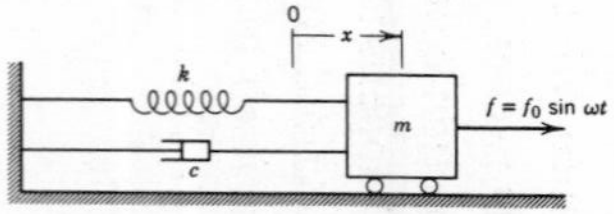 $x \sim$ Eq. 3-2 $\zeta \sim$ Eq. 1-5 $\beta \sim$ Eq. 1-6 $c_c \sim$ Eq. 1-12 $\delta_{st} = f_0\ k$	$\frac{x}{\delta_{st}} =$ Eq. 3-4, 3-5 Fig. 3-1, 3-12	$\frac{\dot{x}}{\beta\delta_{st}} =$ Eq. 3-12, 3-13 Fig. 3-2, 3-12	$\frac{\ddot{x}}{\beta^2\delta_{st}} =$ Eq. 3-14, 3-15 Fig. 3-3, 3-12	$\frac{f_{wall}}{f_0} =$ Eq. 3-16, 3-17 Fig. 3-4, 3-13
2	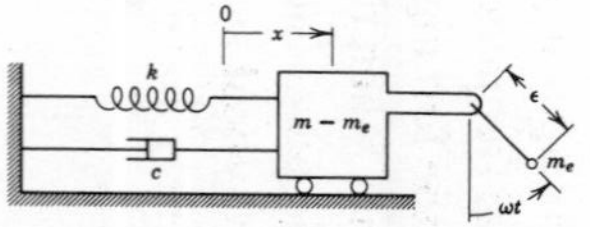 $x \sim$ Eq. 3-18 $\zeta \sim$ Eq. 1-5 $\beta \sim$ Eq. 1-6 $c_c \sim$ Eq. 1-12	$\frac{x}{\epsilon}\frac{m}{m_e} =$ Eq. 3-19, 3-5 Fig. 3-3, 3-12	$\frac{\dot{x}}{\beta\epsilon}\frac{m}{m_e} =$ Eq. 3-20, 3-13 Fig. 3-5, 3-12	$\frac{\ddot{x}}{\beta^2\epsilon}\frac{m}{m_e} =$ Eq. 3-21, 3-15 Fig. 3-6, 3-12	$\frac{f_{wall}}{\beta^2\epsilon m_e} =$ Eq. 3-22, 3-17 Fig. 3-8, 3-13
3	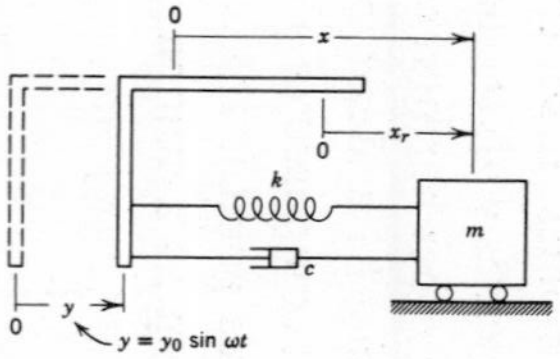 $x_r \sim$ Eq. 3-23 $\zeta \sim$ Eq. 1-5 $\beta \sim$ Eq. 1-6 $c_c \sim$ Eq. 1-12 $x = x_r + \zeta$	$\frac{x_r}{y_0} =$ Eq. 3-19, 3-5 Fig. 3-3, 3-12	$\frac{\dot{x}_r}{\beta y_0} =$ Eq. 3-20, 3-13 Fig. 3-5, 3-12	$\frac{\ddot{x}_r}{\beta^2 y_0} =$ Eq. 3-21, 3-15 Fig. 3-6, 3-12	$\frac{f_{wall}}{\beta^2 y_0 m} =$ Eq. 3-22, 3-17 Fig. 3-8, 3-13
		$\frac{x}{y_0} =$ Eq. 3-24, 3-17 Fig. 3-4, 3-13	$\frac{\dot{x}}{\beta y_0} =$ Eq. 3-25, 3-26 Fig. 3-7, 3-13	$\frac{\ddot{x}}{\beta^2 y_0} =$ Eq. 3-27, 3-28 Fig. 3-8, 3-13	
4	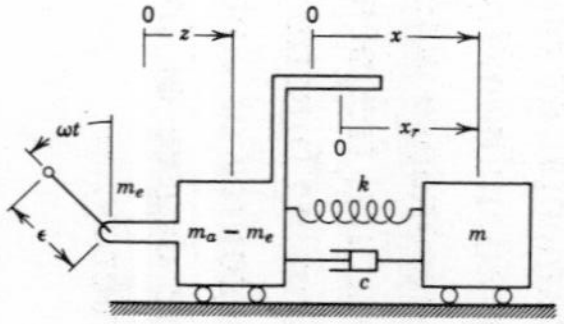 $x_r \sim$ Eq. 3-29 $\zeta \sim$ Eq. 3-30 $\beta \sim$ Eq. 3-31 $c_c \sim$ Eq. 3-32 $x = x_r + z$	$\frac{x_r}{\epsilon}\frac{m_a}{m_e} =$ Eq. 3-19, 3-5 Fig. 3-3, 3-12	$\frac{\dot{x}_r}{\beta\epsilon}\frac{m_a}{m_e} =$ Eq. 3-20, 3-13 Fig. 3-5, 3-12	$\frac{\ddot{x}_r}{\beta^2\epsilon}\frac{m_a}{m_e} =$ Eq. 3-21, 3-15 Fig. 3-6, 3-12	$\frac{f_{wall}}{\beta^2\epsilon m_e}\left(1 + \frac{m_a}{m}\right) =$ Eq. 3-22, 3-17 Fig. 3-8, 3-13
		$\frac{x}{\epsilon}\frac{m}{m_e} =$ Eq. 3-24, 3-17 Fig. 3-4, 3-13	$\frac{\dot{x}}{\beta\epsilon}\frac{m}{m_e} =$ Eq. 3-25, 3-26 Fig. 3-7, 3-13	$\frac{\ddot{x}}{\beta^2\epsilon}\frac{m}{m_e} =$ Eq. 3-27, 3-28 Fig. 3-8, 3-13	
		$\frac{z}{\epsilon}\frac{m_a + m}{m} =$ Eq. 3-33, 3-34 Fig. 3-10, 3-14	$\frac{\dot{z}}{\beta\epsilon}\frac{m_a + m}{m_e} =$ Eq. 3-35, 3-36 Fig. 3-10, 3-14	$\frac{\ddot{z}}{\beta^2\epsilon}\frac{m_a + m}{m_e} =$ Eq. 1-37, 3-38 Fig. 3-11, 3-14	

Table 3-2. Summary of Equations for Use with Table 3-1

$$\zeta = \frac{c}{c_c} \tag{1-5}$$

$$\beta = \sqrt{\frac{k}{m}} \tag{1-6}$$

$$c_c = 2\sqrt{mk} \equiv \frac{2k}{\beta} \equiv 2m\beta \tag{1-12}$$

$$\frac{d^2x}{dt^2} + 2\zeta\beta\frac{dx}{dt} + \beta^2 x = \beta^2 \frac{f_0}{k} \sin \omega t \tag{3-2}$$

$$\frac{x}{\delta_{st}} = \frac{1}{\sqrt{\left[1 - \left(\frac{\omega}{\beta}\right)^2\right]^2 + \left(2\zeta\frac{\omega}{\beta}\right)^2}} \sin(\omega t + \phi_1) \tag{3-4}$$

where

$$\phi_1 = \sin^{-1} \frac{-2\zeta\frac{\omega}{\beta}}{\sqrt{\left[1 - \left(\frac{\omega}{\beta}\right)^2\right]^2 + \left(2\zeta\frac{\omega}{\beta}\right)^2}} = \cos^{-1} \frac{1 - \left(\frac{\omega}{\beta}\right)^2}{\sqrt{\left[1 - \left(\frac{\omega}{\beta}\right)^2\right]^2 + \left(2\zeta\frac{\omega}{\beta}\right)^2}} = \tan^{-1} \frac{\left(-2\zeta\frac{\omega}{\beta}\right)}{\left[1 - \left(\frac{\omega}{\beta}\right)^2\right]} \tag{3-5}$$

$$\frac{\dot{x}}{\beta\delta_{st}} = \frac{\left(\frac{\omega}{\beta}\right)}{\sqrt{\left[1 - \left(\frac{\omega}{\beta}\right)^2\right]^2 + \left(2\zeta\frac{\omega}{\beta}\right)^2}} \sin(\omega t + \phi_2) \tag{3-12}$$

where

$$\phi_2 = \left(\phi_1 + \frac{\pi}{2}\right) = \cos^{-1} \frac{2\zeta\frac{\omega}{\beta}}{\sqrt{\left[1 - \left(\frac{\omega}{\beta}\right)^2\right]^2 + \left(2\zeta\frac{\omega}{\beta}\right)^2}} = \sin^{-1} \frac{1 - \left(\frac{\omega}{\beta}\right)^2}{\sqrt{\left[1 - \left(\frac{\omega}{\beta}\right)^2\right]^2 + \left(2\zeta\frac{\omega}{\beta}\right)^2}} = \tan^{-1} \frac{\left[1 - \left(\frac{\omega}{\beta}\right)^2\right]}{2\zeta\frac{\omega}{\beta}} \tag{3-13}$$

continued

$$\frac{\ddot{x}}{\beta^2\,\delta_{st}} = \frac{\left(\frac{\omega}{\beta}\right)^2}{\sqrt{\left[1-\left(\frac{\omega}{\beta}\right)^2\right]^2+\left(2\zeta\frac{\omega}{\beta}\right)^2}}\sin(\omega t+\phi_3) \tag{3-14}$$

where

$$\phi_3 = (\phi_1+\pi) = \sin^{-1}\frac{2\zeta\frac{\omega}{\beta}}{\sqrt{\left[1-\left(\frac{\omega}{\beta}\right)^2\right]^2+\left(2\zeta\frac{\omega}{\beta}\right)^2}} = \cos^{-1}\frac{-1+\left(\frac{\omega}{\beta}\right)^2}{\sqrt{\left[1-\left(\frac{\omega}{\beta}\right)^2\right]^2+\left(2\zeta\frac{\omega}{\beta}\right)^2}} = \tan^{-1}\frac{2\zeta\frac{\omega}{\beta}}{1-\left(\frac{\omega}{\beta}\right)^2} \tag{3-15}$$

$$\frac{F_{\text{wall}}}{F_0} = \sqrt{\frac{1+\left(2\zeta\frac{\omega}{\beta}\right)^2}{\left[1-\left(\frac{\omega}{\beta}\right)^2\right]^2+\left(2\zeta\frac{\omega}{\beta}\right)^2}}\sin(\omega t+\phi_4) \tag{3-16}$$

where

$$\begin{aligned}\phi_4 &= \cos^{-1}\frac{1-\left(\frac{\omega}{\beta}\right)^2+\left(2\zeta\frac{\omega}{\beta}\right)^2}{\sqrt{\left\{\left[1-\left(\frac{\omega}{\beta}\right)^2\right]^2+\left(2\zeta\frac{\omega}{\beta}\right)^2\right\}\left[1+\left(2\zeta\frac{\omega}{\beta}\right)^2\right]}}\\ &= \sin^{-1}\frac{-\left(2\zeta\frac{\omega}{\beta}\right)\left(\frac{\omega}{\beta}\right)^2}{\sqrt{\left\{\left[1-\left(\frac{\omega}{\beta}\right)^2\right]^2+\left(2\zeta\frac{\omega}{\beta}\right)^2\right\}\left[1+\left(2\zeta\frac{\omega}{\beta}\right)^2\right]}}\\ &= \tan^{-1}\frac{-\left(2\zeta\frac{\omega}{\beta}\right)\left(\frac{\omega}{\beta}\right)^2}{1-\left(\frac{\omega}{\beta}\right)^2+\left(2\zeta\frac{\omega}{\beta}\right)^2}\end{aligned} \tag{3-17}$$

$$\frac{d^2x}{dt^2} + 2\zeta\beta\frac{dx}{dt} + \beta^2 x = \frac{m_e}{m}\,\epsilon\,\omega^2\sin\omega t \tag{3-18}$$

$$\frac{x}{\epsilon}\frac{m}{m_e} = \frac{x_r}{y_0} = \frac{x_r}{\epsilon}\frac{m_a}{m_e} = \frac{\left(\frac{\omega}{\beta}\right)^2}{\sqrt{\left[1-\left(\frac{\omega}{\beta}\right)^2\right]^2 + \left(2\zeta\frac{\omega}{\beta}\right)^2}} \sin(\omega t + \phi_1) \tag{3-19}$$

$$\frac{\dot{x}}{\beta\epsilon}\frac{m}{m_e} = \frac{\dot{x}_r}{\beta y_0} = \frac{\dot{x}_r}{\beta\epsilon}\frac{m_a}{m_e} = \frac{\left(\frac{\omega}{\beta}\right)^3}{\sqrt{\left[1-\left(\frac{\omega}{\beta}\right)^2\right]^2 + \left(2\zeta\frac{\omega}{\beta}\right)^2}} \sin(\omega t + \phi_2) \tag{3-20}$$

$$\frac{\ddot{x}}{\beta^2\epsilon}\frac{m}{m_e} = \frac{\ddot{x}_r}{\beta^2 y_0} = \frac{\ddot{x}_r}{\beta^2\epsilon}\frac{m_a}{m_e} = \frac{\left(\frac{\omega}{\beta}\right)^4}{\sqrt{\left[1-\left(\frac{\omega}{\beta}\right)^2\right]^2 + \left(2\zeta\frac{\omega}{\beta}\right)^2}} \sin(\omega t + \phi_3) \tag{3-21}$$

$$\frac{f_{\text{wall}}}{\beta^2\epsilon m_e} = \frac{f_{\text{wall}}}{\beta^2 y_0 m} = \frac{f_{\text{wall}}}{\beta^2\epsilon m_e}\left(1 + \frac{m_a}{m}\right) = \left(\frac{\omega}{\beta}\right)^2\sqrt{\frac{1 + \left(2\zeta\frac{\omega}{\beta}\right)^2}{\left[1-\left(\frac{\omega}{\beta}\right)^2\right]^2 + \left(2\zeta\frac{\omega}{\beta}\right)^2}} \sin(\omega t + \phi_4) \tag{3-22}$$

$$\frac{d^2x_r}{dt^2} + 2\zeta\beta\frac{dx_r}{dt} + \beta^2 x_r = y_0\omega^2 \sin\omega t \tag{3-23}$$

$$\frac{x}{y_0} = \frac{x}{\epsilon}\frac{m}{m_e} = \frac{x}{\epsilon}\frac{(m + m_a)}{m_e} = \sqrt{\frac{1 + \left(2\zeta\frac{\omega}{\beta}\right)^2}{\left[1-\left(\frac{\omega}{\beta}\right)^2\right]^2 + \left(2\zeta\frac{\omega}{\beta}\right)^2}} \sin(\omega t + \phi_4) \tag{3-24}$$

$$\frac{\dot{x}}{\beta y_0} = \frac{\dot{x}}{\beta\epsilon}\frac{m}{m_e} = \frac{\dot{x}}{\beta\epsilon}\left(\frac{m + m_a}{m_e}\right) = \frac{\omega}{\beta}\sqrt{\frac{1 + \left(2\zeta\frac{\omega}{\beta}\right)^2}{\left[1-\left(\frac{\omega}{\beta}\right)^2\right]^2 + \left(2\zeta\frac{\omega}{\beta}\right)^2}} \sin(\omega t + \phi_5) \tag{3-25}$$

continued

where

$$\phi_5 = \left(\phi_4 + \frac{\pi}{2}\right) = \tan^{-1} \frac{1 - \left(\frac{\omega}{\beta}\right)^2 + \left(2\zeta \frac{\omega}{\beta}\right)^2}{2\zeta \left(\frac{\omega}{\beta}\right)^3} \tag{3-26}$$

$$\frac{\ddot{x}}{\beta^2 y_0} = \frac{\ddot{x}}{\beta^2 \epsilon} \frac{m}{m_e} = \frac{\ddot{x}}{\beta^2 \epsilon} \left(\frac{m + m_a}{m_e}\right) = \left(\frac{\omega}{\beta}\right)^2 \sqrt{\frac{1 + \left(2\zeta \frac{\omega}{\beta}\right)^2}{\left[1 - \left(\frac{\omega}{\beta}\right)^2\right]^2 + \left(2\zeta \frac{\omega}{\beta}\right)^2}} \sin(\omega t + \phi_6) \tag{3-27}$$

where

$$\phi_6 = (\phi_4 + \pi) = \tan^{-1} \frac{2\zeta \left(\frac{\omega}{\beta}\right)^3}{-1 + \left(\frac{\omega}{\beta}\right)^2 - \left(2\zeta \frac{\omega}{\beta}\right)^2} \tag{3-28}$$

$$\frac{d^2 x_r}{dt^2} + 2\zeta\beta \frac{dx_r}{dt} + \beta^2 x_r = \frac{m_e}{m_a} \epsilon \, \omega^2 \sin \omega t \tag{3-29}$$

where

$$\zeta = \frac{c}{2\sqrt{km}} \sqrt{1 + \frac{m}{m_a}} \equiv \frac{c\beta}{2k} \equiv \frac{c}{2\beta m} \left(1 + \frac{m}{m_a}\right) \equiv \frac{c}{c_c} \tag{3-30}$$

$$\beta = \sqrt{\frac{k}{m}} \sqrt{1 + \frac{m}{m_a}} \tag{3-31}$$

$$c_c = \frac{2\sqrt{km}}{\sqrt{1 + \frac{m}{m_a}}} \equiv \frac{2k}{\beta} \equiv \frac{2\beta m}{1 + \frac{m}{m_a}} \tag{3-32}$$

$$\frac{z}{\epsilon} \left(\frac{m + m_a}{m_e}\right) = \sqrt{\frac{\left[1 - \left(1 + \frac{m}{m_a}\right)\left(\frac{\omega}{\beta}\right)^2\right]^2 + \left(2\zeta \frac{\omega}{\beta}\right)^2}{\left[1 - \left(\frac{\omega}{\beta}\right)^2\right]^2 + \left(2\zeta \frac{\omega}{\beta}\right)^2}} \sin(\omega t + \phi_7) \tag{3-33}$$

where

$$\phi_7 = \sin^{-1} \frac{\frac{m}{m_a} 2\zeta \left(\frac{\omega}{\beta}\right)^3}{\sqrt{\left\{\left[1 - \left(\frac{\omega}{\beta}\right)^2\right]^2 + \left(2\zeta \frac{\omega}{\beta}\right)^2\right\}\left\{\left[1 - \left(1 + \frac{m}{m_a}\right)\left(\frac{\omega}{\beta}\right)^2\right]^2 + \left(2\zeta \frac{\omega}{\beta}\right)^2\right\}}}$$

$$= \cos^{-1} \frac{\left[1 - \left(1 + \frac{m}{m_a}\right)\left(\frac{\omega}{\beta}\right)^2\right]\left[1 - \left(\frac{\omega}{\beta}\right)^2\right] + \left(2\zeta \frac{\omega}{\beta}\right)^2}{\sqrt{\left\{\left[1 - \left(\frac{\omega}{\beta}\right)^2\right]^2 + \left(2\zeta \frac{\omega}{\beta}\right)^2\right\}\left\{\left[1 - \left(1 + \frac{m}{m_a}\right)\left(\frac{\omega}{\beta}\right)^2\right]^2 + \left(2\zeta \frac{\omega}{\beta}\right)^2\right\}}} \tag{3-34}$$

$$= \tan^{-1} \frac{\frac{m}{m_a} 2\zeta \left(\frac{\omega}{\beta}\right)^3}{\left[1 - \left(1 + \frac{m}{m_a}\right)\left(\frac{\omega}{\beta}\right)^2\right]\left[1 - \left(\frac{\omega}{\beta}\right)^2\right] + \left(2\zeta \frac{\omega}{\beta}\right)^2}$$

$$\frac{\dot{z}}{\beta\epsilon}\left(\frac{m + m_a}{m_e}\right) = \left(\frac{\omega}{\beta}\right)\sqrt{\frac{\left[1 - \left(1 + \frac{m}{m_a}\right)\left(\frac{\omega}{\beta}\right)^2\right]^2 + \left(2\zeta \frac{\omega}{\beta}\right)^2}{\left[1 - \left(\frac{\omega}{\beta}\right)^2\right]^2 + \left(2\zeta \frac{\omega}{\beta}\right)^2}} \sin(\omega t + \phi_8) \tag{3-35}$$

where

$$\phi_8 = \left(\phi_7 + \frac{\pi}{2}\right) = \tan^{-1} \frac{\left[1 - \left(1 + \frac{m}{m_a}\right)\left(\frac{\omega}{\beta}\right)^2\right]\left[1 - \left(\frac{\omega}{\beta}\right)^2\right] + \left(2\zeta \frac{\omega}{\beta}\right)^2}{-\frac{m}{m_a} 2\zeta \left(\frac{\omega}{\beta}\right)^3} \tag{3-36}$$

$$\frac{\ddot{z}}{\beta^2\epsilon}\left(\frac{m + m_a}{m_e}\right) = \left(\frac{\omega}{\beta}\right)^2\sqrt{\frac{\left[1 - \left(1 + \frac{m}{m_a}\right)\left(\frac{\omega}{\beta}\right)^2\right]^2 + \left(2\zeta \frac{\omega}{\beta}\right)^2}{\left[1 - \left(\frac{\omega}{\beta}\right)^2\right]^2 + \left(2\zeta \frac{\omega}{\beta}\right)^2}} \sin(\omega t + \phi_9) \tag{3-37}$$

where

$$\phi_9 = (\phi_7 + \pi) = \tan^{-1} \frac{-\frac{m}{m_a} 2\zeta \left(\frac{\omega}{\beta}\right)^3}{-\left[1 - \left(1 + \frac{m}{m_a}\right)\left(\frac{\omega}{\beta}\right)^2\right]\left[1 - \left(\frac{\omega}{\beta}\right)^2\right] + \left(2\zeta \frac{\omega}{\beta}\right)^2} \tag{3-38}$$

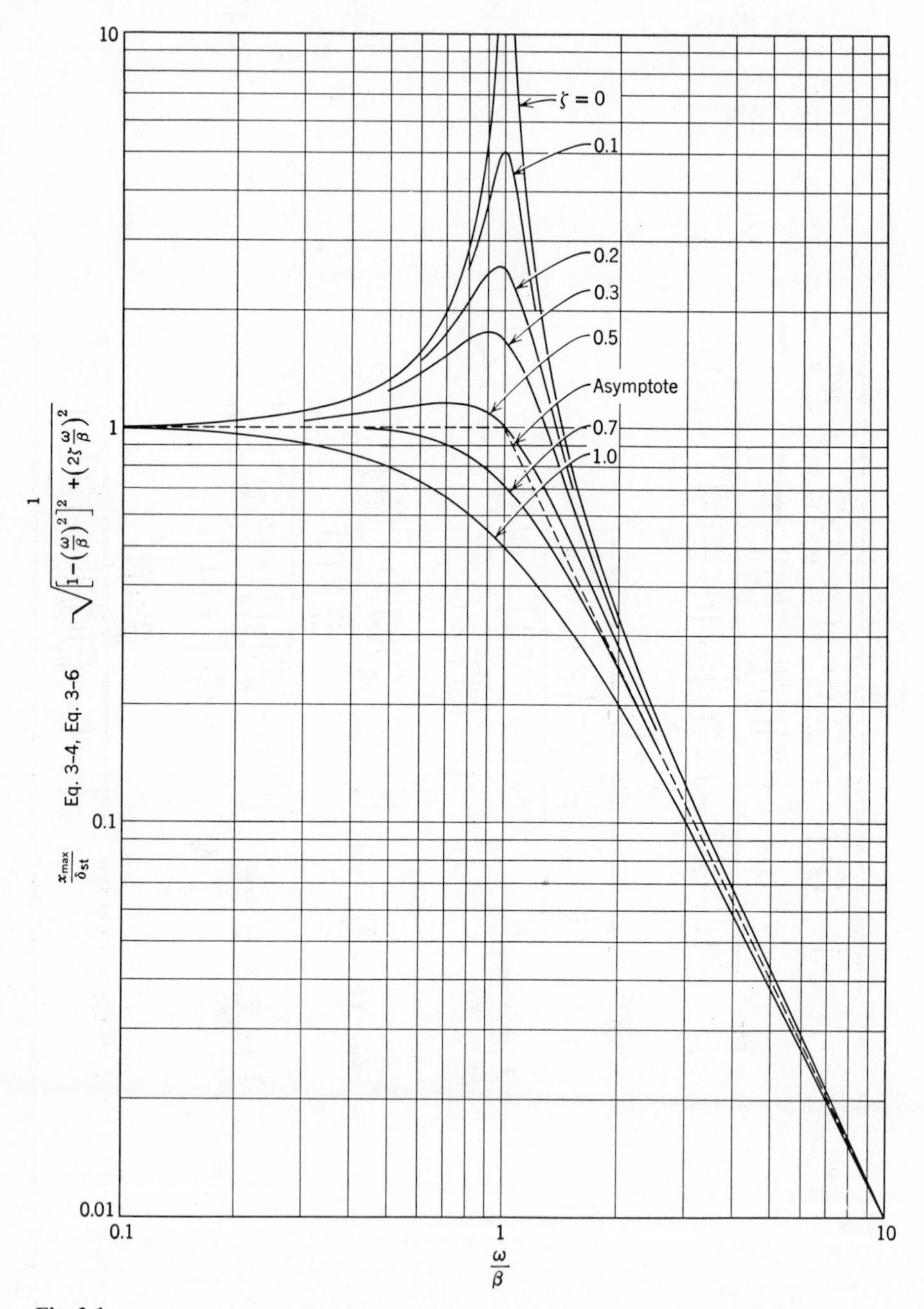

10
1
0.1
0.01
0.1
1
10
ζ = 0
0.1
0.2
0.3
0.5
Asymptote
0.7
1.0
$\frac{\omega}{\beta}$
$\frac{x_{max}}{\delta_{st}}$ Eq. 3-4, Eq. 3-6 $\frac{1}{\sqrt{\left[1-\left(\frac{\omega}{\beta}\right)^2\right]^2+\left(2\zeta\frac{\omega}{\beta}\right)^2}}$

Fig. 3-1

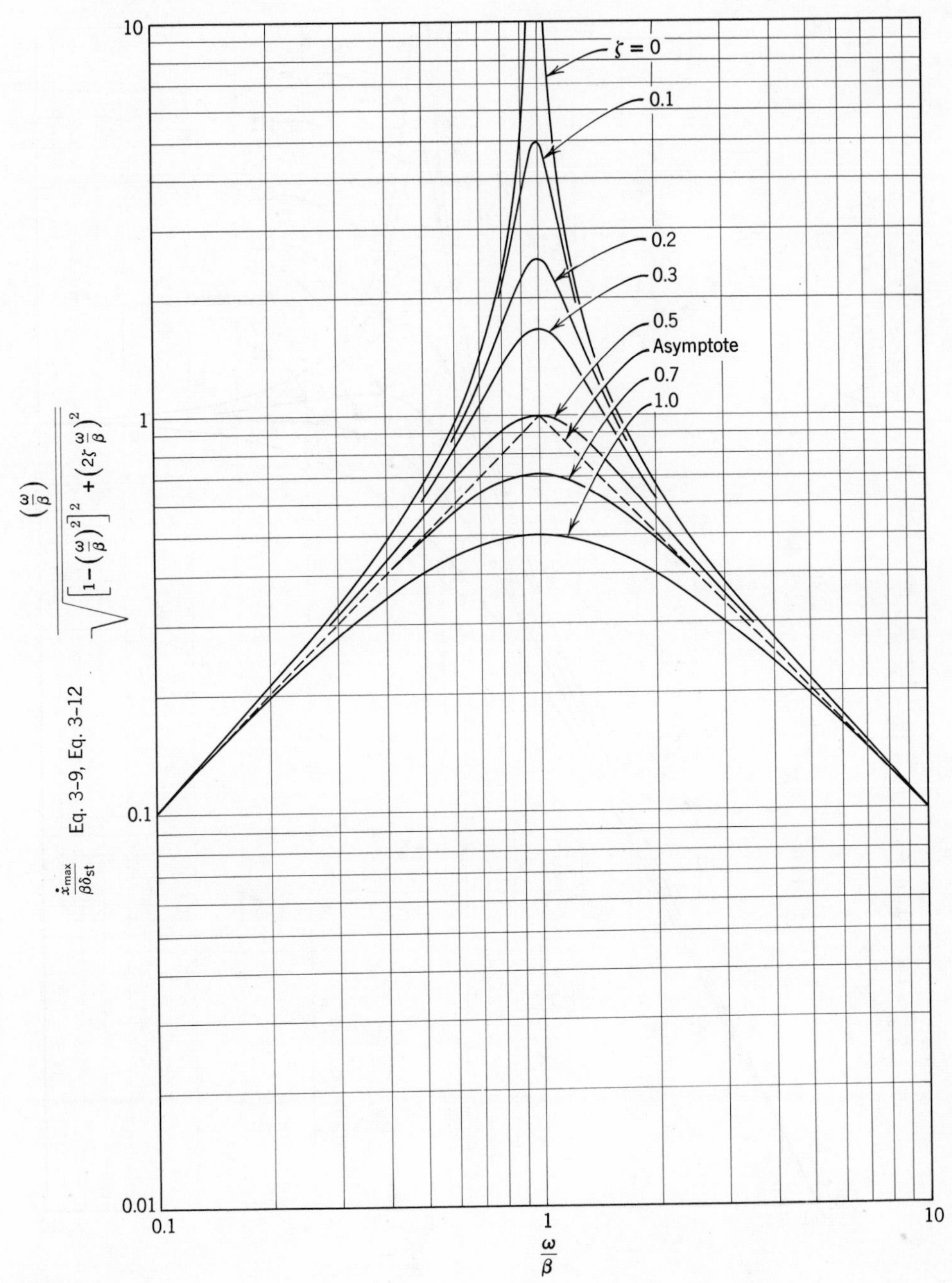

$\zeta = 0$
0.1
0.2
0.3
0.5
Asymptote
0.7
1.0
10
1
0.1
0.01
0.1
1
10
$\frac{\omega}{\beta}$
$\frac{\dot{x}_{max}}{\beta\delta_{st}}$ Eq. 3-9, Eq. 3-12 $\frac{\left(\frac{\omega}{\beta}\right)}{\sqrt{\left[1-\left(\frac{\omega}{\beta}\right)^2\right]^2+\left(2\zeta\frac{\omega}{\beta}\right)^2}}$

Fig. 3-2

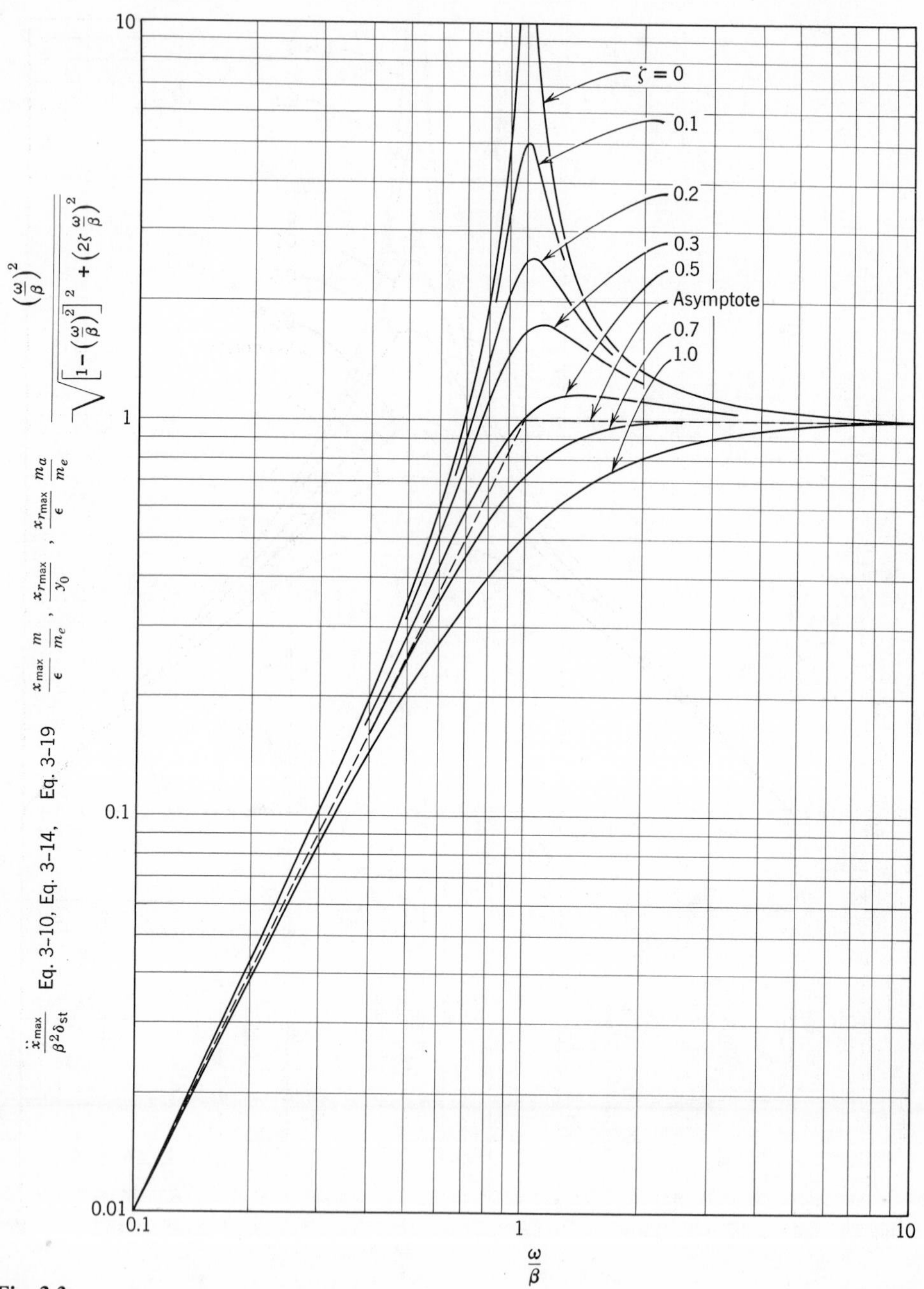

ζ = 0
0.1
0.2
0.3
0.5
Asymptote
0.7
1.0
10
1
0.1
0.01
0.1
1
10
$\frac{\omega}{\beta}$
$\frac{\ddot{x}_{max}}{\beta^2\delta_{st}}$ Eq. 3-10, Eq. 3-14, Eq. 3-19 $\frac{x_{max}}{\epsilon}\frac{m}{m_e}$, $\frac{x_{r\,max}}{y_0}$, $\frac{x_{r\,max}}{\epsilon}\frac{m_a}{m_e}$ $\frac{\left(\frac{\omega}{\beta}\right)^2}{\sqrt{\left[1-\left(\frac{\omega}{\beta}\right)^2\right]^2+\left(2\zeta\frac{\omega}{\beta}\right)^2}}$

Fig. 3-3

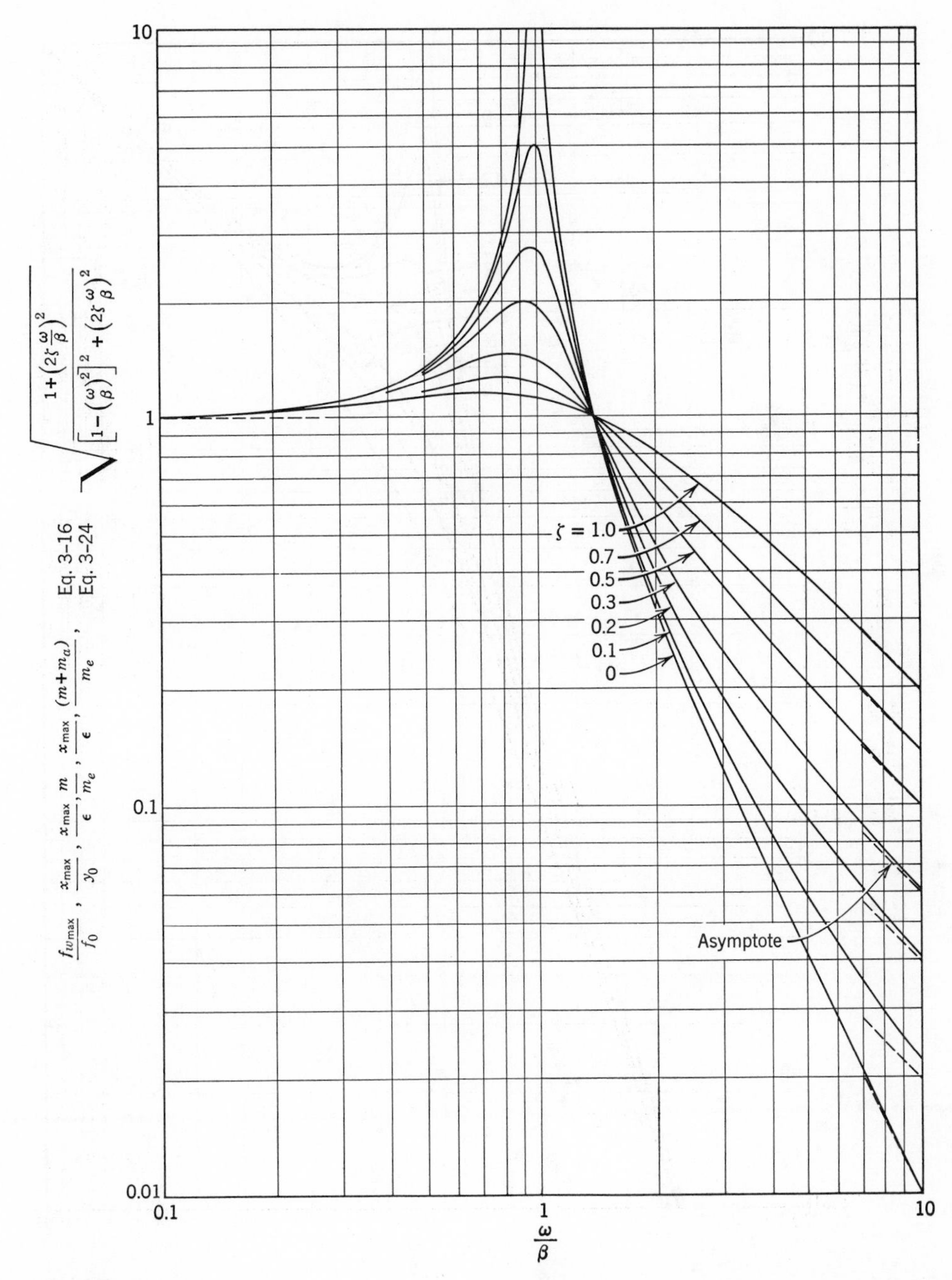

10
1
0.1
0.01
0.1
1
10
$\frac{\omega}{\beta}$
$\frac{f_{w_{max}}}{f_0}$, $\frac{x_{max}}{y_0}$, $\frac{x_{max}}{\epsilon}\frac{m}{m_e}$, $\frac{x_{max}}{\epsilon}\frac{(m+m_a)}{m_e}$, Eq. 3-16 Eq. 3-24 $\sqrt{\frac{1+\left(2\zeta\frac{\omega}{\beta}\right)^2}{\left[1-\left(\frac{\omega}{\beta}\right)^2\right]^2+\left(2\zeta\frac{\omega}{\beta}\right)^2}}$
ζ = 1.0
0.7
0.5
0.3
0.2
0.1
0
Asymptote

Fig. 3-4

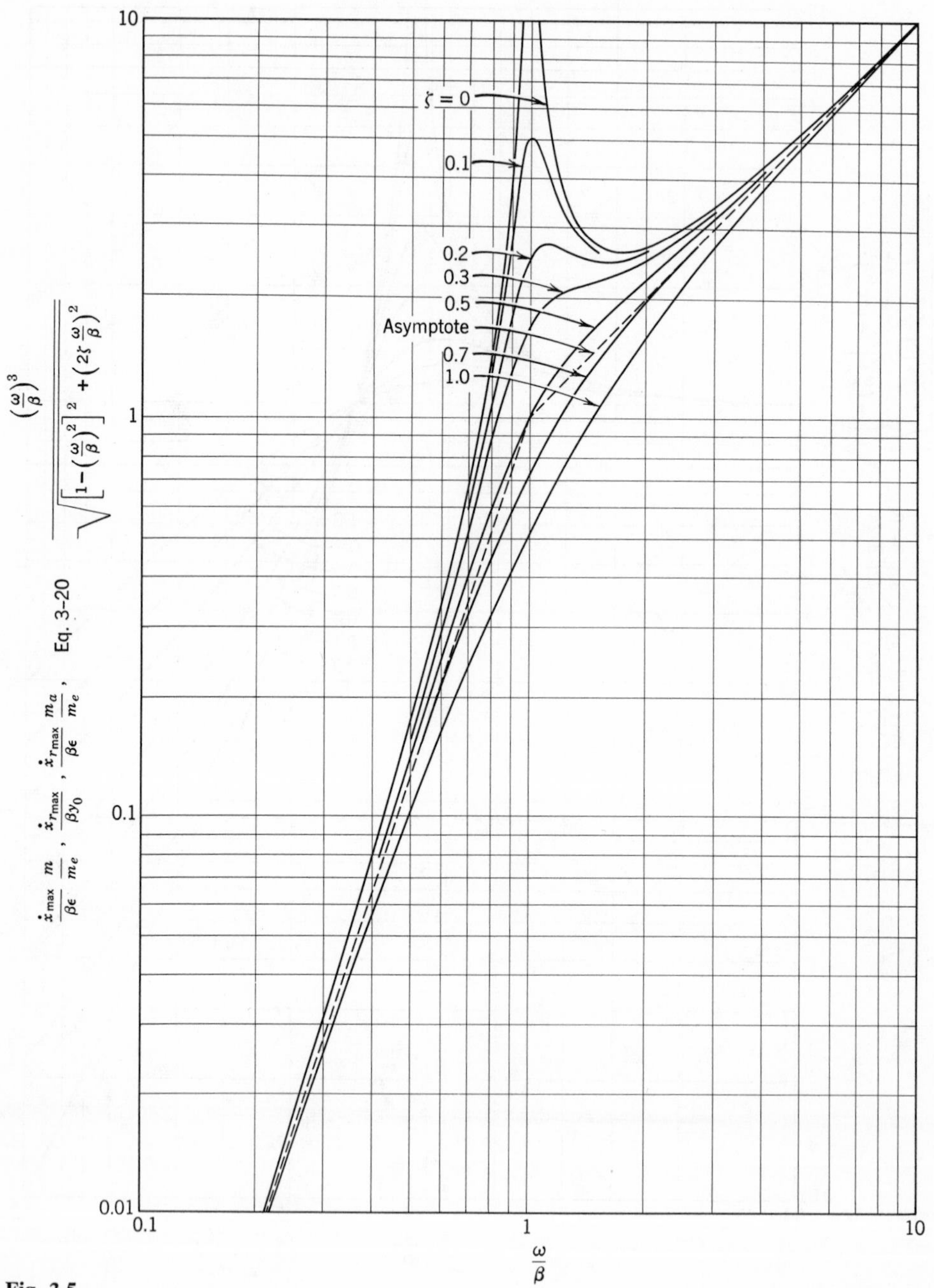

$\zeta = 0$
0.1
0.2
0.3
0.5
Asymptote
0.7
1.0
10
1
0.1
0.01
0.1
1
10
$\frac{\omega}{\beta}$
$\frac{\dot{x}_{\max}}{\beta\epsilon}\frac{m}{m_e}, \quad \frac{\dot{x}_{r_{\max}}}{\beta y_0}, \quad \frac{\dot{x}_{r_{\max}}}{\beta\epsilon}\frac{m_a}{m_e}, \quad$ Eq. 3-20 $\quad \frac{\left(\frac{\omega}{\beta}\right)^3}{\sqrt{\left[1-\left(\frac{\omega}{\beta}\right)^2\right]^2 + \left(2\zeta\frac{\omega}{\beta}\right)^2}}$

Fig. 3-5

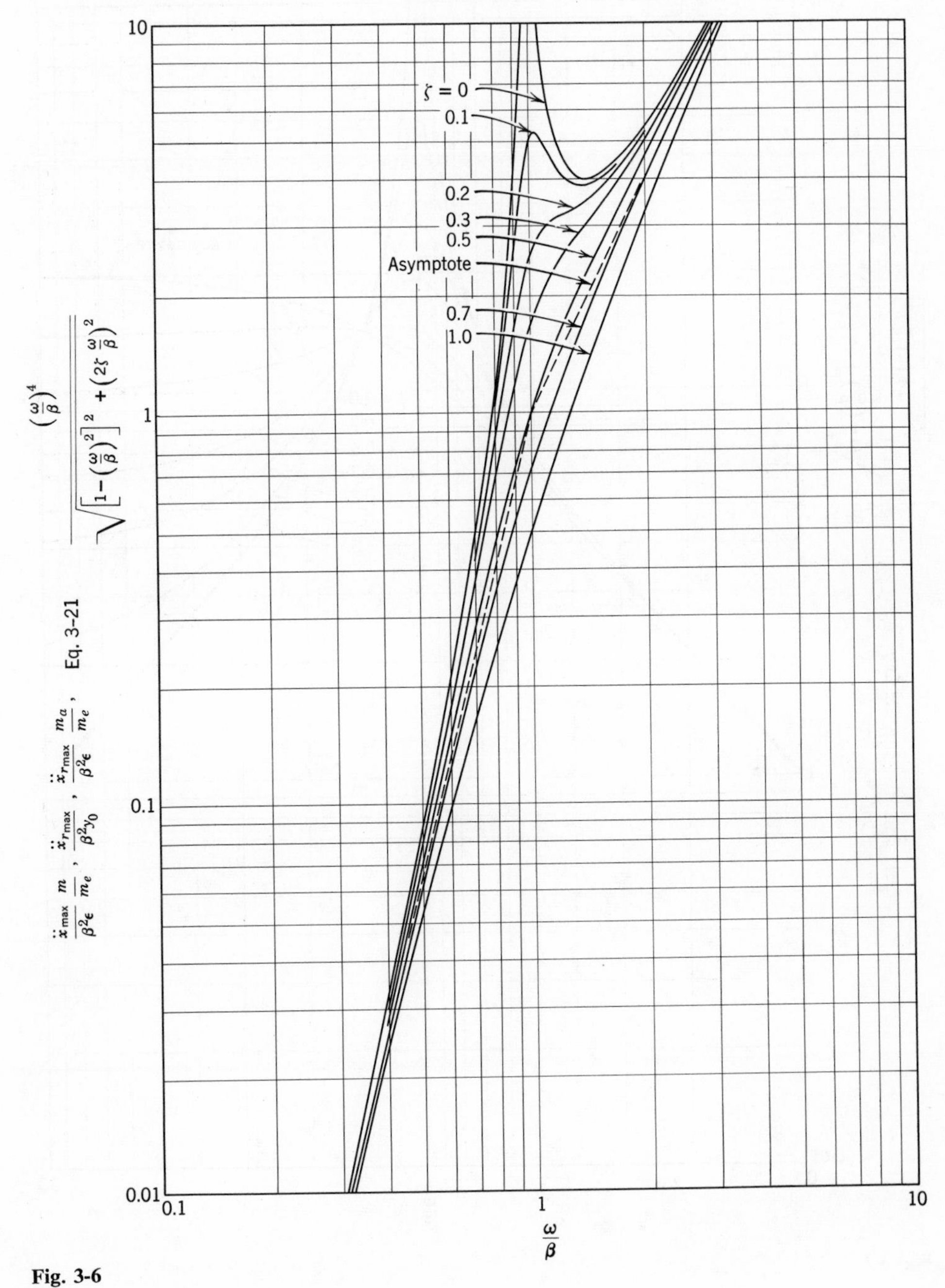

$\frac{\ddot{x}_{\max}}{\beta^2\epsilon}\frac{m}{m_e}$, $\frac{\ddot{x}_{r\max}}{\beta^2 y_0}$, $\frac{\ddot{x}_{r\max}}{\beta^2\epsilon}\frac{m_a}{m_e}$, Eq. 3–21 $\frac{\left(\frac{\omega}{\beta}\right)^4}{\sqrt{\left[1-\left(\frac{\omega}{\beta}\right)^2\right]^2+\left(2\zeta\frac{\omega}{\beta}\right)^2}}$
$\zeta = 0$
0.1
0.2
0.3
0.5
Asymptote
0.7
1.0
10
1
0.1
0.01
0.1
1
10
$\frac{\omega}{\beta}$

Fig. 3-6

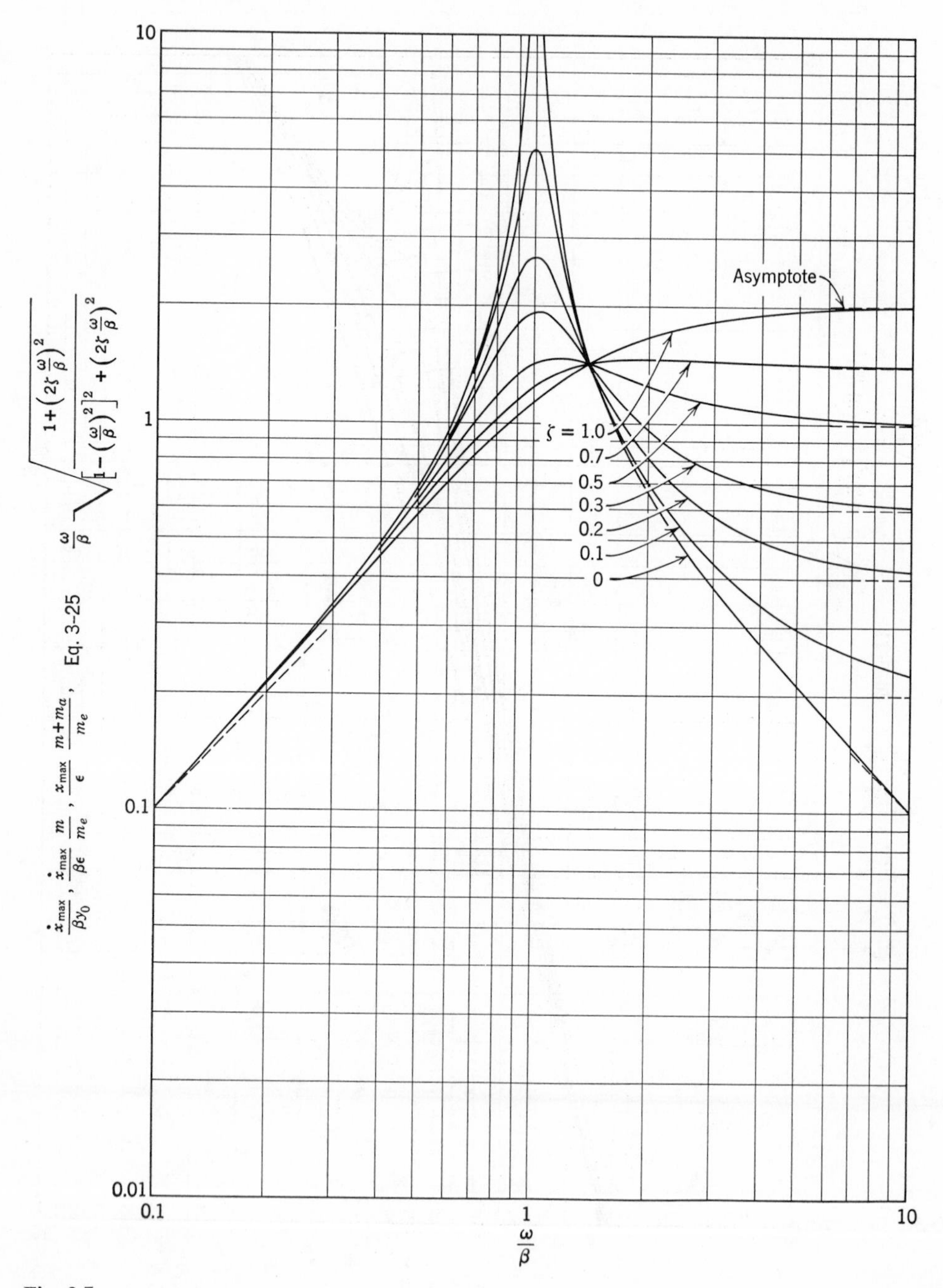

$\frac{\dot{x}_{\max}}{\beta y_0}, \frac{\dot{x}_{\max}}{\beta\epsilon}\frac{m}{m_e}, \frac{x_{\max}}{\epsilon}\frac{m+m_a}{m_e}$, Eq. 3-25 $\frac{\omega}{\beta}\sqrt{\frac{1+\left(2\zeta\frac{\omega}{\beta}\right)^2}{\left[1-\left(\frac{\omega}{\beta}\right)^2\right]^2+\left(2\zeta\frac{\omega}{\beta}\right)^2}}$
Asymptote
$\zeta = 1.0$
0.7
0.5
0.3
0.2
0.1
0
10
1
0.1
0.01
0.1
1
10
$\frac{\omega}{\beta}$

Fig. 3-7

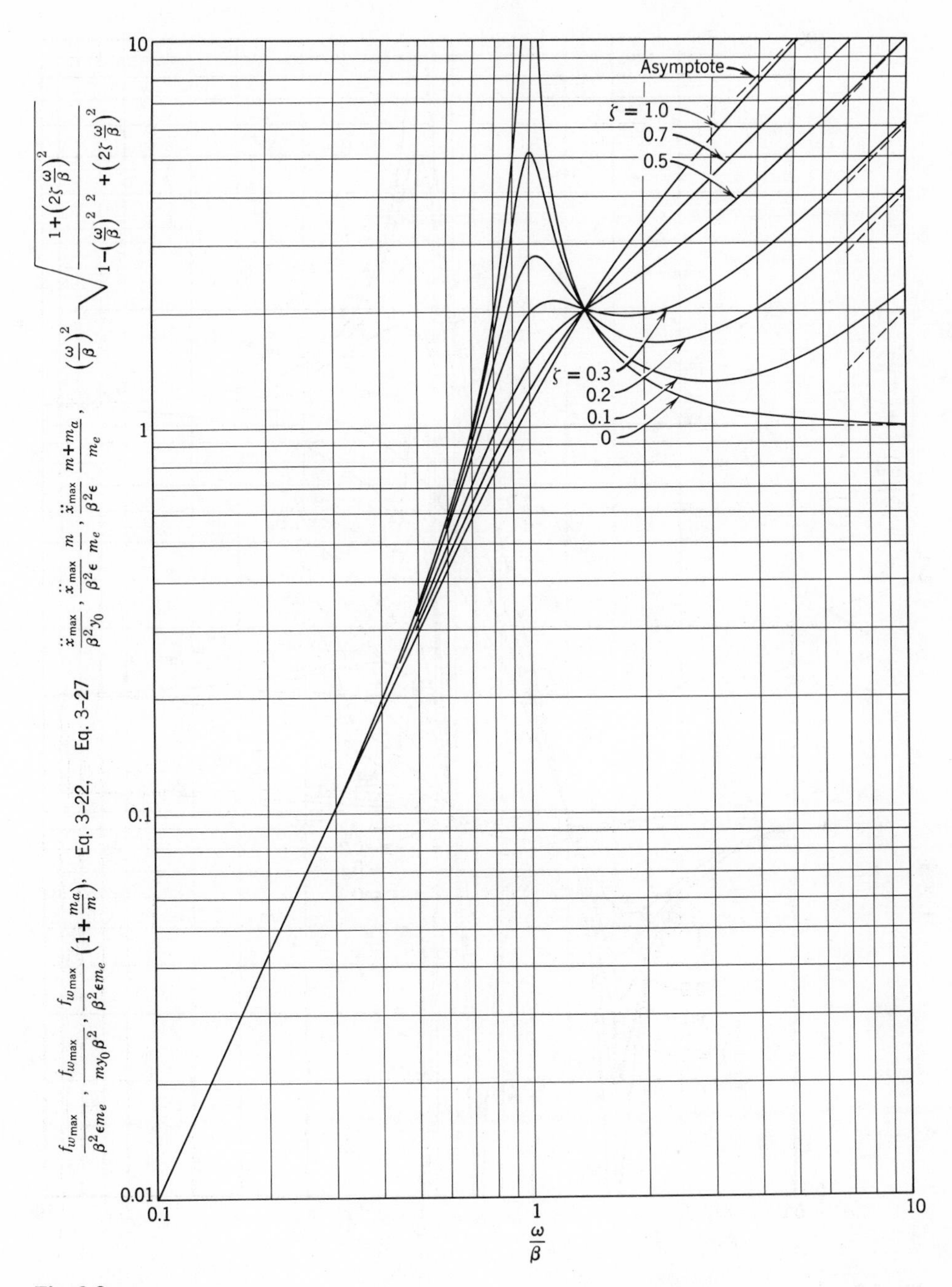

10
1
0.1
0.01
0.1
1
10
$\frac{\omega}{\beta}$
Asymptote
$\zeta = 1.0$
0.7
0.5
$\zeta = 0.3$
0.2
0.1
0
$\frac{f_{w_{\max}}}{\beta^2 \epsilon m_e}, \frac{f_{w_{\max}}}{m y_0 \beta^2}, \frac{f_{w_{\max}}}{\beta^2 \epsilon m_e}\left(1+\frac{m_a}{m}\right)$, Eq. 3-22, Eq. 3-27 $\frac{\ddot{x}_{\max}}{\beta^2 y_0}, \frac{\ddot{x}_{\max}}{\beta^2 \epsilon}\frac{m}{m_e}, \frac{\ddot{x}_{\max}}{\beta^2 \epsilon}\frac{m+m_a}{m_e}, \left(\frac{\omega}{\beta}\right)^2 \sqrt{\frac{1+\left(2\zeta\frac{\omega}{\beta}\right)^2}{\left[1-\left(\frac{\omega}{\beta}\right)^2\right]^2+\left(2\zeta\frac{\omega}{\beta}\right)^2}}$

Fig. 3-8

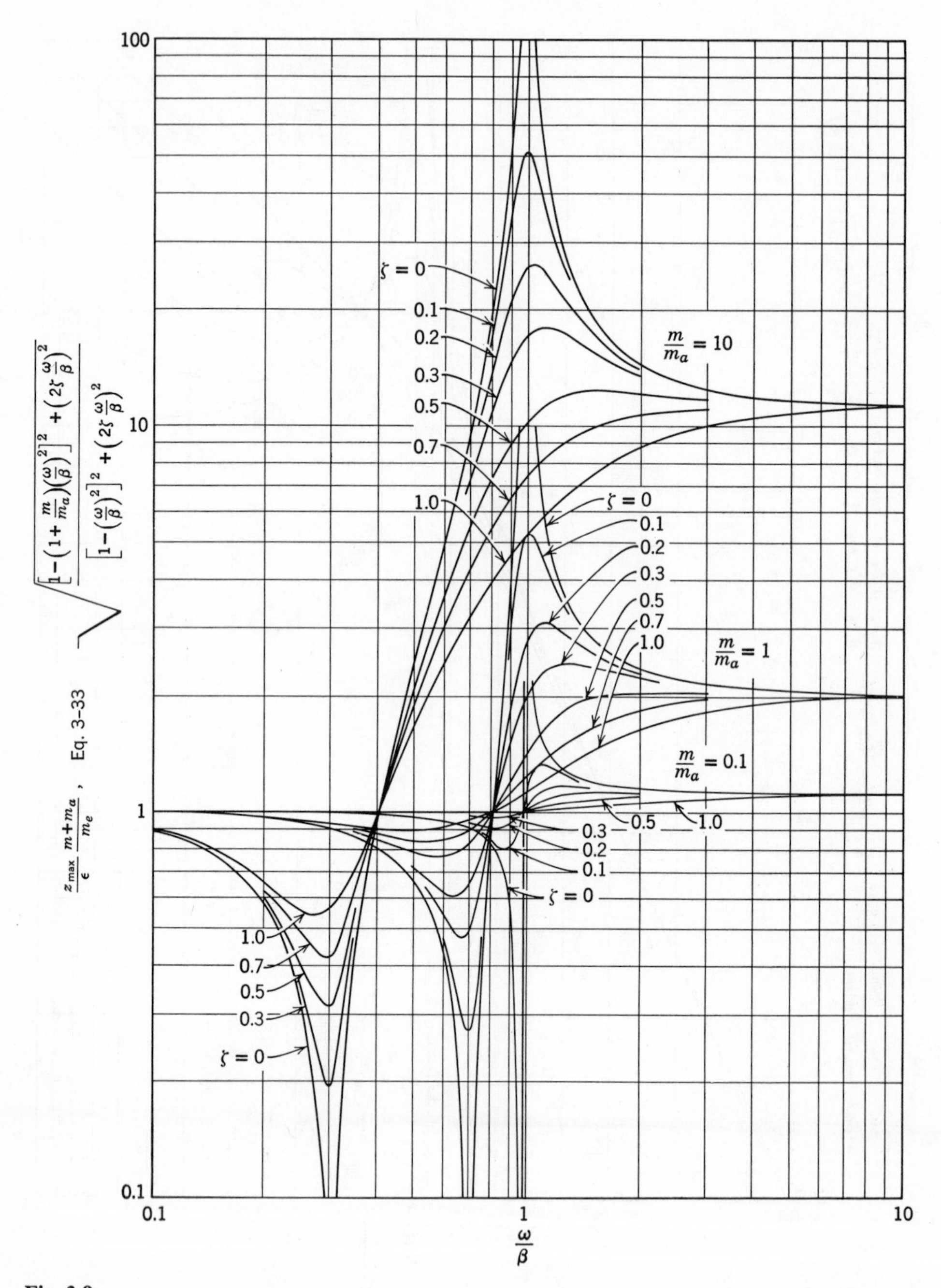

$\frac{z_{\max}}{\epsilon}\frac{m+m_a}{m_e}$, Eq. 3-33 $\sqrt{\frac{\left[1-\left(1+\frac{m}{m_a}\right)\left(\frac{\omega}{\beta}\right)^2\right]^2+\left(2\zeta\frac{\omega}{\beta}\right)^2}{\left[1-\left(\frac{\omega}{\beta}\right)^2\right]^2+\left(2\zeta\frac{\omega}{\beta}\right)^2}}$
100
10
1
0.1
0.1
1
10
$\frac{\omega}{\beta}$
$\zeta = 0$
0.1
0.2
0.3
0.5
0.7
1.0
$\frac{m}{m_a} = 10$
$\zeta = 0$
0.1
0.2
0.3
0.5
0.7
1.0
$\frac{m}{m_a} = 1$
$\frac{m}{m_a} = 0.1$
0.3
0.2
0.1
$\zeta = 0$
0.5
1.0
1.0
0.7
0.5
0.3
$\zeta = 0$

Fig. 3-9

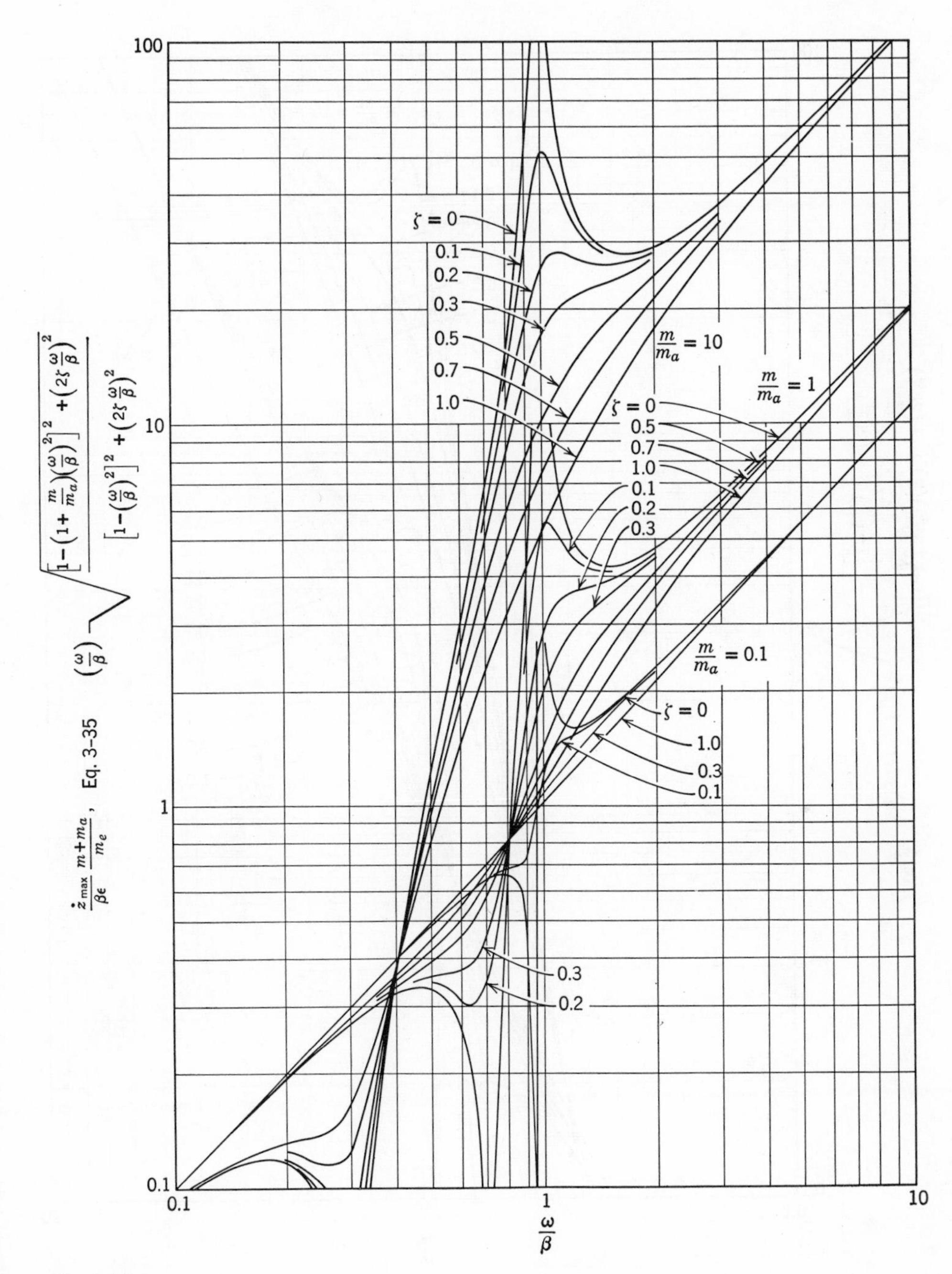

$\frac{\dot{z}_{max}}{\beta\epsilon}\frac{m+m_a}{m_e}$, Eq. 3-35 $\left(\frac{\omega}{\beta}\right)\sqrt{\frac{\left[1-\left(1+\frac{m}{m_a}\right)\left(\frac{\omega}{\beta}\right)^2\right]^2+\left(2\zeta\frac{\omega}{\beta}\right)^2}{\left[1-\left(\frac{\omega}{\beta}\right)^2\right]^2+\left(2\zeta\frac{\omega}{\beta}\right)^2}}$
$\zeta = 0$
0.1
0.2
0.3
0.5
0.7
1.0
$\frac{m}{m_a} = 10$
$\frac{m}{m_a} = 1$
$\zeta = 0$
0.5
0.7
1.0
0.1
0.2
0.3
$\frac{m}{m_a} = 0.1$
$\zeta = 0$
1.0
0.3
0.1
0.3
0.2
100
10
1
0.1
0.1
1
10
$\frac{\omega}{\beta}$

Fig. 3-10

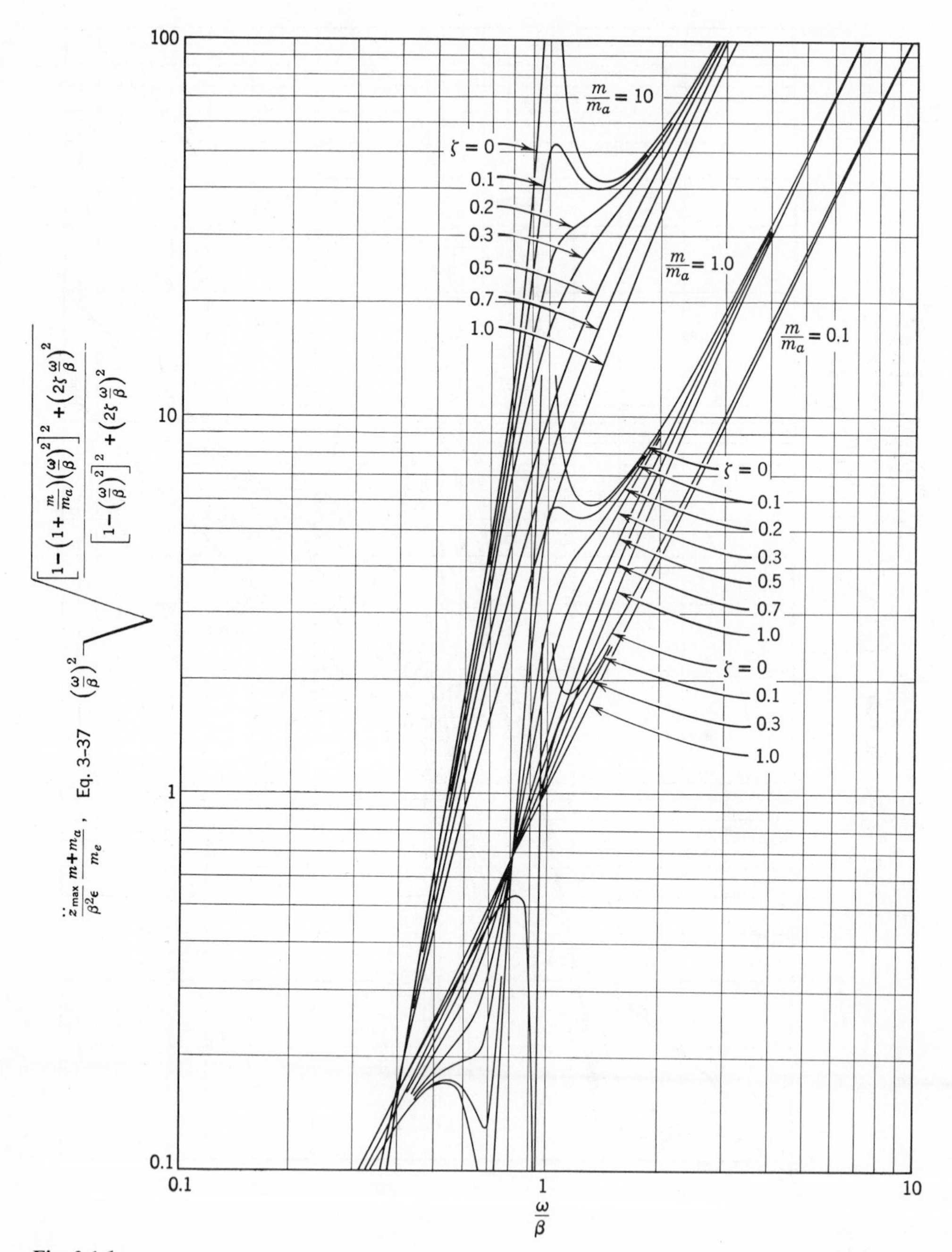

100
10
1
0.1
$\frac{m}{m_a} = 10$
$\zeta = 0$
0.1
0.2
0.3
0.5
0.7
1.0
$\frac{m}{m_a} = 1.0$
$\frac{m}{m_a} = 0.1$
$\zeta = 0$
0.1
0.2
0.3
0.5
0.7
1.0
$\zeta = 0$
0.1
0.3
1.0
$\frac{\ddot{z}_{\max}}{\beta^2 \epsilon} \frac{m+m_a}{m_e}$, Eq. 3-37 $\left(\frac{\omega}{\beta}\right)^2 \sqrt{\frac{\left[1-\left(1+\frac{m}{m_a}\right)\left(\frac{\omega}{\beta}\right)^2\right]^2 + \left(2\zeta\frac{\omega}{\beta}\right)^2}{\left[1-\left(\frac{\omega}{\beta}\right)^2\right]^2 + \left(2\zeta\frac{\omega}{\beta}\right)^2}}$
$\frac{\omega}{\beta}$

Fig. 3-1 1

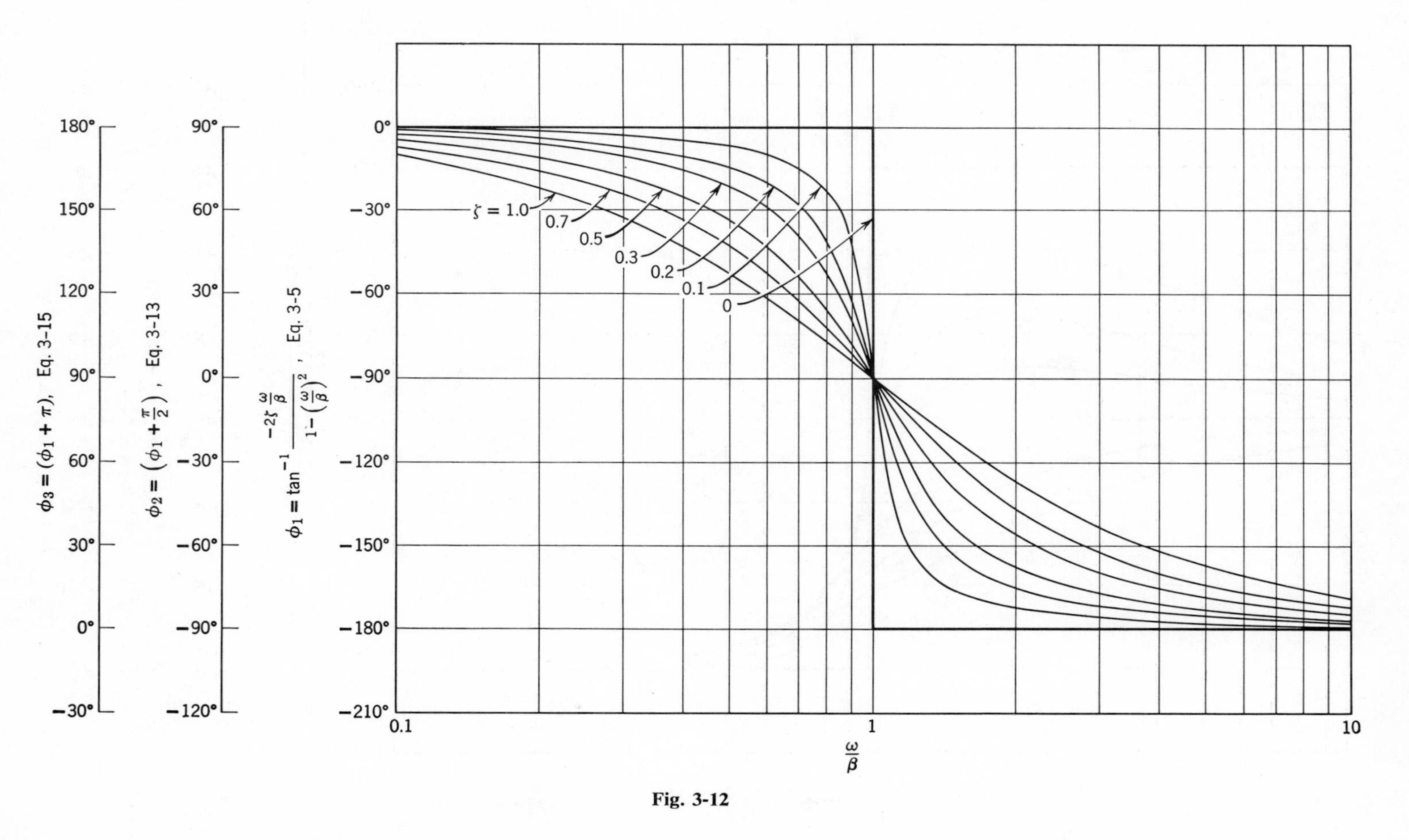

$\phi_3 = (\phi_1 + \pi)$, Eq. 3-15
180°
150°
120°
90°
60°
30°
0°
−30°
$\phi_2 = \left(\phi_1 + \frac{\pi}{2}\right)$, Eq. 3-13
90°
60°
30°
0°
−30°
−60°
−90°
−120°
$\phi_1 = \tan^{-1} \frac{-2\zeta \frac{\omega}{\beta}}{1 - \left(\frac{\omega}{\beta}\right)^2}$, Eq. 3-5
0°
−30°
−60°
−90°
−120°
−150°
−180°
−210°
$\zeta = 1.0$
0.7
0.5
0.3
0.2
0.1
0
0.1
1
10
$\frac{\omega}{\beta}$

Fig. 3-12

Fig. 3-13

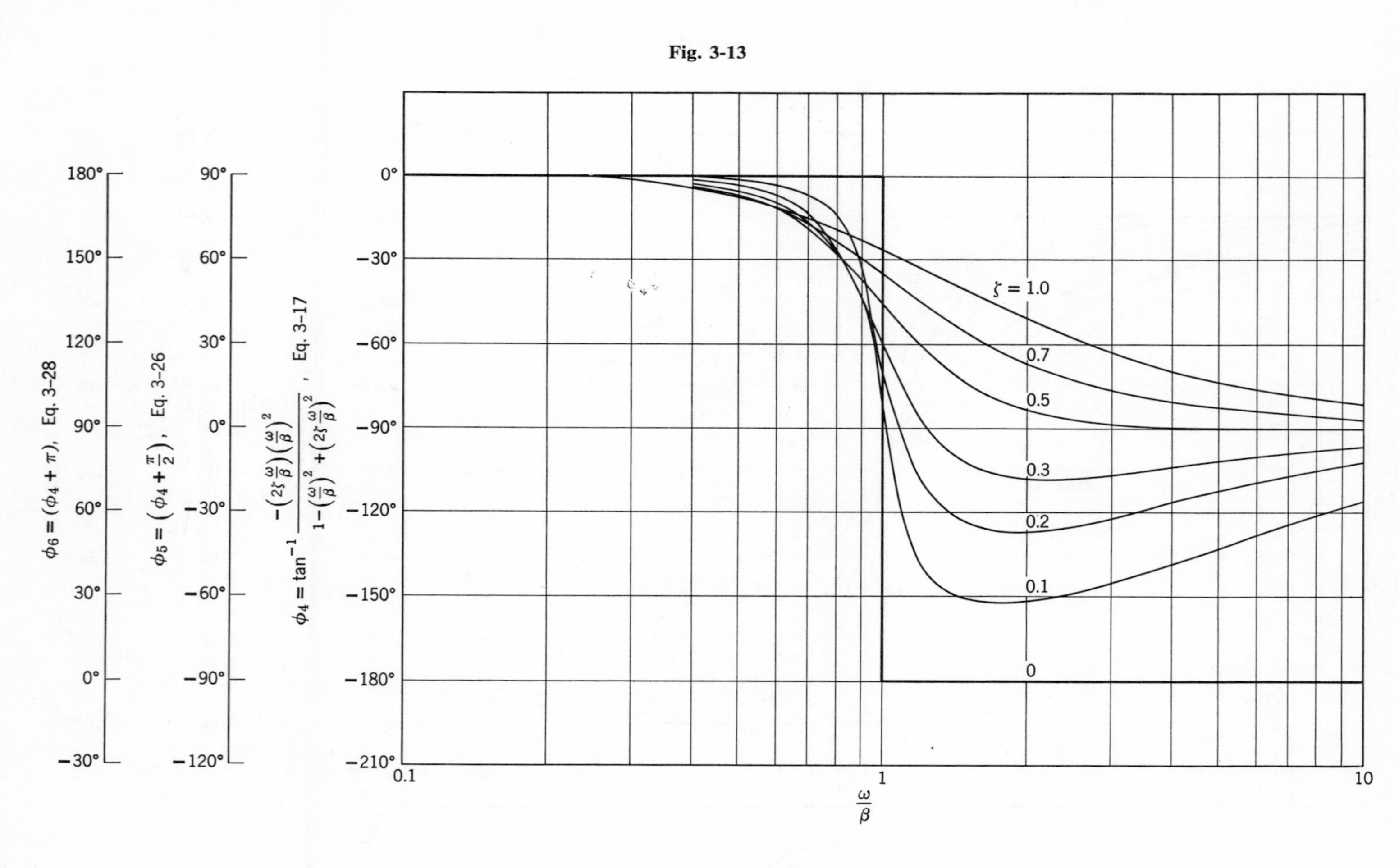
ζ = 1.0
0.7
0.5
0.3
0.2
0.1
0
0°
−30°
−60°
−90°
−120°
−150°
−180°
−210°
0.1
1
10
ω/β
φ4 = tan⁻¹ −(2ζ ω/β)(ω/β)² / 1−(ω/β)² + (2ζ ω/β)², Eq. 3-17
90°
60°
30°
0°
−30°
−60°
−90°
−120°
φ5 = (φ4 + π/2), Eq. 3-26
180°
150°
120°
90°
60°
30°
0°
−30°
φ6 = (φ4 + π), Eq. 3-28

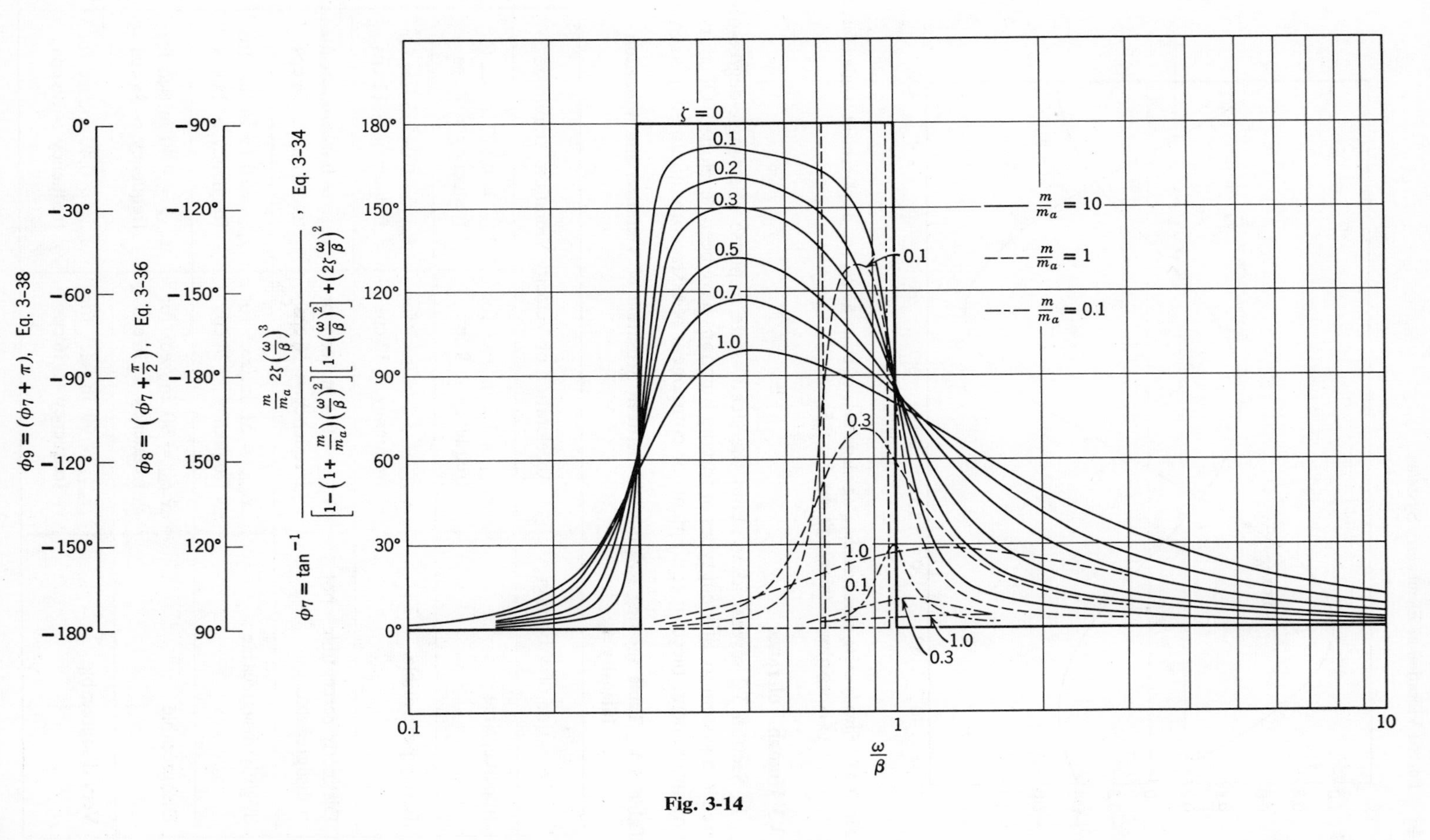
$\phi_9 = (\phi_7 + \pi)$, Eq. 3-38
0°
−30°
−60°
−90°
−120°
−150°
−180°
$\phi_8 = \left(\phi_7 + \frac{\pi}{2}\right)$, Eq. 3-36
−90°
−120°
−150°
−180°
150°
120°
90°
$\phi_7 = \tan^{-1} \dfrac{\frac{m}{m_a} 2\zeta \left(\frac{\omega}{\beta}\right)^3}{\left[1 - \left(1 + \frac{m}{m_a}\right)\left(\frac{\omega}{\beta}\right)^2\right]\left[1 - \left(\frac{\omega}{\beta}\right)^2\right] + \left(2\zeta \frac{\omega}{\beta}\right)^2}$, Eq. 3-34
180°
150°
120°
90°
60°
30°
0°
$\zeta = 0$
0.1
0.2
0.3
0.5
0.7
1.0
0.1
0.3
1.0
0.1
1.0
0.3
$\frac{m}{m_a} = 10$
$\frac{m}{m_a} = 1$
$\frac{m}{m_a} = 0.1$
0.1
1
10
$\frac{\omega}{\beta}$

Fig. 3-14

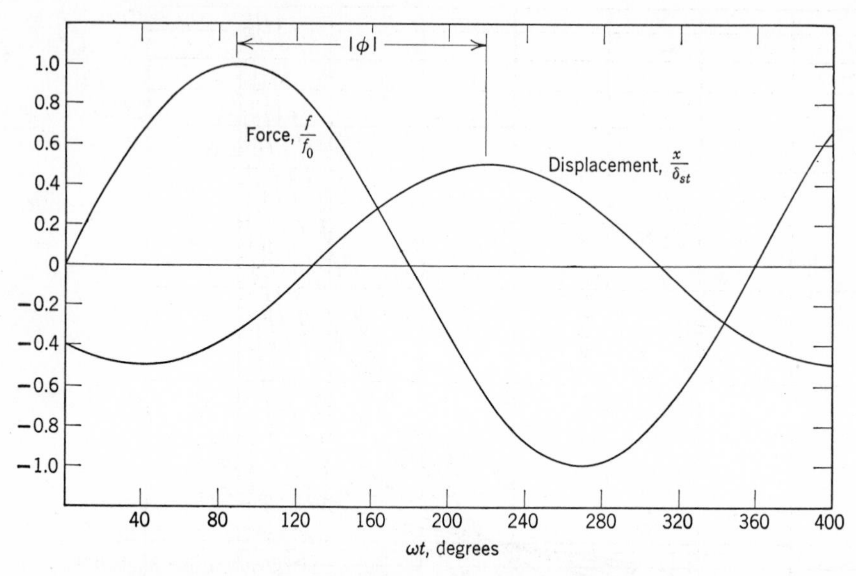

Fig. 3-15 Steady-state vibration showing magnitude of phase angle, $|\phi|$, displacement lagging force (ϕ is negative for this condition). $\zeta = 0.5$; $\omega/\beta = 1.5$

3.3 Human Tolerance

In Section 3.2 several ideas about the steady-state response of a single-degree-of-freedom system to different types of forcing functions have been developed. Of course, any instrument, piece of equipment, or component of a structure mounted in such a

Table 3-3. Table showing Relationship between Sensation of Vibration and Vibration Intensity

Sensation of Vibration	Acceleration or Velocity Vibration Amplitude	
Imperceptible	$\ddot{x}_{max} = 1.2$ in./sec^2 for frequency < 8 cps	$\dot{x}_{max} = 0.022$ in./sec for frequency > 8 cps
Barely perceptible	$\ddot{x}_{max} = 3.5$ in./sec^2 for frequency < 12 cps	$\dot{x}_{max} = 0.047$ in./sec for frequency > 12 cps
Distinctly perceptible—not disagreeable	$\ddot{x}_{max} = 9.3$ in./sec^2 for frequency < 16 cps	$\dot{x}_{max} = 0.094$ in./sec for frequency > 16 cps
Slightly disagreeable	$\ddot{x}_{max} = 31$ in./sec^2 for frequency < 24 cps	$\dot{x}_{max} = 0.19$ in./sec for frequency > 24 cps
Disagreeable	$\ddot{x}_{max} = 90$ in./sec^2 for frequency < 36 cps	$\dot{x}_{max} = 0.40$ in./sec for frequency > 36 cps
Very disagreeable	$\ddot{x}_{max} > 90$ in./sec^2 for frequency < 36 cps	$\dot{x}_{max} > 0.40$ in./sec for frequency > 36 cps

way as to be subjected to forced vibration must be able to withstand the appropriate amplitude, velocity, acceleration, or force imposed. It is of interest to know how much vibration the human anatomy can tolerate. While this is obviously a difficult matter to specify exactly because of the differences between individuals and even differences for the same individual at different times, still some "order-of-magnitude" information is available. Lippert* has summarized the work of many investigators in curves relating amplitude to frequency for various sensation intensities. These curves show that the sensation of vibration seems to be related to the vibration acceleration for low frequencies and the vibration velocities at higher frequencies, as indicated in Table 3-3. These numbers are for vibrations in the direction of the long axis of the human body (vertical vibrations for a person seated), which is the most uncomfortable orientation.

3.4 Overdamped and First-Order Systems

It is convenient at this time to return to the original problem represented by Fig. 1-3 and consider further the overdamped system, for which $\zeta > 1$. Equation 3-4, for forced vibration, is obtained from the third term of Equation 3-3, whose derivation is shown in Example A1-15 of Appendix 1. As shown in that example, this expression arises when the term in the inverse Laplace transform corresponding to the quadratic factor $(s^2 + \omega^2)$ in the denominator of the transform is evaluated; that is, when $s = i\omega$ in the expression

$$\frac{\beta^2\omega\,\delta_{\text{st}}}{s^2 + 2\zeta\beta s + \beta^2}$$

to determine ϕ_i and ϕ_r for use in Equation A1-17. If the system is overdamped, the quadratic factor $(s^2 + 2\zeta\beta s + \beta^2)$ can be factored into two linear factors $[s + (1/T_1)]$ $[s + (1/T_2)]$, so that the magnitude and phase angle for the forced response can eventually be shown to depend on an evaluation of

$$\frac{\delta_{\text{st}}}{(1 + T_1 s)(1 + T_2 s)}$$

when $s = i\omega$ and T_1, and T_2 are related to β and ζ by Equations 3-39

$$T_1 = \frac{1}{\zeta\beta\left(1 + \sqrt{1 - \dfrac{1}{\zeta^2}}\right)}$$

$$T_2 = \frac{1}{\zeta\beta\left(1 - \sqrt{1 - \dfrac{1}{\zeta^2}}\right)} \qquad \text{(3-39)}$$

$$T_1 T_2 = \frac{1}{\beta^2}$$

Therefore, it appears that a plot of amplitude and phase of the function $1/(1 + Ts)$ when $s = i\omega$ might be useful for overdamped systems, and T could assume the value T_1 or T_2. The "time constant," T, has some significance of its own, however, aside from its possible usefulness in the application described above. This is discussed next.

* Lippert, S., "Vibration Standards Proposed," *SAE Journal*, May 1947.

Time Constant for First-Order System. Suppose that in Fig. 1-3 the mass were zero and the force sinusoidal. The differential equation would have been

$$c\frac{dx}{dt} + kx = F_0 \sin \omega t$$

or

$$T\frac{dx}{dt} + x = \frac{F_0}{k} \sin \omega t \tag{3-40}$$

where

$$T = \frac{c}{k}$$

This system will be designated as a first-order system, since it is governed by a first order differential equation, to distinguish it from the overdamped second-order (but single-degree-of-freedom) system governed by Equation 1-4.

The solution of Equation 3-40 is easily obtained by the methods shown in Appendix 1.

$$x = x_0 e^{-t/T} + \delta_{st}\frac{\omega T}{1 + (\omega T)^2} e^{-t/T} + \delta_{st}\frac{1}{\sqrt{1 + (\omega T)^2}} \sin(\omega t + \phi_{10}) \tag{3-41}$$

where

$$\phi_{10} = \sin^{-1}\frac{-\omega T}{\sqrt{1 + (\omega T)^2}} = \cos^{-1}\frac{1}{\sqrt{1 + (\omega T)^2}} = \tan^{-1}(-\omega T) \tag{3-42}$$

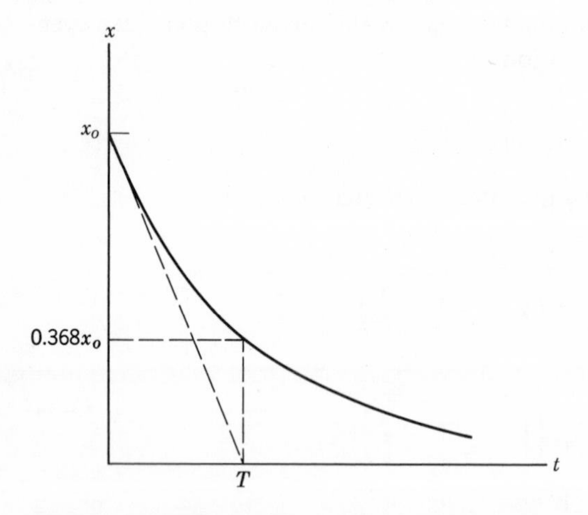

Fig. 3-16 Displacement as function of time for first-order system

The interpretation of Equation 3-41 parallels that of Equation 3-3, and two terms are discerned which decay with time, one depending on the initial displacement and the other started by the force. The third term describes a steady state vibration having amplitude and phase angle. This last term arises from the substitution of $s = i\omega$ in the expression $\delta_{st}/(1 + Ts)$.

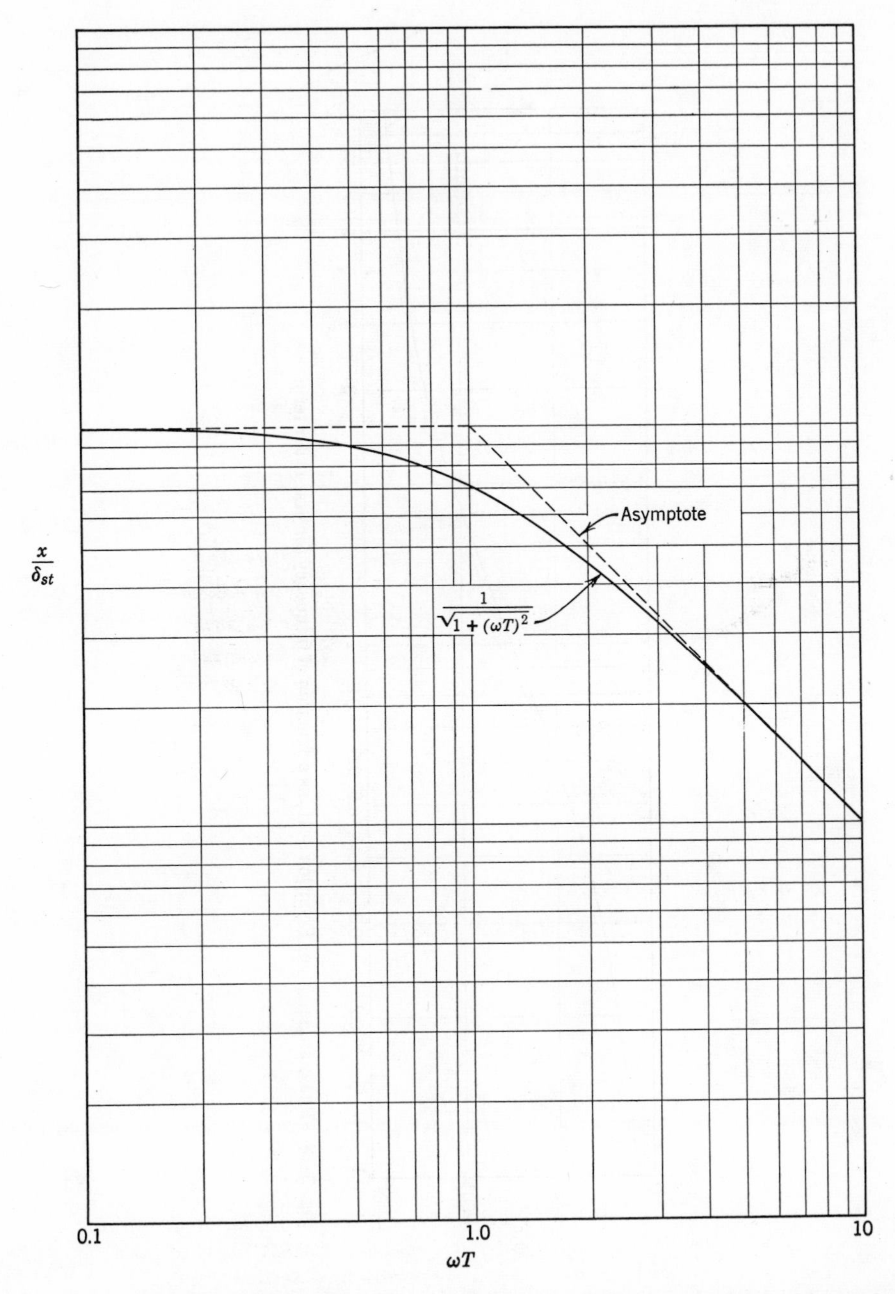

Fig. 3-17 Plot of amplitude of frequency response for first-order term (third term of Equation 3-41)

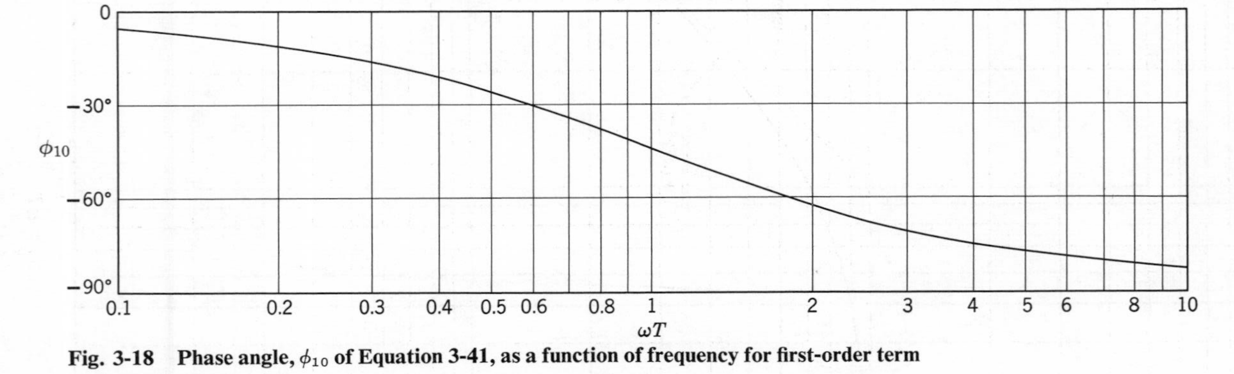

Fig. 3-18 Phase angle, ϕ_{10} of Equation 3-41, as a function of frequency for first-order term

Inspection of the first two terms of Equation 3-41 shows that these terms die out exponentially in the same way that the amplitude of oscillation decreases in Equation 1-8. One physical significance of the time constant, T, is the following: if the displacement continued to die down at the same rate as it started, it would reach zero in the time T. This is easily verified by considering the first term of Equation 3-41,

$$x = x_0 \, e^{-t/T} \quad (\text{at } t = 0, x = x_0)$$

$$\frac{dx}{dt} = -\frac{x_0}{T} e^{-t/T} \quad \left[\text{at } t = 0, \left(\frac{dx}{dt}\right)_0 = -\frac{x_0}{T}\right]$$

$$x_0 + \left(\frac{dx}{dt}\right)_0 T = x_0 - \frac{x_0}{T} T = 0$$

However, the displacement does not really die out this fast, and consequently at the time T, the displacement is $x_0 \, e^{-T/T} = 0.368x_0$. These relationships are illustrated in Fig. 3-16. It is clear then that the smaller the time constant the faster the motion dies out. Since $T = c/k$, small time constants are associated with small damping coefficients or large spring rates.

If there are two such terms in the transfer function (see Appendix 1 for explanation of transfer function), as in the overdamped second-order system discussed earlier, then the displacement is the sum of the two terms, one of which dies out faster than the other. Usually the larger time constant, corresponding to the term which dies out more slowly, is the more significant.

The third term of Equation 3-41, the steady-state term, is plotted in Figs. 3-17 and 3-18. The amplitude decreases only slightly until (ωT) exceeds 1, after which the amplitude varies approximately as $1/\omega T$. When there are two such terms, as in the overdamped second-order system, each of the terms contributes to the amplitude and phase according to the value of ωT_1 and ωT_2. The use of Figs. 3-17 and 3-18 is discussed in more detail in Reference 1.

CHAPTER 4

Transient Vibration of Elementary Systems

4.1 Response to Step Function

Chapter 3 dealt with the response of a system to a harmonic forcing function. Another type of forcing function of considerable interest is the step function. This system is initially at rest in the equilibrium position and a sudden change is made; this change remains constant thereafter. For instance, if the force in Fig. 1-3 suddenly changed from zero to a constant value, the displacement would change from zero to a steady-state value after a period of transient motion. The transient motion is often of more interest than the steady-state value.

Step Force Input. For the system shown in Fig. 1-3, the transfer function* is

$$\frac{X}{F} = \frac{1}{k} \frac{1}{1 + \frac{2\zeta}{\beta} s + \frac{s^2}{\beta^2}} \tag{4-1}$$

If $f(t)$ is $f_0 u(t)$ (the step function of magnitude f_0), then $F(s)$ is f_0/s. Therefore

$$x(t) = \frac{f_0}{k} \mathscr{L}^{-1} \left[\frac{1}{s\left(1 + \frac{2\zeta}{\beta} s + \frac{s^2}{\beta^2}\right)} \right] \tag{4-2}$$

If f_0/k is again designated as δ_{st}, the inverse yields

$$\frac{x}{\delta_{st}} = 1 - \frac{e^{-\zeta\beta t}}{\sqrt{1 - \zeta^2}} \sin\left(\beta\sqrt{1 - \zeta^2}\, t + \phi_{11}\right) \tag{4-3}$$

where

$$\phi_{11} = \sin^{-1}\left(\sqrt{1 - \zeta^2}\right) = \cos^{-1}\zeta = \tan^{-1}\frac{\sqrt{1 - \zeta^2}}{\zeta} \tag{4-4}$$

* The Laplace transform will be used extensively hereafter. Appendix A1-2 contains a review of this subject which may be used for reference.

Figure 4-1 shows the variation of the displacement with time for the step input. It should be noted that for zero damping there is 100% overshoot.

Step Displacement Input. A similar result occurs if the platform of System 3 of Table 3-1 is given a sudden acceleration. The transfer function for X_r/Y is

$$\frac{X_r}{Y} = -\frac{1}{\beta^2}\frac{s^2}{1 + \frac{2\zeta}{\beta}s + \frac{s^2}{\beta^2}}$$

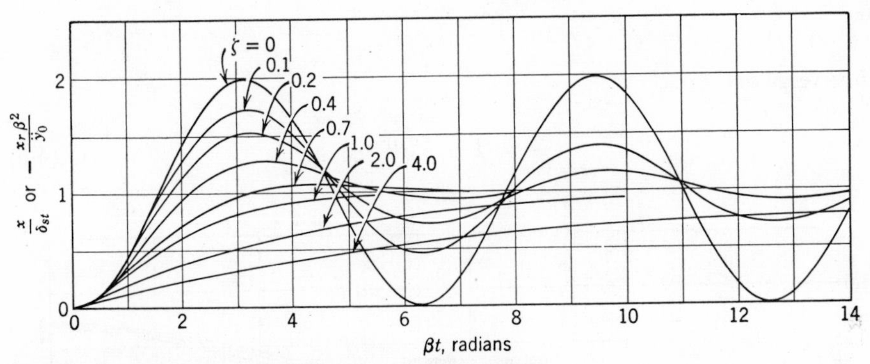

Fig. 4-1 Response of second-order system to step input

Since $s^2 Y$ represents the acceleration d^2y/dt^2, the previous equation could be written

$$\frac{X_r}{\ddot{Y}} = -\frac{1}{\beta^2}\frac{1}{1 + \frac{2\zeta}{\beta}s + \frac{s^2}{\beta^2}}$$

where $\ddot{Y}$ is the transform of d^2y/dt^2, and if a sudden constant acceleration of magnitude $\ddot{y}_0$ is applied, then

$$x_r = -\frac{\ddot{y}_0}{\beta^2}\mathscr{L}^{-1}\frac{1}{s\left(1 + \frac{2\zeta}{\beta}s + \frac{s^2}{\beta^2}\right)}$$

Since this is of the same form as Equation 4-2, Fig. 4-1 also represents

$$-\frac{x_r\beta^2}{\ddot{y}_0}$$

Overdamped Second-Order System. If $\zeta > 1$ (overdamped), then the quadratic in the denominator of Equation 4-2 can be factored to give

$$x = \frac{f_0}{k}\mathscr{L}^{-1}\frac{1}{s(1 + T_1 s)(1 + T_2 s)}$$

where T_1 and T_2 can be determined from Equation 3-39. The inverse transform yields

$$\frac{x}{\delta_{st}} = 1 + \frac{1}{\left(\frac{T_2}{T_1} - 1\right)} e^{-t/T_1} - \frac{1}{\left(1 - \frac{T_1}{T_2}\right)} e^{-t/T_2} \tag{4-5}$$

It is apparent from Equation 4-5 that the third term is more important than the second in preventing the displacement from reaching its final steady-state value, since $T_2 > T_1$. Curves for several overdamped systems are shown in Fig. 4-1.

First-Order System. For the first-order system (Fig. 1-3 with zero mass) the transformed equation for the step forcing function is

$$x = \frac{f_0}{k}\mathscr{L}^{-1}\left[\frac{1}{s(1 + Ts)}\right]$$

where

$$T = \frac{c}{k}$$

The inverse gives

$$\frac{x}{\delta_{st}} = 1 - e^{-t/T} \tag{4-6}$$

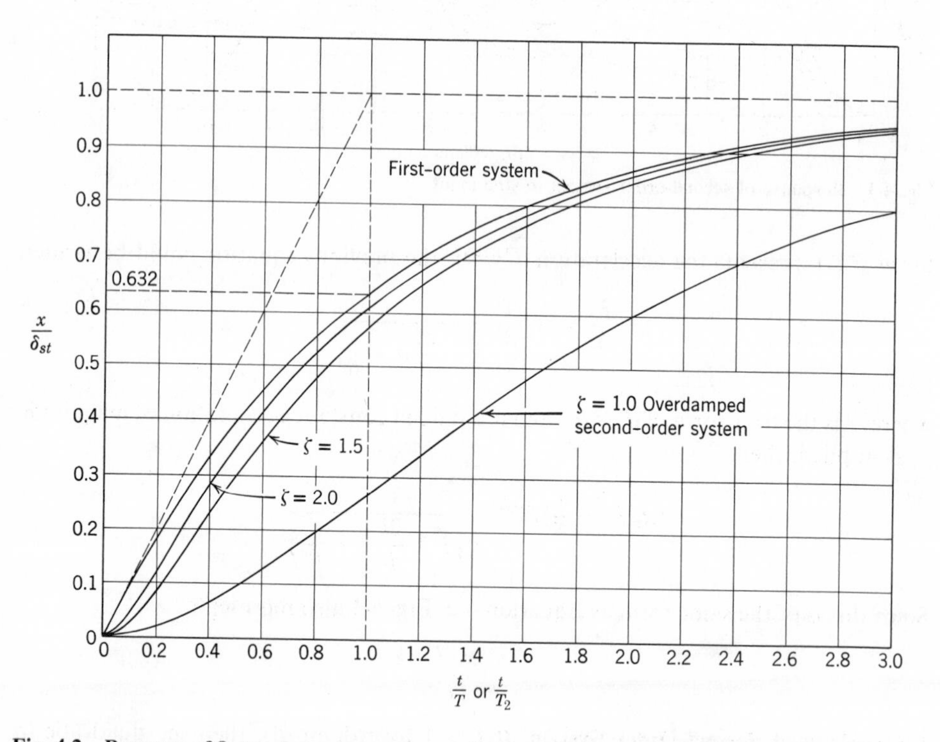

Fig. 4-2 Response of first-order system and second-order overdamped system to step input

Equation 4-6 is plotted in Fig. 4-2. The relationship between this graph and that of Fig. 3-16 is obvious.

Other curves of Fig. 4-2 show the effect of the second time constant in a second-order system. That is, if the time constant T is also T_2, the larger of the two time constants of an overdamped second-order system, the effect of the other time constant, T_1, is shown here. The cases depicted are for $\zeta = 1$, 1.5, and 2. For $\zeta = 1$, of course, the two time constants are equal and the response to the step forcing function becomes

$$\frac{x}{\delta_{st}} = 1 - \left(1 + \frac{t}{T}\right) e^{-t/T} \tag{4-7}$$

For $\zeta = 1.5$, $\beta T_2 = 2.63$ and $T_1 = \dfrac{T_2}{6.92}$

For $\zeta = 2$, $\beta T_2 = 3.73$ and $T_1 = \dfrac{T_2}{13.9}$

These relationships may be obtained from Equation 3-39 and the values substituted in Equation 4-5 to obtain the curves shown in Fig. 4-2. It is apparent from the curves that the effect of the smaller time constant is not very important for overdamped systems if ζ is as great as 2, except near $t = 0$ where the effect produces zero slope.

Example 4-1. An accelerometer is to be constructed from a weight suspended in a box by means of a spring and damper, the relative motion between the box and weight to be used as an indication of the acceleration to which the box is subjected. If the acceleration is of the ramp type, 100 g/sec to a maximum of 10 g, estimate satisfactory values of mass, spring, and damper.

Since Fig. 4-1 indicates that $\zeta = 0.7$ gives a fairly rapid response with small overshoot when subjected to a step acceleration, use this value of damping factor. If the input were a step function instead of a ramp, the response would achieve a value very close to the final value in a time corresponding to about $\beta t = 6$, and would not overshoot more than about 5%. To estimate a satisfactory value for β, it might be assumed that the ramp input is equivalent to a series of small step functions. If it is assumed that indicated acceleration should agree with actual acceleration after the first 10% of the ramp time has elapsed, let $t = 0.01$ sec in the expression $\beta t = 6$ (since the total ramp time is 10/100 or 0.1 sec.) Therefore, $\beta = 600$ rad/sec. A possible set of constants to achieve $\beta \geqq 600$ and $\zeta \doteq 0.7$ is the following: weight = 0.01 lb, spring constant = 10 lb/in., damping constant = 0.02 lb/(in./sec). In Chapter 15 this estimate is checked more accurately. The maximum displacement of the mass under the full acceleration of 10 g is $(10 \times 0.01)/10 = 0.01$ in.; thus it is clear that in a practical instrument this displacement should be converted to an electrical signal.

4.2 Complex Plane Representation of Roots of Characteristic Equation

In all of the foregoing work the denominator of the transfer function is of major importance. For the transfer functions considered in Section 4.1 the denominator is of the same form, namely, some variant of

$$s^2 + 2\zeta\beta s + \beta^2 \quad \text{or} \quad (s + \zeta\beta)^2 + \beta^2(1 - \zeta^2)$$

This expression set equal to zero is known as the "characteristic equation," and the two roots of the characteristic equation for a second order system may be real or complex, depending on whether $|\zeta|$ is greater or less than 1. The factored form of the denominator can then be written as $(s - r_1)(s - r_2)$ where r_1 and r_2 are the roots of the characteristic equation. It is evident that if $\zeta < 1$ these roots are

$$r_1 = -\zeta\beta + i\sqrt{1 - \zeta^2} \quad \text{and} \quad r_2 = -\zeta\beta - i\sqrt{1 - \zeta^2} \tag{4-8}$$

and if $\zeta > 1$ the roots are the negatives of $1/T_1$ and $1/T_2$ of Equation 1-57 or

$$r_1 = -\zeta\beta + \beta\sqrt{\zeta^2 - 1} \quad \text{and} \quad r_2 = -\zeta\beta - \beta\sqrt{\zeta^2 - 1} \tag{4-9}$$

It is instructive to plot these roots on the complex plane as ζ varies throughout its range of possible values, and to correlate this plot with the transient behavior of the system as described by Equations 1-8 to 1-11. This plot is shown in Fig. 4-3. For a given value of β, the roots lie on a circle having a radius equal to β if $-1 < \zeta < 1$, and lie on the real axis if $|\zeta| > 1$.

For $\zeta = 0$, the roots lie on the imaginary axis at the points A. If the value of ζ is increased to some positive value between zero and 1 the roots move to the left along the circle to a point such as B. The position of B in the complex plane indicates most of the information of interest for the transient oscillation. The radius to B represents β, the undamped natural frequency. The projection of B on the imaginary axis is $\beta\sqrt{1 - \zeta^2}$, which is the damped natural frequency. The projection of B on the real axis is $-\zeta\beta$, the constant in the term $e^{-\zeta\beta t}$. The damping factor itself, ζ, is associated

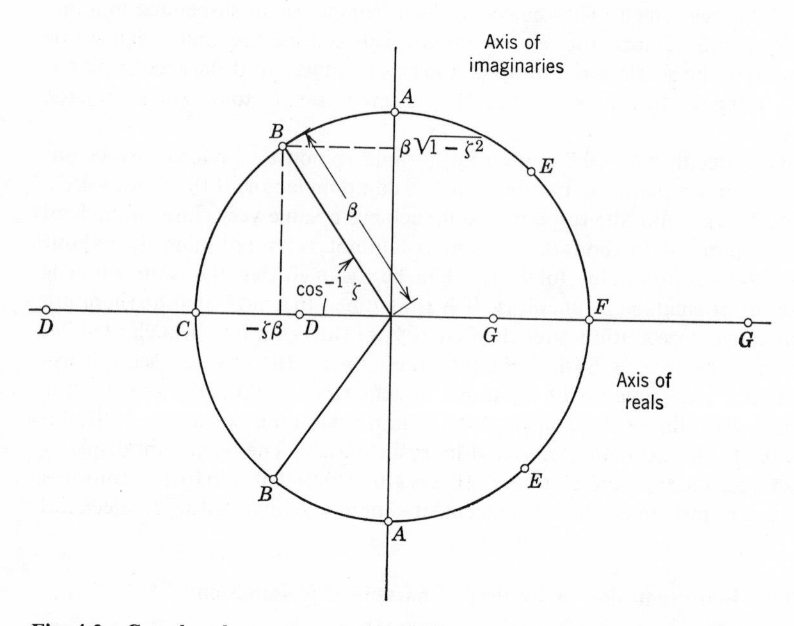

Fig. 4-3 Complex plane representation of the roots of the second-order system

with the angle which the radius to B makes with the real axis. The smaller this angle, the larger is the value of ζ, and the angle is numerically that angle whose cosine is ζ, as indicated in Fig. 4-3. This is also the same as the angle ψ of Equation 1-8 for initial condition $\dot{x}_0 = 0$. If B is on a 45° line, the damping factor is 0.707. As ζ is increased to 1 the two roots come together at the point C and Equation 1-10 applies.

As the damping factor increases further, one root moves toward the origin along the real axis, and the other root moves away from the origin on the real axis as indicated by the points D, which would correspond to ζ of about 1.25 for the positions shown. As ζ increases, the root which approaches the origin is the more significant, as was shown in Section 4.1.

If the roots lie to the right of the imaginary axis, the system is unstable—the instability being more severe with increased distance from the imaginary axis. Roots at

E would result in a divergent oscillation, with ζ between zero and -1, about -0.7 at the position shown. If $\zeta = -1$ the roots coincide at F, and if $\zeta < -1$ the roots take positions along the real axis as indicated at G. For roots located at F or G the divergence would not be accompanied by oscillation. For roots located at G the root which is farther from the origin is the more important, since it would cause the most rapid divergence.

A thorough understanding of the complex plane method of portraying the roots of the characteristic equation and the significance of the location of roots in various regions of the complex plane is especially useful in relating the various aspects of the second-order, single-degree-of-freedom system.

CHAPTER 5

Equivalent Systems

5.1 Rectilinear Motion

The previous chapters have been concerned with the physical problem proposed by Fig. 1-3: a mass moving horizontally, subjected to the effect of a linear spring, linear damper, and an external force which is a function of time only. There are many examples of systems which lead to the same form of differential equation and are therefore governed by the same equations of motion, and the same discussion can be applied.

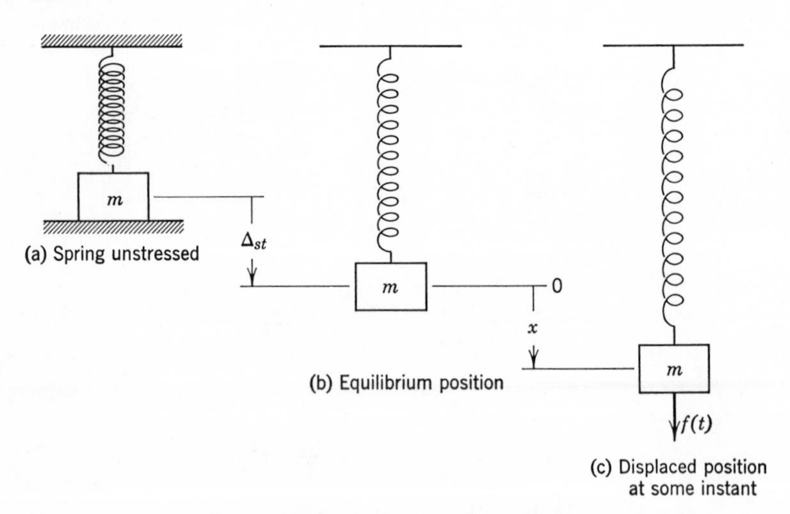

Fig. 5-1 Single-degree-of-freedom system oriented vertically

Effect of Gravity. First, the system may be rotated 90 degrees so that the mass is suspended by the spring (Fig. 5-1). It is clear that nothing has changed except that there is a deflection of the system caused by the constant force of gravity. If the equilibrium position in this system is taken as the zero position for the coordinate x, then the equations of the previous sections are valid. It is interesting to note that the distance, Δ_{st}, is the static deflection of the spring from its own zero stress position caused by the weight, and is equal to mg/k or

$$\Delta_{st} = \frac{mg}{k} \equiv \frac{g}{\beta^2} \tag{5-1}$$

From this, it is evident that the lower the natural frequency of the system, the greater is the static deflection. This sometimes causes trouble in designing spring suspension systems that have low natural frequencies, if these must be operable in various orientations with respect to the earth.

Equivalent Springs and Dampers. Any single-degree-of-freedom system composed of linear elements moving with rectilinear motion can be reduced to an equivalent system such as the one already discussed (Figs. 1-3 or 5-1). All that is necessary is to determine what to use for the mass, spring constant, and damping constant. The following examples demonstrate this.

Example 5-1. A homogeneous solid cylindrical block (Fig. 5-2) of density δ_s, diameter d, and height h floats in liquid of density δ_l. If the block is depressed and then released, it

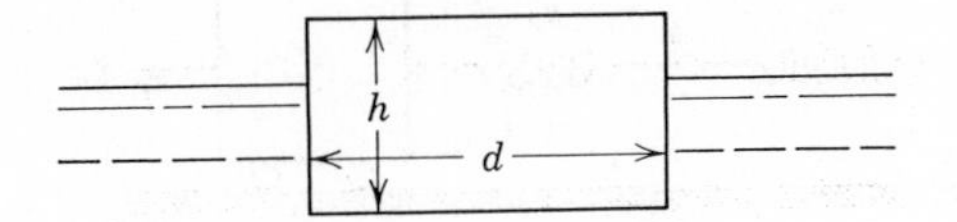

Fig. 5-2

will oscillate up and down at some frequency. If damping is neglected, what is the frequency?

Let x be the displacement downward from the equilibrium position. The buoyant force on the block is the weight of the water displaced or $(\pi/4)\, d^2x\, \delta_l$ in consistent units. The equivalent spring constant is therefore the above force divided by x or

$$k_{equiv} = \frac{\pi}{4} d^2\, \delta_l$$

The natural frequency is

$$\sqrt{\frac{k}{m}} \quad \text{and} \quad m = \frac{\frac{\pi}{4} d^2 k \delta_s}{g}$$

$$\beta = \sqrt{\frac{\frac{\pi}{4} d^2 \delta_l}{\frac{\frac{\pi}{4} d^2 k \delta_s}{g}}} = \sqrt{\frac{g\, \delta_l}{h\, \delta_s}}$$

This equation is valid only for $\delta_s < \delta_l$, for which a flotation equilibrium position exists. For a block of wood 1 ft in height and specific gravity 0.6, in water,

$$\beta = \sqrt{\frac{32.2 \times 1.0}{1.0 \times 0.6}} = 1.32 \text{ rad/sec} = 1.2 \text{ cycles/sec}$$

Example 5-2. A concentrated mass is supported at the end of a cantilever beam. What is the natural frequency if the mass of the beam is neglected?

This is simply a problem of calculating the equivalent spring constant of a cantilever beam. Since the deflection of the end of the beam under a load F would be $FL^3/3EI$ where L is the length of the beam, E is the modulus of elasticity of the beam material, and I is the moment of inertia of the beam, the equivalent spring constant would be load/deflection

$$= \frac{F}{\frac{FL^3}{3EI}} = \frac{3EI}{L^3}$$

and the natural frequency

$$= \sqrt{\frac{3EI}{ML^3}} \text{ rad/sec}$$

Elements in Parallel and in Series. Two or more springs may be employed in parallel or series, as illustrated in Fig. 5-3. For the springs in parallel (Fig. 5-3*a*), both springs undergo the same deflection. For the springs in series (Fig. 5-3*b*), both springs are subjected to the same force.

The total force necessary to extend the springs acting in parallel is the sum of the forces required to extend each spring, or

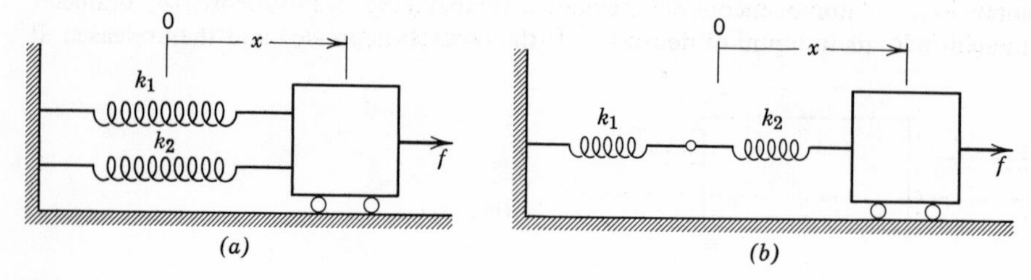

Fig. 5-3

$$f = f_1 + f_2 = k_1x + k_2x = (k_1 + k_2)x$$

An equivalent single spring may be defined which has an equivalent spring constant given by df/dx, or for springs acting in parallel,

$$k_{eq} = k_1 + k_2 \tag{5-2}$$

For springs operating in series, the total deflection is the sum of the deflection of each spring, both subjected to the same load, or

$$x = x_1 + x_2 = \frac{f}{k_1} + \frac{f}{k_2} = \left(\frac{1}{k_1} + \frac{1}{k_2}\right) f$$

An equivalent single spring having the same value of df/dx for springs in series is therefore

$$k_{eq} = \frac{1}{1/k_1 + 1/k_2} \tag{5-3}$$

A similar discussion for dampers would establish Equation 5-4 for an equivalent damping constant for dampers in parallel and Equation 5-5 for dampers in series.

$$c_{eq} = c_1 + c_2 \quad \text{(parallel)} \tag{5-4}$$

$$c_{eq} = \frac{1}{1/c_1 + 1/c_2} \quad \text{(series)} \tag{5-5}$$

Masses attached rigidly together so that their displacement must coincide can be considered to be in parallel and an equation similar to Equations 5-2 and 5-4 is easily derived.

$$m_{eq} = m_1 + m_2 \quad \text{(parallel)} \tag{5-6}$$

Combination of masses in a way analogous to springs or dampers in series would represent an artificial concept of little use.

Example 5-3. Neglecting damping and weight of the cantilever beam, determine an expression for the natural frequency of the system shown in Fig. 5-4.

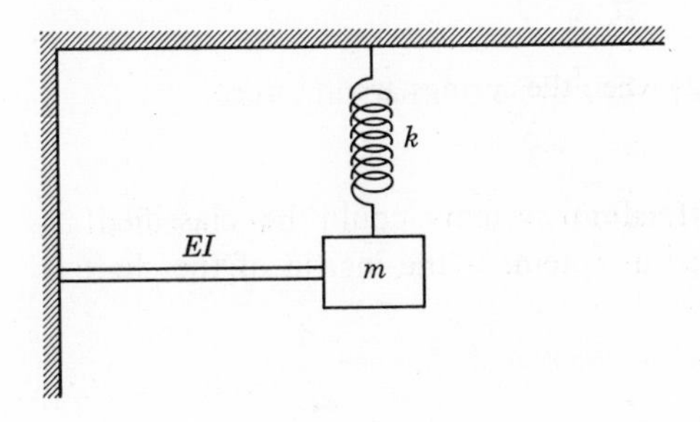

Fig. 5-4

Let x be the downward displacement of the mass. The static force required to deflect the spring x inches is kx. The static force required to deflect the end of the beam x inches is $3EIx/L^3$. The total static force required to deflect the mass x inches is $kx + 3EIx/L^3$, and the equivalent spring constant is force/deflection $= k + 3EI/L^3$. The natural frequency is $\sqrt{(k + 3EI/L^3)/m}$. This problem illustrates the fact that when two springs are employed in parallel the equivalent spring constant is obtained from Equation 5-2 or $k_{eq} = k_1 + k_2$. Notice that the deflection is common to both springs when the springs are in parallel.

Example 5-4. Neglecting damping and weight of the cantilever beam, determine an expression for the natural frequency of the system depicted in Fig. 5-5.

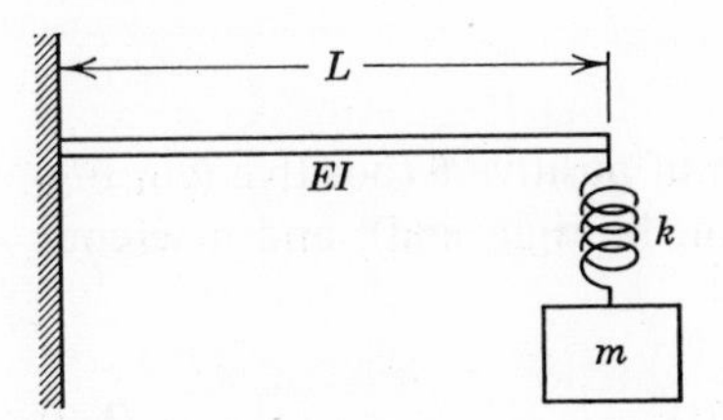

Fig. 5-5

Let x be the downward movement of the mass. A static load of f lb on the bottom of the spring would produce a deflection of the spring of f/k units. Also, f lb would exist on the end of the beam which would therefore deflect downward a distance $fL^3/3EI$. Thus, the total deflection at the bottom of the spring caused by load f would be $f/k + fL^3/3EI$. The equivalent spring constant is therefore

$$\frac{f}{\frac{f}{k} + \frac{fL^3}{3EI}} = \frac{1}{\frac{1}{k} + \frac{L^3}{3EI}}$$

and the natural frequency is

$$\sqrt{\frac{k}{m} \frac{1}{1 + \frac{kL^3}{3EI}}}$$

This problem illustrates the fact that when two springs are employed in series the equivalent spring constant is obtained from Equation 5-5 or

$$\frac{1}{k_{eq}} = \frac{1}{k_1} + \frac{1}{k_2}$$

Notice that the load is common to both springs when the springs are in series.

5.2 Angular Motion

Another large group of one-degree-of-freedom systems could be classified as torsional systems. Figure 5-6 represents such a system. If the inertia of the shaft is

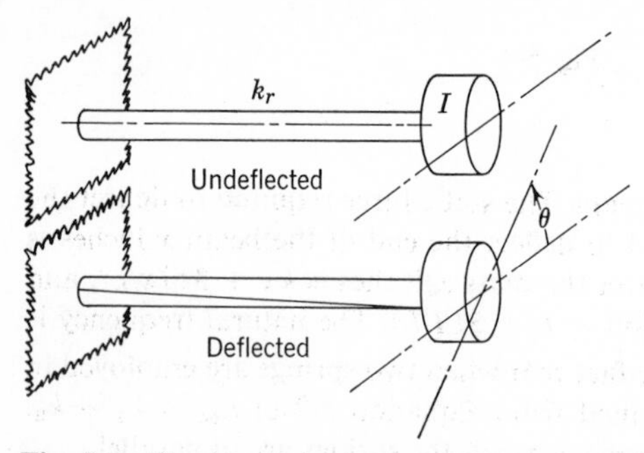

Fig. 5-6 Torsional one-degree-of-freedom system.

neglected and if there is no damping, the differential equation of motion with no externally applied torque would be (setting moment of inertia of mass times angular acceleration equal to torque):

$$I \frac{d^2\theta}{dt^2} = -k_r\theta$$

If there were an applied torque, $Q(t)$, in the direction of positive θ (positive θ in Fig. 5-6 is defined as counterclockwise when viewed from the right end), and a viscous damper, c_r, the above equation would become

$$I \frac{d^2\theta}{dt^2} + c_r \frac{d\theta}{dt} + k_r = Q(t) \tag{5-7}$$

which is, by comparison with Equation 1-2, the same form as the differential equation derived for rectilinear motion. Therefore the above equation could be represented by Equation 1-4, where

$$\beta^2 = \frac{k_r}{I}$$

$$\zeta = \frac{c_r}{c_{c_r}} = \frac{c_r}{2\sqrt{Ik_r}} = \frac{c_r\beta}{2k_r} = \frac{c_r}{2\beta I} \quad (5\text{-}8)$$

$$c_{c_r} = 2\sqrt{Ik_r} = \frac{2k_r}{\beta} = 2I\beta$$

and earlier discussions of the previous sections apply without change, except for the above definitions and the fact that the spring constant k_r is a rotational spring constant and has dimensions of torque per angular displacement (usually lb-ft per radian), and the damping constant c_r is torque per angular velocity (usually lb-ft per rad/sec). Also $f(t)$ in Equation 1-4 becomes $Q(t)$ and has dimensions of lb-ft instead of just pounds.

Example 5-5 What is the natural frequency in torsion of a 2-ft diameter disc, weighing 100 lb, supported on a steel shaft that is 1 in. in diameter and 3 ft long? Neglect damping.

The torsional deflection of such a shaft with a steady torque, Q, applied to the end would be QL/GJ where G is the shear modulus and J the polar moment of inertia, $\pi d^4/32$. Therefore the torsional spring constant would be

$$k_r = \frac{Q}{QL/GJ} = \frac{GJ}{L} = \frac{\pi}{32}\frac{d^4G}{L}$$

For this problem,

$$k_r = \frac{\pi}{32}\,\frac{1^4 \times 11 \times 10^6}{3 \times 12} = 3.00 \times 10^4 \text{ lb-in./rad} = 2500 \text{ lb-ft/rad}$$

The moment of inertia is the mass times the square of the radius of gyration. For a disc, the radius of gyration squared is $d^2/8$.

$$I = \frac{M\,d^2}{8} = \frac{100}{32.2} \times \frac{2^2}{8} = 0.777 \text{ slug ft}^2$$

The natural frequency is therefore

$$\beta = \sqrt{\frac{k_r}{I}} = \sqrt{\frac{2500}{0.777}} = 56.8 \text{ rad/sec} = 9.03 \text{ cps}$$

Example 5-6. What is the natural frequency, for small oscillations, of a pendulum whose length between c.g. and point of suspension is L and whose radius of gyration about the c.g. is ρ?

The moment of inertia of this mass about the point of suspension is $m\rho^2 + mL^2$. The restoring torque about the point of suspension is

$$mgL \sin\theta \approx mgL\theta$$

for θ small, so that the equivalent rotational spring constant would be

$$\frac{mgL\theta}{\theta} = mgL$$

The natural frequency is

$$\beta = \sqrt{\frac{mgL}{m(\rho^2 + L^2)}} = \sqrt{\left(\frac{g}{L}\right)\frac{1}{1 + \left(\frac{\rho}{L}\right)^2}}$$

If the mass were small and the length large (like a steel ball on a long string) then $\rho/L \to 0$ and the natural frequency would become $\sqrt{g/L}$ rad/sec. For large angles of oscillation the restoring torque is not proportional to θ, and the differential equation is not linear; thus the above equation for natural frequency would be in error for such circumstances.

Example 5-7. A rectangular block of wood of density δ_s, floats in a liquid of density, δ_l (Fig. 5-7). If the block is rotated and released, what is its natural " rocking " frequency? Neglect friction: assume small angles.

Let the length of the block (into the paper) be one unit. The horizontal components of hydrostatic pressure against the block cancel each other; the sum of vertical components of hydrostatic pressure against the block equals the weight of the block; and the sum of the moments about the c.g. of the block in terms of the angle θ will yield the desired spring constant.

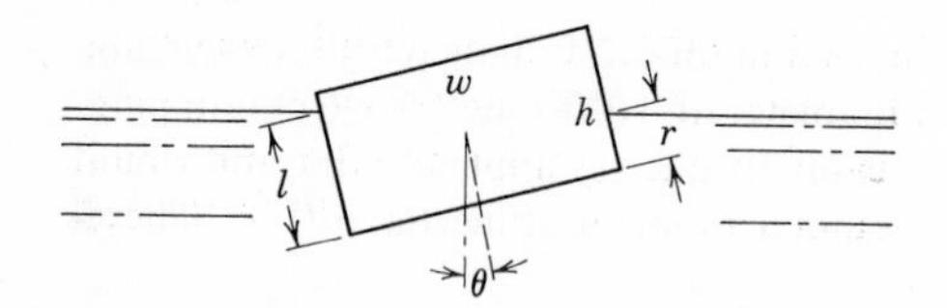

Fig. 5-7

$$\textit{Left face}\text{: moment in } +\theta \text{ direction} = +\delta_l \frac{l\cos\theta}{2} l\left(\frac{h}{2} - \frac{l}{3}\right)$$

$$\textit{bottom}\text{: moment in } +\theta \text{ direction} = -\delta_l \left(\frac{l-r}{2}\right)(\cos\theta)w\left(\frac{2}{3}w - \frac{1}{2}w\right)$$

$$\textit{Right face}\text{: moment in } +\theta \text{ direction} = -\delta_l \frac{r\cos\theta}{2} r\left(\frac{h}{2} - \frac{r}{3}\right)$$

also

$$\text{weight} = \delta_s wh = \delta_l \frac{r+l}{2} w$$

and

$$l = r + w\tan\theta$$

When this equation is simplified algebraically, the moment in $+\theta$ direction becomes

$$\delta_l\left[-\frac{w^3}{12} + \frac{wh^2}{2}\left(\frac{\delta_s}{\delta_l}\right)\left(1 - \frac{\delta_s}{\delta_l}\right)\right]\sin\theta - \delta_l\frac{w^3}{24}\cos\theta\tan^3\theta$$

For small angles $\quad \sin\theta \doteq \theta \quad \tan\theta \doteq \theta \quad \cos\theta \doteq 1$

so that the last term becomes negligible and the spring constant becomes

$$k_r = \frac{\delta_l w^3}{12}\left[1 - 6\left(\frac{h}{w}\right)^2\left(\frac{\delta_s}{\delta_l}\right)\left(1 - \frac{\delta_s}{\delta_l}\right)\right]$$

From this, it is seen that k_r might become negative for certain combinations of block dimensions and densities. This means that the " restoring " moment really becomes a moment tending to increase deflection. (Thus, a block with a square cross section, $h = w$, having a specific gravity of 0.5, would not float in water with one side level but, instead, with the diagonal level. For such cases, a different expression for k_r would have to be derived for small angular deflections from the equilibrium position.)

The moment of inertia can be obtained from the radius of gyration squared about the c.g. of this block,

$$\frac{1}{12}\frac{(wh^3 + hw^3)}{wh}$$

or

$$\frac{1}{12}(h^2 + w^2)$$

and thus

$$I = \delta_s \frac{wh}{12g}(h^2 + w^2)$$

and the natural frequency becomes

$$\beta = \sqrt{\frac{g}{h}\frac{\left[1 - 6\left(\frac{h}{w}\right)^2\left(\frac{\delta_s}{\delta_l}\right)\left(1 - \frac{\delta_s}{\delta_l}\right)\right]}{\frac{\delta_s}{\delta_l}\left[1 + \left(\frac{h}{w}\right)^2\right]}}$$

Therefore, for $\delta_s/\delta_l = 0.5$ and $h/w = 0.5$, $h = 1''$,

$$\beta = 19.6 \text{ rad/sec} = 3.12 \text{ cps}$$

This can be confirmed by floating a block and tapping it by hand at its resonant frequency.

5.3 Combined Rectilinear and Angular Motion

A single-degree-of-freedom system may be composed of elements that involve both

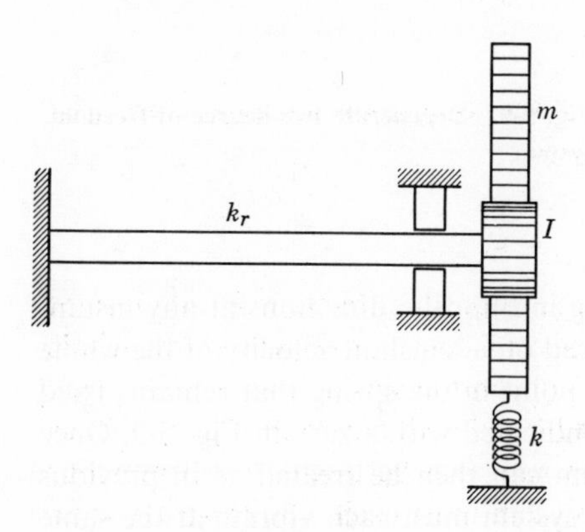

Fig. 5-8

rectilinear and angular motion. Although such systems are usually more conveniently analyzed with energy methods, a simple example is given here for comparison with the systems considered previously.

Example 5-8. Figure 5-8 represents a shaft that is flexible torsionally but supported by a bearing that prevents bending deflections of the shaft. The shaft drives a rack and pinion, one end of the rack being attached by a spring to a fixed point. The rack is guided, and has mass m; and the pinion has a moment of inertia, I, and radius R, to the point of contact with the pinion. The shaft mass is neglected. What is the natural frequency of this system?

Let θ = angle of rotation of the pinion from the position of equilibrium. Then θR = linear displacement of mass m from its position of equilibrium. Call this x. Then $m\ddot{x} = -kx + f$ where f is the force of the pinion on the rack in the $+x$ direction. The mass at this instant will then produce a torque on the pinion in the $+\theta$ direction of $-fR$. Therefore, $I\ddot{\theta} = -k_r\theta - fR$. Since $x = \theta R$ and $\ddot{x} = \ddot{\theta}R$, x and $\ddot{x}$ can be eliminated to obtain

$$\ddot{\theta} + \frac{k_r + kR^2}{I + mR^2}\,\theta = 0$$

so that the natural frequency is

$$\sqrt{\frac{k_r + kR^2}{I + mR^2}}$$

5.4 Degenerate Two-Degree-of-Freedom System

Sometimes a system involving either rectilinear or angular motion will not be fixed at one end, as was true for most of the previous examples (for instance, Fig. 5-9). For

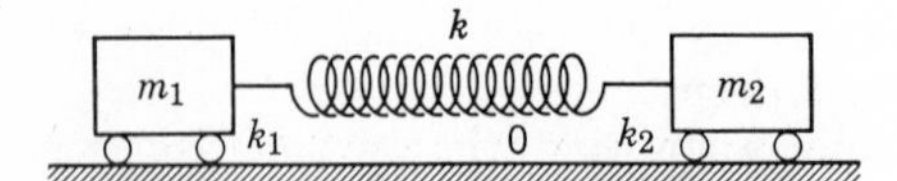

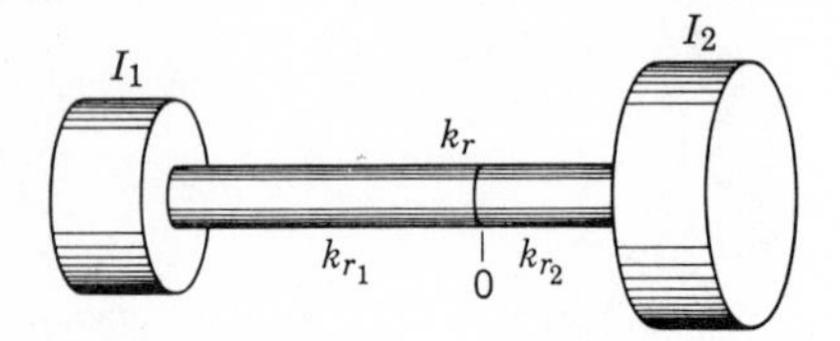

Fig. 5-9 Degenerate two-degree-of-freedom system

such systems the masses will have to be moving in opposite directions at any instant (or at least such a movement can be superimposed on a constant velocity of the whole system), and consequently there must be some point in the spring that remains fixed in space. This point is called a "node" and is indicated with a zero in Fig. 5-9. Once the node is determined, each part of the system can then be treated as in previous examples. It is clear that the two halves of the system must each vibrate at the same frequency. Thus

$$\frac{k_1}{m_1} = \frac{k_2}{m_2}$$

Also the total deflection of the spring under any load is the sum of the two individual deflections or

$$\frac{f}{k} = \frac{f}{k_1} + \frac{f}{k_2}$$

By using these equations together it is easy to show that

$$k_1 = \left(1 + \frac{m_1}{m_2}\right) k \qquad \text{and} \quad k_2 = \left(1 + \frac{m_2}{m_1}\right) k$$

and therefore that

$$\beta^2 = \frac{m_1 + m_2}{m_1 m_2} k \equiv \frac{k}{m_1}\left(1 + \frac{m_1}{m_2}\right) \equiv \frac{k}{m_2}\left(1 + \frac{m_2}{m_1}\right) \tag{5-9}$$

Equation 5-9 shows that the natural frequency of such a system is increased over the value that either mass would have if the other mass were fixed instead of free. If a damper were also included between m_1 and m_2, the above value of β (undamped natural frequency) would be valid, and the earlier equations and discussions of freely vibrating systems would apply, but with the following definitions:

$$\begin{aligned} c_c &= 2\sqrt{k\left(\frac{m_1 m_2}{m_1 + m_2}\right)} \equiv \frac{2k}{\beta} \equiv \frac{2m_1 m_2}{m_1 + m_2}\,\beta \\ \zeta &= \frac{c}{c_c} \equiv \frac{c}{2}\sqrt{\frac{m_1 + m_2}{k m_1 m_2}} \equiv \frac{c\beta}{2k} \equiv \frac{c(m_1 + m_2)}{2\beta m_1 m_2} \end{aligned} \tag{5-10}$$

The damped natural frequency would be

$$\beta_d = \beta\sqrt{1 - \zeta^2}$$

CHAPTER 6

Two-Degree-of-Freedom Systems

6.1 Differential Equations of Motion

The discussion of the two-degrees-of-freedom system will begin with two masses in rectilinear motion—a setup similar to the one-degree system of Fig. 1-3. The physical problem is idealized as shown in Fig. 6-1. In this figure the coordinates x_1 and x_2 are

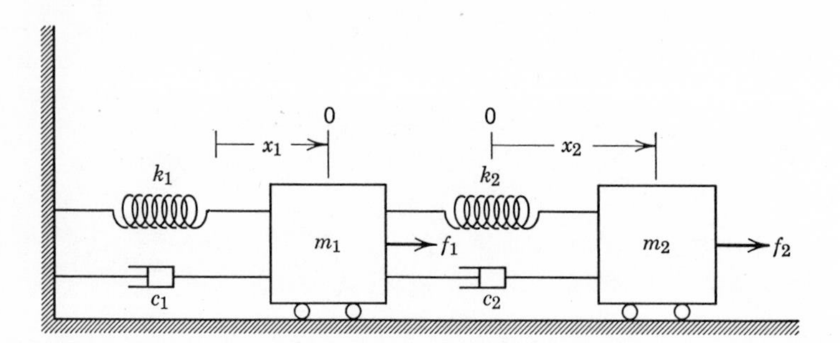

Fig. 6-1 Basic two-degree-of-freedom system

measured from the fixed position in space where each mass would come to rest if the forces were removed. Each coordinate has a positive value if the corresponding mass is to the right of that particular zero position. Forces f_1 and f_2 are functions of time only (unspecified at present).

Although the same equation would result no matter what configuration is assumed, let Fig. 6-1 represent the system at an instant when x_2 is greater than x_1 and both are positive. Also both masses have velocities in the positive direction, $\dot{x}_2$ being larger than $\dot{x}_1$. At the instant depicted, therefore, both springs and both dampers will be in tension at their respective connections to both masses. The left spring and damper will produce forces toward the left on mass m_1, and the right spring and damper will produce forces toward the left on m_2, but toward the right on m_1. The mathematical expression of Newton's law for each mass is

$$\begin{aligned} m_1\ddot{x}_1 &= -c_1\dot{x}_1 - k_1x_1 + c_2(\dot{x}_2 - \dot{x}_1) + k_2(x_2 - x_1) + f_1 \\ m_2\ddot{x}_2 &= -c_2(\dot{x}_2 - \dot{x}_1) - k_2(x_2 - x_1) + f_2 \end{aligned} \tag{6-1}$$

For the present, f_1 and f_2 and c_1 and c_2 are assumed to be zero. Therefore, the result will be the "natural" vibration, undamped. The effects of the damping and forcing functions will be considered later. Upon rearranging, this becomes

$$\begin{aligned} m_1\ddot{x}_1 + (k_1 + k_2)x_1 - k_2x_2 &= 0 \\ -k_2x_1 + m_2\ddot{x}_2 + k_2x_2 &= 0 \end{aligned} \tag{6-2}$$

6.2 Undamped Natural Vibration

Classical Solution of Differential Equation. There are several ways to proceed. If classical differential-equation techniques were used, the first of Equations 6-2 could be solved for x_2 in terms of x_1, this differentiated twice to obtain an expression for $\ddot{x}_2$, and then both x_2 and $\ddot{x}_2$ substituted in the second of Equations 6-2 to obtain a fourth-order equation in x_1.

$$x_2 = \frac{m_1}{k_2}\ddot{x}_1 + \frac{k_1 + k_2}{k_2}x_1$$

$$\ddot{x}_2 = \frac{m_1}{k_2}x_1^{\mathrm{IV}} + \frac{k_1 + k_2}{k_2}\ddot{x}_1$$

$$-k_2x_1 + \frac{m_2m_1}{k_2}x_1^{\mathrm{IV}} + m_2\frac{k_1 + k_2}{k_2}\ddot{x}_1 + k_2\frac{m_1}{k_2}\ddot{x}_1 + \frac{k_2(k_1 + k_2)}{k_2}x_1 = 0$$

Simplifying,

$$\frac{d^4x_1}{dt^4} + \left(\frac{k_1 + k_2}{m_1} + \frac{k_2}{m_2}\right)\frac{d^2x_1}{dt^2} + \frac{k_1k_2}{m_1m_2}x_1 = 0 \tag{6-3}$$

This fourth-order homogeneous equation is readily solved by the method described in Appendix 1. The result would involve expressions such as $A_1 e^{i\beta_1 t}$, $A_2 e^{-i\beta_1 t}$, $A_3 e^{i\beta_2 t}$, and $A_4 e^{-i\beta_2 t}$, which could then be converted to the appropriate trigonometric functions. Since x_2 is defined in terms of x_1, an expression for x_2 is also available. The constants would depend on the initial values of x_1 and x_2 and $\dot{x}_1$ and $\dot{x}_2$. However, rather than continue this solution, Equation 6-2 will be solved by Laplace transform methods.

Solution by Laplace Transform. The transform of each of Equations 6-2 is taken.

$$\begin{aligned} [m_1s^2 + (k_1 + k_2)]X_1 - k_2X_2 &= m_1sx_{1_0} + m_1\dot{x}_{1_0} \\ -k_2X_1 + (m_2s^2 + k_2)X_2 &= m_2sx_{2_0} + m_2\dot{x}_{2_0} \end{aligned} \tag{6-4}$$

In these equations, x_{1_0} is the initial value of coordinate x_1, $\dot{x}_{1_0}$ is its initial rate of change or velocity, etc., and the functions X_1 and X_2 are functions of s rather than t.

These are now two simultaneous algebraic equations in X_1 and X_2 instead of two simultaneous differential equations in x_1 and x_2. The solution of these equations yields

$$X_1 = \frac{(m_1 m_2 s^3 + m_1 k_2 s)x_{1_0} + (m_1 m_2 s^2 + m_1 k_2)\dot{x}_{1_0} + m_2 k_2 s x_{2_0} + m_2 k_2 \dot{x}_{2_0}}{m_1 m_2 s^4 + [m_1 k_2 + m_2(k_1 + k_2)]s^2 + k_1 k_2}$$

$$X_2 = \frac{m_1 k_2 s x_{1_0} + m_1 k_2 \dot{x}_{1_0} + [m_1 m_2 s^3 + m_2(k_1 + k_2)s]x_{2_0} + [m_1 m_2 s^2 + m_2(k_1 + k_2)]\dot{x}_{2_0}}{m_1 m_2 s^4 + [m_1 k_2 + m_2(k_1 + k_2)]s^2 + k_1 k_2} \tag{6-5}$$

The inverse transformation of Equations 6-5 requires that the denominator be in factored form. These factors could be obtained by setting the denominator equal to zero and solving for the roots of the algebraic equation in s. The characteristic equation is then

$$s^4 + \left(\frac{k_1 + k_2}{m_1} + \frac{k_2}{m_2}\right) s^2 + \frac{k_1 k_2}{m_1 m_2} = 0 \tag{6-6}$$

Since this is a quadratic in s^2, it is easily determined that

$$s^2 = -\beta_1^2 \quad \text{and} \quad s^2 = -\beta_2^2$$

where

$$\beta_1^2 = \frac{1}{2}\left(\frac{k_1 + k_2}{m_1} + \frac{k_2}{m_2}\right)\left[1 - \sqrt{1 - \frac{4\dfrac{k_1 k_2}{m_1 m_2}}{\left(\dfrac{k_1 + k_2}{m_1} + \dfrac{k_2}{m_2}\right)^2}}\,\right]$$

$$\beta_2^2 = \frac{1}{2}\left(\frac{k_1 + k_2}{m_1} + \frac{k_2}{m_2}\right)\left[1 + \sqrt{1 - \frac{4\dfrac{k_1 k_2}{m_1 m_2}}{\left(\dfrac{k_1 + k_2}{m_1} + \dfrac{k_2}{m_2}\right)^2}}\,\right] \tag{6-7}$$

It is easy to show that the second term under the radical is always a number between zero and $+1$, so that β_1^2 and β_2^2 are real positive numbers, and therefore $\beta_2^2 > \beta_1^2$ for all combinations of positive spring constants. Thus the characteristic equation becomes

$$(s^2 + \beta_1^2)(s^2 + \beta_2^2) = 0$$

and the denominator of Equations 6-5 can be manipulated to contain these same two factors. It is apparent then that when Equation A1-17 of Appendix 1 is applied to obtain the inverse of Equations 6-5, terms involving $\sin \beta_1 t$, $\cos \beta_1 t$, $\sin \beta_2 t$, $\cos \beta_2 t$ will result. Therefore, β_1 and β_2 are natural frequencies. It is seen that the solution of the characteristic equation yields the natural frequencies—in this instance, the undamped natural frequencies.

If the inverse transformations of Equations 6-5 are taken, the results are

$$\begin{aligned} x_1 = \frac{1}{(\beta_2^2 - \beta_1^2)}\Bigg\{&\left[\left(\frac{k_2}{m_2} - \beta_1^2\right) x_{1_0} + \frac{k_2}{m_1} x_{2_0}\right] \cos \beta_1 t \\ &+ \frac{1}{\beta_1}\left[\left(\frac{k_2}{m_2} - \beta_1^2\right)\dot{x}_{1_0} + \frac{k_2}{m_1}\dot{x}_{2_0}\right] \sin \beta_1 t \\ &- \left[\left(\frac{k_2}{m_2} - \beta_2^2\right) x_{1_0} + \frac{k_2}{m_1} x_{2_0}\right] \cos \beta_2 t \\ &- \beta_2\left[\left(\frac{k_2}{m_2} - \beta_2^2\right)\dot{x}_{1_0} + \frac{k_2}{m_1}\dot{x}_{2_0}\right] \sin \beta_2 t\Bigg\} \end{aligned}$$

$$x_2 = \frac{1}{(\beta_2^2 - \beta_1^2)} \left\{ \left[\frac{k_2}{m_2} x_{1_0} + \left(\frac{k_1 + k_2}{m_1} - \beta_1^2 \right) x_{2_0} \right] \cos \beta_1 t \right.$$

$$+ \frac{1}{\beta_1} \left[\frac{k_2}{m_2} \dot{x}_{1_0} + \left(\frac{k_1 + k_2}{m_1} - \beta_1^2 \right) \dot{x}_{2_0} \right] \sin \beta_1 t$$

$$- \left[\frac{k_2}{m_2} x_{1_0} + \left(\frac{k_1 + k_2}{m_1} - \beta_2^2 \right) x_{2_0} \right] \cos \beta_2 t$$

$$\left. - \frac{1}{\beta_2} \left[\frac{k_2}{m_2} \dot{x}_{1_0} + \left(\frac{k_1 + k_2}{m_1} - \beta_1^2 \right) \dot{x}_{2_0} \right] \sin \beta_2 t \right\} \tag{6-8}$$

Normal Modes of Vibration. It is apparent from Equations 6-8 that the motion of each mass is composed of two oscillations of different frequencies added together. The thought arises that there might be some combination of initial conditions which would cause one or the other of these oscillations to be missing. For example, if the initial velocities were both zero, the sine terms would be missing from Equations 6-8. Then if x_{1_0} and x_{2_0} are chosen to make the coefficient of $\cos \beta_2 t$ zero in the equation for x_1, the same relationship will also make the coefficient of $\cos \beta_2 t$ zero in the equation for x_2. Both x_1 and x_2 would then oscillate at the single frequency β_1. By a similar procedure, initial values of x_{1_0} and x_{2_0} could be chosen which would cause the coefficients of $\cos \beta_1 t$ to go to zero, leaving only the oscillation at the frequency β_2. To eliminate the β_2 frequency, it would be necessary to have

$$\frac{x_{1_0}}{x_{2_0}} = \frac{\dfrac{k_2}{m_1}}{\beta_2^2 - \dfrac{k_2}{m_2}}$$

If x_{1_0} is substituted from the above equation into Equations 6-8, then

$$x_1 = \frac{\dfrac{k_2}{m_1}}{\beta_2^2 - \dfrac{k_2}{m_2}} x_{2_0} \cos \beta_1 t \qquad \text{and} \quad x_2 = x_{2_0} \cos \beta_1 t$$

These two equations state that x_1 and x_2 both oscillate at the same frequency (and only one of the two possible frequencies) and that their motion is such that their coordinates have the same ratio at all times

$$\left(\frac{x_1}{x_2} \right)_1 = \frac{\dfrac{k_2}{m_1}}{\beta_2^2 - \dfrac{k_2}{m_2}} \tag{6-9}$$

An algebraic exercise would show that the above ratio is always a positive number less than 1. This means that at any given instant each mass is on the same side of its equilibrium point (the movements are in phase), but that x_2 is always greater than x_1 according to the ratio expressed by Equation 6-9. This is illustrated in Fig. 6-2.

When a system is capable of vibrating with more than one frequency but is actually vibrating at only one of its possible natural frequencies, the system is said to be vibrating in one of its "normal modes." The description of the normal mode is some equation—in this instance, Equation 6-9, which specifies how the various elements of the system move in relation to each other. In the problem just discussed the motion occurred at the frequency β_1, which was the lower frequency. The mode of vibration associated with the lowest natural frequency of a system is referred to as the first mode. The next higher frequency is the second, and so on.

If the β_1 motion had been eliminated instead of β_2 by making the right choice of initial conditions in Equations 6-8, a similar analysis would have shown that the second mode is described by

$$\left(\frac{x_1}{x_2}\right)_2 = \frac{-\dfrac{k_2}{m_1}}{\dfrac{k_2}{m_2} - \beta_1{}^2} \tag{6-10}$$

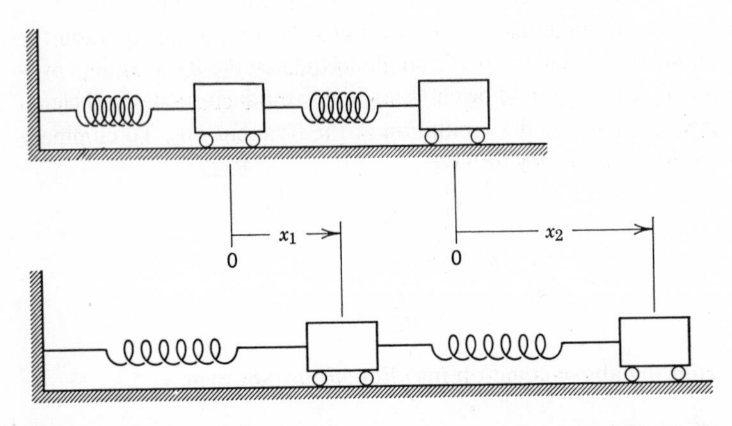

Fig. 6-2 First normal mode of vibration of a two-degree-of-freedom system

Of course, it would be necessary to deflect the coordinates in this same ratio initially, if the motion is to have none of the first mode motion in it. Again, an exercise in algebra would show that this ratio is always a negative number, but this time either greater or less than -1, depending on the magnitude of the springs and masses. Therefore, the amplitude of the oscillation of x_2 about its neutral point may be either greater or less than the amplitude of x_1, but its displacement from the neutral point is always in the opposite direction. This is illustrated in Fig. 6-3.

In general, a two-degree system oscillates with both modes and both frequencies present. (It takes certain combinations of initial conditions to cause it to oscillate in only one mode, as was seen.) Once the oscillation is started, it would continue indefinitely (no damping), with the same amount of each mode always present. However, the two modes have different frequencies, with one frequency not necessarily an even multiple of the other. An observer might easily think that the motion is quite erratic and irregular because of the superposition of simultaneous modes. In some systems the two frequencies might be rather close together. Then each of the masses would appear to oscillate sometimes with larger amplitude, sometimes with smaller amplitude, according to whether the contribution from one mode is reinforcing or counteracting the contribution from the other mode. If the effects add together for one mass, they subtract for the other. That is, when x_1 has its largest apparent amplitude (actually, the sum of two amplitudes—see Equations 6-8), x_2 has its smallest apparent amplitude, and vice versa. Thus, the total energy in the oscillation appears to wander back and forth from one coordinate to the other. This is sometimes referred to as "wandering energy." The apparent increases and decreases in amplitude because of the superposition of the two oscillations of nearly equal frequency are termed "beats," and the "beat frequency" is the frequency at which the maximum amplitude occurs, which is also the difference in the two almost equal frequencies. However, it is important to remember that there is a constant amount of each of the *normal modes* present, even if the amplitude of each of the coordinates varies.

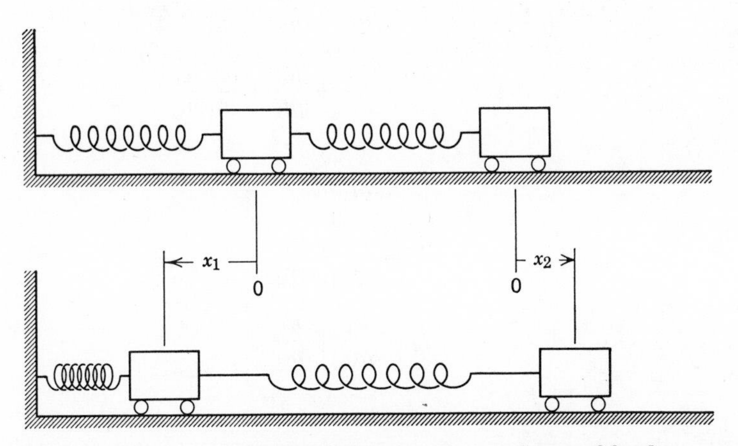

Fig. 6-3 Second normal mode of vibration of a two-degree-of-freedom system

The concept of normal modes and the simultaneous oscillation of a two-degree-of-freedom system in each of two normal modes is of great importance. Systems having a greater number of degrees of freedom also oscillate simultaneously in each of several normal modes—as many normal modes as there are degrees of freedom.

6.3 Natural Vibration with Damping

If the effect of damping in the original problem is included, the following equations in the transforms are obtained.

$$X_1 = \frac{(s^3 + b_1 s^2 + b_2 s + b_3)x_{1_0} + (s^2 + d_1 s + d_2)\dot{x}_{1_0} + e_1 s x_{2_0} + (g_1 s + g_2)\dot{x}_{2_0}}{s^4 + a_1 s^3 + a_2 s^2 + a_3 s + a_4}$$

$$X_2 = \frac{(h_1 s + h_2)x_{1_0} + (i_1 s + i_2)\dot{x}_{1_0} + (s^3 + j_1 s^2 + j_2 s + j_3)x_{2_0} + (s^2 + l_1 s + l_2)\dot{x}_{2_0}}{s^4 + a_1 s^3 + a_2 s^2 + a_3 s + a_4} \tag{6-11}$$

where

$$a_1 = \frac{c_1}{m_1} + \frac{c_2}{m_2} + \frac{c_2}{m_1} \qquad g_2 = \frac{k_2}{m_1} \quad (= e_1)$$

$$a_2 = \frac{k_1}{m_1} + \frac{k_2}{m_2} + \frac{k_2}{m_1} + \frac{c_1}{m_1}\frac{c_2}{m_2} \qquad h_1 = \frac{k_2}{m_2} \quad (= d_2)$$

$$a_3 = \frac{c_1}{m_1}\frac{k_2}{m_2} + \frac{c_2}{m_2}\frac{k_1}{m_1} \qquad h_2 = \frac{k_2}{m_2}\frac{c_1}{m_1} - \frac{k_1}{m_1}\frac{c_2}{m_2}$$

$$a_4 = \frac{k_1}{m_1}\frac{k_2}{m_2} \qquad i_1 = \frac{c_2}{m_2} \quad (= d_1)$$

$$b_1 = \frac{c_1}{m_1} + \frac{c_2}{m_2} + \frac{c_2}{m_1} \quad (= a_1) \qquad i_2 = \frac{k_2}{m_2} \quad (= d_2 = g_1)$$

$$b_2 = \frac{k_2}{m_2} + \frac{c_1}{m_1}\frac{c_2}{m_2} \qquad j_1 = \frac{c_1}{m_1} + \frac{c_2}{m_2} + \frac{c_2}{m_1} \quad (= a_1 = b_1)$$

$$b_3 = \frac{c_1}{m_1}\frac{k_2}{m_2} \qquad j_2 = \frac{k_1}{m_1} + \frac{k_2}{m_1} + \frac{c_1}{m_1}\frac{c_2}{m_2}$$

$$d_1 = \frac{c_2}{m_2} \qquad j_3 = \frac{k_1}{m_1}\frac{c_2}{m_2}$$

$$d_2 = \frac{k_2}{m_2} \qquad l_1 = \frac{c_1}{m_1} + \frac{c_2}{m_1}$$

$$e_1 = \frac{k_2}{m_1} \qquad l_2 = \frac{k_1}{m_1} + \frac{k_2}{m_1}$$

$$g_1 = \frac{c_2}{m_1}$$

These equations are presented here, although no attempt is made to take the inverse transformation. In a specific problem, numbers would be available for the various parameters, and the inverse could be taken. However, it is instructive to consider how the inverse might be taken and what would be the form of the result. First, the denominator would be factored into two quadratic factors, so that the denominator would become

$$(s^2 + 2\zeta_1\beta_1 s + \beta_1^2)(s^2 + 2\zeta_2\beta_2 s + \beta_2^2)$$

or

$$[(s + \zeta_1\beta_1)^2 + \beta_1^2(1 - \zeta_1^2)][(s + \zeta_2\beta_2)^2 + \beta_2^2(1 - \zeta_2^2)] \tag{6-12}$$

It should be pointed out that the value of β_1 and β_2 in the above equation cannot be obtained from Equation 6-7 if there is damping present. However, β_1 and β_2 in Equation 6-12 are often referred to as "undamped natural frequencies" of the damped system, even though they are not numerically equal to the frequencies of the corresponding undamped system calculated from Equation 6-7.

Application of Equation A1-17 (Appendix 1) to the problem of obtaining the inverse, as was done for the inverse of the undamped equations, results in equations similar to Equations 6-8, except that where there were $\beta_1 t$ and $\beta_2 t$ in the sine and cosine terms, there are now $\beta_1\sqrt{1-\zeta_1^2}\,t$ and $\beta_2\sqrt{1-\zeta_2^2}\,t$ or the damped natural frequencies corresponding to the individual damping factors. As stated previously the numerical values of β_1 and β_2 would be slightly different from the values that they would have if the dampers were zero—see Example 6-1. Also there would be a factor $e^{-\zeta_1\beta_1 t}$ multiplying the $\sin\beta_1\sqrt{1-\zeta_1^2}\,t$ and $\cos\beta_1\sqrt{1-\zeta_1^2}\,t$ terms and a similar factor $e^{-\zeta_2\beta_2 t}$ multiplying the $\sin\beta_2\sqrt{1-\zeta_2^2}\,t$ and $\cos\beta_2\sqrt{1-\zeta_2^2}\,t$ terms. These factors show that all motion would eventually cease.

Application of concepts learned in the study of the single-degree-of-freedom system can now help in the visualization of this motion. If ζ_1 and ζ_2 were both between zero and $+1$ there would be two damped oscillations existing simultaneously, each damping out at a rate depending on the damping factor. If the factors were about the same, then the higher frequency oscillation would decay in less time, leaving only the first mode. (They would both decay in the same number of cycles, but that would require less time for the higher frequency mode.)

It is recalled that the damped natural frequency is not appreciably different from the undamped natural frequency unless ζ is greater than about 0.1. Most unintentional damping (such as structural damping) is less than this, so that usually no significant error is made in calculating natural frequencies of the multiple degree system from the simpler equations for zero damping.

The amount of each mode which is present again depends on the initial conditions, as in the undamped case, but the coefficients of the various terms are, of course, affected by the damping constant. Just as for the undamped system, it would be possible to choose initial conditions so that the system would oscillate in either of the two possible modes with the other mode absent, except that with damping the motion would decay. Also the description of the mode is more involved, a phase angle other than 0° or 180° being involved as well as the coordinate ratios. This is clarified in Example 6-1.

Of course, either damping factor (or both) might be greater than 1; if so, that particular mode would decay without oscillation. Also, if either damping factor were negative, the system would be unstable. (For the system depicted in Fig. 6-1 a negative damping factor could not result, since energy can only be dissipated in this system.)

6.4 Forced Vibration

Sinusoidal Forcing Function. Attention is now directed to the effect of the forces which act on the system. As in the one-degree system, the forcing functions of major interest are sinusoidal for steady-state vibration, and step function for transient motion. The sinusoidal forces would also produce some transients which would die out, and the motion remaining would be the response of principal interest.

Since this is a linear system, the effects of the two forces could be evaluated separately and then superimposed. Therefore, there is really no need to consider both forces in this discussion. Actually, there would be four transfer functions of interest: X_1/F_1, X_1/F_2, X_2/F_1, and X_2/F_2. Only X_1/F_2 and X_2/F_2 will be considered. The motion resulting from the initial conditions is not considered. Although motion resulting from the initial conditions could be superimposed on the forced motion, this motion dies out anyway, so that after a long time only the forced motion remains. The transformed equations are

$$[m_1 s^2 + (c_1 + c_2)s + (k_1 + k_2)]X_1 - (c_2 s + k_2)X_2 = F_1$$
$$-(c_2 s + k_2)X_1 + (m_2 s^2 + c_2 s + k_2)X_2 = F_2$$

Solving these simultaneously gives

$$X_1 = \frac{(s^2 + d_1 s + d_2)F_1/m_1 + (g_1 s + g_2)F_2/m_2}{(s^2 + 2\zeta_1\beta_1 s + \beta_1^2)(s^2 + 2\zeta_2\beta_2 s + \beta_2^2)}$$
$$X_2 = \frac{(d_1 s + d_2)F_1/m_1 + (s^2 + l_1 s + l_2)F_2/m_2}{(s^2 + 2\zeta_1\beta_1 s + \beta_1^2)(s^2 + 2\zeta_2\beta_2 s + \beta_2^2)} \tag{6-13}$$

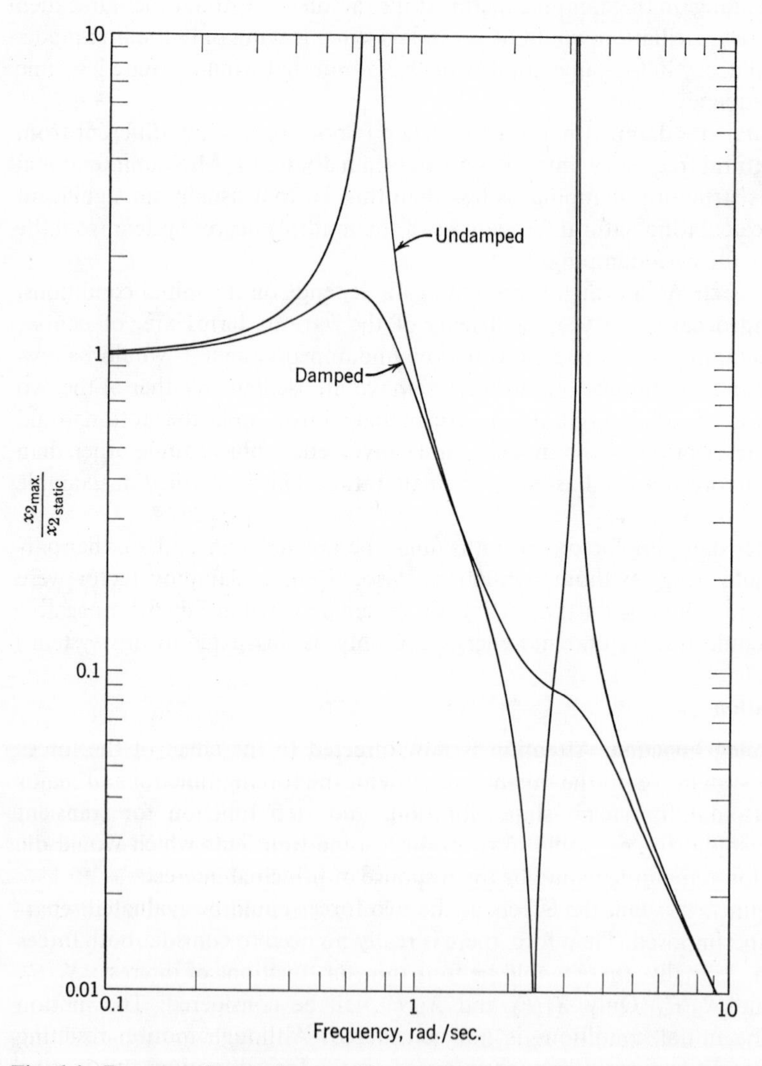

Fig. 6-4 Response of a two-degree-of-freedom system to a sinusoidal forcing function

where the constants are defined in Equations 6-11 and 6-12. Now, if F_1 is zero and F_2 is

$$\frac{f_{2_0}\omega}{(s^2 + \omega^2)}$$

(transform of f_{2_0} sin ωt), the inverse transform corresponding to the $(s^2 + \omega^2)$ factor in the denominator is the only term in the inverse which does not decay. This term, therefore, leads to the mathematical description of the forced vibration. The full inverse is not developed here, but it is apparent that the magnitude of the denominator of both X_1 and X_2 can be manipulated to become

$$\left\{\left[1 - \left(\frac{\omega}{\beta_1}\right)^2\right]^2 + \left(\frac{2\zeta_1\omega}{\beta_1}\right)^2\right\}\left\{\left[1 - \left(\frac{\omega}{\beta_2}\right)^2\right]^2 + \left(\frac{2\zeta_2\omega}{\beta_2}\right)^2\right\}$$

Each quantity within braces is familiar from the single-degree-of-freedom discussion

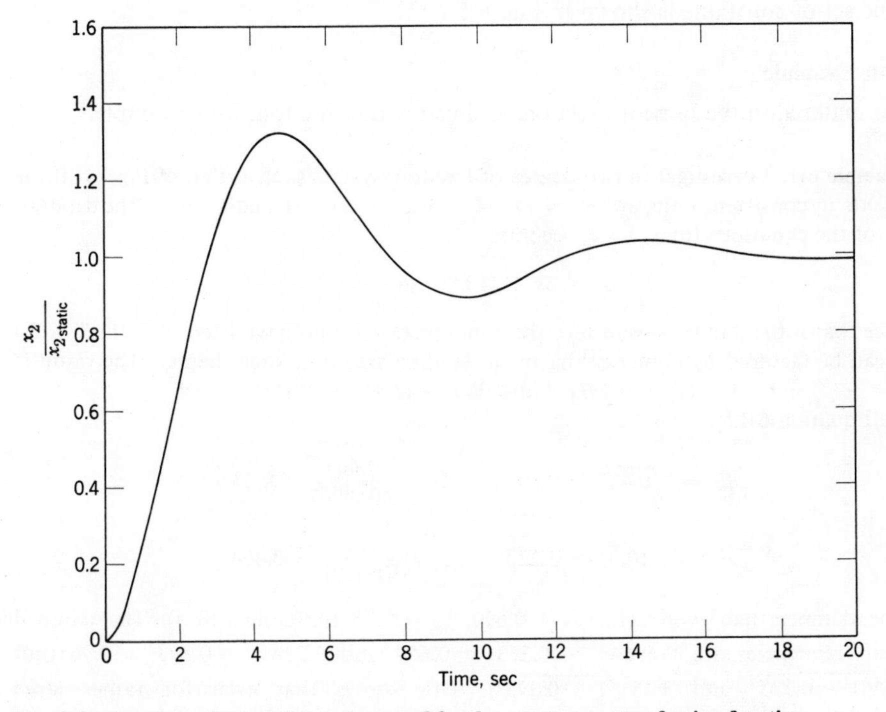

Fig. 6-5 Response of damped two-degree-of-freedom system to step forcing function

and thus two undamped resonant frequencies are recognized: one at the natural frequency β_1, and one at β_2. If the damping factors are small and the natural frequencies β_1 and β_2 are well spread, the resonant frequencies for the damped system occur at the damped natural frequencies, the same as for the single-degree-of-freedom system; that is, at $\beta_1\sqrt{1 - \zeta_1^2}$ and $\beta_2\sqrt{1 - \zeta_2^2}$. A plot of amplitude for a specific set of constants is shown in Fig. 6-4. Because of the large number of possible configurations, a set of charts similar to Figs. 3-1 to 3-14 for the single-degree system cannot be developed here. A general method for obtaining such charts is explained in Reference 1.

Step Forcing Function. Now, consider the step forcing function. Again it is convenient to analyze only one of the forces at a time, the complete response then being the sum of the responses to each force. Therefore, in Equation 6-13, let $F_1 = 0$ and $F_2 = f_{2_0}/s$, the transform of the step function. After a period of time the transients would die out and the system would come to rest with $x_1 = f_{2_0}/k_1$ and $x_2 = f_{2_0}/k_1 + f_{2_0}/k_2$. These are the terms in the inverse transform of X_1 and X_2 which derive from the s in the denominator. Then there are oscillatory terms, if ζ_1 and ζ_2 are less than 1, corresponding to each of the other factors in the denominator of Equations 6-13. The resulting transient displacement of each mass is the sum of these terms. If there is no damping, then since the two natural frequencies are not, in general, integral multiples of one another, there will be some time at which the contribution of each frequency term will be in phase, so that the maximum deflections should be twice the steady-state values, or $x_{1_{max}} = 2f_{2_0}/k_1$ and $x_{2_{max}} = 2f_{2_0}/k_1 + 2f_{2_0}/k_2$. This is similar to the 100% overshoot of the single-degree system. The response of a two-degree system for a specific set of constants is shown in Fig. 6-5.

6.5 An Example

The material in the previous sections is illustrated in the following example.

Example 6-1. Investigate a two-degree-of-freedom system such as that of Fig. 6-1 if the constants in consistent units are $m_1 = m_2 = c_1 = c_2 = k_1 = 1$ and $k_2 = 5$. The denominator of the equations for x_1 or x_2 becomes

$$s^4 = 3s^3 + 12s^2 + 6s + 5$$

(Notice that if the dampers were zero the denominator would have been $s^4 + 11s^2 + 5$.) This can be factored by numerical means to be discussed in a later chapter. The result is

$$(s^2 + 0.463s + 0.483)(s^2 + 2.53s + 10.35)$$

From Equation 6-12,

$$\beta_1 = \sqrt{0.483} = 0.696, \qquad \zeta_1 = \frac{0.463}{2(0.696)} = 0.333$$

$$\beta_2 = \sqrt{10.35} = 3.22, \qquad \zeta_2 = \frac{2.53}{2(3.22)} = 0.393$$

(If the dampers had been zero, $\beta_1 = 0.690$, $\beta_2 = 3.25$ for comparison). The damped natural frequencies are $0.696\sqrt{1 - 0.333^2} = 0.657$ and $3.22\sqrt{1 - 0.393^2} = 2.96$ (not $0.690\sqrt{1 - 0.333^2}$ and $3.25\sqrt{1 - 0.393^2}$). This shows that even for rather large damping the natural frequencies are not greatly different from what would be computed if the dampers were assumed zero—0.657 compared with 0.690 and 2.96 compared with 3.25.

Now, when the forces are zero, Equations 6-11 become

$$X_1 = \frac{(s^3 + 3s^2 + 6s + 5)x_{1_0} + (s^2 + s + 5)\dot{x}_{1_0} + 5sx_{2_0} + (s + 5)\dot{x}_{2_0}}{[(s + 0.232)^2 + 0.657^2][(s + 1.267)^2 + 2.96^2]}$$

$$X_2 = \frac{(5s + 4)x_{1_0} + (s + 5)\dot{x}_{1_0} + (s^3 + 3s^2 + 7s + 1)x_{2_0} + (s^2 + 2s + 6)\dot{x}_{2_0}}{[(s + 0.232)^2 + 0.657^2][(s + 1.267)^2 + 2.96^2]}$$

If Equation A1-17 (Appendix 1) is applied to taking these inverses, the result is, after a tedious calculation,

$$x_1 = e^{-0.232t}[(0.390x_{1_0} - 0.045\dot{x}_{1_0} + 0.549x_{2_0} - 0.0053\dot{x}_{2_0}) \cos 0.657t + (0.505x_{1_0} + 0.705\dot{x}_{1_0} - 0.109x_{2_0} + 0.766\dot{x}_{2_0}) \sin 0.657t]$$

$$+ e^{-1.267t}[(0.610x_{1_0} + 0.045\dot{x}_{1_0} - 0.549x_{2_0} + 0.0053\dot{x}_{2_0}) \cos 2.96t + (0.182x_{1_0} + 0.195\dot{x}_{1_0} - 0.168x_{2_0} - 0.169\dot{x}_{2_0}) \sin 2.96t]$$

. . . .

$$x_2 = e^{-0.232t}[(0.458x_{1_0} - 0.0053\dot{x}_{1_0} + 0.592x_{2_0} + 0.042\dot{x}_{2_0}) \cos 0.657t + (0.529x_{1_0} + 0.766\dot{x}_{1_0} - 0.153x_{2_0} + 0.840\dot{x}_{2_0}) \sin 0.657t]$$

$$+ e^{-1.267t}[(-0.458x_{1_0} + 0.0053\dot{x}_{1_0} + 0.411x_{2_0} - 0.042x_{2_0}) \cos 2.96t + (-0.276x_{1_0} - 0.1693\dot{x}_{1_0}\ 0.257x_{2_0} + 0.137\dot{x}_{2_0}) \sin 2.96t]$$

To excite only one of the normal modes (for instance, the second one), it would be necessary to choose the initial conditions x_{1_0}, $\dot{x}_{1_0}$, x_{2_0}, and $\dot{x}_{2_0}$ so that the factors multiplying cos $0.657t$ and sin $0.657t$ in both the x_1 and x_2 expressions are zero. Actually, if the initial conditions are chosen so that the factors multiplying the cos $0.657t$ and sin $0.657t$ in x_1 are zero, these same conditions should cause the factors in the x_2 equation to be zero. This offers a check on the accuracy. For the above problem if $\dot{x}_{2_0} = 0$, it can be found from the x_1 equation that $x_{1_0}/x_{2_0} = -1.28$ and $\dot{x}_{1_0}/x_{2_0} = 1.07$; from the x_2 equation if $\dot{x}_{2_0} = 0$ $x_{1_0}/x_{2_0} = -1.28$ and $\dot{x}_{1_0}/x_{2_0} = 1.08$, a satisfactory check for slide-rule calculations.

If only the first mode were to be excited, calculation using the x_1 equation would require $\dot{x}_{2_0} = 0$, $x_{1_0}/x_{2_0} = 0.898$, and $\dot{x}_{1_0}/x_{2_0} = 0.022$; from the x_2 equation the conditions are $\dot{x}_{2_0} = 0$, $x_{1_0}/x_{2_0} = 0.898$, and $\dot{x}_{1_0}/x_{2_0} = 0.057$. The discrepancy can be traced to differences of numbers which are themselves nearly equal. More significant figures would be required in all of the calculations to avoid this difficulty.

To illustrate the method of determining the steady-state response to the sinusoidal forcing functions, suppose the desired response is that of x_2 caused by the force f_2. Then the corresponding transfer function is

$$\frac{X_2}{F_2} = \frac{(s^2 + 2s + 6)}{(s^2 + 0.463s + 0.483)(s^2 + 2.53s + 10.35)}$$

$$= \frac{\frac{6}{5}\left[1 + \frac{2(0.408)}{2.45}s + \left(\frac{s}{2.45}\right)^2\right]}{\left[1 + \frac{2(0.333)}{0.696}s + \left(\frac{s}{0.696}\right)^2\right]\left[1 + \frac{2(0.393)}{3.22}s + \left(\frac{s}{3.22}\right)^2\right]}$$

The second form is more convenient for identifying the factors necessary for application of the methods of Reference 1. For

$$F_2 = \frac{f_{2_0}\omega}{(s^2 + \omega^2)}$$

corresponding to $f_{2_0} \sin \omega t$, Equation A1-14 (Appendix 1) would show that the inverse can be obtained by substitution of $i\omega$ for s in the above transfer function. However, the response plot is more easily obtained by the methods described in Reference 1. The result is shown in Fig. 6-4.

The response of the system to the step input can be determined by using $F_2 = f_{2_0}/s$ which is the transform of the step function of magnitude, f_{2_0}.

$$X_2 = f_{2_0} \frac{s^2 + 2s + 6}{s(s^2 + 0.463s + 0.483)(s^2 + 2.53s + 10.35)}$$

Corresponding to the s in the denominator is a term in the inverse which is simply $1.2f_0$. This is the final steady value of the deflection, which agrees with

$$\frac{f_{2_0}}{k_1} + \frac{f_{2_0}}{k_2} = f_{2_0}\left(1 + \frac{1}{5}\right) = x_{2_{\text{static}}}$$

The complete inverse, by applying Equation A1-17 (Appendix 1), is

$$x_2 = f_{2_0}\,[1.2 + e^{-0.232t}\,(-1.166\cos 0.657t - 0.351\sin 0.657t) + e^{-1.267t}(-0.034\cos 2.96t - 0.029\sin 2.96t)]$$

where $1.2f_{2_0}$ also is $x_{2_{\text{static}}}$. This equation is plotted in Fig. 6-5. Note that the higher frequency term in the above equation for x_2 has a very small initial amplitude and is rapidly damped out, so that the plot of Fig. 6-5 is very similar to the response of the one-degree-of-freedom system to a step input. This is not always to be expected, but is merely a consequence of the numerical parameters chosen.

6.6 One Mass, Two Coordinate System

In the previous discussion two masses were involved, with the motion of each mass restricted to one direction. If one mass is supported in such a way that it can move in a plane (as depicted schematically in Fig. 6-6), restrained by springs so that k_x is the

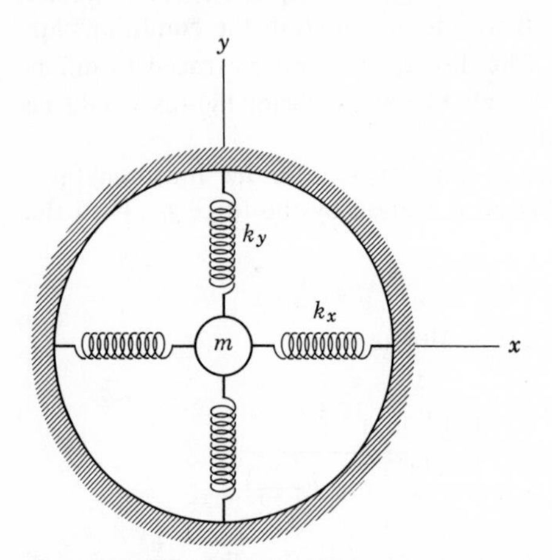

Fig. 6-6 Two-degree-of-freedom system, motion in a plane

sum of the spring constants acting in the x direction and similarly for k_y, a two-degree-of-freedom system also results. Imagine that the mass is free to move in the horizontal plane, supported against gravity by friction-free rollers (not shown), and that the zero for the x and y coordinates is the position of equilibrium. For the condition as shown, It is intuitively obvious that the two normal modes are at right angles to each other and the mass could vibrate in either normal mode without exciting the other. (It is assumed that the deflections are small, of course.) The frequency of either mode is readily computed as $\sqrt{k_x/m}$ or $\sqrt{k_y/m}$. If both modes are present, the mass will trace out a pattern which depends on the initial conditions and the ratio of the frequencies. Such patterns are called Lissajous figures. If there were dampers colinear with the springs, the individual modes would decay as for single degree systems.

Spring Constants. If the springs which restrain the mass were not oriented at right angles to each other, a slight complication occurs. Figure 6-7 illustrates a configuration in which the springs are chosen arbitrarily. A displacement in the x direction produces a force in both the x and y directions. Therefore, motion in the x direction would be "coupled" with motion in the y direction. For spring 1, a deflection x causes a deflection of the spring of $x \cos \psi_1$, while y causes deflection $y \sin \psi_1$. The force on the mass in the $+x$ direction is $-k_1(x \cos \psi_1 + y \sin \psi_1) \cos \psi_1$. The force on the mass in the

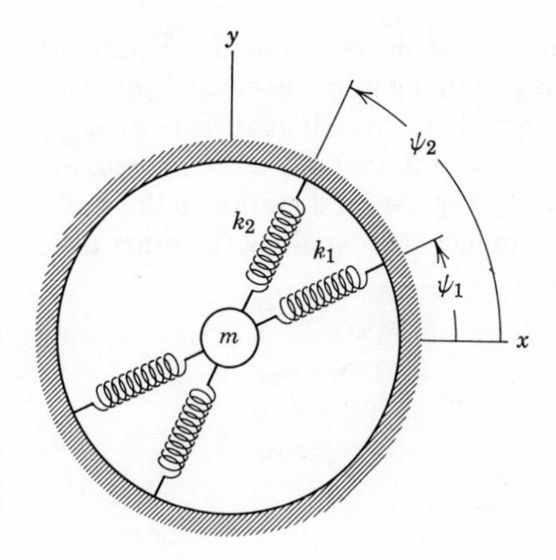

Fig. 6-7 Springs not aligned with axes

$+y$ direction is $-k_1(x \cos \psi_1 + y \sin \psi_1) \sin \psi_1$. It is convenient to define effective spring constants as follows.

k_{xx} force in $-x$ direction per unit displacement in $+x$ direction

k_{xy} force in $-x$ direction per unit displacement in $+y$ direction

k_{yx} force in $-y$ direction per unit displacement in $+x$ direction

k_{yy} force in $-y$ direction per unit displacement in $+y$ direction

If there are n springs, these effective spring constants become

$$k_{xx} = \sum_{i=1}^{n} k_i \cos^2 \psi_i$$

$$k_{xy} = k_{yx} = \sum_{i=1}^{n} k_i \sin \psi_i \cos \psi_i \tag{6-14}$$

$$k_{yy} = \sum_{i=1}^{n} k_i \sin^2 \psi_i$$

(Note that k_{xx} and k_{yy} must always be positive, but that k_{xy} may be either positive or negative.)

It may be that the arbitrary choice of x and y axes was not the most convenient. Let the axes be rotated as in Fig. 6-8 and new spring constants determined for use with the new axis system. If the spring constants in the x' and y' directions are defined in the same way ($k_{x'x'}$ the force in the $-x'$ direction per unit displacement in the $+x'$ direction, etc.) it is possible to demonstrate the following relationships between spring constants.

$$\begin{aligned} k_{x'x'} &= k_{xx} \cos^2 \theta + 2k_{xy} \sin \theta \cos \theta + k_{yy} \sin^2 \theta \\ k_{x'y'} &= k_{y'x'} = (k_{yy} - k_{xx}) \sin \theta \cos \theta + k_{xy}(\cos^2 \theta - \sin^2 \theta) \\ k_{y'y'} &= k_{xx} \sin^2 \theta - 2k_{xy} \sin \theta \cos \theta + k_{yy} \cos^2 \theta \end{aligned} \tag{6-15}$$

These equations are similar to the equations for elastic bodies under combined stresses in two dimensions, and to the equations pertaining to moments and products of inertia about axes rotated relative to each other. This suggests that there must be some angle θ_p which would cause $k_{x'y'}$ to become zero. If this set of axes were used, the problem would revert to the problem represented by Fig. 6-6, and motion in the direction of one of these "principal axes" would not induce motion along the other axis. Then the modes would be "uncoupled."

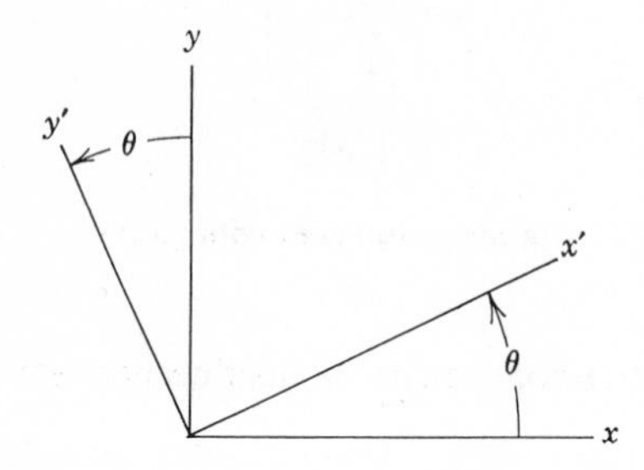

Fig. 6-8. Rotation of axes

The angle to the principal axis is determined by setting $k_{x'y'} = 0$. Then the values of $k_{x'x'_p}$ and $k_{y'y'_p}$ along these principal axes can be determined using this value of θ_p. The results are

$$\begin{aligned} \theta_p &= \frac{1}{2} \tan^{-1} \left(\frac{2k_{xy}}{(k_{xx} - k_{yy})} \right) \\ k_{x'x'_p} &= \frac{k_{xx} + k_{yy}}{2} + \sqrt{\left(\frac{k_{xx} - k_{yy}}{2} \right)^2 + k_{xy}^2} \\ k_{y'y'_p} &= \frac{k_{xx} + k_{yy}}{2} - \sqrt{\left(\frac{k_{xx} - k_{yy}}{2} \right)^2 + k_{xy}^2} \end{aligned} \tag{6-16}$$

where the subscript p denotes "principal."

Orthogonality of Normal Modes. It is a significant property of vibrating systems that the normal modes are "orthogonal." In the problem just discussed the normal modes were seen to lie at right angles to each other, so the orthogonality of the modes might suggest perpendicularity. The term has a broader meaning, however, which is simply that the system can oscillate in one of its normal modes without exciting another of its normal modes.

Sometimes it is possible, at a glance, to determine how to define coordinates so that they will measure the amount of a normal mode present (as for Fig. 6-6), although sometimes a short calculation is required, as was just discussed. For other systems, even simple systems such as that represented by Fig. 6-1, a rather extensive calculation is necessary before a coordinate can be defined which will measure directly the amount of a normal mode present. In such a system the coordinates which suggest themselves by the physical nature of the problem (x_1 and x_2 in Fig. 6-1) are coupled together, so that if x_1 oscillates, x_2 cannot remain zero. Each of the differential equations which describe the motion contains terms involving both of the variables. If the coordinates measured directly the deflection in a normal mode (as in Fig. 6-6), each differential equation would contain only one of the variables. The use of different coordinates to represent the same physical system is frequently used in the following chapters.

CHAPTER 7

Energy Methods and Generalized Properties

7.1 Kinetic and Potential Energy

It is often easier to make use of energy relationships in formulating the mathematical description of a system than it is to use Newton's law relating forces and torques with linear and angular accelerations. Two forms of energy—kinetic and potential—are of interest in the discussion which follows. Both of these represent a capacity to do work, and consequently might be conceptually visualized as "stored work." In this context, "work" has the technical meaning associated with the movement of a force through a displacement (or a torque through an angle), and thus work, kinetic energy, and potential energy all have the dimensions of foot-pounds. Kinetic energy is energy stored in the form of a moving mass (or masses), and work could be performed by the mass while slowing down. Potential energy may be visualized as stored "energy of position." For instance, if an elastic body is deformed, work must be done on the body to produce the deformation. This work is stored in the fibers of the body and is potentially recoverable. Similarly, work would be required to lift a mass in a gravity field, and this work is potentially recoverable and can be considered as potential energy.

In a vibrating system, both forms of energy are present. If the total energy (kinetic plus potential) stored in a system remains constant with time, the system is said to be conservative, and the energy is alternately converted from one form to the other. Figure 1-1 represents such a system for a one-degree-of-freedom configuration. Since the spring of Fig. 1-1 is linear, the amount of energy stored in the spring when deflected through the distance, x, can be computed by determining the amount of work done on the spring, or

$$dw = d(\text{P.E.}) = f\,dx = (kx)\,dx$$

$$\text{Potential energy} = k\int_0^x x\,dx = \tfrac{1}{2}kx^2 \tag{7-1}$$

Similarly, the kinetic energy corresponding to the velocity of the mass could be computed by considering the work done by a force on a free mass to accelerate it up to a velocity, v, as follows. Since $f = m(dv/dt)$ and $dx = v\,dt$, the work done in dt time is

$$dw = d(\text{K.E.}) = f\,dx = \left(m\frac{dv}{dt}\right)(v\,dt) = mv\,dv$$

$$\text{Kinetic energy} = m\int_{v=0}^{v} v\,dv = \tfrac{1}{2}mv^2 \tag{7-2}$$

7.2 Rayleigh Method

Single-Degree System. For a one-degree-of-freedom system oscillating freely at its natural frequency, the potential energy stored in the spring is maximum when the deflection is maximum, and at this point the velocity is zero so the kinetic energy is zero. On the other hand, when the deflection is zero (and, therefore, potential energy is zero), the velocity is maximum so that the kinetic energy is maximum. It is possible to compute the natural frequency by taking advantage of the fact that the total energy remains constant and therefore the same at both of the above instants. Assuming harmonic motion,

$$x = x_{\max}\sin\beta t$$

$$v = \frac{dx}{dt} = x_{\max}\,\beta\cos\beta t$$

Setting maximum potential energy equal to maximum kinetic energy results in

$$\frac{1}{2}kx^2_{\max} = \frac{1}{2}m(x_{\max}\beta)^2 \qquad \text{or} \qquad \beta^2 = \frac{k}{m}$$

This is known to be the correct frequency for the one-degree system.

This method, which is known as the Rayleigh method, is often useful in computing the natural frequencies of more complex conservative systems. For instance, Example 5-8 required a certain amount of thought and logic which could have been avoided by setting the maximum potential energy, $\frac{1}{2}k_r\theta^2_{\max} + \frac{1}{2}k(\theta_{\max}R)^2$, and the maximum kinetic energy, $\frac{1}{2}I(\beta\theta_{\max})^2 + \frac{1}{2}m(\beta\theta_{\max}R)^2$, equal and solving for β.

Two-Degree Systems. For systems having more than a single degree of freedom, it is necessary to know the natural modes before this method can be used. For example, consider the system of Fig. 6-1 (with zero damping), and let all of the masses and springs have unit values. If the analysis of Section 6.2 were applied to this system, it would be found that the natural frequencies are $\beta_1 = 0.618$ and $\beta_2 = 1.620$, and the modes are defined by the ratios $(x_1/x_2)_1 = 0.617$ and $(x_1/x_2)_2 = -1.615$. If only the modes had been known, the frequencies could have been calculated by the Rayleigh method as follows:

$$\text{P.E.} = \frac{1}{2}k_1x_1^2 + \frac{1}{2}k_2(x_2 - x_1)^2$$

and for the first mode

$$\text{P.E.}_{\max} = \frac{1}{2}(1)(0.617x_{2_{\max}})^2 + \frac{1}{2}(1)(x_{2_{\max}} - 0.617x_{2_{\max}})^2 = \frac{1}{2}0.527x_{2_{\max}}^2$$

$$\text{K.E.} = \frac{1}{2}m_1\dot{x}_1^2 + \frac{1}{2}m_2\dot{x}_2^2$$

and for the first mode

$$\text{K.E.}_{max} = \frac{1}{2}(1)(\beta_1 0.617 x_{2_{max}})^2 + \frac{1}{2}(1)(\beta_1 x_{2_{max}})^2 = \frac{1}{2}1.380\beta_1{}^2 x_{2_{max}}^2$$

$$\beta_1 = \sqrt{\frac{0.527}{1.380}} = 0.618 \quad \text{(the correct value)}$$

A similar calculation for β_2 would also result in the correct value. However, in this calculation the modes had to be known before the calculation for frequency could be made. Even if the mode had not been known, it might have been possible to make a good estimate of the modal configuration. For instance, in this example the first mode could be estimated by determining the relative deflection of the two masses in response to a static load applied on the second mass. This would result in a relative deflection $x_1/x_2 = \frac{1}{2}$ instead of 0.617. If this had been used in the previous computation, the result would have been $\beta_1 = 0.633$ instead of the correct value of 0.618. Notice that the frequency computed by this approximation of the modal description is somewhat greater than the correct value. It is possible to demonstrate that the computed frequency (computed by the Rayleigh method) of the first mode must attain its minimum value when the true modal description is used to determine the potential and kinetic energies. Other assumed modal descriptions lead to higher calculated frequencies. For systems having two natural frequencies, the values computed with erroneous assumed modal descriptions are greater than the true value of the first mode frequency and less than the true value of the second mode frequency. For systems having many natural frequencies, the values computed by the Rayleigh method approach "stationary" values when the modal descriptions approach the corresponding correct descriptions. This suggests that frequencies and mode descriptions for conservative systems could be obtained by the use of either differential calculus or variational calculus, whichever is appropriate. However, the Lagrange equations, discussed next, exploit a different application of variational calculus to dynamic systems.

7.3 Lagrange Equations for Conservative Systems

Ordinary Coordinates. The Rayleigh method is convenient, when applicable, because energies are scalar quantities and usually are easier to determine and manipulate than the vector quantities associated with Newton's law. However, it was seen that the usefulness of the method is somewhat limited because of the necessity of knowing, or being able to estimate, the mode descriptions in advance of the computation (although this disadvantage may be overcome to a certain extent by variational methods, as indicated previously). It is desirable to be able to use potential and kinetic energies, rather than forces and accelerations, in the differential equations of motion. The attempt to do this leads to the formulation known as Lagrange's equations, which are important not only because they greatly facilitate the setup of the mathematical model from the physical model, but also because of important generalizations leading to improved conceptual insight. Therefore, consider once again the familiar Newtonian equation for a single-degree-of-freedom system:

$$m\frac{d^2x}{dt^2} + kx = 0$$

or also

$$\frac{d}{dt}(m\dot{x}) + kx = 0 \tag{7-3}$$

If the kinetic energy at a given instant is T and the potential energy is V, then

$$\begin{aligned} T &= \frac{1}{2}m\dot{x}^2 \\ V &= \frac{1}{2}kx^2 \end{aligned} \tag{7-4}$$

It is clear that

$$\frac{\partial T}{\partial \dot{x}} = m\dot{x} \quad \text{and} \quad \frac{\partial V}{\partial x} = kx$$

thus Equation 2-17 could be written

$$\frac{d}{dt}\left(\frac{\partial T}{\partial \dot{x}}\right) + \frac{\partial V}{\partial x} = 0 \tag{7-5}$$

This is Lagrange's equation for the one-degree-of-freedom system of Fig. 1-1. An analogous procedure could be used to show that the system represented by Fig. 2-1, with no damping or external forces, would lead to the two equations:

$$\begin{aligned} \frac{d}{dt}\left(\frac{\partial T}{\partial \dot{x}_1}\right) + \frac{\partial V}{\partial x_1} &= 0 \\ \frac{d}{dt}\left(\frac{\partial T}{\partial \dot{x}_2}\right) + \frac{\partial V}{\partial x_2} &= 0 \end{aligned} \tag{7-6}$$

However, here, this will simply be accepted and checked to see if these two equations yield the correct differential equations, which are Equations 6-2. Since

$$T = \frac{1}{2}m_1\dot{x}_1^2 + \frac{1}{2}m_2\dot{x}_2^2 \quad \text{and} \quad V = \frac{1}{2}k_1x_1^2 + \frac{1}{2}k_2(x_2 - x_1)^2$$

it is immediately evident that Equations 6-2 do result from Equations 7-6.

Generalized Coordinates. Now suppose that it were desired to use completely arbitrary coordinates to define the configuration of a system, not necessarily any geometric distance or angle in the physical problem. Such coordinates are called "generalized coordinates." As an example, suppose that in the problem depicted by Fig. 6-1 two coordinates, q_1 and q_2, are defined as follows:

q_1 is a coordinate such that when $q_1 = 1$ (and $q_2 = 0$), $x_1 = 2$ and $x_2 = 4$

q_2 is a coordinate such that when $q_2 = 1$ (and $q_1 = 0$), $x_1 = -1$ and $x_2 = 1$

It is apparent that neither q_1 nor q_2 is a physical distance in Fig. 6-1, although it might be possible to imagine some weightless mechanical linkages which would provide a direct indication of what q_1 and q_2 would be for a given configuration. However, the physical existence of such a linkage is not necessary, and the definition above is sufficient to specify what such a linkage would have to accomplish.

From the definitions, it is possible to write equations relating the q's and x's.

$$x_1 = 2q_1 - q_2 \quad \text{and} \quad x_2 = 4q_1 + q_2$$
$$\dot{x}_1 = 2\dot{q}_1 - \dot{q}_2 \quad \text{and} \quad \dot{x}_2 = 4\dot{q}_1 + \dot{q}_2 \tag{7-7}$$

Algebraic manipulation yields

$$q_1 = \frac{1}{6}x_1 + \frac{1}{6}x_2 \quad \text{and} \quad q_2 = -\frac{2}{3}x_1 + \frac{1}{3}x_2$$
$$\dot{q}_1 = \frac{1}{6}\dot{x}_1 + \frac{1}{6}\dot{x}_2 \quad \text{and} \quad \dot{q}_2 = -\frac{2}{3}\dot{x}_1 + \frac{1}{3}\dot{x}_2 \tag{7-8}$$

It is important to know whether Equations 7-6 remain of the same form when written in terms of these new coordinates, q_1 and q_2, or whether they assume some other form. Eventually, it is desirable to determine forms for these equations which are valid for any coordinates selected, not just the specific ones chosen here.

The expression $\partial T/\partial \dot{x}_1$ implies the derivative of T with respect to $\dot{x}_1$ with all other variables in the expression for T considered as constants. It is useful to use subscripts to indicate what variables are held constant when partial derivatives are written. In this instance, $(\partial T/\partial \dot{x}_1)_{\dot{x}_2}$ must be replaced with terms involving $(\partial T/\partial \dot{q}_1)_{\dot{q}_2}$ and $(\partial T/\partial \dot{q}_2)_{\dot{q}_1}$, and since both $\dot{q}_1$ and $\dot{q}_2$ vary with both variables $\dot{x}_1$ and $\dot{x}_2$,

$$\left(\frac{\partial T}{\partial \dot{x}_1}\right)_{\dot{x}_2} = \left(\frac{\partial T}{\partial \dot{q}_1}\right)_{\dot{q}_2}\left(\frac{\partial \dot{q}_1}{\partial \dot{x}_1}\right)_{\dot{x}_2} + \left(\frac{\partial T}{\partial \dot{q}_2}\right)_{\dot{q}_1}\left(\frac{\partial \dot{q}_2}{\partial \dot{x}_1}\right)_{\dot{x}_2}$$
$$\left(\frac{\partial T}{\partial \dot{x}_2}\right)_{\dot{x}_1} = \left(\frac{\partial T}{\partial \dot{q}_1}\right)_{\dot{q}_2}\left(\frac{\partial \dot{q}_1}{\partial \dot{x}_2}\right)_{\dot{x}_1} + \left(\frac{\partial T}{\partial \dot{q}_2}\right)_{\dot{q}_1}\left(\frac{\partial \dot{q}_2}{\partial \dot{x}_2}\right)_{\dot{x}_1}$$
$$\left(\frac{\partial V}{\partial x_1}\right)_{x_2} = \left(\frac{\partial V}{\partial q_1}\right)_{q_2}\left(\frac{\partial q_1}{\partial x_1}\right)_{x_2} + \left(\frac{\partial V}{\partial q_2}\right)_{q_1}\left(\frac{\partial q_2}{\partial x_1}\right)_{x_2} \tag{7-9}$$
$$\left(\frac{\partial V}{\partial x_2}\right)_{x_1} = \left(\frac{\partial V}{\partial q_1}\right)_{q_2}\left(\frac{\partial q_1}{\partial x_2}\right)_{x_1} + \left(\frac{\partial V}{\partial q_2}\right)_{q_1}\left(\frac{\partial q_2}{\partial x_2}\right)_{x_1}$$

The factors $(\partial \dot{q}_1/\partial \dot{x}_1)_{\dot{x}_2} = \frac{1}{6}$, $(\partial \dot{q}_1/\partial \dot{x}_2)_{\dot{x}_1} = \frac{1}{6}$ etc., are obtained from Equations 7-8 rather than 7-7, since Equation 7-8 has the proper variables held constant. When these are substituted in Equations 7-9 and those results in 7-6, the following equations are eventually obtained, in which the subscripts indicating which variables are held constant have been dropped.

$$\frac{d}{dt}\left(\frac{\partial T}{\partial \dot{q}_1}\right) + \frac{\partial V}{\partial q_1} = 0$$
$$\frac{d}{dt}\left(\frac{\partial T}{\partial \dot{q}_2}\right) + \frac{\partial V}{\partial q_2} = 0 \tag{7-10}$$

Equations 7-10 are of the same form as Equation 7-6. It is easy to show that the same equations will result if the relationships between the coordinates are linear such as those of Equations 7-7, no matter what the constants, provided that q_1 and q_2 are independent. (That is, it would not be satisfactory to have $q_1 = x_1 + x_2$ and $q_2 = 2x_1 + 2x_2$, for instance, because then q_2 would not be independent of q_1, but would simply be $2q_1$.)

Equations 7-10 are not as general as they should be. For some choices of coordinate systems the kinetic energy may depend on coordinates, q_i, as well as rates of change of coordinates, $\dot{q}_i$, and another term will appear, and the more general form of Lagrange's equations for conservative systems with two coordinates is

$$\frac{d}{dt}\left(\frac{\partial T}{\partial \dot{q}_1}\right) - \frac{\partial T}{\partial q_1} + \frac{\partial V}{\partial q_1} = 0$$

$$\frac{d}{dt}\left(\frac{\partial T}{\partial \dot{q}_2}\right) - \frac{\partial T}{\partial q_2} + \frac{\partial V}{\partial q_2} = 0 \qquad (7\text{-}11)$$

This form also can be developed from Equations 7-6. It is an exercise in calculus. If the reader wishes to accept Equations 7-11 without following the rest of this rather lengthy development, little will be lost. However, it is included in Appendix III for reference.

Example 7-1. A simple example of a system for which the kinetic energy expression contains a function of the coordinate is that shown in Fig. 7-1. The gravity field is vertical and downward. In this problem it is assumed for the sake of simplicity that the angles which

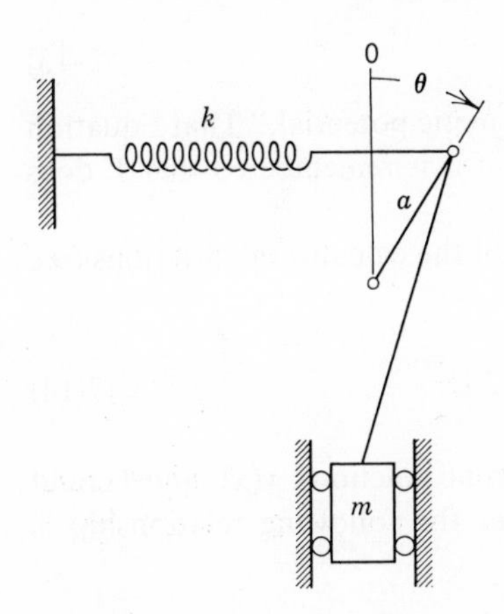

Fig. 7-1

the lines from the spring and mass make with the horizontal and vertical are small enough to neglect, but θ is not necessarily small. The equilibrium position is at the point marked 0. The downward deflection of the mass is $(a - a\cos\theta)$. The velocity of the mass is then $a\dot{\theta}\sin\theta$, and the kinetic energy must be a function of θ as well as $\dot{\theta}$.

$$T = \frac{1}{2} ma^2\dot{\theta}^2 \sin^2\theta$$

$$V = \frac{1}{2} ka^2 \sin^2\theta - mg(a - a\cos\theta)$$

Applying Equation 7-11, only once, of course, since there is only one variable,

$$\frac{\partial T}{\partial \dot{\theta}} = ma^2\dot{\theta}\sin^2\theta$$

$$\frac{d}{dt}\left(\frac{\partial T}{\partial \dot{\theta}}\right) = ma^2(\ddot{\theta}\sin^2\theta + 2\dot{\theta}^2\sin\theta\cos\theta)$$

$$\frac{\partial T}{\partial \theta} = ma^2\dot{\theta}^2 \sin \theta \cos \theta$$

$$\frac{\partial V}{\partial \theta} = ka^2 \sin \theta \cos \theta - mga \sin \theta$$

When these are combined according to Equation 7-11 and reduced, the result is

$$\frac{d^2\theta}{dt^2} + \left(\frac{d\theta}{dt}\right)^2 \cot \theta + \frac{k}{m} \cot \theta = \frac{g}{a} \csc \theta$$

This example illustrates the ease with which the use of the Lagrange equation yields the differential equation of motion. This is one of the chief advantages of this method of analysis, although the equation is also the basis for other powerful concepts, as will be seen.

7.4 Minimization of the Lagrangian

Lagrange's equation is also written in the form

$$\frac{d}{dt}\left(\frac{\partial L}{\partial \dot{q}_i}\right) - \frac{\partial L}{\partial q_i} = 0 \tag{7-12}$$

where

$$L = T - V \tag{7-13}$$

The function L is called the "Lagrangian," also the "kinetic potential." That Equation 7-12 is the equivalent of Equation 7-11 is easily seen if it is remembered that V does not contain $\dot{q}$; thus $\partial L/\partial \dot{q} = \partial T/\partial \dot{q}$.

The form of Equation 7-12 suggests an application of the calculus of variations (see Appendix 1). Briefly stated, if $y = y(x)$ and

$$I = \int_{x_a}^{x_b} F(x, y, y', y'', \text{etc.})\, dx \tag{7-14}$$

the integral, I, would take on different values for different functions, $y(x)$, and I could be maximized or minimized by choosing $y(x)$ so that the following relationship is satisfied.

$$\frac{\partial F}{\partial y} - \frac{d}{dx}\left(\frac{\partial F}{\partial y'}\right) + \frac{d^2}{dx^2}\left(\frac{\partial F}{\partial y''}\right) - \cdots = 0 \tag{7-15}$$

Equation 7-15 results in a differential equation, the solution of which would yield the particular $y(x)$ which would maximize or minimize I. Translated into the variables of the dynamics problem, where t is the independent variable, if L is a function of t, q, $\dot{q}$, and

$$I = \int_{t_a}^{t_b} L(t, q, \dot{q})\, dt \tag{7-16}$$

then Equation 7-15 would become the same as Equation 7-12 if the integral, I, in Equation 7-16 were to be minimized. If there were several coordinates, so that

$$L = L(t, q_1, \dot{q}_1, q_2, \dot{q}_2, \text{etc.})$$

and

$$I = \int_{t_a}^{t_b} L(t, q_1, \dot{q}_1, q_2, \dot{q}_2, \text{etc.})\, dt \tag{7-17}$$

then the application of the calculus of variations would lead to the set of simultaneous equations implied by the subscript i in Equation 7-12.

Hamilton's Principle. This is "Hamilton's principle," a fundamental principle of dynamics. It states that if I is defined as in Equation 7-17 and if at t_a and t_b all of the coordinates have specified values $q_{1_a}, q_{1_b}, q_{2_a}, q_{2_b}$, and if the total energy of the system remains constant, then the mathematical expression of the way that q_1 and q_2 vary between these limits must be such that I will be a minimum. Several alternative ways of writing Equation 7-17 are common. Since $L = T - V$ and $T + V = C$, Equation 7-17 might be written $I = \int_{t_a}^{t_b} (2T - C)\, dt$, and minimizing $(2T - C)$ is the same as minimizing $2T$, since $\int_{t_1}^{t_2} C\, dt$ is the same, regardless of how T varies between t_1 and t_2. Thus, instead of minimizing I in Equation 7-17, it would be possible to minimize A in

$$A = \int_{t_a}^{t_b} 2T\, dt \tag{7-18}$$

where A is the "action" between two configurations of the system, a and b. Also, if p is the "generalized momentum" such that

$$p = \frac{\partial T}{\partial \dot{q}} = \frac{2T}{\dot{q}},$$

then

$$\int_{t_a}^{t_b} 2T\, dt = \int_{t_a}^{t_b} \frac{2T}{\dot{q}} \dot{q}\, dt = \int_{t_a}^{t_b} p \frac{dq}{dt}\, dt = \int_{t_a}^{t_b} p\, dq$$

so that another way of writing Equation 7-18 for one-coordinate systems is

$$A = \int_{q_a}^{q_b} p\, dq \tag{7-19}$$

For the more inclusive case of several coordinates, the generalized momenta are defined as

$$p_1 = \frac{\partial L}{\partial \dot{q}_1}, \qquad p_2 = \frac{\partial L}{\partial \dot{q}_2}$$

or

$$p_i = \frac{\partial L}{\partial \dot{q}_i} = \frac{\partial T}{\partial \dot{q}_i} \tag{7-20}$$

It is possible to show that with this definition $2T = \sum_i p_i \dot{q}_i$ so that

$$A = \int_{t_a}^{t_b} (p_1 \dot{q}_1 + p_2 \dot{q}_2 + \cdots)\, dt$$

and, since $\dot{q}\, dt = dq/dt)\, dt = dq$, etc.,

$$A = \int_a^b (p_1\, dq_1 + p_2\, dq_2 + \cdots) \tag{7-21}$$

In the forms of Equation 7-18, 7-19, and 7-21, the restriction of constant energy ($T + V = C$) must be imposed in such a way that Equation 7-17 results. Therefore, Equation 7-17 is the most useful form for application of the calculus of variations, leading to Equation 7-12. Equations 7-18, 7-19, and 7-21 are interesting because of the concepts contained therein, rather than in the solution of problems. Another name for Hamilton's principle is "Principle of Least Action."

Development of Hamilton's Principle for a Simple System. It is not intuitively obvious that the integral of the Lagrangian between two configurations of a system should be minimum. Perhaps the fact that Lagrange's equations result from this postulate, and that they can also be derived as was done earlier, is sufficient evidence to convince the reader of the validity of this principle. If the principle were merely stated and accepted, then the Lagrange equations could be developed easily by using the calculus of variations. This is certainly neater and shorter, but perhaps less convincing. The development which follows is intended to make this principle more appealing to the intuition.

It is desired to show that $\int_{t_1}^{t_2} L\,dt$ should be a minimum for the naturally occurring motion. This will be done for the simplest configuration, from which extension to more complex systems can be made. The development is based on the calculus of variations. (For additional discussion of this subject, see Appendix 1.) A comparison will be made between $\int_{t_1}^{t_2} L\,dt$ for the correct motion and for motion slightly different or varied from the correct motion, except that the configuration is required to be the same at t_1 and t_2 for both the correct and incorrect descriptions of the motion.

Consider a mass free to move in the x direction and subject to an external force directed in the positive x direction. Newton's law is $m(d^2x/dt^2) = f$ or

$$m\frac{d^2x}{dt^2} - f = 0 \tag{7-22}$$

This is a description of the naturally occurring motion, and the $x(t)$ which is the solution of this equation is the correct $x(t)$ or the correct "path," where this word implies a relationship between *position* and *time*.

If the force, f, can be expressed as a function of x only, then there will be a potential energy "field," V, which will itself be a function of x. If the potential energy is designated as zero at $x = x_1$ (datum point for V), the work done *by* the force field *on* the mass when the mass is moved from x_1 to x is $\int_{x_1}^{x} f\,dx$. Therefore, the potential energy field at x is less than at x_1 by this same amount, or

$$V = -\int_{x_1}^{x} f\,dx \tag{7-23}$$

In Equation 7-23, x is considered an independent variable. However, in Equation 7-22, t is the independent variable and x is the dependent variable. It might be imagined that the correct "path," represented by the solution of Equation 7-22, is "varied" by a small amount, δx, where δx is an arbitrary function of time. The new path, $x + \delta x$, is not the naturally occurring path. If the potential energy at a given instant along the correct path is specified by Equation 7-23, then at the same instant along the varied, or incorrect, path the potential energy will be

$$V + \delta V = -\int_{x_1}^{x+\delta x} f\,dx \tag{7-24}$$

Subtraction of Equation 7-23 from Equation 7-24 shows the variation of the potential energy from the correct value at the same instant to be:

$$\delta V = -\int_{x_1}^{x+\delta x} f\,dx + \int_{x_1}^{x} f\,dx = -\int_{x}^{x+\delta x} f\,dx$$

or, since δx is a small distance, f can be considered constant from x to $x + \delta x$, and

$$\delta V = -f\,\delta x \tag{7-25}$$

Now, return to Equation 7-22, multiply through by δx, and integrate from t_1 to t_2.

$$\int_{t_1}^{t_2} \left(m\frac{d^2x}{dt^2} - f\right)(\delta x)\,dt = 0 \tag{7-26}$$

It has already been seen that if f is derivable from a potential energy field, $-f\,\delta x = \delta V$. Now, consider the first term in Equation 7-26, and integrate by parts.

$$\int_{t_1}^{t_2} m\frac{d^2x}{dt^2}(\delta x)\,dt = \int_{t_1}^{t_2} u\,dv = uv\int_{t_1}^{t_2} - \int_{t_1}^{t_2} v\,du$$

where
$$u = \delta x, \qquad dv = m\frac{d^2x}{dt^2}\,dt$$

and therefore
$$du = \frac{d(\delta x)}{dt}\,dt, \quad v = m\frac{dx}{dt}$$

$$\int_{t_1}^{t_2} m\frac{d^2x}{dt^2}(\delta x)\,dt = m\left(\frac{dx}{dt}\right)(\delta x)\Big]_{t_1}^{t_2} - \int_{t_1}^{t_2} m\left(\frac{dx}{dt}\right)\frac{d(\delta x)}{dt}\,dt \tag{7-27}$$

It is recalled that $(x + \delta x)$ is an imaginary path varied from the true path an arbitrary amount δx at each value of t. However, at t_1 and t_2 the incorrect and correct paths must be the same; that is, x_1 is the same for either path, or δx at $t_1 = 0$. Similarly, δx at $t_2 = 0$. Therefore, the first term on the right in Equation 7-27 vanishes. Now consider the second term,

$$\int_{t_1}^{t_2} = m\left(\frac{dx}{dt}\right)\frac{d(\delta x)}{dt}\,dt$$

In this integral the expression $d(\delta x)/dt$ can be replaced with $\delta\dot{x}$ (where $\dot{x} = dx/dt$), or the time rate of change of the variation of x from the true value is the same as the variation of the velocity from the true value. (This is discussed in more detail in Appendix 1.) Therefore

$$\int_{t_1}^{t_2} - m\dot{x}\frac{d(\delta x)}{dt}\,dt = \int_{t_1}^{t_2} - m\dot{x}\,\delta\dot{x}\,dt \tag{7-28}$$

Now consider what is meant by the variation of velocity squared. On the varied path, velocity squared is

$$(\dot{x} + \delta\dot{x})^2 = \dot{x}^2 + 2\dot{x}(\delta\dot{x}) + (\delta\dot{x})^2$$

and for small values of $\delta\dot{x}$ the last term can be neglected. The variation of velocity squared from the true value is therefore

$$\delta(\dot{x}^2) = (\dot{x} + \delta\dot{x})^2 - \dot{x}^2 = 2\dot{x}(\delta\dot{x})$$

The right side of Equation 7-28 is therefore

$$\int_{t_1}^{t_2} -\frac{1}{2} m\, \delta(\dot{x}^2)\, dt \qquad \text{or also} \qquad \int_{t_1}^{t_2} -\delta\left(\frac{1}{2} m\dot{x}^2\right) dt$$

Since $\frac{1}{2}m\dot{x}^2$ is the kinetic energy, T, the quantity $\delta(\frac{1}{2}m\dot{x}^2)$ is the variation of T. It is seen that Equation 7-26 can be converted to

$$-\int_{t_1}^{t_2} [\delta T + f(\delta x)]\, dt = 0 \tag{7-29}$$

and when f is derivable from a potential energy, this becomes

$$-\int_{t_1}^{t_2} (\delta T - \delta V)\, dt = 0 \qquad \text{or} \qquad \int_{t_1}^{t_2} \delta(T - V)\, dt = 0$$

The last form shown is also

$$\delta\left[\int_{t_1}^{t_2} (T - V)\, dt\right] = 0$$

or (7-30)

$$\delta\left[\int_{t_1}^{t_2} L\, dt\right] = 0$$

Equation 7-30 has now been derived from Newton's law (Equation 7-22), and it states that for a path differing from the path prescribed by Newton's law by a very small, arbitrary, amount, δx, at any t except the end points t_1 and t_2, the integral of $(T - V)$ will be the same as for the correct path. That is, when the correct description of the motion as a function of time has been determined, the variation of the integral will approach zero for small differences from this description. Thus, it is seen that Equation 7-30 is equivalent to Newton's law for a conservative system or where the force f is the negative gradient of the potential energy ($f = -dV/dx$).

Equation 7-30 also states that $\int_{t_1}^{t_2} L\, dt$ is either maximum or minimum on the correct path, and although it has not been shown here, it is true that the integral is at its minimum value rather than the maximum. This can be seen by checking a very simple case. Suppose that the force is zero, so that $V = 0$. If the mass remains stationary between t_1 and t_2, then $T = 0$ and $\int_{t_1}^{t_2} (T - V)\, dt = 0$. Now suppose that the displacement is zero at t_1 and t_2, but not zero at some intermediate times. This would require a velocity, and no matter whether the velocity were in the positive or negative direction, the kinetic energy would be positive, so that $\int_{t_1}^{t_2} (T - V)\, dt > 0$ for any other description of the motion. Of course, these other descriptions are erroneous; thus, for this particular example, $\int_{t_1}^{t_2} L\, dt$ for the correct description of the motion is seen to be less than for incorrect descriptions, and therefore this "extremum" is a minimum rather than a maximum.

It should be noted that Equation 7-29 is true even if f is not derivable from a potential energy function. If f is derivable from a potential energy function, then Equation 7-30 applies. If part of the force f is derivable from a potential energy function and another part (for example, f_a) is not, then Equation 7-29 would become

$$\delta\left[\int_{t_1}^{t_2} L\, dt\right] = \int_{t_1}^{t_2} f_a(\delta x)\, dt \tag{7-31}$$

The preceding discussion was limited to a very simple system in order to facilitate the concepts involved. It is possible to expand the development to complex systems with many degrees of freedom, using essentially the same procedure, but this will not be done here.

A simple example is now presented in order to illustrate several of the points introduced in the discussion.

Example 7-2. Investigate the motion of a mass in a constant gravity field.

Assume that a mass is projected from a point $x = 0$ and $y = 0$ at a time $t = 0$ with velocities v_{x_0} and v_{y_0} in the positive x and y directions. Positive x is measured horizontally, and positive y is measured vertically upward from the zero point. Since, in this problem, a constant gravity field is assumed, the potential energy is $V = mgy$. (This assumes that the zero for potential energy corresponds to $y = 0$.) The kinetic energy is $T = \frac{1}{2}m(\dot{x}^2 + \dot{y}^2)$:

$$L = T - V = \frac{1}{2}m(\dot{x}^2 + \dot{y}^2) - mgy$$

$$\frac{\partial L}{\partial \dot{x}} = m\dot{x} \qquad \frac{\partial L}{\partial x} = 0 \qquad \frac{\partial L}{\partial \dot{y}} = m\dot{y} \qquad \frac{\partial L}{\partial y} = -mg$$

Application of Equations 7-12 to the x and y coordinates results in $m\ddot{x} = 0$ and $m\ddot{y} - (-mg) = 0$ which, of course, lead to the equations

$$x = v_{x_0}t \qquad \text{and} \quad y = v_{y_0}t - \frac{1}{2}gt^2$$

when the integrations are performed and the initial conditions applied.

Now consider the application of Equation (7-18). If $A = \int_0^{t_b} 2\,\frac{1}{2}\,m\,(\dot{x}^2 + \dot{y}^2)\,dt$ and the calculus of variations is applied to minimize this integral without first using the restriction $T + V = C$, the result is

$$\frac{d}{dt}(2m\dot{x}) = 0 \qquad \text{and} \quad \frac{d}{dt}(2m\dot{y}) = 0$$

which is obviously erroneous. This error results because the system has not been forced to move in such a way that the total energy remains constant during the interval $t = 0$ to $t = t_b$. The principle of least action requires this stipulation. If $T = C - V$ is used for one of the T's in $\int_0^{t_2} 2T\,dt$ before minimizing, the correct equations result. On the other hand if $C - V$ is substituted for both T's, an erroneous result again occurs because the mathematical manipulations again do not force the total energy to be constant. These results illustrate the desirability of using the principle of least action to minimize I of Equation 7-17, rather than A of Equation 7-18, for actual problem solving.

If it were desired to use Equation 7-21 it would also be found more convenient to convert back to Equation 7-18 and then to Equation 7-17 before minimizing.

$$A = \int^b p_1\,dq_1 + p_2\,dq_2 + \cdots = \int p_1 \frac{dq_1}{dt}\,dt + p_2 \frac{dq_2}{dt}\,dt + \cdots$$

$$= \int_{ta}^{t_b} (p_1\dot{q}_1 + p_2\dot{q}_2 + \cdots)\,dt = \int_{ta}^{t_b} 2T\,dt = \int_{ta}^{t_b} (T + C - V)\,dt$$

Since the variation of $C\,dt$ is zero, the form 7-17 appears and the result is the same as before. Again it is clear that Equation 7-17 is the most useful form for problem solving. In the form 7-17 it is not necessary to specify mathematically that the total energy must remain constant during the motion in order that the integral should be a minimum (although it does remain constant, of course), whereas in the other forms this must be specified and inserted before taking the integral.

Now let the integral $I = \int_0^{t_b} L\,dt$ for two possible solutions be compared to see whether the integral for the correct solution is actually less than for the incorrect one. The correct solution is known to be

$$x = v_{x0}t \qquad y = v_{y0}t - \frac{1}{2}gt^2$$

With these equations the Lagrangian function becomes

$$L = T - V = \frac{1}{2}m[v_{x0}^2 + (v_{y0} - gt)^2] - mg[v_{y0}t - \frac{1}{2}gt^2]$$

The integral $\int_0^{t_b} L\,dt$, after evaluation, reduces to

$$I = \frac{1}{2}m[(v_{x0}^2 + v_{y0}^2)t_b - 2v_{y0}\,gt_b^2 + \frac{2}{3}g^2t_b^3]$$

If the limit t_b is chosen for convenience as $2v_{y0}/g$, the result is

$$I = \frac{m}{g}\left[-\frac{1}{3}v_{y0}^3 + v_{x0}^2v_{y0}\right]$$

The above limit on t_b causes the vertical displacement at t_b to be zero.

Suppose that the following erroneous descriptions of the vertical component of the motion are assumed.

$$v_y = \frac{1}{2}v_{y0} \qquad \text{for} \quad 0 < t < \frac{v_{y0}}{g}$$

$$v_y = -\frac{1}{2}v_{y0} \qquad \text{for} \quad \frac{v_{y0}}{g} < t < \frac{2v_{y0}}{g}$$

(The velocity is constant upward, followed by constant downward.)
This description of the velocity would cause the same displacement at the end of $t_b = 2v_{y0}/g$ seconds as the correct solution, which is necessary for the comparison since the system must have the same configuration at the end of the time interval. Taking advantage of the symmetry,

$$L = T - V = \frac{1}{2}m\left[v_{x0}^2 + \left(\frac{1}{2}v_{y0}\right)^2\right] - mg\left(\frac{1}{2}v_{y0}t\right) \qquad \text{for} \quad 0 < t < \frac{v_{y0}}{g}$$

$$I = 2\int_0^{v_{y0}/g} L\,dt = \frac{m}{g}\left[-\frac{1}{4}v_{y0}^3 + v_{x0}^2v_{y0}\right]$$

Comparison with the integral for the correct description shows that integral to be less, as it should. Notice that this erroneous description of the motion does not maintain constant total energy during the time interval. As mentioned earlier, this restriction is not necessary if Equation 7-17 is used.

Now if the same comparisons are made using Equation 7-18 the action for the correct description can be shown to be

$$A = 2\int_0^{v_{y0}/g} 2\left(\frac{1}{2}m\right)\left[v_{x0}^2 + (v_{y0} - gt)^2\right]dt = 2\frac{m}{g}\left[\frac{1}{3}v_{y0}^3 + v_{x0}^2v_{y0}\right]$$

For the incorrect description, the result is

$$A = 2\int_0^{v_{y0}/g} 2\left(\frac{1}{2}m\right)\left[v_{x0}^2 + \left(\frac{1}{2}v_{y0}\right)^2\right] dt = 2\frac{m}{g}\left[\frac{1}{4}v_{y0}^3 + v_{x0}^2 v_{y0}\right]$$

Here, the integral for the correct function is greater than for the incorrect function, which appears to violate the principle of least action. However, the restriction was not observed that the total energy must remain constant during the motion, and the same constant for both paths, if Equation 7-18 is used. This accounts for the discrepancy.

A proper comparison would require that the total energy for the incorrect path be the same as for the correct path, and remain constant throughout the time interval, and that the configuration for either path be the same at the beginning and end of the interval. It is possible to observe the restriction in the example chosen by requiring the mass to move in the horizontal plane, perpendicular to both the x and y directions (for instance, the z direction), with whatever velocity is necessary to maintain the proper total energy. The mathematical description of this velocity during the first half of the time interval is

$$v_z = \sqrt{\frac{3}{4}v_{y0}^2 - gv_{y0}t}$$

During the second half, the velocity is reversed symmetrically so that the correct displacement at the end of the time interval results. The result is now

$$A = 2\int_0^{v_{y0}/g} 2\frac{1}{2}m\left[v_{x0}^2 + \left(\frac{1}{2}v_{y0}\right)^2 + \left(\frac{3}{4}v_{y0}^2 - gv_{y0}t\right)\right] dt = 2\frac{m}{g}\left[\frac{1}{2}v_{y0}^3 + v_{x0}v_{y0}\right]$$

Comparison of this value with the value for the correct description resolves the apparent conflict with the principle of least action, since the action for the correct motion is less.

It has been the purpose of this example to investigate some of the details implied by the Lagrange equation in its various forms. The concepts illustrated can be applied to more difficult problems.

7.5 Generalized Forces

Heretofore in the discussion of Lagrange's equations only conservative systems have been considered, for which the forces are functions of the dependent coordinates (or displacements).

The modifications necessary when some of the forces involved are functions of the independent variable (time) will be investigated next. The simple system of Fig. 1-3, but with no damper, will be used for this discussion, where the force is a function of time.

Equation 7-5 becomes

$$\frac{d}{dt}\left(\frac{\partial T}{\partial \dot{x}}\right) + \frac{\partial V}{\partial x} = f(t) \tag{7-32}$$

This equation, written in terms of the general coordinate q, is

$$\frac{d}{dt}\left(\frac{\partial T}{\partial \dot{q}}\right) - \frac{\partial T}{\partial q} + \frac{\partial V}{\partial q} = Q(t) \tag{7-33}$$

where $Q(t)$ is a "generalized force," a function of time.

The manner in which the left side of Equation 7-33 results from Equation 7-32 has already been discussed. Now it is necessary to find out how $Q(t)$ is determined from

$f(t)$. This can be accomplished by considering the amount of work done in a small time interval dt. During this time interval the coordinate x changes by the amount dx, and the coordinate q changes by the amount dq. The work done by the force during the interval dt is $f\,dx$. Of course, the work must be the same, regardless of the coordinates used, and thus $Q\,dq = f\,dx$, or

$$Q = f\frac{dx}{dq} \tag{7-34}$$

Since dx/dq would be known, the generalized force could be determined.

Now, if more than one dependent variable is involved, (the problem represented by Fig. 6-1, but again without the dampers), the equations are

$$\begin{aligned} \frac{d}{dt}\left(\frac{\partial T}{\partial \dot{x}_1}\right) + \frac{\partial V}{\partial x_1} &= f_1(t) \\ \frac{d}{dt}\left(\frac{\partial T}{\partial \dot{x}_2}\right) + \frac{\partial V}{\partial x_2} &= f_2(t) \end{aligned} \tag{7-35}$$

which, when transformed to the generalized coordinates, become

$$\begin{aligned} \frac{d}{dt}\left(\frac{\partial T}{\partial \dot{q}_1}\right) - \frac{\partial T}{\partial q_1} + \frac{\partial V}{\partial q_1} &= Q_1(t) \\ \frac{d}{dt}\left(\frac{\partial T}{\partial \dot{q}_2}\right) - \frac{\partial T}{\partial q_2} + \frac{\partial V}{\partial q_2} &= Q_2(t) \end{aligned} \tag{7-36}$$

It is again necessary to determine Q_1 and Q_2, the generalized forces. In the time, dt, the coordinates change by the amounts dx_1, dx_2, dq_1, dq_2, and the work done is the same in either system.

$$F_1\,dx_1 + F_2\,dx_2 = Q_1\,dq_1 + Q_2\,dq_2 \tag{7-37}$$

Since x_1 and x_2 are really functions of q_1 and q_2, the differentials can be formed in the usual way,

$$\begin{aligned} x_1 &= x_1(q_1, q_2) \qquad & dx_1 &= \frac{\partial x_1}{\partial q_1}\,dq_1 + \frac{\partial x_1}{\partial q_2}\,dq_2 \\ x_2 &= x_2(q_1, q_2) \qquad & dx_2 &= \frac{\partial x_2}{\partial q_1}\,dq_1 + \frac{\partial x_2}{\partial q_2}\,dq_2 \end{aligned} \tag{7-38}$$

Equations 7-39 follow without difficulty from 7-37 and 7-38:

$$\begin{aligned} Q_1 &= F_1\frac{\partial x_1}{\partial q_1} + F_2\frac{\partial x_2}{\partial q_1} \\ Q_2 &= F_1\frac{\partial x_1}{\partial q_2} + F_2\frac{\partial x_2}{\partial q_2} \end{aligned} \tag{7-39}$$

It would be just as valid, of course, to use

$$\begin{aligned} q_1 &= q_1(x_1, x_2) \qquad & dq_1 &= \frac{\partial q_1}{\partial x_1}\,dx_1 + \frac{\partial q_1}{\partial x_2}\,dx_2 \\ q_2 &= q_2(x_1, x_2) \qquad & dq_2 &= \frac{\partial q_2}{\partial x_1}\,dx_1 + \frac{\partial q_2}{\partial x_2}\,dx_2 \end{aligned}$$

in which instance, after solving for dx_1 and dx_2, and using Equation 7-37,

$$Q_1 = \frac{F_1 \dfrac{\partial q_2}{\partial x_2} - F_2 \dfrac{\partial q_2}{\partial x_1}}{\dfrac{\partial q_1}{\partial x_1}\dfrac{\partial q_2}{\partial x_2} - \dfrac{\partial q_2}{\partial x_1}\dfrac{\partial q_1}{\partial x_2}}$$

$$Q_2 = \frac{F_2 \dfrac{\partial q_1}{\partial x_1} - F_1 \dfrac{\partial q_1}{\partial x_2}}{\dfrac{\partial q_1}{\partial x_1}\dfrac{\partial q_2}{\partial x_2} - \dfrac{\partial q_2}{\partial x_1}\dfrac{\partial q_1}{\partial x_2}} \tag{7-40}$$

Equations 7-40 could have been deduced directly from Equation 7-35, without assuming the existence of Q_1 and Q_2, which was done in writing Equation 7-36. This would automatically have resulted from the manipulations which were performed on Equations A3-9 to obtain Equation A3-10 if F_1 and F_2 had appeared instead of zero on the right side of Equations A3-9.

It is apparent that the generalized forces could also be obtained from the equation

$$Q_i = \frac{\partial w}{\partial \dot{q}_i} \tag{7-41}$$

where w is the rate of production of work by all external forces in terms of the $\dot{q}$ coordinate system.

As a result of the foregoing analysis, it is seen that a generalized force is a "force" which does the same amount of work when the corresponding generalized coordinate changes a small amount as the actual forces do when their coordinates change by the amount corresponding to the change in the generalized coordinate. This is a very useful concept, which will be exploited in subsequent chapters.

Example 7-3. Equations 7-7 and 7-8 relate two specific sets of coordinates which could describe the configuration of a two-degree system such as that of Fig. 6-1. Suppose that the dampers are zero and the forces are $f_1 = f_{1_0} \sin \omega t$ and $f_2 = K_2 t$. If the problem were to be worked in terms of the q coordinates instead of the x coordinates, what are the generalized forces which "drive" the q equations?

From Equations 7-39 and 7-7:

$$Q_1 = (f_{1_0} \sin \omega t)(2) + (K_2 t)(4)$$

$$Q_2 = (f_{1_0} \sin \omega t)(-1) + (K_2 t)(1)$$

Also, from Equations 7-40 and 7-8:

$$Q_1 = \frac{(f_{1_0} \sin \omega t)\dfrac{1}{3} - K_2 t\left(-\dfrac{2}{3}\right)}{\left(\dfrac{1}{6}\right)\left(\dfrac{1}{3}\right) - \left(-\dfrac{2}{3}\right)\left(\dfrac{1}{6}\right)}$$

$$Q_2 = \frac{(K_2 t)\dfrac{1}{6} - (f_{1_0} \sin \omega t)\dfrac{1}{6}}{\left(\dfrac{1}{6}\right)\left(\dfrac{1}{3}\right) - \left(-\dfrac{2}{3}\right)\left(\dfrac{1}{6}\right)}$$

To check these results with work done in dt time, suppose that in dt time q_1 deflects 1 unit and q_2 deflects 1 unit. The total work done is $(Q_1)(1) + (Q_2)(1)$, and if the above values of Q_1 and Q_2 are used, this becomes $f_{1_0} \sin \omega t + 5(\zeta t)$. If $q_1 = 1$ and $q_2 = 1$ then $x_1 = 1$ and $x_2 = 5$. The work done is $(f_1)(1) + (f_2)(5) = f_{1_0} \sin \omega t + 5(K_2 t)$, checking the value above.

Since, in the q coordinate system,

$$T = \frac{1}{2} m_1(2\dot{q}_1 - \dot{q}_2)^2 + \frac{1}{2} m_2 (4\dot{q}_1 + \dot{q}_2)^2$$

$$V = \frac{1}{2} k_1(2q_1 - q_2)^2 + \frac{1}{2} k_2(2q_1 + 2q_2)^2$$

the differential equations of motion in the q coordinates, using Equations 7-36, become

$$(4m_1 + 16m_2)\frac{d^2q_1}{dt^2} + (-2m_1 + 4m_2)\frac{d^2q_2}{dt^2} + (4k_1 + 4k_2)q_1 + (-2k_1 + 4k_2)q_2 = f_{1_0} \sin \omega t + 4K_2 t$$

$$(-2m_1 + 4m_2)\frac{d^2q_1}{dt^2} + (m_1 + m_2)\frac{d^2q_2}{dt^2} + (-2k_1 + 4k_2)q_1 + (k_1 + 4k_2)q_1 = -f_{1_0} \sin \omega t + K_2 t$$

Example 7-4. In Example 7-1, suppose that a force $f_0 u(t)$, is applied on the mass in the downward direction. What generalized force should be used with the coordinate θ?

The work done by the force is $F\,ds$. Since $s = a - a \cos \theta$, $ds = a \sin \theta \, d\theta$. For the same work, $Q\,d\theta = fa \sin \theta \, d\theta$ or $Q = f_0 \sin \theta \, u(t)$. The differential equation is then

$$\frac{d}{dt}(ma^2\dot{\theta} \sin^2 \theta) - ma^2\dot{\theta}^2 \sin \theta \cos \theta + ka^2 \sin \theta \cos \theta - mga \sin \theta = f_0 a (\sin \theta)u(t)$$

or, after reducing,

$$\frac{d^2\theta}{dt^2} + \left(\frac{d\theta}{dt}\right)^2 \cot \theta + \frac{k}{m} \cot \theta = \frac{g}{a} \csc \theta + \frac{f_0}{ma} \csc \theta u(t)$$

Notice that in this example the generalized "force," Q, actually is a moment.

7.6 Lagrange Equations for Non-Conservative Systems

Dissipation Function for Viscous Dampers. The application of Lagrange equations to conservative systems and to systems having external forces which are functions only of time has been demonstrated. It remains to determine how to apply the Lagrange equations to nonconservative systems, particularly systems with viscous dampers, such as those of Figs. 1-3 and 6-1.

To get started, consider the simple system of Fig. 1-3 and, taking a clue from the previous work with conservative systems, attempt to find some sort of energy relationship which would yield the correct term in the differential equation and which would remain of the same form when transformed to other coordinates. The desired term is $c(dx/dt)$. A "dissipation function" is defined as one half of the actual dissipation of energy per unit time, or, for viscous dampers,

$$\mathscr{F}_d = \frac{1}{2} c\dot{x}^2 \tag{7-42}$$

Note the similarity to the kinetic energy ($\frac{1}{2}m\dot{x}^2$) and potential energy terms ($\frac{1}{2}kx^2$); however, the dimension of this variable is energy per unit time rather than just energy. The partial derivative of this function with respect to $\dot{x}$ yields the correct term, and thus, if this works equally well for other systems and coordinates, the Lagrange equation for the system of Fig. 1-3 could be written as

$$\frac{d}{dt}\left(\frac{\partial L}{\partial \dot{x}}\right) - \frac{\partial L}{\partial x} + \frac{\partial \mathscr{F}_d}{\partial \dot{x}} = f \tag{7-43}$$

It is not difficult to show that when this is transformed to the q coordinate system the result is the same, or Equation 7-44 below. However, the two-degree system, discussed below, is more significant and includes the one-degree system as a special case, so Equation 7-44 is not developed here.

$$\frac{d}{dt}\left(\frac{\partial L}{\partial \dot{q}}\right) - \frac{\partial L}{\partial q} + \frac{\partial \mathscr{F}_d}{\partial \dot{q}} = Q \tag{7-44}$$

For two coordinates, equations similar to Equation 7-6 are written, but with the dissipation function term included.

$$\frac{d}{dt}\left(\frac{\partial T}{\partial \dot{x}_1}\right) + \frac{\partial V}{\partial x_1} + \frac{\partial \mathscr{F}_d}{\partial \dot{x}_1} = f_1$$

$$\frac{d}{dt}\left(\frac{\partial T}{\partial \dot{x}_1}\right) + \frac{\partial V}{\partial x_2} + \frac{\partial \mathscr{F}_d}{\partial \dot{x}_2} = f_2$$

In these equations, $\mathscr{F}_d$ is one half of the rate of total energy dissipation by all dampers in the system. Now consider the transformations to the general coordinates q_1 and q_2. The transformation of the dissipation function terms proceeds exactly like the kinetic energy terms, except that the derivative with respect to time is not taken. If Equations A3-9 and A3-10 are re-examined with this in mind, it is easily seen that the terms $\partial \mathscr{F}_d/\partial \dot{q}_1$ and $\partial \mathscr{F}_d/\partial \dot{q}_2$ will occur in the final equations, but not terms $\partial \mathscr{F}_d/\partial q_1$ and $\partial \mathscr{F}_d/\partial q_2$, similar to the terms $\partial T/\partial q_1$ and $\partial T/\partial q_2$ which appear as a result of the differentiation with respect to time. Therefore, the final Lagrange equations for the two-coordinate system with viscous damping (which could be extended to multiple-coordinate systems) are

$$\begin{aligned} \frac{d}{dt}\left(\frac{\partial L}{\partial \dot{q}_1}\right) - \frac{\partial L}{\partial q_1} + \frac{\partial \mathscr{F}_d}{\partial \dot{q}_1} &= Q_1 \\ \frac{d}{dt}\left(\frac{L\partial}{\partial \dot{q}_2}\right) - \frac{\partial L}{\partial q_2} + \frac{\partial \mathscr{F}_d}{\partial \dot{q}_2} &= Q_2 \end{aligned} \tag{7-45}$$

Now, as in the conservative system, it would be possible to convert to still another set of coordinates, for example z, if desired, and the equation would remain the same except that z and $\dot{z}$ would replace q and $\dot{q}$, and new functions would replace Q_1 and Q_2. One of the most useful applications of this property is that the energy dissipated can be computed in terms of the most convenient coordinates and then expressed in terms of other coordinates which might be more convenient for the solution of the problem, with the assurance that the partial derivatives with respect to the new coordinates can still be used in the same way. (The same can also be said of the potential energy and kinetic energy terms, for that matter.) For instance, in Fig. 6-1, coordinates x_1 and x_2

are measured from fixed points in space. These are convenient for the calculation of kinetic energy, which is merely $\frac{1}{2}m_1\dot{x}_1^2 + \frac{1}{2}m_2\dot{x}_2^2$. However, the potential energy stored in k_2 is more conveniently computed from the stretch of this spring. Thus, a coordinate system consisting of x_1 and x_3, where $x_3 = x_2 - x_1$, would be more convenient for calculating potential energy, which would then be $\frac{1}{2}k_1x_1^2 + \frac{1}{2}k_2x_3^2$. This latter coordinate system would also be more convenient for calculation of the dissipation function, which would be $\frac{1}{2}c_1\dot{x}_1^2 + \frac{1}{2}c_2\dot{x}_3^2$, but would be less convenient for calculating kinetic energy, which would be $\frac{1}{2}m_1\dot{x}_1^2 + \frac{1}{2}m_2(\dot{x}_1 + \dot{x}_3)^2$. In working the problem it is a comfort to know that either set of coordinates can be used (x_1 and x_2 or x_1 and x_3) to compute the kinetic energy, potential energy, and dissipation functions, and after these functions have been computed, they can be converted to the other set if desired for solution by Lagrange's equations, and these equations will not assume some other form for the second set of coordinates.

Example 7-5. Check whether the dissipation function term leads to the correct expressions for the system of Fig. 6-1.

$$\text{Rate of energy dissipation} = c_1\dot{x}_1^2 + c_2(\dot{x}_2 - \dot{x}_1)^2$$

$$\mathcal{F}_d = \frac{1}{2}c_1\dot{x}_1^2 + \frac{1}{2}c_2(\dot{x}_2 - \dot{x}_1)^2$$

In the equation for m_1 the damping terms should be

$$\frac{\partial \mathcal{F}_d}{\partial \dot{x}_1} = c_1\dot{x}_1 - c_2(\dot{x}_2 - \dot{x}_1)$$

In the equation for m_2 the damping terms should be

$$\frac{\partial \mathcal{F}_d}{\partial \dot{x}_2} = c_2(\dot{x}_2 - \dot{x}_1)$$

These are seen to be the correct terms (Equations 6-1 with these terms transposed to the left side).

Dissipation Function for Nonviscous Dampers. It should be emphasized that the definition of the dissipation function as one half of the rate of energy dissipation is really applicable only to systems with viscous damping; that is, to systems in which the damping force is proportional to the velocity and oppositely directed. (It is not necessarily a linear term in the coordinates used, however.) This is different from the potential energy term, which does not require a linear spring, but only that the potential energy be a function of the coordinates. Although somewhat disappointing because of the lack of generality, the dissipation function must be selected to suit the damper, if the damper is nonviscous. This and other significant points are illustrated in the examples which follow.

Example 7-6. Discuss the application of Lagrange's equation to a simple one-degree-of-freedom system such as Fig. 1-3, but with springs and dampers of both linear and nonlinear types.

If the springs and dampers are linear,

$$V = \frac{1}{2}kx^2 \qquad T = \frac{1}{2}m\dot{x}^2$$

$$\mathcal{F}_d = \frac{1}{2}c\dot{x}^2 \qquad Q = f$$

and the application of Lagrange's equation results in

$$m\ddot{x} + c\dot{x} + kx = f$$

which, of course, is correct. If the spring were one in which the restoring force is proportional to x^3, for instance, the potential energy stored in the spring would be

$$V = \int_0^x kx^3\,dx = \frac{1}{4}kx^4$$

Since

$$\frac{\partial V}{\partial x} = kx^3$$

as required, the differential equation resulting from the application of the Lagrange's equation is correct. If the restoring force were proportional to x^2, then $V = \frac{1}{3}kx^3$ and $\partial V/\partial x$ would still give kx^2, the correct term. However, there is a complication here, since when x becomes negative the potential energy term, V, becomes negative. It is clear that the potential energy stored in the spring can never be negative if it is zero in the undeflected position. This problem would have to be worked with $V = \frac{1}{3}kx^3$ when x is positive and $V = -\frac{1}{3}kx^3$ when x is negative to give the correct result. The equations which result from one expression do not apply to the other.

If the damping force were proportional to $\dot{x}^3$, the rate of energy dissipation is $(c\dot{x}^3)\dot{x}$ or $c\dot{x}^4$. If the definition of the dissipation function as one half of the rate of energy dissipation is used, then $\mathscr{F}_d = \frac{1}{2}c\dot{x}^4$ and $\partial\mathscr{F}_d/\partial\dot{x} = 2c\dot{x}^3$. This is not the correct expression for the damping force, which should be $c\dot{x}^3$. This difficulty could be avoided by defining the dissipation function as $\frac{1}{4}c\dot{x}^4$ instead of $\frac{1}{2}c\dot{x}^4$. If the damping force were proportional to $\dot{x}^2$, it would be necessary to use $\mathscr{F}_d = \frac{1}{3}c\dot{x}^3$ in order to get the correct expression, and also to use $-\frac{1}{3}c\dot{x}^3$ for $\dot{x}$ negative, as with the potential energy term. It appears, then, that it is possible to use the dissipation function concept for nonviscous dampers provided that the dissipation function is defined as $\mathscr{F}_d = \int f(\dot{x})\,d\dot{x}$ where $f(\dot{x})$ is the resistance to motion as a function of the velocity, and due caution is observed in regard to positive and negative velocities.

It is of interest to check the validity of transforming to another coordinate. First, suppose $y = x/2$, and it is desired to set up the equations in terms of y.

$$T = \frac{1}{2}m\dot{x}^2 = \frac{1}{2}m(2\dot{y})^2 = 2m\dot{y}^2$$

$$V = \frac{1}{2}kx^2 = \frac{1}{2}k(2y)^2 = 2ky^2$$

$$\mathscr{F}_d = \frac{1}{2}c\dot{x}^2 = \frac{1}{2}c(2\dot{y})^2 = 2c\dot{y}^2$$

$$Q = f\frac{dx}{dy} = 2f$$

The differential equation resulting from the Lagrange equation would become

$$4m\ddot{y} + 4ky + 4c\dot{y} = 2f$$

If this is set up by Newton's equations

$$m\left[\frac{d^2(2y)}{dt^2}\right] + c\left[\frac{d(2y)}{dt}\right] + k(2y) = f$$

which is obviously the same result. If the spring force were proportional to x^3, or $(2y)^3$,

$$V = \frac{1}{4}kx^4 = \frac{1}{4}k(2y)^4 = 4ky^4$$

The differential equation as derived from the Lagrange equation would be

$$4m\ddot{y} + 16ky^3 + 4c\dot{y} = 2f$$

and from Newton's equation

$$m\left[\frac{d^2(2y)}{dt^2}\right] + c\left[\frac{d(2y)}{dt}\right] + k(2y)^3 = f$$

which checks. If the damping force were proportional to $\dot{x}^3$ and the dissipation function computed according to $\int c\dot{x}^3 d\dot{x}$,

$$\mathscr{F}_d = \frac{1}{4}c\dot{x}^4 = \frac{1}{4}c(2\dot{y})^4 = 4c\dot{y}^4$$

The differential equation from Lagrange is

$$4m\ddot{y} + 16ky^3 + 16c\dot{y}^3 = 2f$$

and from Newton is

$$m\frac{d^2(2y)}{dt^2} + c\left[\frac{d(2y)}{dt}\right]^3 + k(2y)^3 = f$$

which also checks.

Now, suppose that the relationship between coordinates is not a linear one. Let $y^2 = x$ and let $x > 0$:

$$T = \frac{1}{2}m\dot{x}^2 = \frac{1}{2}m(2y\dot{y})^2 = 2my^2\dot{y}^2$$

$$V = \frac{1}{2}kx^2 = \frac{1}{2}k(y^2)^2 = \frac{1}{2}ky^4$$

$$\mathscr{F}_d = \frac{1}{2}c\dot{x}^2 = \frac{1}{2}c(2y\dot{y})^2 = 2cy^2\dot{y}^2$$

$$Q = f\frac{dx}{dy} = 2fy$$

The differential equation from Lagrange eventually simplifies to

$$2my\ddot{y} + 2m\dot{y}^2 + 2cy\dot{y} + ky^2 = f$$

The differential equation from Newton's law is

$$m\frac{d^2(y^2)}{dt^2} + c\frac{d(y^2)}{dt} + ky^2 = f$$

which, when expanded, checks the above. Similarly if the damping force varies as $\dot{x}^3$ and the dissipation function is $\frac{1}{4}c\dot{x}^4$, either the Newtonian or Lagrange equations would lead to the following differential equation:

$$2my\ddot{y} + 2m\dot{y}^2 + 8cy^3\dot{y}^3 + ky^2 = f$$

This example has illustrated the fact that the dissipation function is one half of the rate of energy dissipation for viscous dampers only, but that the concept may be used for non-viscous dampers if the dissipation function is properly selected; also that the transformation to coordinates in which the damping terms are not linear is valid for a properly chosen dissipation function.

Example 7-7. Check whether a dissipation function constructed as in Example 7-6 yields correct results for a two-degree system.

Referring to Fig. 6-1, suppose that damper No. 2 is not a viscous damper, but produces a resisting force proportional to $\dot{x}^3$. Then, using the coordinates x_1 and x_3, where $x_3 = x_2 - x_1$,

$$\mathscr{F}_d = \frac{1}{2} c_1 \dot{x}_1^2 + \frac{1}{4} c_2 \dot{x}_3^4$$

It is already clear that this would yield the correct equation in these coordinates. In the x_1 and x_2 coordinate system,

$$\mathscr{F}_d = \frac{1}{2} c_1 \dot{x}_1^2 + \frac{1}{4} c_2 (\dot{x}_2 - \dot{x}_1)^4$$

and it is equally clear that the differential equation derived from the Lagrange equations is the same as that derived from Newton's law.

Now, referring to Fig. 6-6, for a single mass free to move in a plane, suppose that viscous dampers are added which are aligned with the springs. If the dampers were of the same strength, the effect would be the same as if the motion took place in a viscous fluid. It is evident that the force would be opposite the direction of motion, and that the use of $\mathscr{F}_d = \frac{1}{2}c(\dot{x}^2 + \dot{y}^2)$ would result in the correct equations.

If the viscous dampers were of different strength, it is clear that $\mathscr{F}_d = \frac{1}{2}c_x\dot{x}^2 + \frac{1}{2}c_y\dot{y}^2$ would yield the correct equations although, in this instance, the resultant damping force would not be colinear with the resultant velocity. If the damping force were proportional to the square of the absolute velocity and colinear with the absolute velocity vector (motion in a fluid), the dissipation function would be $\mathscr{F}_d = \frac{1}{3}c(\sqrt{\dot{x}^2 + \dot{y}^2})^3$ according to the suggested rule. The corresponding force term in the Lagrange equation would then become $c\sqrt{\dot{x}^2 + \dot{y}^2}\,\dot{x}$ or $c\sqrt{\dot{x}^2 + \dot{y}^2}\,\dot{y}$. These are the correct magnitudes for forces to be used in the respective Newtonian equations. If the damping were due to nonviscous dampers of different strengths, or even different functions in the two directions, it is evident that the respective forces for use in Newton's law would result from $\partial\mathscr{F}_d/\partial\dot{x}$ and $\partial\mathscr{F}_d/\partial\dot{y}$ if

$$\mathscr{F}_d = \int f_x(\dot{x})\,d\dot{x} + \int f_y(\dot{y})\,d\dot{y}$$

where $f_x(\dot{x})$ means force in the x direction as a function of $\dot{x}$, with a similar definition for $f_y(\dot{y})$.

7.7 Generalized Quantities

Principal Coordinates. An important concept, which has not been specifically emphasized previously, is that often forces, masses, spring constants, and damping constants can be replaced with equivalent "generalized" values of these quantities—when this is convenient—these generalized quantities being associated with their corresponding generalized coordinates. When the generalized coordinates are also normal (or principal) coordinates, and the system is linear, it is possible to consider each coordinate as if it measured the deflection of a one-degree-of-freedom system, and then superimpose the results of these one-degree systems to determine the over-all performance.

The reason why this can be done is apparent from the Lagrange equation.

$$\frac{d}{dt}\left(\frac{\partial T}{\partial \dot{q}_i}\right) - \frac{\partial T}{\partial q_i} + \frac{\partial V}{\partial q_i} + \frac{\partial \mathscr{F}_d}{\partial \dot{q}_i} = Q_i$$

For rectilinear coordinates and coordinates related to rectilinear coordinates by linear transformation equations (such as Equations 7-7), the equation is

$$\frac{d}{dt}\left(\frac{\partial T}{\partial \dot{q}_i}\right) + \frac{\partial V}{\partial \dot{q}_i} + \frac{\partial \mathscr{F}_d}{\partial \dot{q}_i} = Q_i$$

If the differential equations resulting from this equation are linear, and each equation contains only one of the variables, the equations are uncoupled and the coordinates are normal coordinates. For this to occur it would be necessary for the functions to have the following forms, where the c's are constants:

$$T = c_{T_1}\dot{q}_1^{\,2} + c_{T_1}\dot{q}_2^{\,2} + \cdots + c_{T_i}\dot{q}_i^{\,2} + \cdots$$

$$V = c_{V_1}q_1^{\,2} + c_{V_2}q_2^{\,2} + \cdots + c_{V_i}q_i^{\,2} + \cdots$$

$$\mathscr{F}_d = c_{f_1}\dot{q}_1^{\,2} + c_{f_2}\dot{q}_2^{\,2} + \cdots c_{f_i}\dot{q}_i^{\,2} + \cdots$$

The differential equations would then become

$$2c_{T_1}\ddot{q}_1 + 2c_{V_1}q_1 + 2c_{f_1}\dot{q}_1 = Q_1$$

$$2c_{T_2}\ddot{q}_2 + 2c_{V_2}q_2 + 2c_{f_2}\dot{q}_2 = Q_2$$

$$2c_{T_i}\ddot{q}_i + 2c_{V_i}q_i + 2c_{f_i}\dot{q}_i = Q_1$$

Each of these is the equation for a single-degree-of-freedom system, and consequently it is possible to designate the factors multiplying the quantities, q_i, $\dot{q}_i$, and $\ddot{q}_i$, as K_i, C_i, and M_i, respectively, and name them "generalized spring constant," "generalized damping coefficient," and "generalized mass" for the ith mode.

From the above formulation it is seen that all of the kinetic energy corresponding to the velocity of the q_i coordinate is represented by the single term, $\frac{1}{2}M_i\dot{q}_i^{\,2}$. The generalized mass for the ith mode is then the "mass," M_i, moving at the velocity, $\dot{q}_i$, so that the expression, $\frac{1}{2}M_i\dot{q}_i^{\,2}$, accounts for all of the kinetic energy attributable to $\dot{q}_i$. This mass may not have the dimensions of mass, but $\frac{1}{2}M_i\dot{q}_i^{\,2}$ must have the dimensions of energy.

Similarly, the generalized spring constant, K_i, used in the expression, $\frac{1}{2}K_iq_i^{\,2}$, accounts for all of the potential energy attributable to the deflection, q_i. Again, K_i may not have the dimensions of a spring constant, but $\frac{1}{2}K_iq_i^{\,2}$ has the dimensions of energy.

The generalized damping coefficient, C_i, accounts for all of the energy dissipation associated with the velocity, $\dot{q}_i$, when used in the expression, $\frac{1}{2}C_i\dot{q}_i^{\,2}$.

The generalized force, Q_i, is a "force" such that the work done by all of the external forces on the system when q_i changes an amount, dq_i, can be calculated by $Q_i\,dq_i$. This was discussed in connection with Equation 7-41 and Examples 7-3 and 7-4.

Although the use of generalized quantities in complex systems will be illustrated in subsequent sections, it is of interest to re-examine the simple two-degree system of Fig. 6-1 in this light. Assume no damping and let the masses and springs have unit values.

Equations 6-7, 6-9, and 6-10 establish the modes and frequencies, which were seen earlier to be

$$\beta_1 = 0.618$$

$$\beta_2 = 1.620$$

$$\left(\frac{x_1}{x_2}\right)_1 = 0.617$$

$$\left(\frac{x_1}{x_2}\right)_2 = -1.615$$

Let generalized (principal) coordinates be defined so that

$$x_1 = 0.617q_1 - 1.615q_2$$

$$x_2 = q_1 + q_2$$

and therefore, solving for q_1 and q_2,

$$q_1 = 0.448x_1 + 0.725x_2$$

$$q_2 = -0.448x_1 + 0.277x_2$$

Now q_1 and q_2 are normal, or principal coordinates, each specifying directly the displacement in a normal mode. The generalized mass for the first mode can be computed as follows (letting $q_2 = 0$ and equating kinetic energies):

$$\frac{1}{2}M_1\dot{q}_1^{\,2} = \frac{1}{2}m_1\dot{x}_1^{\,2} + \frac{1}{2}m_2\dot{x}_2^{\,2}$$

$$= \frac{1}{2}(1)(0.617\dot{q}_1)^2 + \frac{1}{2}(1)(\dot{q}_1)^2$$

$$M_1 = 1.380$$

Similarly, the generalized spring constant for this mode is

$$\frac{1}{2}K_1q_1^{\,2} = \frac{1}{2}k_1x_1^{\,2} + \frac{1}{2}k_2(x_2 - x_1)^2$$

$$= \frac{1}{2}(1)(0.617q_1)^2 + \frac{1}{2}(1)(q_1 - 0.617q_1)^2$$

$$K_1 = 0.525$$

Calculations for the second mode result in

$$M_2 = 3.61, \qquad K_2 = 9.44$$

Now each mode can be considered as a single-degree system similar to Fig. 1-1, and the natural frequencies are, as expected,

$$\beta_1 = \sqrt{\frac{K_1}{M_1}} = \sqrt{\frac{0.525}{1.380}} = 0.617$$

$$\beta_2 = \sqrt{\frac{K_2}{M_2}} = \sqrt{\frac{9.44}{3.61}} = 1.620$$

Suppose that a force, $f_1 = 1.0$ (Fig. 6-1), is suddenly applied and remains constant. The generalized forces in the two modes are

$$Q_1\,dq_1 = f_1\,dx_1 = 1(0.617\,dq_1) \qquad \text{or} \quad Q_1 = 0.617$$

$$Q_2\,dq_2 = f_1\,dx_1 = 1(-1.615\,dq_2) \qquad \text{or} \quad Q_2 = -1.615$$

Now the equivalent one-degree systems are similar to Fig. 1-3 with zero damping, and the solutions are familiar.

$$q_1 = \frac{Q_1}{K_1}(1 - \cos\beta_1 t) = 1.175(1 - \cos 0.617t)$$

$$q_2 = \frac{Q_2}{K_2}(1 - \cos\beta_2 t) = -0.171(1 - \cos 1.620t)$$

If the actual coordinate displacements were desired, these are easily obtained from

$$\begin{aligned} x_1 &= 0.617q_1 - 1.615q_2 \\ &= 0.725(1 - \cos 0.617t) + 0.276(1 - \cos 1.620t) \\ x_2 &= q_1 + q_2 \\ &= 1.175(1 - \cos 0.617t) - 0.171(1 - \cos 1.620t) \end{aligned}$$

(Some slide-rule error has accumulated here, since the constant terms should be 1.000 for each variable.)

Some additional insight can also be achieved here by returning to the unforced system and considering the possible inertia coupling of the two modes, as follows. Let "inertia forces" for Mode 1 be computed from the accelerations of the masses. Thus the forces exerted by the masses on the system when oscillating in Mode 1 would be

$$f_1 = -m_1\ddot{x}_1 = -m_1\left(\frac{\partial x_1}{\partial q_1}\right)\ddot{q}_1 = -(1)(0.617)\ddot{q}_1$$

$$f_2 = -m_2\ddot{x}_2 = -m_2\left(\frac{\partial x_2}{\partial q_1}\right)\ddot{q}_1 = -(1)(1)\ddot{q}_1$$

If these are considered as external forces acting on the system as far as Mode 2 is concerned, the generalized force exciting q_2 is obtained from

$$Q_2\,dq_2 = f_1\,dx_1 + f_2\,dx_2 = f_1\left(\frac{\partial x_1}{\partial q_2}\right)dq_2 + f_2\left(\frac{\partial x_2}{\partial q_2}\right)dq_2$$

$$Q_2 = -\left[m_1\left(\frac{\partial x_1}{\partial q_1}\right)\left(\frac{\partial x_1}{\partial q_2}\right) + m_2\left(\frac{\partial x_2}{\partial q_1}\right)\left(\frac{\partial x_2}{\partial q_2}\right)\right]\ddot{q}_1$$

$$Q_2 = -\,[1(0.617)(-1.615) + 1(1)(1)]\ddot{q}_1$$

$$Q_2 = 0$$

A similar calculation would show that the generalized force in Mode 1 of inertia loads developed in a natural oscillation in Mode 2 is also zero. This merely means that the coordinates q_1 and q_2 are not inertia-coupled. This was already known, of course, since q_1 and q_2 were selected to be normal (or principal) coordinates. This is another manifestation of the orthogonality of the natural modes.

Similarly, the spring coupling between normal coordinates is zero, as can easily be confirmed by showing that the combination of forces necessary to cause a deflection of one normal mode will result in zero generalized force in the other normal mode or modes, as follows. Deflections corresponding to q_1 are $x_1 = (\partial x_1/\partial q_1)q_1$ and $x_2 = (\partial x_2/\partial q_1)q_1$. Forces in the positive x_1 and x_2 directions, which must be applied to maintain these deflections, are:

$$f_1 = k_1 x_1 - k_2(x_2 - x_1) = (k_1 + k_2)\frac{\partial x_1}{\partial q_1} q_1 - k_2 \frac{\partial x_2}{\partial q_1} q_1$$

$$f_2 = k_2(x_2 - x_1) = k_2 \frac{\partial x_2}{\partial q_1} q_1 - k_2 \frac{\partial x_1}{\partial q_1} q_1$$

These forces produce generalized force, Q_2, exciting q_2.

$$Q_2\, dq_2 = f_1\, dx_1 + f_2\, dx_2 = f_1 \frac{\partial x_1}{\partial q_2}\, dq_2 + f_2 \frac{\partial x_2}{\partial q_2}\, dq_2$$

$$Q_2 = \left\{\left[(k_1 + k_2)\frac{\partial x_1}{\partial q_1} - k_2 \frac{\partial x_2}{\partial q_1}\right]\frac{\partial x_1}{\partial q_2} + \left[k_2 \frac{\partial x_2}{\partial q_1} - k_2 \frac{\partial x_1}{\partial q_1}\right]\frac{\partial x_2}{\partial q_2}\right\} q_1$$

$$Q_2 = \{[(2)(0.617) - (1)(1)](-1.615) + [(1)(1) - (1)(0.617)](1)\}q_1$$

$$Q_2 = 0$$

Thus, if a deflection of one principal coordinate occurs, the spring forces developed do not cause a change of other principal coordinates.

Coupling of Generalized Coordinates. Although it is sometimes advantageous to make use of similar generalized quantities even if the generalized coordinates are not principal coordinates, usually it is less confusing to use the Lagrange equation directly, in which instance all of the expressions which couple the coordinates develop automatically. However, as one example illustrating a possible application, suppose that the dampers in the system were not zero. Then the generalized coordinates previously selected would be uncoupled for spring and inertia forces, but the damping forces could cause coupling between these coordinates. These forces could be considered as external generalized forces, as follows. Let both of the damping coefficients be unity, for convenience. If velocity $\dot{q}_1$ occurs, damping forces are developed on the masses in the positive x_1 and x_2 directions, which are

$$f_1 = -c_1\dot{x}_1 + c_2(\dot{x}_2 - \dot{x}_1) = \left[-(c_1 + c_2)\frac{\partial x_1}{\partial q_1} + c_2 \frac{\partial x_2}{\partial q_1}\right]\dot{q}_1$$

$$f_2 = -c_2(\dot{x}_2 - \dot{x}_1) = \left[c_2 \frac{\partial x_1}{\partial q_1} - c_2 \frac{\partial x_2}{\partial q_1}\right]\dot{q}_1$$

The generalized forces in the q_1 and q_2 coordinates are

$$Q_1 = f_1 \frac{\partial x_1}{\partial q_1} + f_2 \frac{\partial x_2}{\partial q_1} = -0.527\dot{q}_1$$

$$Q_2 = f_1 \frac{\partial x_1}{\partial q_1} + f_2 \frac{\partial x_2}{\partial q_2} = 0\dot{q}_1$$

If $\dot{q}_2$ occurs, similar computations lead to

$$Q_1 = 0\dot{q}_2$$

$$Q_2 = -9.45\dot{q}_2$$

Consideration of each coordinate as a single-degree system with an external forcing function leads to

$$M_1\ddot{q}_1 + K_1q_1 = Q_2 = -0.527\dot{q}_1 + 0\dot{q}_2$$

$$M_2\ddot{q}_2 + K_2q_2 = Q_2 = 0\dot{q} - 9.45\dot{q}_2$$

or

$$1.38\ddot{q}_1 + 0.527\dot{q}_1 + 0.525q_1 = 0$$

$$3.61\ddot{q}_2 + 9.45\dot{q}_2 + 9.44q_2 = 0$$

These are uncoupled; thus, for this combination of masses, springs, and dampers q_1 and q_2 are still principal coordinates, and consequently the constants, 0.527 and 9.45, are also "generalized damping coefficients" in the two normal modes. This would not be true in general. For instance, if the damping coefficient, c_2, were zero, and $c_1 = 1$ as before, a similar calculation would result in the coupled equations:

$$1.38\ddot{q}_1 + 0.380\dot{q}_1 - 1.00\dot{q}_2 + 0.525q_1 = 0$$

$$3.61\ddot{q}_2 - 1.00\dot{q}_1 + 2.61\dot{q}_2 + 9.44q_2 = 0$$

These equations could have been developed, with less thought required, from the Lagrange equation, for which

$$T = \frac{1}{2}M_1\dot{q}_1^2 + \frac{1}{2}M_2\dot{q}_2^2 = \frac{1}{2}(1.380)\dot{q}_1^2 + \frac{1}{2}(3.61)\dot{q}_2^2$$

$$V = \frac{1}{2}K_1q_1^2 + \frac{1}{2}K_2q_2^2 = \frac{1}{2}(0.525)q_1^2 + \frac{1}{2}(9.44)q_2^2$$

$$\mathscr{F}_d = \frac{1}{2} \times \text{rate of energy dissipation} = \frac{1}{2}c_1\dot{x}_1^2 = \frac{1}{2}c_1\left(\frac{\partial x_1}{\partial q_1}\dot{q}_1 + \frac{\partial x_1}{\partial q_2}\dot{q}_2\right)^2$$

$$\mathscr{F}_d = \frac{1}{2}(0.617\dot{q}_1 - 1.615\dot{q}_2)^2$$

Other applications of the concept of generalized quantities will occur in subsequent portions of the text.

7.8 Hamilton Equations

Although the Lagrange equations are usually more useful in actual solutions of physical problems, there is another formulation which is very powerful and provides additional insight into the principles of dynamics. Accordingly, this chapter concludes with a short discussion of Hamilton's equations for conservative systems.

It is convenient to start with a system having rectilinear coordinates, such as Fig. 6-1 without dampers. It is recalled that the generalized momenta (from Equation 7-20) are

$$p_{x_1} = \frac{\partial L}{\partial \dot{x}_1} = \frac{\partial T}{\partial \dot{x}_1} = m_1\dot{x}_1$$

$$p_{x_2} = \frac{\partial L}{\partial \dot{x}_2} = \frac{\partial T}{\partial \dot{x}_2} = m_2\dot{x}_2$$

It is clear that for this system

$$T = \frac{1}{2} m_1 \dot{x}_1^{\,2} + \frac{1}{2} m_2 \dot{x}_2^{\,2} = \frac{1}{2\,m_1} p_{x_1}{}^2 + \frac{1}{2\,m_2} p_{x_2}{}^2$$

The kinetic energy is therefore a function of the generalized momenta.

The Hamiltonian, H, is formed, which is simply the total energy, $T + V$, but in terms of momenta and coordinates rather than velocities and coordinates. Therefore

$$\frac{\partial H}{\partial x_1} = \frac{\partial T}{\partial x_1} + \frac{\partial V}{\partial x_1}$$
$$\frac{\partial H}{\partial p_{x_1}} = \frac{\partial T}{\partial p_{x_1}} + \frac{\partial V}{\partial p_{x_1}} \tag{7-46}$$

In the rectilinear coordinate system, T is not a function of the x's, and in any system V is not a function of $\dot{x}$'s. Therefore $\partial V/\partial p_{x_1} = 0$ and $\partial T/\partial x_1 = 0$ in the above equations. Also, $\partial L/\partial x_1 = -\partial V/\partial x_1$, since $L = T - V$, so that the first equation becomes $\partial H/\partial x_1 = -\partial L/\partial x_1$. Since $\partial T/\partial p_{x_1} = p_{x_1}/m_1 = m_1\dot{x}_1/m_1 = \dot{x}_1$ the second equation becomes $\partial H/\partial p_{x_1} = \dot{x}_1$. Since the Lagrange equation is $(d/dt)p_{x_1} - \partial L/\partial x_1 = 0$ for conservative systems with no external forces, it is evident that Equations 7-46 and similar equations for x_2 become

$$\frac{\partial H}{\partial x_1} = -\frac{dp_{x_1}}{dt} \qquad \frac{\partial H}{\partial p_{x_1}} = \frac{dx_1}{dt}$$
$$\frac{\partial H}{\partial x_2} = -\frac{dp_{x_2}}{dt} \qquad \frac{\partial H}{\partial p_{x_2}} = \frac{dx_2}{dt} \tag{7-47}$$

These four first-order Hamilton equations relating the p's and x's to t replace the two second-order Lagrange equations which relate the x's to t.

Now it is necessary to prove that the Hamilton equations hold true for general coordinates, not just rectilinear coordinates. For this purpose, the Hamiltonian is defined as

$$H = \sum_i p_i \dot{q}_i - L \tag{7-48}$$

which will be shown later to be the total energy. In this form, L must be expressed in terms of p's and q's. For a two-degree-of-freedom system, the above definition becomes

$$H = p_1\dot{q}_1 + p_2\dot{q}_2 - L$$

Expressions are needed for $\partial H/\partial p_1$, $\partial H/\partial q_1$, $\partial H/\partial p_2$, and $\partial H/\partial q_2$, and if there were more than two coordinates, similar partials for the others. Even though the Hamiltonian, H, appears to be a function of p_1, $\dot{q}_1$, p_2, $\dot{q}_2$, it is to be regarded as a function of p_1, q_1, p_2, q_2; and L is also a function of these variables, which must be regarded as independent variables when the above partials are formed. Also, since p_1 and p_2 are both functions of $\dot{q}_1$, q_1, $\dot{q}_2$ q_2, it is possible to regard $\dot{q}_1$ and $\dot{q}_2$ as functions of p_1, p_2, q_1, q_2. The partials required can therefore be written as

$$\left(\frac{\partial H}{\partial p_1}\right)_{p_2 q_1 q_2} = \dot{q}_1 + p_1\left(\frac{\partial \dot{q}_1}{\partial p_1}\right)_{p_2 q_1 q_2} + p_2\left(\frac{\partial \dot{q}_2}{\partial p_1}\right)_{p_2 q_1 q_2} - \left(\frac{\partial L}{\partial p_1}\right)_{p_2 q_1 q_2}$$
$$\left(\frac{\partial H}{\partial q_1}\right)_{p_1 p_2 q_2} = p_1\left(\frac{\partial \dot{q}_1}{\partial q_1}\right)_{p_1 p_2 q_2} + p_2\left(\frac{\partial \dot{q}_2}{\partial q_1}\right)_{p_1 p_2 q_2} - \left(\frac{\partial L}{\partial q_1}\right)_{p_1 p_2 q_2}$$

where the subscripts indicate which variables are constant. Since L was originally a function of $q_1, \dot{q}_1, q_2, \dot{q}_2$, and $\dot{q}_1$ and $\dot{q}_2$ are functions of p_1, p_2, q_1, q_2, the partials $\partial L/\partial p_1$ and $\partial L/\partial q_1$ can be obtained as follows.

$$\left(\frac{\partial L}{\partial p_1}\right)_{p_2 q_1 q_2} = \left(\frac{\partial L}{\partial \dot{q}_1}\right)_{q_1 q_2 \dot{q}_2} \left(\frac{\partial \dot{q}_1}{\partial p_1}\right)_{p_2 q_1 q_2} + \left(\frac{\partial L}{\partial \dot{q}_2}\right)_{q_1 q_2 \dot{q}_1} \left(\frac{\partial \dot{q}_2}{\partial p_1}\right)_{p_2 q_1 q_2}$$

$$\left(\frac{\partial L}{\partial q_1}\right)_{p_1 p_2 q_2} = \left(\frac{\partial L}{\partial \dot{q}_1}\right)_{q_1 q_2 \dot{q}_2} \left(\frac{\partial \dot{q}_1}{\partial q_1}\right)_{p_1 p_2 q_2} + \left(\frac{\partial L}{\partial \dot{q}_2}\right)_{q_1 q_2 \dot{q}_1} \left(\frac{\partial \dot{q}_2}{\partial q_1}\right)_{p_1 p_2 q_2} + \left(\frac{\partial L}{\partial q_1}\right)_{q_2 \dot{q}_1 \dot{q}_2}$$

When it is recalled that by definition

$$\left(\frac{\partial L}{\partial \dot{q}_1}\right)_{q_1 q_2 \dot{q}_2} = p_1 \quad \text{and} \quad \left(\frac{\partial L}{\partial \dot{q}_2}\right)_{q_1 q_2 \dot{q}_2} = p_2$$

and that Lagrange's equation is

$$\left(\frac{\partial L}{\partial q_1}\right)_{q_2 \dot{q}_1 \dot{q}_2} = \frac{d}{dt}\left(\frac{\partial L}{\partial \dot{q}_1}\right)_{q_1 q_2 \dot{q}_2} = \frac{dp_1}{dt}$$

it is possible to substitute and combine to obtain the Hamilton equations for general coordinates:

$$\frac{\partial H}{\partial p_1} = \frac{dq_1}{dt} \qquad \frac{\partial H}{\partial q_1} = -\frac{dp_1}{dt}$$
$$\frac{\partial H}{\partial p_2} = \frac{dq_2}{dt} \qquad \frac{\partial H}{\partial q_2} = -\frac{dp_2}{dt} \tag{7-49}$$

The modifications to these equations which become necessary if there are external generalized forces or dissipation functions are left as an exercise for the reader.

It is still necessary to show that the Hamiltonian, as defined by Equation 7-48 is equivalent to the total energy. This can be demonstrated for the two-degree-of-freedom system as follows. H will be $T + V$ if $\sum_i p_i\dot{q}_i = 2T$. It is easy enough to show that this is true when the time rate of change of a single coordinate defines the velocity of the corresponding mass. This has already been done for the rectilinear coordinate system in connection with the development of Equations 7-46. It would always be possible to define such a set of coordinates, and then transform to some other coordinate system with a set of equations which would relate the two coordinate systems. Since it is known that $2T = \sum_i p_{x_i}\dot{x}_i$, where the x's are chosen as explained above, if it can be shown that $\sum_i p_i\dot{q}_i = \sum_i p_{x_i}\dot{x}_i$ for any transformation equations relating the q's and x's, then the desired result that $\sum_i p_i\dot{q}_i = 2T$ will have been demonstrated. In these equations it must be remembered that, by definition, the momentum terms are $p_x = \partial L/\partial \dot{x} = \partial T/\partial \dot{x}$ and $p = \partial L/\partial \dot{q} = \partial T/\partial \dot{q}$.

For a two-degree system,

$$2T = p_{x_1}\dot{x}_1 + p_{x_2}\dot{x}_2 = \frac{\partial T}{\partial \dot{x}_1}\frac{dx_1}{dt} + \frac{\partial T}{\partial \dot{x}_2}\frac{dx_2}{dt} \tag{7-50}$$

Now, $x_1 = x_1(q_1, q_2)$ and $x_2 = x_2(q_1, q_2)$, so

$$\frac{dx_1}{dt} = \frac{\partial x_1}{\partial q_1}\frac{dq_1}{dt} + \frac{\partial x_1}{\partial q_2}\frac{dq_2}{dt}$$
$$\frac{dx_2}{dt} = \frac{\partial x_2}{\partial q_1}\frac{dq_1}{dt} + \frac{\partial x_2}{\partial q_2}\frac{dq_2}{dt} \tag{7-51}$$

Expressions are needed for $\partial T/\partial \dot{x}_1$ and $\partial T/\partial \dot{x}_2$, which should also involve $\partial x_1/\partial q_1$, $\partial x_1/\partial q_2$, etc. These could be obtained by writing an expression for $\partial T/\partial \dot{q}_1$ and $\partial T/\partial \dot{q}_2$ and solving these simultaneously for $\partial T/\partial \dot{x}_1$ and $\partial T/\partial \dot{x}_2$:

$$\begin{aligned} \frac{\partial T}{\partial \dot{q}_1} &= \frac{\partial T}{\partial \dot{x}_1}\frac{\partial \dot{x}_1}{\partial \dot{q}_1} + \frac{\partial T}{\partial \dot{x}_2}\frac{\partial \dot{x}_2}{\partial \dot{q}_1} \\ \frac{\partial T}{\partial \dot{q}_2} &= \frac{\partial T}{\partial \dot{x}_1}\frac{\partial \dot{x}_1}{\partial \dot{q}_2} + \frac{\partial T}{\partial \dot{x}_2}\frac{\partial \dot{x}_2}{\partial \dot{q}_2} \end{aligned} \tag{7-52}$$

It can be demonstrated (Appendix 3, Equations A3-6) that $\partial \dot{x}_1/\partial \dot{q}_1 = \partial x_1/\partial q_1$, etc.; thus, if Equations 7-52 are solved for $\partial T/\partial \dot{x}_1$ and $\partial T/\partial \dot{x}_2$ and these results and Equations 7-51 substituted into Equation 7-50, the desired result is obtained.

$$2T = \frac{\partial T}{\partial \dot{q}_1}\frac{dq_1}{dt} + \frac{\partial T}{\partial \dot{q}_2}\frac{dq_2}{dt} = p_1\dot{q}_1 + p_2\dot{q}_2 \tag{7-53}$$

This same procedure could be followed for the multiple-degree-of-freedom system. The final stage, proving $2T = \sum_i p_i\dot{q}_i$, could be accomplished easily by use of matrix algebra, an exercise left for the reader.

As was mentioned earlier, the Lagrange equation is more easily used than the Hamilton equations, and although the following example is very easily solved with the Lagrange equation, the Hamilton equations will be used for purposes of illustration.

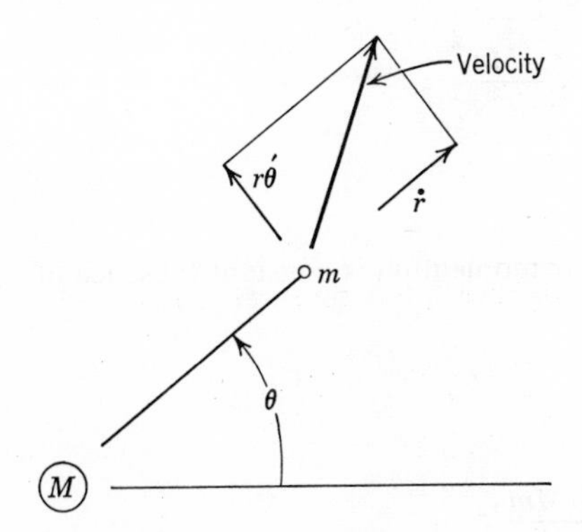

Fig. 7-2

Example 7-8. Derive the equations of motion for a satellite of the earth, using polar coordinates and ignoring the effects of other bodies (Fig. 7-2). Assume that the mass of the earth is concentrated at its center (this is valid for a homogeneous sphere).

The gravitational attraction between the earth and a satellite is given by GMm/r^2, where G is the universal gravitation constant, M is the mass of the earth, m the mass of the satellite and r the distance between the satellite and the center of the earth. If the potential energy of the satellite is zero at R_0, then the potential energy at the radius r is

$$\int_{R_0}^{r} \frac{GMm}{r^2}\, dr$$

or

$$V = GMm\left(\frac{1}{R_0} - \frac{1}{r}\right)$$

(R_0 could be the radius at the earth's surface, if desired.) The kinetic energy of the satellite in terms of the radius and an angle θ from some reference line is

$$T = \frac{1}{2} m[\dot{r}^2 + (r\dot{\theta})^2]$$

Since $\partial T/\partial \dot{r} = p_r$ and $\partial T/\partial \dot{\theta} = p_\theta$,

$$p_r = m\dot{r} \qquad \text{and} \quad p_\theta = mr^2\dot{\theta}$$

In terms of p's, then, the various functions required are

$$T = \frac{1}{2}\frac{p_r^2}{m} + \frac{1}{2}\frac{p_\theta^2}{mr^2}$$

$$L = T - V = \frac{1}{2}\frac{p_r^2}{m} + \frac{1}{2}\frac{p_\theta^2}{mr^2} + \frac{GMm}{r} - \frac{GMm}{R_0}$$

$$H = 2T - L$$

$$H = p_r\dot{r} + p_\theta\dot{\theta} - \frac{1}{2}\frac{p_r^2}{m} - \frac{1}{2}\frac{p_\theta^2}{mr^2} - \frac{GMm}{r} + \frac{GMm}{R_0}$$

$$H = \frac{1}{2}\frac{p_r^2}{m} + \frac{1}{2}\frac{p_\theta^2}{mr^2} - \frac{GMm}{r} + \frac{GMm}{R_0}$$

(Note that this expression for H is also $T + V$.) The Hamiltonian is now in terms of momenta and coordinates, and Equations 7-49 can be applied. These give $p_r = m(dr/dt)$ and $p_\theta = mr^2(d_\theta/dt)$, which were already known, and

$$\frac{dp_r}{dt} = -\frac{\partial H}{\partial r} = \frac{p_\theta^2}{mr^3} - \frac{GMm}{r^2}$$

$$\frac{dp_\theta}{dt} = -\frac{\partial H}{\partial \theta} = 0$$

The second of these equations states that the angular momentum is constant (absence of torque), or

$$mr^2\dot{\theta} = c$$

The first of the equations yields

$$\frac{d}{dt}(m\dot{r}) = mr\dot{\theta}^2 - \frac{GMm}{r^2}$$

The two terms on the right of this equation are recognizable as "centrifugal force" and the force due to the gravitational attraction. These equations govern the motion of the satellite. They will not be integrated here, since the purpose of this example was only to demonstrate the use of the Hamilton equations.

CHAPTER 8

Numerical Solution for Undamped Multiple-Degree-of-Freedom Systems

8.1 Matrix Equations

It is clear from the discussion in Chapter 7 that the Lagrange and Hamilton equations apply equally well to several degrees of freedom. However, the solution of simultaneous equations which results from the application of these methods to multiple-degree-of-freedom problems becomes very difficult if the differential equations are not linear. The discussion which follows applies only to linear systems; that is, spring loads are proportional to displacement, and dampers if any are of the viscous type. Most multiple-

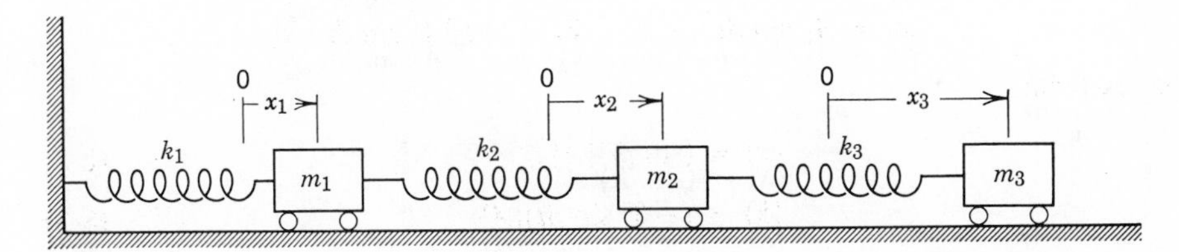

Fig. 8-1

degree-of-freedom systems encountered in applications have more degrees of freedom than three; however, since three-degree systems are representative of these systems and are satisfactory for illustration purposes, they will be used in this discussion. The reader will be able to extend the methods described to the higher-order systems.

The first system to be considered is that depicted in Fig. 8-1, in which there are no dampers. As in the previous systems, the deflections are measured from the fixed points in space where the masses would be at rest if there were no loads in the springs. What is required is a method of determining the normal modes and natural frequencies corresponding to the modes. The differential equations, easily obtained by use of either Newtons' law or Lagrange's equation, are the following:

$$\begin{aligned} m_1\ddot{x}_1 + 0\ddot{x}_2 + 0\ddot{x}_3 + (k_1 + k_2)x_1 - k_2x_2 + 0x_3 &= 0 \\ 0\ddot{x}_1 + m_2\ddot{x}_2 + 0\ddot{x}_3 - k_2x_1 + (k_2 + k_3)x_2 - k_3x_3 &= 0 \\ 0\ddot{x}_1 + 0\ddot{x}_2 + m_3\ddot{x}_3 + 0x_1 - k_3x_2 + k_3x_3 &= 0 \end{aligned}$$

The equations are written in the form shown, with zero coefficients as indicated in order to facilitate the formation of matrix equations. The terms involving the masses can be written as the product of two matrices, and the same is true with regard to the spring terms. Therefore, in matrix form, these equations would become

$$\begin{bmatrix} m_1 & 0 & 0 \\ 0 & m_2 & 0 \\ 0 & 0 & m_3 \end{bmatrix} \begin{Bmatrix} \ddot{x}_1 \\ \ddot{x}_2 \\ \ddot{x}_3 \end{Bmatrix} + \begin{bmatrix} (k_1 + k_2) & -k_2 & 0 \\ -k_2 & (k_2 + k_3) & -k_3 \\ 0 & -k_3 & k_3 \end{bmatrix} \begin{Bmatrix} x_1 \\ x_2 \\ x_3 \end{Bmatrix} = \begin{Bmatrix} 0 \\ 0 \\ 0 \end{Bmatrix}$$

or

$$[M]\{\ddot{x}\} + [K]\{x\} = \{0\} \tag{8-1}$$

The braces indicate column matrices. The square matrices are the "inertia matrix" and "stiffness matrix," and these are designated $[M]$ and $[K]$, respectively. In other problems the individual elements might not be similar to these, so the elements, in general, would be indicated as

$$\begin{bmatrix} M_{11} & M_{11} & M_{13} \\ M_{21} & M_{22} & M_{23} \\ M_{31} & M_{32} & M_{33} \end{bmatrix} \quad \text{and} \quad \begin{bmatrix} K_{11} & K_{12} & K_{13} \\ K_{21} & K_{22} & K_{23} \\ K_{31} & K_{32} & K_{33} \end{bmatrix}$$

In a natural mode of vibration, every coordinate will have the same frequency (and either the same phase or 180° difference in phase, which can be manifested by a sign difference), so that

$$\begin{aligned} x_1 &= A_1 \sin \beta t & \ddot{x}_1 &= -\beta^2 A_1 \sin \beta t \\ x_2 &= A_2 \sin \beta t & \ddot{x}_2 &= -\beta^2 A_2 \sin \beta t \\ x_3 &= A_3 \sin \beta t & \ddot{x}_3 &= -\beta^2 A_3 \sin \beta t \end{aligned}$$

In matrix form

$$\{x\} = (\sin \beta t)\{A\} \tag{8-2}$$

$$\{\ddot{x}\} = (-\beta^2 \sin \beta t)\{A\} \tag{8-3}$$

The terms in parentheses in these equations are simply scalar multipliers. When these equations are substituted in Equation 8-1 and the scalar $\sin \beta t$, is divided out, the following matrix equation is obtained.

$$-\beta^2[M]\{A\} + [K]\{A\} = \{0\}$$

Premultiplying both sides of this equation by $[K]^{-1}$ yields

$$-\beta^2[K]^{-1}[M]\{A\} + \{A\} = \{0\}$$

or

$$\{A\} = \beta^2[U]\{A\} \tag{8-4}$$

where

$$[U] = [K]^{-1}[M] \tag{8-5}$$

The array represented by $[U]$ is called the "dynamic matrix" (also "dynamical matrix"). It might appear from Equation 8-4 that $\beta^2[U]$ would have to be the unit matrix.

However, $[U]$ is determined by physical constants and, therefore, $\beta^2[U]$ is not necessarily the unit matrix. What is required is a combination of β^2 and $\{A\}$ that will satisfy Equation 8-4.

A particular set of numbers for the column matrix $\{x\}$ or $\{A\}$ is called a "vector" (the elements of the column matrix being the components of the vector) and a column matrix which satisfies Equation 8-4 is often called a "solution vector."

8.2 Flexibility and Stiffness Matrices

Flexibility Matrix. Before proceeding with the solution of Equation 8-4, it is advisable to digress momentarily and investigate the physical meaning of the matrix, $[K]^{-1}$. This matrix is known as the "flexibility matrix" or the "matrix of influence coefficients," and will be designated hereafter as $[\delta]$. The elements of this matrix are the various influence coefficients, as now defined. Imagine a static unit load applied in the positive direction of one of the coordinates. That coordinate and all other coordinates will deflect by various amounts. If the unit load is applied at some other point in the positive direction of the corresponding coordinate, the deflections are different, in general. These deflections, caused by unit loads, are influence coefficients.

δ_{11} = deflection of coordinate q_1 caused by unit load applied at q_1 with no other loads acting on the structure

δ_{12} = deflection of coordinate q_1 caused by unit load applied at q_2 with no other loads acting on the structure

δ_{21} = deflection of coordinate q_2 caused by unit load applied at q_1 with no other loads acting on the structure

etc. The matrix $[\delta]$ is then formed as

$$\begin{bmatrix} \delta_{11} & \delta_{12} & \delta_{13} & \cdots \\ \delta_{21} & \delta_{22} & \delta_{23} & \cdots \\ \delta_{32} & \delta_{32} & \delta_{33} & \cdots \\ \cdot & \cdot & \cdot & \cdot \end{bmatrix}$$

Now the problem proposed by Fig 8-1 could be approached from a different direction, using these influence coefficients. Imagine static loads f_1, f_2, f_3, applied on the three masses in the positive direction of the x's. These loads are not unit loads, but the deflections caused by them can be computed from the influence coefficients.

$$\left(\delta_{11} = \frac{\partial x_1}{\partial f_1}, \qquad \delta_{12} = \frac{\partial x_1}{\partial f_2}, \qquad \delta_{21} = \frac{\partial x_2}{\partial f_1}, \text{ etc.}\right)$$

Since the springs are all linear, and therefore deflections caused by different loads can be added to obtain the total deflection,

$$x_1 = \delta_{11} f_1 + \delta_{12} f_2 + \delta_{13} f_3$$

$$x_2 = \delta_{21} f_1 + \delta_{22} f_2 + \delta_{23} f_3$$

$$x_3 = \delta_{31} f_1 + \delta_{32} f_2 + \delta_{33} f_3$$

or

$$\{x\} = [\delta]\{f\} \tag{8-6}$$

Now these static loads will be replaced by dynamic inertia loads. This can be justified by remembering that when the system is oscillating in a normal mode, all coordinates oscillate with the same frequency and maintain fixed ratios with the other coordinates, so that all inertia forces maintain fixed ratios with the other inertia forces. Thus the force exerted by the third spring on the third mass in the $+x_3$ direction at a given instant would be $-m_3\beta^2 A_3 \sin \beta t$ if $x_3 = A_3 \sin \beta t$. The inertia force of the mass on the spring would then be $f_3 = +m_3\beta^2 A_3 \sin \beta t$. Therefore, $\{f\} = (\beta^2 \sin \beta t)[M]\{A\}$. If this is substituted for $\{f\}$, and $(\sin \beta t)\{A\}$ is substituted for $\{x\}$ in Equation 8-6, and the scalar multiplier $\sin \beta t$ is divided out, the result is

$$\{A\} = \beta^2[\delta][M]\{A\} \tag{8-7}$$

A comparison of Equations 8-7 and 8-4 shows that

$$[\delta] = [K]^{-1} \tag{8-8}$$

as asserted earlier. It may be easier to calculate the elements for $[\delta]$ than for $[K]$, although such is not the case for the system of Fig. 8-1. For this system, $[\delta]$ is determined to be

$$[\delta] = \begin{bmatrix} \frac{1}{k_1} & \frac{1}{k_1} & \frac{1}{k_1} \\ \frac{1}{k_1} & \left(\frac{1}{k_1} + \frac{1}{k_2}\right) & \left(\frac{1}{k_1} + \frac{1}{k_2}\right) \\ \frac{1}{k_1} & \left(\frac{1}{k_2} + \frac{1}{k_2}\right) & \left(\frac{1}{k_1} + \frac{1}{k_2} + \frac{1}{k_3}\right) \end{bmatrix}$$

It is easily verified that this is the inverse of $[K]$ by simply multiplying the two matrices together.

Stiffness Matrix. Another interpretation of the stiffness matrix may be obtained from Equation 8-6. If $\{x\} = [\delta]\{f\}$ relates deflections $\{x\}$ to arbitrary loads $\{f\}$, then $\{f\} = [\delta]^{-1}\{x\} = [K]\{x\}$ would relate loads $\{f\}$ to arbitrary deflections $\{x\}$. This matrix equation represents the algebraic equations,

$$f_1 = K_{11}x_1 + K_{12}x_2 + K_{13}x_3$$

$$f_2 = K_{21}x_1 + K_{22}x_2 + K_{23}x_3$$

$$f_3 = K_{31}x_1 + K_{32}x_2 + K_{33}x_3$$

The algebraic equations preceding Equation 8-6 were obtained by superposition of deflections caused by forces acting separately. In a similar way the above equations could be considered as the statement of a superposition theorem, possible because of the linearity of the system, except that here the effects of individual deflections are superimposed to produce a force. That is, the equations above state the following line of reasoning. Suppose that three arbitrary deflections, x_1, x_2, x_3, are imposed on the system. What loads, f_1, f_2, f_3, are required to maintain this deflection pattern? If x_1 is applied first, maintaining x_2 and x_3 zero, certain loads will be required at the three stations in order to maintain this pattern. These loads are proportional to x_1, and may be designated as $K_{11}x_1$ on Station 1, $K_{21}\,x_1$ on Station 2, and $K_{31}x_1$ on Station 3. If then deflection x_2 is applied, some more loads will be required at the three stations,

$K_{12}x_1$, $K_{22}x_2$, and $K_{32}x_3$, respectively, these additional loads being the same as those which would be calculated if x_2 were applied alone, x_1 and x_3 being maintained at zero. In a similar way the third deflection would cause additional loads, so that finally the loads at the three stations would be the sum of the contributions from each of the three arbitrary deflections, resulting in the algebraic equations relating forces to deflections.

$$f_1 = K_{11}x_1 + K_{12}x_2 + K_{13}x_3$$

$$f_2 = K_{21}x_1 + K_{22}x_2 + K_{23}x_3$$

$$f_3 = K_{31}x_1 + K_{32}x_2 + K_{33}x_3$$

Thus if x_1 were unity and x_2 and x_3 were maintained at zero, the loads necessary at the three stations would be K_{11}, K_{21}, and K_{31}. Therefore, a definition of the elements of the stiffness matrix is available which is analogous to the definition of the elements of the flexibility matrix.

It is recalled that the element, δ_{13}, in the flexibility matrix is defined as the deflection of Station 1 when a unit load is applied in the positive direction at Station 3, and loads at all other stations are zero. Similarly, the stiffness element, K_{13}, could be defined as the load at Station 1 resulting from a unit deflection at Station 3, *when the deflections at all other stations are maintained at zero*. With this definition the stiffness matrix for the system of Fig. 8-1 can be written directly, as follows. Suppose that unit deflection is given to Station 1, but all other stations are maintained at zero deflection. It is easily seen that the forces of springs 1 and 2 have the magnitudes k_1 and k_2 and the force of spring 3 is zero. Therefore, the force required at Station 1 is $(k_1 + k_2)$, in the positive direction, and at Station 2 is $-k_2$, while the force at Station 3 is zero. That is, $K_{11} = k_1 + k_2$, $K_{21} = -k_2$, and $K_{31} = 0$. The other elements of the stiffness matrix of Equation 8-1 are easily obtained in the same way.

Reciprocal Relationship. It is instructive to start with these definitions and show that $[\delta]$ and $[K]$ are reciprocals of each other. Since the system is linear, the matrix equations relating loads and deflections are

$$\{q\} = [\delta]\{Q\}$$

$$\{Q\} = [K]\{q\}$$

If the first of these equations is substituted in the second,

$$\{Q\} = [K][\delta]\{Q\}$$

Although it appears from this equation that $[K][\delta] = [1]$, this conclusion should not be drawn immediately. (In Equation 8-4 the product $\beta^2[U]$ is not $[1]$ for instance.) However, it is easily shown that $[K][\delta] = [1]$ if it is noted that $\{Q\} = [K][\delta]\{Q\}$ must be true for arbitrary load patterns. For instance, if $Q_1 \neq 0$, $Q_2 = 0$, $Q_3 = 0$, etc., then from the first equation

$$q_1 = \delta_{11}Q_1$$

$$q_2 = \delta_{21}Q_1$$

$$q_3 = \delta_{31}Q_1$$

etc.

When these are substituted in the second equation

$$\{Q\} = [K]\{q\} = Q_1[K]\begin{Bmatrix}\delta_{11}\\ \delta_{21}\\ \delta_{31}\end{Bmatrix}$$

$$Q_1 = Q_1(K_{11}\delta_{11} + K_{12}\delta_{21} + K_{13}\delta_{31} + \cdots)$$

$$Q_2 = Q_1(K_{21}\delta_{11} + K_{22}\delta_{21} + K_{23}\delta_{31} + \cdots)$$

$$Q_3 = Q_1(K_{31}\delta_{11} + K_{32}\delta_{21} + K_{33}\delta_{31} + \cdots)$$

etc.

Since $Q_1 \neq 0$, but Q_2 and $Q_3 = 0$, it is clear that the expressions in parentheses must be 1, 0, 0, respectively, and these expressions are the elements of the first column of the product $[K][\delta]$. In a similar manner the other elements of this product could be shown to be the rest of the unit matrix.

The definitions of elements of flexibility and stiffness matrices are repeated and summarized below.

δ_{ij} is the displacement of coordinate i when unit load is applied at Station j in the positive direction and all other loads are zero. Thus, in terms of generalized coordinates and forces, $\delta_{ij} = \partial q_i/\partial Q_j$.

K_{ij} is the load required in the direction of coordinate i when unit displacement occurs at Station j and all other displacements are zero. In terms of generalized coordinates and forces, $K_{ij} = \partial Q_i/\partial q_j$.

8.3 Symmetry of Matrices

It may have been noticed that both $[\delta]$ and $[K]$ are symmetrical matrices in the previous sections, and that $[M]$ is a diagonal matrix. This is a result of the coordinates chosen. It is easily shown that the $[\delta]$ matrix is symmetrical if the coordinates measure the deflection from a fixed position in space. This can be done by considering the total amount of energy stored in the structure when two loads are applied. Suppose that f_1 is applied, and afterward f_2 is applied. The amount of work done on the system and therefore stored in the springs when f_1 is applied is $\frac{1}{2}f_1x_1$, or $\frac{1}{2}f_1^2\,\delta_{11}$. When f_2 is applied, f_1 is already in place and does some more work when the system deflects under the action of f_2. The total amount of work done when f_2 is applied is $\frac{1}{2}f_2^2\delta_{22} + f_1f_2\delta_{12}$. Therefore the total energy stored in the springs is $\frac{1}{2}f_1^2\delta_{11} + \frac{1}{2}f_2^2\delta_{22} + f_1f_2\delta_{12}$. If the order of application of the loads is reversed, the result is $\frac{1}{2}f_1^2\delta_{11} + \frac{1}{2}f_2^2\delta_{22} + f_1f_2\delta_{21}$. Since the energy stored in the springs must be the same, regardless of order (the energy is a function of coordinate displacements only), it is clear that $\delta_{12} = \delta_{21}$, and the argument can be immediately extended to the other elements, showing that $[\delta]$ and therefore $[K]$ are symmetrical. When $[\delta]$ and $[K]$ are symmetrical, the inertia matrix is also symmetrical. However, the multiplication $[\delta][M]$ to obtain the dynamic matrix $[U]$ does not necessarily result in a symmetrical matrix.

It would be possible to choose coordinates in such a way that $[\delta]$, $[K]$, and $[M]$ are not symmetrical. For example, suppose that in Fig. 8-1 the coordinates were defined as the amount by which each spring stretches rather than the deflection from a fixed point in space. The three equations would then become

$$m_1\ddot{x}_1 + 0\ddot{x}_2 + 0\ddot{x}_3 + k_1x_1 - k_2x_2 + 0x_3 = 0$$
$$m_2\ddot{x}_1 + m_2\ddot{x}_2 + 0\ddot{x}_3 + 0x_1 + k_2x_2 - k_3x_3 = 0$$
$$m_3\ddot{x}_1 + m_3\ddot{x}_2 + m_3\ddot{x}_3 + 0x_1 + 0x_2 + k_3x_3 = 0$$

For this case

$$[M] = \begin{bmatrix} m_1 & 0 & 0 \\ m_2 & m_2 & 0 \\ m_3 & m_3 & m_3 \end{bmatrix}, \qquad [K] = \begin{bmatrix} k_1 & -k_2 & 0 \\ 0 & k_2 & -k_3 \\ 0 & 0 & k_3 \end{bmatrix},$$

and also $[\delta]$ is easily written as

$$[\delta] = \begin{bmatrix} \frac{1}{k_1} & \frac{1}{k_1} & \frac{1}{k_1} \\ 0 & \frac{1}{k_2} & \frac{1}{k_2} \\ 0 & 0 & \frac{1}{k_3} \end{bmatrix}$$

Clearly $[\delta]$ is still the inverse of $[K]$, but the matrices are not symmetrical. However, three equations could be constructed from the above three for which the matrices would be symmetrical. For instance, if the first equation were replaced by the sum of the three equations and the second equation by the sum of the second and third equations and the third equation left unchanged, the new matrices would again be symmetrical:

$$[M] = \begin{bmatrix} (m_1 + m_2 + m_3) & (m_2 + m_3) & m_3 \\ (m_2 + m_3) & (m_2 + m_3) & m_3 \\ m_3 & m_3 & m_3 \end{bmatrix}$$

$$[K] = \begin{bmatrix} k_1 & 0 & 0 \\ 0 & k_2 & 0 \\ 0 & 0 & k_3 \end{bmatrix}$$

Inherent in the physical problem is the property of symmetry, even though with some choices of coordinates the symmetry is not immediately evident. (It is interesting to note that if Lagrange's equation instead of Newton's equation were used to formulate the differential equation, the matrices would be symmetrical, regardless of the choice of coordinates.) It is also clear from the above examples that the inertia matrix, $[M]$, even when symmetrical, is not necessarily a diagonal matrix, although in many problems the selection of coordinates which seems most natural does result in a diagonal matrix.

8.4 Solution of Matrix Equations

Solution of Equation 8-4 or 8-7 can be accomplished by any of several different methods.

To be of practical use, any of the methods have to be programmed for solution by digital computer if the number of coordinates becomes larger than about 4 or 5. It is recalled that the A's in the column matrices of Equation 8-4 are the values of the coordinates. It would be possible to define other coordinates in terms of these coordinates. For instance, a new set of coordinates, $\{B\}$, could be defined so that

$$\{A\} = [N_1]\{B\} \qquad \text{or} \quad \{B\} = [N_1]^{-1}\{A\}$$

These matrix equations represent equations such as 7-7 and 7-8 for the two-degree system. If this value of $\{A\}$ is used in Equation 8-4, then

$$[N_1]\{B\} = \beta^2[U][N_1]\{B\}$$

Still other coordinates might be defined in terms of these coordinates; for instance,

$$\{B\} = [N_2]\{C\} \qquad \text{or} \quad \{C\} = [N_2]^{-1}\{B\}$$

If this expression were substituted for $\{B\}$ above, then

$$[N_1][N_2]\{C\} = \beta^2[U][N_1][N_2]\{C\}$$

This process could be repeated as many times as desired. All of the intermediate matrices could be combined into one, with the following result.

$$[N]\{Y\} = \beta^2[U][N]\{Y\} \tag{8-9}$$

where

$$[N]\{Y\} = \{A\} \qquad \text{or} \quad \{Y\} = [N]^{-1}\{A\} \tag{8-10}$$

If Equation 8-9 is now premultiplied by $[N]^{-1}$, the result is

$$\{Y\} = \beta^2[N]^{-1}[U][N]\{Y\} \tag{8-11}$$

If the product $[N]^{-1}[U][N]$ is a diagonal matrix, the elements of the column matrix $\{Y\}$ are normal coordinates, or "principal" coordinates, and the value of β for each normal mode can be immediately determined. This will be illustrated in Example 8-1.

Diagonalization Transformation. Evidently, it is desirable to try to determine a matrix $[N]$ so that the above product results in a diagonal matrix. This can be accomplished by an iterative process, using only four elements in each step. To see how this works, consider the multiplication of second-order matrices, as follows. It is desired to determine the elements of $[N]$ so that $[N]^{-1}[U][N]$ is a diagonal matrix. We need $[N]^{-1}$, which is easily shown to be

$$[N]^{-1} = \frac{1}{(N_{11}N_{22} - N_{12}N_{21})}\begin{bmatrix} N_{22} & -N_{12} \\ -N_{21} & N_{11} \end{bmatrix}$$

The desired product is then

$$\frac{1}{(N_{11}N_{22} - N_{12}N_{21})}\begin{bmatrix} N_{22} & -N_{12} \\ -N_{21} & N_{11} \end{bmatrix}\begin{bmatrix} U_{11} & U_{12} \\ U_{21} & U_{22} \end{bmatrix}\begin{bmatrix} N_{11} & N_{12} \\ N_{21} & N_{22} \end{bmatrix}$$

In order that the product should be a diagonal matrix, the upper right and lower left elements must be zero. This provides two equations. It is convenient to have the term $N_{11}N_{22} - N_{12}N_{21} = 1$ so that these factors do not have to be accounted for when the iterative procedure is used. Finally, for convenience, it is possible to let $N_{11} = N_{22}$, if this is desired. When the matrices are multiplied out and the first three of these restrictions applied, the following equations result.

$$[N] = \begin{bmatrix} N_{11} & N_{12} \\ N_{21} & N_{22} \end{bmatrix} \qquad [N]^{-1} = \begin{bmatrix} N_{22} & -N_{12} \\ -N_{21} & N_{11} \end{bmatrix} \tag{8-12}$$

$$\left.\begin{aligned} N_{11}N_{22} &= \frac{1}{2}\,\frac{1}{1 + \dfrac{(U_{22} - U_{11})^2}{4U_{12}U_{21}}\left[1 + \sqrt{1 + \dfrac{4U_{12}U_{21}}{(U_{22} - U_{11})^2}}\right]} \\ N_{21} &= N_{11}\frac{U_{22} - U_{11}}{2U_{12}}\left[1 + \sqrt{1 + \frac{4U_{12}U_{21}}{(U_{22} - U_{11})^2}}\right] \\ N_{12} &= -N_{22}\frac{U_{22} - U_{11}}{2U_{21}}\left[1 + \sqrt{1 + \frac{4U_{12}U_{21}}{(U_{22} - U_{11})^2}}\right] \end{aligned}\right\} \tag{8-13}$$

These results can be used with general subscripts i and j in an iterative manner, as will be demonstrated in the following example.

Example 8-1. Referring to Fig 8-1, let $M_1 = 1$, $M_2 = 2$, $M_3 = 3$, $k_1 = k_2 = k_3 = 1$.

Then

$$[\delta] \begin{bmatrix} 1 & 1 & 1 \\ 1 & 2 & 2 \\ 1 & 2 & 3 \end{bmatrix} \qquad [M] = \begin{bmatrix} 1 & 0 & 0 \\ 0 & 2 & 0 \\ 0 & 0 & 3 \end{bmatrix} \qquad [U] = \begin{bmatrix} 1 & 2 & 3 \\ 1 & 4 & 6 \\ 1 & 4 & 9 \end{bmatrix}$$

The computation will begin with the largest off-diagonal numbers, namely, 4 and 6.
Applying Equations 8-13, with $U_{22} = 4$, $U_{23} = 6$, $U_{22} = 4$, $U_{33} = 9$,

$$[N_1] = \begin{bmatrix} 1 & 0 & 0 \\ 0 & 0.523 & -1.047 \\ 0 & 0.696 & 0.523 \end{bmatrix} \qquad [N_1]^{-1} = \begin{bmatrix} 1 & 0 & 0 \\ 0 & 0.523 & 1.047 \\ 0 & -0.696 & 0.523 \end{bmatrix}$$

Multiplying out the matrices $[N_1]^{-1}[U][N_1]$ produces the following result. Call this matrix $[V_2]$

$$[V_2] = \begin{bmatrix} 1 & 3.13 & -0.520 \\ 1.57 & 12.03 & 0 \\ -0.173 & 0 & 0.997 \end{bmatrix}$$

Again the largest off-diagonal elements, 3.13 and 1.57, will be selected for the next computation. When zeros are produced at these positions, new numbers unfortunately replace the present zeros in $[V_2]$. However, if the process is repeated over and over the numbers which are not on the diagonal become smaller in comparison with the numbers on the diagonal until finally the off-diagonal terms are small enough to be considered zero. It is apparent that the process requires automatic machine calculation to be practical. The next step, then, uses

$$V_{11} = 1, \ V_{12} = 3.13, \ V_{21} = 1.57, \ V_{22} = 12.03$$

Use of Equations 8-13 now results in

$$[N_2] = \begin{bmatrix} 0.190 & -1.390 & 0 \\ 0.695 & 0.190 & 0 \\ 0 & 0 & 1 \end{bmatrix} \qquad [N_2]^{-1} = \begin{bmatrix} 0.190 & 1.390 & 0 \\ -0.695 & 0.190 & 0 \\ 0 & 0 & 1 \end{bmatrix}$$

which when substituted in $[N_2]^{-1}[V_2][N_2]$ yields

$$[V_3] = \begin{bmatrix} 12.51 & 0 & -0.0988 \\ 0 & 0.572 & 0.361 \\ -0.0329 & 0.240 & 0.997 \end{bmatrix}$$

It is seen that the zeros in $[V_2]$ have been replaced with numbers, but all the numbers off the diagonal are smaller than the corresponding numbers in the original matrix, $[U]$. Three more iterations will produce zeros in all off-diagonal positions, as far as slide-rule accuracy is concerned. The final diagonal matrix is

$$[V] = [V_6] = \begin{bmatrix} 1.16 & 0 & 0 \\ 0 & 0.422 & 0 \\ 0 & 0 & 12.60 \end{bmatrix}$$

It is desirable to have the final product of the $[N]$ matrices. This is

$$[N] = [N_1][N_2][N_3][N_4][N_5] = \begin{bmatrix} -0.450 & -1.240 & -0.329 \\ -0.506 & 0.477 & -0.636 \\ 0.315 & -0.0778 & -0.840 \end{bmatrix}$$

The inverse is
$$[N]^{-1} = \begin{bmatrix} -0.444 & -1.002 & 0.933 \\ -0.615 & 0.474 & -0.1183 \\ -0.1090 & -0.419 & -0.830 \end{bmatrix}$$

As a check on the accuracy, $[V_6]$ should be obtainable from $[N]$ as follows

$$[V_6] = [N]^{-1}[U][N]$$

However, when this is checked through the result is

$$[N]^{-1}[U][N] = \begin{bmatrix} 1.102 & 0 & 0.025 \\ 0 & 0.418 & 0.018 \\ 0 & 0 & 12.43 \end{bmatrix}$$

The slight discrepancy is probably the result of accumulation of slide-rule errors; consequently, these values of $[V]$ and $[N]$ are assumed correct.

$$\{Y\} = \beta^2[V]\{Y\} \qquad [V] = \text{diagonal}$$

$$\{A\} = [N]\{Y\}$$

Numerically these are

$$Y_1 = \beta^2 1.16\, Y_1 \qquad A_1 = -0.450\, Y_1 - 1.240\, Y_2 - 0.329\, Y_3$$

$$Y_2 = \beta^2 0.422\, Y_2 \qquad A_2 = -0.506\, Y_1 + 0.477\, Y_2 - 0.636\, Y_3$$

$$Y_3 = \beta^2 12.60\, Y_3 \qquad A_3 = 0.315\, Y_1 - 0.0778\, Y_2 - 0.840\, Y_3$$

The first set of equations can be satisfied for appropriate combinations of

$$\beta^2 = \frac{1}{1.16} = 0.862 \quad \text{or} \quad Y_1 = 0$$

$$\beta^2 = \frac{1}{0.422} = 2.37 \quad \text{or} \quad Y_2 = 0$$

$$\beta^2 = \frac{1}{12.60} = 0.0795 \quad \text{or} \quad Y_3 = 0$$

It is clear that if $\beta^2 = 0.862$, Y_2 and Y_3 must be zero. Y_1 does not have to be zero and the amplitudes of vibration of the masses are fixed fractions of Y_1. Thus, Y_1 is the amplitude of a normal coordinate, say y_1, and the normal mode for the frequency $\sqrt{0.862}$ is $A_1 = -0.450\,Y_1$ $A_2 = -0.506\,Y_1$, $A_3 = 0.315\,Y_1$. For this frequency the first and second masses are always moving in the direction opposite to the third mass (indicated by the negative sign). Similarly, for $\beta^2 = 2.37$, the first and third mass move opposite the second, and for $\beta^2 = 0.0795$ the masses all move in the same direction. It is conventional to designate the "first" mode as the lowest frequency mode, the second mode as the next highest, etc. The fact that the first mode happens to be designated by Y_3 in this instance is merely accidental, depending only on when the computation is stopped. It is apparent that the columns of the $[N]$ matrix are the "modal columns" and that these are associated with frequencies determined from the $[V]$ matrix.

A variation of the foregoing method can be used taking advantage of symmetry if either the $[K]$ matrix or the $[M]$ matrix is a diagonal matrix in the equation.

$$[K]\{A\} = \beta^2[M]\{A\} \tag{8-14}$$

If the $[K]$ matrix is diagonal the $[M]$ matrix is symmetrical, and if $[M]$ is diagonal $[K]$ is symmetrical. The object is to convert the diagonal matrix to the unit matrix without destroying the symmetry of the other matrix. Suppose, for instance, that $[M]$ is a diagonal matrix. Then it would be possible to find a new set of coordinates $\{B\}$ such that $\{A\} = [N_1]\{B\}$ where $[N_1]$ is a diagonal matrix whose elements are the reciprocals of the square roots of the corresponding elements of $[M]$. Substituting for $\{A\}$ in Equation 8-14 and premultiplying both sides by $[N_1]$ (instead of $[N_1]^{-1}$) would give

$$[N_1][K][N_1]\{B\} = \beta^2[N_1][M][N_1]\{B\}$$

where the matrix $[N_1][M][N_1]$ is now the unit matrix and $[N_1][K][N_1]$ is still symmetrical. The new matrix equation is similar in form to Equations 8-4 or 8-7. That is, $\{B\} = 1/\beta^2[V_1]\{B\}$, where $[V_1] = [N_1][K][N_1]$ and $[V_1]$ is symmetrical. For the succeeding operations the $[V]$ matrices will all be symmetrical. For symmetrical matrices it is possible to prove that the $[N]$ matrices become

$$[N] = \begin{bmatrix} \cos\theta & \sin\theta \\ -\sin\theta & \cos\theta \end{bmatrix} \qquad [N]^{-1} = \begin{bmatrix} \cos\theta & -\sin\theta \\ \sin\theta & \cos\theta \end{bmatrix} \tag{8-15}$$

where

$$\tan 2\theta = \frac{2V_{12}}{V_{22} - V_{11}} \tag{8-16}$$

and, of course, $V_{12} = V_{21}$

Example 8-2. Solve Example 8-1 taking advantage of symmetry and diagonal $[M]$ matrix. The example uses the numerical matrices

$$\beta^2 \begin{bmatrix} 1 & 0 & 0 \\ 0 & 2 & 0 \\ 0 & 0 & 3 \end{bmatrix} \{A\} = \begin{bmatrix} 2 & -1 & 0 \\ -1 & 2 & -1 \\ 0 & -1 & 1 \end{bmatrix} \{A\}$$

If $[N_1] = \begin{bmatrix} 1 & 0 & 0 \\ 0 & \frac{1}{\sqrt{2}} & 0 \\ 0 & 0 & \frac{1}{\sqrt{3}} \end{bmatrix}$ and $[N_1]\{B\} = \{A\}$

$$\beta^2 \begin{bmatrix} 1 & 0 & 0 \\ 0 & 1 & 0 \\ 0 & 0 & 1 \end{bmatrix} \{B\} = \begin{bmatrix} 1 & 0 & 0 \\ 0 & \frac{1}{\sqrt{2}} & 0 \\ 0 & 0 & \frac{1}{\sqrt{3}} \end{bmatrix} \begin{bmatrix} 2 & -1 & 0 \\ -1 & 2 & -1 \\ 0 & -1 & 1 \end{bmatrix} \begin{bmatrix} 1 & 0 & 0 \\ 0 & \frac{1}{\sqrt{2}} & 0 \\ 0 & 0 & \frac{1}{\sqrt{3}} \end{bmatrix} \{B\}$$

$$\beta^2\{B\} = \begin{bmatrix} 2 & -0.707 & 0 \\ -0.707 & 1.00 & -0.408 \\ 0 & -0.408 & 0.333 \end{bmatrix} \{B\} = [V_1]\{B\}$$

After this the example proceeds as before but using Equations 8-15 and 8-16. Let $V_{11} = 2$, $V_{12} = V_{21} = -0.707$, $V_{22} = 1$. This gives $\tan 2\theta = 2(-0.707)/(1 - 2) = 1.414$, $2\theta = 54.8°$, $\theta = 27.4°$

$$N_{11} = N_{22} = \cos 27.4° = 0.889$$

$$N_{12} = -N_{21} = \sin 27.4° = 0.460$$

$$[N_2] = \begin{bmatrix} 0.889 & 0.460 & 0 \\ -0.460 & 0.889 & 0 \\ 0 & 0 & 1 \end{bmatrix}$$

$$[N_2]^{-1} = \begin{bmatrix} 0.889 & -0.460 & 0 \\ 0.460 & 0.889 & 0 \\ 0 & 0 & 1 \end{bmatrix}$$

As before, it is necessary to compute $[N_2]^{-1}[V][N_2]$ or

$$[V_2] = \begin{bmatrix} 0.889 & -0.460 & 0 \\ 0.460 & 0.889 & 0 \\ 0 & 0 & 1 \end{bmatrix} \begin{bmatrix} 2 & -0.707 & 0 \\ -0.707 & 1 & -0.408 \\ 0 & -0.408 & 0.333 \end{bmatrix} \begin{bmatrix} 0.889 & 0.460 & 0 \\ -0.460 & 0.889 & 0 \\ 0 & 0 & 1 \end{bmatrix}$$

$$[V_2] = \begin{bmatrix} 2.370 & 0 & 0.188 \\ 0 & 0.635 & -0.362 \\ 0.188 & -0.362 & 0.333 \end{bmatrix}$$

The iteration then proceeds as in Example 8-1. In this computation the numbers in the diagonal of the final $[V]$ matrix will be β^2 rather than $1/\beta^2$. The final $[V]$ matrix after four more iterations is

$$[V] = \begin{bmatrix} 2.39 & 0 & 0 \\ 0 & 0.875 & 0 \\ 0 & 0 & 0.0806 \end{bmatrix}$$

These numbers compare with 2.37, 0.862, and 0.0795 determined in Example 8-1. The final $[N]$ matrix, which represents the modal columns, is

$$[N] = \begin{bmatrix} 0.880 & 0.444 & 0.1905 \\ -0.335 & 0.497 & 0.365 \\ 0.0548 & -0.323 & 0.482 \end{bmatrix}$$

When these are compared with the modal columns from Example 8-1, the relative magnitudes are in good agreement. Another effective way to check the accuracy of the final results is to substitute these results back into the original equations to see if the modal columns yield the same frequency as the values obtained from the diagonal elements of $[V]$, as follows. In the equation $\beta^2[M]\{A\} = [K]\{A\}$ the lowest frequency mode is

$A_1 = 0.1905$, $A_2 = 0.365$, $A_3 = 0.482$, and the numerical values for $[M]$ and $[K]$ are known. The following three equations result.

$$\beta^2(1)(0.1905) = 2(0.1905) - 1(0.365) + 0(0.482)$$

$$\beta^2(2)(0.365) = -1(0.1905) + 2(0.365) - 1(0.482)$$

$$\beta^2(3)(0.482) = 0(0.1905) - 1(0.365) + 1(0.482)$$

These equations give $\beta^2 = 0.084, 0.079, 0.081$ to compare with the value 0.0806 from $[V]$. Three similar equations for the next lowest frequency mode yield $\beta^2 = 0.882, 0.922, 0.890$ to compare with 0.875 from $[V]$. For the highest frequency mode the values are $\beta^2 = 2.38$, 2.39, 2.38 to compare with 2.39 from $[V]$. These are all acceptable checks considering the possibility of slide-rule error accumulation.

It is easy to see how to use the symmetrical matrix technique illustrated in the last example even if neither the $[M]$ nor $[K]$ matrix were diagonal. One or the other of these matrices would be reduced to a diagonal matrix and then to a unit matrix, after which the other matrix would be reduced to a diagonal matrix. One of the advantages of working with symmetrical matrices is that the symmetry reduces the number of computations required. Even when $[M]$ and $[K]$ matrices are not symmetrical, there is an inherent symmetry which means that they can be made symmetrical by some manipulation before starting the iteration procedure.

Example 8-3. Starting with the original matrix equation of Example 8-1, make the matrices symmetrical before beginning the iteration.

$$\beta^2[U]\{A\} = \{A\} \qquad \text{where} \quad [U] = \begin{bmatrix} 1 & 2 & 3 \\ 1 & 4 & 6 \\ 1 & 4 & 9 \end{bmatrix}$$

A possible procedure is to find a diagonal matrix, $[N_0]$, such that $[N_0]^{-1}[U][N_0]$ is a symmetrical matrix. Postmultiplying by a diagonal matrix multiplies the columns, while premultiplying multiplies the rows. The immediate choice for $[N_0]^{-1}$ and $[N_0]$ would be

$$[N_0]^{-1} = \begin{bmatrix} 1 & 0 & 0 \\ 0 & \sqrt{2} & 0 \\ 0 & 0 & \sqrt{3} \end{bmatrix} \qquad [N_0] = \begin{bmatrix} 1 & 0 & 0 \\ 0 & \dfrac{1}{\sqrt{2}} & 0 \\ 0 & 0 & \dfrac{1}{\sqrt{3}} \end{bmatrix}$$

If this is tried, the result for $[N_0]^{-1}[U][N_0]$ is symmetrical as suspected:

$$\begin{bmatrix} 1 & \sqrt{2} & \sqrt{3} \\ \sqrt{2} & 4 & \sqrt{24} \\ \sqrt{3} & \sqrt{24} & 9 \end{bmatrix}$$

In any equation of the form $\{A\} = \beta^2[\delta][M]\{A\}$ where $[\delta]$ is symmetrical and $[M]$ is diagonal, the matrix equation can be prepared so that symmetry may be retained as follows. If the matrix equation is premultiplied by $[M]$,

$$[M]\{A\} = \beta^2[M][\delta][M]\{A\}$$

the combination $[M][\delta][M]$ is symmetrical. However, the matrix on the left side of the equation is diagonal rather than unit. This diagonal matrix can be reduced to a unit matrix without spoiling the symmetry by the same transformation as was used in Example 8-2; that is, by letting

$$\{A\} = [N_0]\{B\}$$

where $[N_0]$ is a diagonal matrix whose elements are the reciprocals of the square roots of the corresponding elements of $[M]$. Then, premultiplying by $[N_0]$ yields the unit matrix on the left side and a symmetrical matrix on the right, or

$$[N_0][M][N_0]\{B\} = \beta^2[N_0][M][\delta][M][N_0]\{B\}$$

or

$$\{B\} = \beta^2[V_0]\{B\}$$

$$\text{where } \{A\} = [N_0]\{B\} \qquad \text{and} \qquad [V_0] = [N_1][\delta][N_1]$$

and $[N_1]$ is a diagonal matrix whose elements are the square roots of the corresponding diagonal $[M]$ matrix. In this example

$$[\delta] = \begin{bmatrix} 1 & 1 & 1 \\ 1 & 2 & 2 \\ 1 & 2 & 3 \end{bmatrix} \qquad [M] = \begin{bmatrix} 1 & 0 & 0 \\ 0 & 2 & 0 \\ 0 & 0 & 3 \end{bmatrix} \qquad [N_0] = \begin{bmatrix} 1 & 0 & 0 \\ 0 & \dfrac{1}{\sqrt{2}} & 0 \\ 0 & 0 & \dfrac{1}{\sqrt{3}} \end{bmatrix} \qquad [N_1] = \begin{bmatrix} 1 & 0 & 0 \\ 0 & \sqrt{2} & 0 \\ 0 & 0 & \sqrt{3} \end{bmatrix}$$

$$[V_0] = \begin{bmatrix} 1 & 0 & 0 \\ 0 & \sqrt{2} & 0 \\ 0 & 0 & \sqrt{3} \end{bmatrix} \begin{bmatrix} 1 & 1 & 1 \\ 1 & 2 & 2 \\ 1 & 2 & 3 \end{bmatrix} \begin{bmatrix} 1 & 0 & 0 \\ 0 & \sqrt{2} & 0 \\ 0 & 0 & \sqrt{3} \end{bmatrix} = \begin{bmatrix} 1 & \sqrt{2} & \sqrt{3} \\ \sqrt{2} & 4 & \sqrt{24} \\ \sqrt{3} & \sqrt{24} & 9 \end{bmatrix}$$

Example 8-4. The previous examples can also be represented by the matrix equation

$$\beta^2 \begin{bmatrix} 1 & 1 & 1 \\ 1 & 3 & 3 \\ 1 & 3 & 6 \end{bmatrix} \{A\} = \begin{bmatrix} 2 & 1 & 1 \\ 1 & 2 & 1 \\ 1 & 1 & 1 \end{bmatrix} \{A\}$$

Here there are no diagonal matrices, but the matrices are all symmetrical. It is assumed that the necessary transformation for producing a diagonal matrix is not known or immediately evident. Of course, the equation could be premultiplied by the inverse of either matrix, producing the unit matrix on one side, but the matrix on the other side would not be a symmetrical matrix and the problem then would be similar to that of Example 8-1. To take advantage of symmetry, first one of these matrices and then the other can be operated upon in the manner shown in Example 8-2. The first $[N]$ matrix can be determined from the elements of the matrix on the left side of the equation.

$$V_{22} = 3, \quad V_{23} = 3, \quad V_{33} = 6$$

$$\tan 2\theta = \frac{2(3)}{6-3} = 2, \quad \theta = 31.7°, \quad \cos\theta = 0.852, \quad \sin\theta = 0.525$$

$$[N_1] = \begin{bmatrix} 1 & 0 & 0 \\ 0 & 0.852 & 0.525 \\ 0 & -0.525 & 0.852 \end{bmatrix} \qquad [N_1]^{-1} = \begin{bmatrix} 1 & 0 & 0 \\ 0 & 0.852 & -0.525 \\ 0 & 0.525 & 0.852 \end{bmatrix}$$

These matrices must be used to operate on the matrices on both sides of the equation by multiplying out $[N_1]^{-1}[V][N_1]$. The new matrix equation would become

$$\beta^2 \begin{bmatrix} 1 & 0.327 & 1.377 \\ 0.327 & 0.524 & 0 \\ 1.377 & 0 & 7.87 \end{bmatrix} \{B\} = \begin{bmatrix} 2 & 0.327 & 1.377 \\ 0.327 & 0.831 & 0.898 \\ 1.377 & 0.898 & 2.170 \end{bmatrix} \{B\}$$

The calculation would now be continued as in previous examples, reducing first the left matrix to a diagonal matrix and then to a unit matrix as in Example 8-2, after which the matrix resulting on the right would be reduced to a diagonal matrix.

Matrix Iteration for Modal Column. The method which has been described obtains simultaneously all the natural frequencies and modal columns. This is sometimes an advantage. It also has the advantage of being easily understood. However, it may be that only the lowest frequency mode or several lowest frequency modes are of interest. While the method described above can be considerably shortened and still be applicable for this problem, there is another iteration procedure attributable to Duncan and Collar* and very well summarized in Reference 10. The theory will not be repeated here, but the example will again be worked out using this procedure, which is very easy to apply even if the theory is somewhat involved.

Example 8-5. Rework Example 8-1 using the matrix iteration method of Duncan and Collar.

$$\{A\} = \beta^2[U]\{A\} \qquad \text{where} \quad [U] = \begin{bmatrix} 1 & 2 & 3 \\ 1 & 4 & 6 \\ 1 & 4 & 9 \end{bmatrix}$$

This equation really represents three equations

$$A_1 = \beta^2[1A_1 + 2A_2 + 3A_3]$$

$$A_2 = \beta^2[1A_1 + 4A_2 + 6A_3]$$

$$A_3 = \beta^2[1A_1 + 4A_2 + 9A_3]$$

If values for A_1, A_2, and A_3 are assumed and placed in the right side of these equations, new values can be calculated and used in the right side to calculate new values, etc. It will be found that the process converges on the first, or lowest frequency, mode, no matter what initial assumptions were made. Assume initially that $A_1 = 3$, $A_2 = 6$, $A_3 = 9$, for example, the last column of the $[U]$ matrix. Let this be "normalized" by dividing through by A_3, for example, so that the first assumed column is $A_1 = 0.333$, $A_2 = 0.667$, $A_3 = 1$. When these are substituted in the three foregoing equations, the new values are $A_1 = 4.667\beta^2$, $A_2 = 9\beta^2$, $A_3 = 12\beta^2$. If this is normalized again by dividing by $12\beta^2$, $A_1 = 0.389$, $A_2 = 0.750$, $A_3 = 1$. These values may be used for a second iteration. The following columns summarize the procedure.

$\{A\}_1$	$\{A\}_2$	$\{A\}_3$	$\{A\}_4$
0.333	0.389	0.395	0.395
0.667	0.750	0.758	0.758
1	1	1	1

When two normalized columns are exactly alike to as many significant figures as desired, the procedure can be stopped. In this calculation, with only slide-rule accuracy, any further iteration would give the same results. Thus, the first mode is $A_1 = 0.395$, $A_2 = 0.758$, $A_3 = 1$. This agrees with the first mode calculated in Example 8.1, normalized on A_3. When these values of A_1, A_2, and A_3 are substituted into the three foregoing equations, the same value of β^2 is obtained from all three equations; namely, $\beta^2 = 0.0805$. If two more decimal

* W. J. Duncan and A. R. Collar, "A Method for the Solution of Oscillation Problems by Matrices," *Philosophical Magazine*, 1934.

points were carried, using a desk calculator or digital computor instead of a slide rule, the more exact column for $\{A\}$ would be

$$\begin{Bmatrix} 0.39522 \\ 0.75864 \\ 1.00000 \end{Bmatrix}$$

In order to obtain the second mode, it is necessary to apply a condition which will prevent convergence on the first mode. This is essentially setting the normal coordinate or principal coordinate corresponding to the first mode equal to zero. The proof is postponed until later (see Section 8.7), but the procedure for accomplishing this is as follows. Form a row matrix from the modal column by transposing the column and then taking the product $[B]^{(1)} = \{\tilde{A}\}[M]$. Then form a square matrix $[S]$ from the elements of $[B]^{(1)}$, as follows:

$$[S] = \begin{bmatrix} 0 & -\dfrac{B_2{}^{(1)}}{B_1{}^{(1)}} & -\dfrac{B_3{}^{(1)}}{B_1{}^{(1)}} \\ 0 & 1 & 0 \\ 0 & 0 & 1 \end{bmatrix}$$

The reason for the foregoing formulation is that the coordinates can be prevented from oscillating in the first mode by setting $\{\tilde{A}\}[M]\{A\} = 0$, or

$$[B]^{(1)}\{A\} = 0 \qquad \text{or} \quad B_1{}^{(1)}A_1 + B_2{}^{(1)}A_2 + B_3{}^{(1)}A_3 = 0$$

Then A_1 can be given in terms of A_2 and A_3 as

$$A_1 = 0A_1 - \frac{B_2{}^{(1)}}{B_1{}^{(1)}}A_2 - \frac{B_3{}^{(1)}}{B_1{}^{(1)}}A_3$$

$$A_2 = 0A_1 + 1A_2 + 0A_3$$

$$A_3 = 0A_1 + 0A_2 + 1A_3$$

Now $\{A\} = [S]\{A\}$ where $[S]$ is the previous matrix. The superscript applied to $[B]^{(1)}$ is to distinguish this matrix from the similar matrix used for determining the third mode, which would then be $[B]^{(2)}$.

Now postmultiply the original dynamic matrix $[U]$ by this $[S]$ and use the new matrix in the same way as the original dynamic matrix to obtain the second mode. Numerically,

$$[B]^{(1)} = [0.395 \quad 0.758 \quad 1.000]\begin{bmatrix} 1 & 0 & 0 \\ 0 & 2 & 0 \\ 0 & 0 & 3 \end{bmatrix} = [0.395 \quad 1.516 \quad 3.000]$$

$$[S] = \begin{bmatrix} 0 & -3.84 & -7.60 \\ 0 & 1 & 0 \\ 0 & 0 & 1 \end{bmatrix}$$

$$[U]_2 = [U][S] = \begin{bmatrix} 1 & 2 & 3 \\ 1 & 4 & 6 \\ 1 & 4 & 9 \end{bmatrix}\begin{bmatrix} 0 & -3.84 & -7.60 \\ 0 & 1 & 0 \\ 0 & 0 & 1 \end{bmatrix} = \begin{bmatrix} 0 & -1.84 & -4.60 \\ 0 & 0.16 & -1.60 \\ 0 & 0.16 & 1.40 \end{bmatrix}$$

Now the iteration can proceed as before, where $\{A\} = \beta^2[U]_2\{A\}$ or

$$A_1 = \beta^2(0A_1 - 1.84A_2 - 4.60A_3)$$

$$A_2 = \beta^2(0A_1 + 0.16A_2 - 1.60A_3)$$

$$A_3 = \beta^2(0A_1 + 0.16A_2 + 1.40A_3)$$

and for a start the last column of the $[U]_2$ matrix can again be used, although any other assumption would lead to the same final result. The following columns summarize the results.

$\{A\}_1$	$\{A\}_2$	$\{A\}_3$	$\{A\}_4$	$\{A\}_5$	$\{A\}_6$	$\{A\}_7$	$\{A\}_8$
−3.29	−2.08	−1.600	−1.473	−1.430	−1.410	−1.400	−1.400
−1.143	−1.490	−1.580	−1.617	−1.627	−1.630	−1.630	−1.630
1.000	1.000	1.000	1.000	1.000	1.000	1.000	1.000

When these values are substituted in the three foregoing equations, all three equations give $\beta^2 = 0.876$. However, if these values of $\{A\}$ are used with the original dynamic matrix,

$$A_1 = \beta^2(A_1 + 2A_2 + 3A_3)$$
$$A_2 = \beta^2(A_1 + 4A_2 + 6A_3)$$
$$A_3 = \beta^2(A_1 + 4A_2 + 9A_3)$$

the values of β^2 obtained are 0.843, 0.848, and 0.925. This discrepancy indicates a loss of accuracy in the process of obtaining $[U]_2$ from $[U]$. If the third mode were calculated with the previous results, even greater discrepancies would be observed. The reason for the final inaccuracy is that the first mode was not accurate enough. If the accurate values of A_1 A_2, A_3, obtained with the digital computer are used,

$$A_1 = 0.39522, \quad A_2 = 0.75864, \quad A_3 = 1.00000$$

more accurate $[S]$ and $[U]_2$ matrices become

$$[S] = \begin{bmatrix} 0 & -3.8391 & -7.5907 \\ 0 & 1 & 0 \\ 0 & 0 & 1 \end{bmatrix}$$

$$[U]_2 = \begin{bmatrix} 0 & -1.83910 & -4.59070 \\ 0 & 0.16090 & -1.59070 \\ 0 & 0.16090 & -1.40930 \end{bmatrix}$$

The more accurate second mode then becomes

$$A_1 = -1.4210$$
$$A_2 = -1.6070$$
$$A_3 = 1.0000$$

For these numbers, $\beta^2 = 0.8690$ from all three equations. Incidentally, these results indicate the magnitude of error in the slide-rule computations for Example 8-1, and also show the necessity for carrying more significant figures than three in the first iteration if the second mode is to be accurate to three significant figures. With larger matrices even greater accuracy is necessary if the higher modes are to be correct.

To determine the third mode, it is necessary to repeat the procedure used for the second mode. Using $[U]_2$ to obtain $[U]_3$ the matrix $[B]^{(2)}$ must first be calculated

$$[B]^{(2)} = [-1.4210 \quad -1.6070 \quad 1.0000] \begin{bmatrix} 1 & 0 & 0 \\ 0 & 2 & 0 \\ 0 & 0 & 3 \end{bmatrix} = [-1.4210 \quad -3.2142 \quad 3.0000]$$

Now, $[S]$ can be formed from the elements of $[B]^{(2)}$ and $[B]^{(1)}$ as follows. Using the two equations

$$B_1^{(1)}A_1 + B_2^{(1)}A_2 + B_3^{(1)}A_3 = 0$$
$$B_1^{(2)}A_1 + B_2^{(2)}A_2 + B_3^{(2)}A_3 = 0$$

A_2 can be determined in terms of A_3 exclusively by eliminating A_1

$$A_1 = 1A_1 + 0A_2 + 0A_3$$

$$A_2 = 0A_1 + 0A_2 + \frac{B_1{}^{(2)}B_3{}^{(1)} - B_1{}^{(1)}B_3{}^{(2)}}{B_1{}^{(1)}B_2{}^{(2)} - B_1{}^{(2)}B_2{}^{(1)}} A_3$$

$$A_3 = 0A_1 + 0A_2 + 1A_3$$

If there were other modes, the foregoing procedure could be extended. Numerically, then

$$[S] = \begin{bmatrix} 1 & 0 & 0 \\ 0 & 0 & -6.151 \\ 0 & 0 & 1 \end{bmatrix}$$

and

$$[U]_3 = [U]_2[S] = \begin{bmatrix} 0 & -1.8391 & -4.5907 \\ 0 & 0.1609 & -1.5907 \\ 0 & 0.1609 & 1.4093 \end{bmatrix} \begin{bmatrix} 1 & 0 & 0 \\ 0 & 0 & -6.151 \\ 0 & 0 & 1 \end{bmatrix}$$

$$[U]_3 = \begin{bmatrix} 0 & 0 & 6.7222 \\ 0 & 0 & -2.5805 \\ 0 & 0 & 0.41952 \end{bmatrix}$$

It is easy to show that the last column of this matrix is the modal column for the third mode. Normalized on A_3 it is

$$A_1 = 16.025$$

$$A_2 = -6.151$$

$$A_3 = 1.000$$

When these numbers are used with the original dynamic matrix, $\beta^2 = 2.3836$ from all these equations, checking the accuracy of the calculation. Note that the above modal column also checks that determined in Example 8-1 for the high-frequency mode. It is not necessary to use both $[B]^{(1)}\{A\}^{(1)} = 0$ and $[B]^{(2)}\{A\}^{(2)} = 0$ in forming $[S]$ as long as $[S]$ postmultiplies $[U]_2$ rather than $[U]_1$, since $[U]_2$ already contains the restriction $[B]^{(1)}\{A\}^{(1)} = 0$. Thus, the matrix

$$[S] = \begin{bmatrix} 1 & 0 & 0 \\ \dfrac{-1.421}{-3.214} & 0 & \dfrac{3}{-3.214} \\ 0 & 0 & 1 \end{bmatrix}$$

would have been satisfactory.

Another way of determining this mode would be as follows. The equation $\beta^2[U]\{A\} = \{A\}$ could also be written as $\beta^2\{A\} = [U]^{-1}\{A\}$. When this equation is iterated as before, the convergence is on the highest frequency mode instead of the lowest frequency mode. The matrix $[U]^{-1}$ is $[M]^{-1}[K]$, which in this example is

$$\begin{bmatrix} 2 & -1 & 0 \\ -0.50000 & 1 & -0.50000 \\ 0 & -0.33333 & 0.33333 \end{bmatrix}$$

Iteration yields the same modal column previously obtained.

Modal Column from Characteristic Equation. In the two methods described earlier, the frequency is determined either after the modal column or simultaneously with it. It is also possible first to determine the frequency and then the corresponding mode. This is done by solving the characteristic equation. The transforms of Equations 8-1 are

$$\begin{aligned}
&\left(s^2 + \frac{k_1 + k_2}{m_1}\right) X_1 && -\frac{k_2}{m_1} X_2 && 0X_3 && = \frac{sx_{1_0} + \dot{x}_{1_0}}{m_1} \\
&-\frac{k_2}{m_2} X_1 && \left(s^2 + \frac{k_2 + k_3}{m_2}\right) X_2 && -\frac{k_3}{m_2} X_3 && = \frac{sx_{2_0} + \dot{x}_{2_0}}{m_2} \\
&0X_1 && -\frac{k_3}{m_3} X_2 && \left(s^2 + \frac{k_3}{m_3}\right) X_3 && = \frac{sx_{3_0} + \dot{x}_{3_0}}{m_3}
\end{aligned} \tag{8-17}$$

The algebraic solution for any of the variables would involve a polynomial in the numerator and a polynomial in the denominator, both obtained from determinants. The factors of the polynomial in the denominator are of fundamental importance in the inverse transform, which is the description of the motion in the time domain. These factors can be found from setting the denominator equal to zero, which is the characteristic equation.

$$\begin{vmatrix}
\left(s^2 + \frac{k_1 + k_2}{m_1}\right) & -\frac{k_2}{m_1} & 0 \\
-\frac{k_2}{m_2} & \left(s^2 + \frac{k_2 + k_3}{m_2}\right) & -\frac{k_3}{m_2} \\
0 & -\frac{k_3}{m_3} & \left(s^2 + \frac{k_3}{m_3}\right)
\end{vmatrix} = 0 \tag{8-18}$$

Some such determinant will be involved in any linear vibration problem. The solution of such problems is so important that ways have been devised for solution by digital computer. The determinant may be expanded and the resulting polynomial solved for the values of s^2 which satisfy the equation. These values are the values of $(-\beta^2)$, where the β's are the natural frequencies. Once these are determined, the modal columns may be determined from the matrix equation, Equation 8-4.

Example 8-6. Solve the problem of Example 8-1 by solution of the characteristic equation.

Numerically, the following equation results from the use of Equation 8-17

$$\begin{vmatrix}
(s^2 + 2) & -1 & 0 \\
-\frac{1}{2} & (s^2 + 1) & -\frac{1}{2} \\
0 & -\frac{1}{3} & (s^2 + \frac{1}{3})
\end{vmatrix} = 0$$

The characteristic equation is

$$s^6 + \frac{10}{3}s^4 + \frac{7}{3}s^2 + \frac{1}{6} = 0$$

The roots of this equation are $s^2 = -2.38, -0.869, -0.0805$ determined by synthetic division, since they are all known to be real. (if there had been damping in the problem the roots would either be real or would occur in conjugate complex pairs.)

To obtain the modal column corresponding to the first mode, use $\beta^2 = 0.0805$

$$\{A\} = 0.0805[U]\{A\}$$

or

$$A_1 = 0.0805(1A_1 + 2A_2 + 3A_3)$$

$$A_2 = 0.0805(1A_1 + 4A_2 + 6A_3)$$

$$A_3 = 0.0805(1A_1 + 4A_2 + 9A_3)$$

These can be expressed in ratios as

$$0.9195\frac{A_1}{A_3} - 0.1610\frac{A_2}{A_3} = 0.2415$$

$$-0.0805\frac{A_1}{A_3} + 0.678\frac{A_2}{A_3} = 0.4830$$

$$-0.0805\frac{A_1}{A_3} - 0.322\frac{A_2}{A_3} = -0.276$$

Any two of these equations can be used to solve for A_1/A_3 and A_2/A_3, and these results substituted into the third equation as an accuracy check. In this instance $A_1/A_3 = 0.3952$ and $A_2/A_3 = 0.7586$ satisfy the equations, so the modal column is $\{0.3952 \quad 0.7586 \quad 1.0000\}$, as was determined in Example 8-5. If the other values of β^2 were used, similar equations would generate the other two modal columns.

8.5 Effect of Light Damping

Several methods have been described for determining the natural frequencies and normal modes of a conservative system of several degrees of freedom. If the actual damping in a system is small, these methods are satisfactory for damped systems too. For heavily damped systems a somewhat different procedure is required. One such procedure is described in Chapter 9, but first a very short example illustrating one way of estimating the effect of small amounts of damping is now given.

Example 8-7. In the problem of the last several examples (Fig. 7-1) suppose that a damper with a constant of 0.1 exists between the wall and the first mass and another of 0.2 has its terminals connected to the first and third mass. Estimate the effect of these dampers on the motion.

Assuming that this amount of damping is small, the undamped frequencies and mode shapes can be found as in the previous examples. Now consider the first mode (lowest frequency mode), and the corresponding generalized coordinate, y_1. The generalized mass for this coordinate could be considered as the amount of mass which would possess the same kinetic energy when in motion with the velocity $\dot{y}_1$ as the actual masses with their actual velocities possess. Thus, if the generalized mass is designated as M_1, and if the coordinate y_1 is chosen such that $x_1 = 0.395y_1$, $x_2 = 0.759y_1$, $x_3 = 1y_1$ (the first mode), then the kinetic energy with $m_1 = 1$, $m_2 = 2$, $m_3 = 3$ is

$$\frac{1}{2}m_1\dot{y}_1^2 = \frac{1}{2}m_1\dot{x}_1^2 + \frac{1}{2}m_2\dot{x}_2^2 + \frac{1}{2}m_3\dot{x}_3^2$$

$$\frac{1}{2}m_1\dot{y}_1^2 = \frac{1}{2}(1)(0.395\dot{y}_1)^2 + \frac{1}{2}(2)(0.759\dot{y}_1)^2 + \frac{1}{2}(3)(1.000\dot{y}_1)^2$$

so that the generalized mass is

$$M_1 = 4.31$$

Similarly, the corresponding generalized spring constant, K_1 could be obtained by setting the potential energies equal.

$$\frac{1}{2}K_1y_1^2 = \frac{1}{2}k_1x_1^2 + \frac{1}{2}k_2(x_2 - x_1)^2 + \frac{1}{2}k_3(x_3 - x_2)^2$$

$$= \frac{1}{2}(1)(0.395y_1)^2 + \frac{1}{2}(1)(0.159y_1 - 0.395y_1)^2 + \frac{1}{2}(1)(1y_1 - 0.759y_1)^2$$

$$K_1 = 0.348$$

Notice that $\beta_1^2 = K_1/M_1 = 0.0806$, the correct value of the frequency. A generalized damper, C_1 could be defined which would produce the same energy dissipation at the velocity $\dot{y}_1$, as the actual dampers do at their actual velocities in this mode. This assumes that the coupling between modes which may occur as a result of the light damping can be neglected. In this instance the velocity across the second damper's terminals is $(\dot{x}_3 - \dot{x}_1)$, and consequently,

$$C_1\dot{y}_1^2 = C_1\dot{x}_1^2 + C_2(\dot{x}_3 - \dot{x}_1)^2$$

$$C_1\dot{y}_1^2 = 0.1(0.395\dot{y}_1)^2 + 0.2(1\dot{y}_1 - 0.395\dot{y}_1)^2$$

$$C_1 = 0.0888$$

It is apparent that as far as this mode is concerned the problem can be approximated by the single-degree-of-freedom problem indicated in Fig. 8-2.

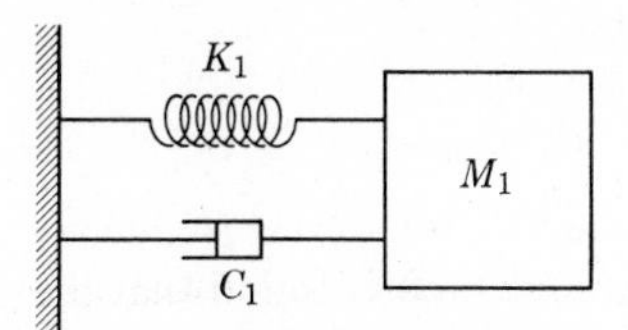

Fig. 8-2

The damping factor for this mode is

$$\zeta_1 = \frac{C_1}{2\sqrt{M_1K_1}} = 0.0362$$

or 3.62% of critical. A similar analysis for the other two modes would show 7.24% critical for the second mode and 6.82% for the third. These are all low enough so that the assumption of small damping is probably satisfactory. These modes would all die out at the corresponding rates.

8.6 Excitation of the Normal Modes

The amount of each mode present in the motion is often of interest. This would depend on the initial conditions. The amount of each mode present could be determined as follows, using $[N]$ as the modal column matrices.

$$\{x\} = [N]\{y\} \qquad \text{and} \quad \{\dot{x}\} = [N]\{\dot{y}\}$$

$$\{y\} = [N]^{-1}\{x\} \qquad \text{and} \quad \{\dot{y}\} = [N]^{-1}\{\dot{x}\}$$

If the initial values of x and $\dot{x}$ are known, the corresponding initial values of the generalized coordinates and velocities can be easily determined, as explained in Example 8-8.

Example 8-8. For the problem of the previous examples, determine the amount of each mode initially present if a static force of 1 unit is applied to m_3 and then released with zero initial velocity.

The initial static deflections are $x_1 = 1$, $x_2 = 2$, $x_3 = 3$. The initial amplitudes of the three normal coordinates will be $\{y\} = [N]^{-1}\{x\}$. If the modal columns are defined according to Example 8-1, the inverse matrix is already available for that example.

$$[N] = \begin{bmatrix} 0.450 & 1.2400 & 0.329 \\ 0.506 & -0.477 & 0.636 \\ -0.315 & 0.0778 & 0.840 \end{bmatrix} \qquad [N]^{-1} = \begin{bmatrix} 0.444 & 1.002 & -0.933 \\ 0.615 & -0.474 & 0.1183 \\ 0.1090 & 0.419 & 0.830 \end{bmatrix}$$

Since these columns are not arranged in the order of frequency, it is necessary to be careful in interpreting the results. This could be accounted for by redefining the matrix as follows,

$$x_1 = 0.450y_2 + 1.240y_3 + 0.329y_1$$

$$x_2 = 0.506y_2 - 0.477y_3 + 0.636y_1$$

$$x_3 = -0.315y_2 + 0.0778y_3 + 0.840y_1$$

$$\{y\} = \begin{Bmatrix} y_2 \\ y_3 \\ y_1 \end{Bmatrix} = [N]^{-1} \begin{Bmatrix} x_1 \\ x_2 \\ x_3 \end{Bmatrix}$$

$$y_2 = 0.444x_1 + 1.002x_2 - 0.933x_3$$

$$y_3 = 0.615x_1 - 0.474x_2 + 0.1183x_3$$

$$y_1 = 0.1090x_1 + 0.419x_2 + 0.830x_3$$

Now the subscripts of the y's have their customary significance of 1 for lowest frequency mode, 2 for next higher, etc. Substituting the values of x_1, x_2, and x_3, it is found that the initial values of the normal coordinates are

$$y_1 = 3.437 \qquad y_2 = -0.351 \qquad y_3 = 0.0219$$

This means that the motion will consist of these simultaneous oscillations at the three natural frequencies, the amplitudes of the three masses in the first mode being $A_1 = 3.437 \times 0.329$, $A_2 = 3.437 \times 0.636$, $A_3 = 3.437 \times 0.840$. In the second mode the amplitudes of the three masses are 0.351×0.450, 0.351×0.506, and 0.351×0.315 respectively, and so on for the third mode.

It must also be remembered that these normal coordinates are defined according to the matrix $[N]$. If the modal columns were to be defined with unity for x_3 as in some of the examples, the corresponding initial values of normal coordinates would be changed by the ratios of the x_3's.

$$y_1 = 0.840(3.437) = 2.88$$

$$y_2 = -0.315(-0.351) = 0.1107$$

$$y_3 = 0.0778(0.0219) = 0.001718$$

The particular initial condition chosen excites primarily the first mode. Whatever damping there might be in the system would suppress the higher modes in a shorter time than the first mode, and since they also start with smaller values, only the first mode of vibration would be significant after a short time.

8.7 Additional Comments on Matrix Methods

Matrix formulation of the dynamic equations for conservative systems and solution of these equations by matrix means have been discussed. Implicit in these methods are certain properties of conservative, linear systems which are now discussed.

Positive Definite Quadratic Form. Consider the kinetic and potential energy functions used in the Lagrange equations for a typical system, say the system of Fig. 8-1.

$$T = \frac{1}{2} m_1 \dot{x}_1^2 + \frac{1}{2} m_2 \dot{x}_2^2 + \frac{1}{2} m_3 \dot{x}_3^2$$

$$V = \frac{1}{2} k_1 x_1^2 + \frac{1}{2} k_2 (x_2 - x_1)^2 + \frac{1}{2} k_3 (x_3 - x_2)^2$$

$$= \frac{1}{2} (k_1 + k_2) x_1^2 - k_2 x_1 x_2 + \frac{1}{2} (k_2 + k_3) x_2^2 - k_3 x_2 x_3 + \frac{1}{2} k_3 x_3^2$$

The last form of V shows that the potential energy function is composed of a set of terms which typically are of the form $cx_i x_j$, and are in fact obtained by expanding and summing expressions such as $(c_a x_i + c_b x_j)^2$, where c_a and c_b may be positive or negative real constants, but the expression $(c_a x_i + c_b x_j)^2$ obviously must be positive and real, regardless of the values of c_a, c_b, x_i, or x_j. An expression formed of the sum of terms, all of which are proportional to products of two of the variables, is said to be of "quadratic form." If the expression is zero or positive for any and all combinations of the variables (except identically zero values of the variables), the expression is said to be "positive," or "positive semidefinite." If the expression *must* be greater than zero, it is "positive definite." Similar definitions for "negative," "negative semidefinite," and "negative definite" also apply for an expression whose value may be, or is definitely, less than zero.

According to these definitions, it is clear that the potential energy function, v, for the system of Fig. 8-1, is of positive-definite, quadratic form, since it must always be positive (except when all the coordinates are identically zero, but this configuration is excluded from the definition). By inspection of the expanded form of V it is apparent that it is not necessary for all of the individual terms in the expression to be positive; only the sum of all of them must be positive. However, all of the individual terms of the form cx_i^2 must be positive. Otherwise, for example, if there were a term such as $-2x_1^2$ in the expression for V, it would be possible for V to have a negative value if all the other variables except x_1 were zero and x_1 were nonzero.

It is possible to express the potential energy function as the product of three matrices, as follows:

$$V = [x_1 \; x_2 \; x_3] \begin{bmatrix} \frac{1}{2}(k_1 + k_2) & -\frac{1}{2} k_2 & 0 \\ -\frac{1}{2} k_2 & \frac{1}{2}(k_2 + k_3) & -\frac{1}{2} k_3 \\ 0 & -\frac{1}{2} k_3 & -\frac{1}{2} k_3 \end{bmatrix} \begin{Bmatrix} x_1 \\ x_2 \\ x_3 \end{Bmatrix}$$

or, in general,

$$V = \frac{1}{2}\{\tilde{x}\}[K]\{x\} \tag{8-19}$$

Similarly, any quadratic form could be so expressed, and the square matrix between the row and column coordinate matrices is called the matrix of the quadratic form. If this matrix is singular (determinant of the matrix = 0), the quadratic form is said to be singular. It is not sufficient that the matrix be nonsingular if the quadratic form is to be either positive or negative.

A sufficient condition for insuring that a quadratic form is positive-definite is that all of the determinants of successively larger square submatrices of the matrix, shown in Equation 8-20, shall be positive. For this example, for all positive values of the spring constants,

$$\left.\begin{array}{ll}
\left|\frac{1}{2}(k_1 + k_2)\right| > 0 & \text{or } K_{11} > 0 \\[2ex]
\begin{vmatrix} \frac{1}{2}(k_1 + k_2) & -\frac{1}{2}k_2 \\ -\frac{1}{2}k_2 & \frac{1}{2}(k_2 + k_3) \end{vmatrix} > 0 & \text{or} \begin{vmatrix} K_{11} & K_{12} \\ K_{21} & K_{22} \end{vmatrix} > 0 \\[2ex]
\begin{vmatrix} \frac{1}{2}(k_1 + k_2) & -\frac{1}{2}k_2 & 0 \\ -\frac{1}{2}k_2 & \frac{1}{2}(k_2 + k_3) & -\frac{1}{2}k_3 \\ 0 & -\frac{1}{2}k_3 & \frac{1}{2}k_3 \end{vmatrix} > 0 & \text{or} \begin{vmatrix} K_{11} & K_{12} & K_{13} \\ K_{21} & K_{22} & K_{23} \\ K_{31} & K_{32} & K_{33} \end{vmatrix} > 0
\end{array}\right\} \tag{8-20}$$

etc.

Accordingly, V is a positive-definite quadratic function of the variables x_1, x_2, and x_3. This was already known, of course, since it is computed from the sum of squares of real numbers. A positive definite quadratic form for the potential energy function insures that the system is statically stable, or tends to return to the equilibrium configuration when displaced, since the displaced configuration has a higher potential energy than the equilibrium configuration. If any of the determinants had been zero, the potential energy function would have been a positive semidefinite function of the coordinates. This corresponds to a neutrally stable system, or one for which there is at least one possible deflection configuration which would not tend to return to the "equilibrium," or reference, configuration, because the potential energy is the same in either configuration. If some of the determinants of Equation 8-20 were negative, the quadratic function would be negative and the system would be unstable. That is, any initial displacement from the "equilibrium," or reference, configuration would increase further, since the potential energy of the displaced configuration is less than that of the reference configuration. Obviously, this could not occur for the system of Fig. 8-1.

The kinetic energy function, T, is also of the quadratic form and also positive-definite. In the particular instance chosen for this illustration, where the matrix of the quadratic form is a diagonal matrix,

$$T \quad [\dot{x}_1 \quad \dot{x}_2 \quad \dot{x}_3] \begin{bmatrix} \frac{1}{2}m_1 & 0 & 0 \\ 0 & \frac{1}{2}m_2 & 0 \\ 0 & 0 & \frac{1}{2}m_3 \end{bmatrix} \begin{Bmatrix} \dot{x}_1 \\ x_2 \\ \dot{x}_3 \end{Bmatrix}$$

but in general, whether $[M]$ is diagonal or not,

$$T = \frac{1}{2}\{\tilde{\dot{x}}\}[M]\{\dot{x}\} \tag{8-21}$$

The fact that $[M]$ in this example is diagonal is a consequence of the selection of coordinates, but even if some other selection of coordinates resulted in a non-diagonal matrix, it would still be the matrix of a positive-definite form since kinetic energy must be positive.

Application of the Lagrange equation to the function $(T - V)$ results in the matrix equation, Equation 8-1; then use of Equation 8-2 leads to the matrix equation, Equation 8-4. It is seen that the inertia matrix used in the matrix formulations of this chapter is the matrix of a positive-definite quadratic form. The stiffness matrix for the examples discussed was also the matrix of a positive-definite quadratic form. However, the possibility exists that this matrix could be the matrix of a positive semidefinite form for some systems in which the "equilibrium," or reference, position is a position of neutral stability. If the reference position were a position of unstable equilibrium, this matrix could even be the matrix of a negative quadratic form, but this is of minor interest. Proofs of the convergence of the matrix iteration techniques used in this chapter are facilitated by the assumption that at least the inertia matrix is the matrix of a positive-definite quadratic form. In the unusual instances where this matrix is singular (and therefore the matrix of a semidefinite form), a different formulation could be made for which the inertia matrix would not be singular.

Matrix Formulation for Generalized Quantities. The generalized quantities discussed in Section 7.7 can also be expressed conveniently in matrix form. Let the matrix $\{x\}$ represent a column matrix (or vector) of ordinary coordinates, perhaps as defined by Fig. 8-1, $\{q\}$ a column matrix (or vector) of generalized coordinates, and $\{y\}$ a column matrix (or vector) of principal coordinates. Equation 8-22 expresses the system dynamic relationships in terms of the ordinary coordinates.

$$[M]\{\ddot{x}\} + [K]\{x\} = \{f\} \tag{8-22}$$

In this equation the matrix $\{f\}$ is a column matrix of forcing functions. For the system of Figure 8-1 the column would be formed from the values of the actual forces on the three masses. Similar relationships exist which describe the system in terms of the general coordinates and the principal coordinates.

$$[M_q]\{\ddot{q}\} + [K_q]\{q\} = \{Q\} \tag{8-23}$$

$$[M_p]\{\ddot{y}\} + [K_p]\{y\} = \{Q_p\} \tag{8-24}$$

In Equation 8-24 both $[M_p]$ and $[K_p]$ should be diagonal matrices, since coupling of the principal coordinates must be avoided. $\{Q\}$ and $\{Q_p\}$ are generalized forces. Transformation relationships between coordinate systems can be expressed by the matrix equations

$$\{x\} = [G]\{q\} \tag{8-25}$$

$$\{x\} = [N]\{y\} \tag{8-26}$$

$[N]$ is a square matrix formed from the solution vectors of the unforced system. That is, the columns $\{x\}$ which satisfy $[M]\{\ddot{x}\} = -[K]\{x\}$ are arrayed as follows:

$$[N] = \begin{bmatrix} N_{11} & N_{12} & \cdots & N_{1j} & \cdots \\ N_{21} & N_{22} & \cdots & N_{2j} & \cdots \\ \cdot & \cdot & \cdot & \cdot & \cdot \\ N_{i1} & N_{i2} & \cdots & N_{ij} & \cdots \end{bmatrix} \tag{8-27}$$

The columns $\begin{Bmatrix} N_{1j} \\ N_{2j} \\ \cdots \\ N_{ij} \\ \cdots \end{Bmatrix}$ are the foregoing solution vectors $\begin{Bmatrix} x_1 \\ x_2 \\ \cdots \\ \dot{x}_i \\ \cdots \end{Bmatrix}$ which satisfy $[M]\{\ddot{x}\} = -[K]\{x\}$ for the various modes.

For the principal coordinate system, substitution of Equation 8-26 in Equation 8-22 yields

$$[M][N]\{\ddot{y}\} + [K][N]\{y\} = \{f\} \tag{8-28}$$

It might be thought that the matrices $[M][N]$ and $[K][N]$ are the corresponding principal matrices $[M_p]$ and $[K_p]$ of Equatoin 8-26. However, the forcing function matrix $\{f\}$ is not the matrix of generalized forces $\{Q_p\}$ of Equation 8-24, and the products $[M][N]$ and $[K][N]$ are not necessarily diagonal matrices. Conversion of Equation 8-28 to Equation 8-24 is accomplished by premultiplying Equation 8-28 by the transpose of $[N]$, as will be shown subsequently, so that

$$[\tilde{N}][M][N]\{\ddot{y}\} + [\tilde{N}][K][N]\{y\} = [\tilde{N}]\{f\}$$

Similarly, for generalized coordinates,

$$[\tilde{G}][M][G]\{\ddot{q}\} + [\tilde{G}][K][G]\{q\} = [\tilde{G}]\{f\}$$

Comparison of these equations with Equation 8-23 and 8-24 shows that

$$\left.\begin{aligned} [M_q] &= [\tilde{G}][M][G] \\ [K_q] &= [\tilde{G}][K][G] \end{aligned}\right\} \tag{8-29}$$

$$\left.\begin{aligned} [M_p] &= [\tilde{N}][M][N] \\ [K_p] &= [\tilde{N}][K][N] \end{aligned}\right\} \tag{8-30}$$

That premultiplication of Equation 8-28 by $[\tilde{N}]$ will accomplish the desired diagonalization can be shown by consideration of the potential and kinetic energies, as follows.

As was pointed out earlier (Equation 8-19) the total potential energy, V, is in general expressed by

$$V = \frac{1}{2}\{\tilde{x}\}[K]\{x\}$$

Substituting $\{x\} = [N]\{y\}$ and $\{\tilde{x}\} = \{\tilde{y}\}[\tilde{N}]$ from Equation 8-26,

$$V = \frac{1}{2}\{\tilde{y}\}[\tilde{N}][K][N]\{y\} \tag{8-31}$$

The potential energy in terms of principal coordinates is also

$$V = \frac{1}{2}(K_{p_{11}}y_1^2 + K_{p_{22}}y_2^2 + \cdots + K_{p_{jj}}y_j^2 + \cdots) \tag{8-32}$$

where obviously $K_{p_{jj}}$ must be the generalized spring constant for the jth mode, since all of the potential energy attributable to the deflection y_j is represented by the single term $\frac{1}{2}K_{p_{jj}}y_j^2$. All cross-product terms in Equation 8-32 are zero; that is, such terms as $K_{p_{21}}y_1y_2$ or $K_{p_{12}}y_1y_2$ are zero because the off-diagonal elements of $[K_p]$ are zero.

Orthogonality Relationships. If Equation 8-31 is expanded and studied it will be seen that this requirement is equivalent to

$$\{\tilde{N}_i\}[K]\{N_j\} = 0 \tag{8-33}$$

where $\{N_i\}$ and $\{N_j\}$ are two different modal columns.

Equation 8-33 expresses in matrix form an orthogonality relationship for normal modes; that is, normal modes are not spring coupled. A similar argument using kinetic energy results in

$$\{\tilde{N}_i\}[M]\{N_j\} = 0 \tag{8-34}$$

stating that normal modes are not inertia coupled.

Equations 8-33 and 8-34 can also be verified by writing the general matrix equation $[K]\{x\} = \beta^2[M]\{x\}$ for two normal modes, thus:

$$[K]\{N\}_i = \beta_i^2[M]\{N\}_i, \quad \text{and} \quad \{\tilde{N}\}_j[K]\{N\}_i = \beta_i^2\{\tilde{N}\}_j[M]\{N\}_i$$

$$[K]\{N\}_j = \beta_j^2[M]\{N\}_j, \quad \text{and} \quad \{\tilde{N}\}_i[K]\{N\}_j = \beta_j^2\{\tilde{N}\}_i[M]\{N\}_j$$

Since the transpose of the product of three matrices is the product of the individual transposes in reverse order (reversal rule), the first of these equations could be transposed to give

$$\{\tilde{N}\}_i[\tilde{K}]\{N\}_j = \beta_i^2\{N\}_i[\tilde{M}]\{N\}_j$$

and since $[K]$ and $[M]$ may be considered to be symmetrical (or could have been made symmetrical by judicious manipulations of the equations), $[\tilde{K}] = [K]$ and $[\tilde{M}] = [M]$. This transposed equation and the second equation can then be combined to obtain

$$(\beta_i^2 - \beta_j^2)\{\tilde{N}\}_i[M]\{N\}_j = \{\tilde{N}\}_i[K]\{N\}_j(1 - 1) = 0$$

Since $\beta_i^2 \neq \beta_j^2$, Equation 8-34 results, and then since $\beta_j^2 \neq 0$, Equation 8-33 develops.

Generalized Spring and Mass for Principal Coordinates. Using Equation 8-33 in Equation 8-31 it is possible to verify that all potential energy terms attributable to principal coordinate y_j are accounted for by the matrix multiplication

$$\frac{1}{2}\{\tilde{N}_j\}[K]\{N_j\}y_j^2$$

Comparison of this expression with Equation 8-32 shows that the generalized spring constant corresponding to a principal coordinate can be computed from

$$K_{p_j} = \{\tilde{N}_j\}[K]\{N_j\} \tag{8-35}$$

A similar argument dealing with the kinetic energy would show that the generalized mass for a principal coordinate can be computed from

$$M_{p_j} = \{\tilde{N}_j\}[M]\{N_j\} \tag{8-36}$$

Frequently the inertia matrix in the ordinary coordinate system is a diagonal matrix, in which instance Equation 8-36 simplifies to

$$M_{p_j} = \sum_i M_{ii}N_{ij}^2 \tag{8-37}$$

It is apparent from Equations 8-35 and 8-36 that at least the left side of Equation 8-24 will result from premultiplying Equation 8-28 by the transpose of $[\tilde{N}]$.

$$[\tilde{N}][M][N]\{\ddot{y}\} + [\tilde{N}][K][N]\{y\} = [\tilde{N}]\{f\} \tag{8-38}$$

If the right side of this equation is also the column of generalized forces corresponding to the principal coordinates, $\{y\}$, then Equation 8-24 is satisfactory for use with the inertia and stiffness matrices computed from Equation 8-30.

Generalized Force. Generalized forces associated with generalized coordinates and also with principal coordinates can be calculated as follows. The work done by the external forces applied in the positive direction of the ordinary coordinates during small displacements is $\{\widetilde{dx}\}\{f\}$ if $\{f\}$ is a column matrix of forcing functions. In the generalized coordinate system the work is $\{\widetilde{dq}\}\{Q\}$. Substitution from Equation 8-25 for $\{\widetilde{dx}\} = \{\widetilde{dq}\}[G]$ results in

$$\{\widetilde{dq}\}[\tilde{G}]\{f\} = \{\widetilde{dq}\}\{Q\} = Q_1\,dq_1 + Q_2\,dq_2 + \cdots + Q_j\,dq_j + \cdots$$

Therefore, comparison on each side of this equation of the work attributable to a change dq_j shows that the generalized force for a generalized coordinate may be calculated from

$$Q_j = \{\tilde{G}_j\}\{f\} \tag{8-39}$$

If the generalized coordinates are also principal coordinates, there is no difference in the development and

$$Q_{p_j} = \{\tilde{N}_j\}\{f\} \tag{8-40}$$

This completes the conversion of Equation 8-28 to 8-24.

By analogy, Equation 8-23 may be written for generalized coordinates which are not principal coordinates, the only difference being that the matrices $[M_q]$ and $[K_q]$ from Equation 8-29 are not necessarily diagonal, and there are no orthogonality relationships similar to Equations 8-33 and 8-34. Since $[M_q]$ and $[K_q]$ are not necessarily diagonal, generalized masses and spring constants computed by equations of the same form as Equation 8-35 and 8-36 do not have the same significance as when the generalized coordinates are also principal coordinates. (See Example 8-9).

Since Equation 8-24 is applicable for static as well as dynamic conditions, and since $[K_p]$ is a diagonal matrix, it is clear that stiffness and flexibility matrices relating principal coordinates and their corresponding generalized forces are diagonal matrices. This was implicit in the discussion, but is worth noting explicitly.

Example 8-9. Investigate generalized quantities for the first mode for Examples 8-1 and 8-5.

These two examples both dealt with the same physical system but were normalized differently. For Example 8-1 the transformation between ordinary coordinates and principal coordinates is defined by

$$\{x\} = [N]\{y\} \text{ where } [N] = \begin{bmatrix} 0.329 & -0.450 & 1.240 \\ 0.636 & -0.506 & -0.477 \\ 0.840 & 0.315 & 0.0778 \end{bmatrix}$$

(The columns have been rearranged so that the first column corresponds to the first mode, the second column to the second mode, and the third column to the third mode.) From Equations 8-35 and 8-36, for the first mode,

$$K_{p_1} = [0.329 \quad 0.636 \quad 0.840] \begin{bmatrix} 2 & -1 & 0 \\ -1 & 2 & -1 \\ 0 & -1 & 1 \end{bmatrix} \begin{Bmatrix} 0.329 \\ 0.636 \\ 0.840 \end{Bmatrix} = 0.244$$

$$M_{p_1} = [0.329 \quad 0.636 \quad 0.840] \begin{bmatrix} 1 & 0 & 0 \\ 0 & 2 & 0 \\ 0 & 0 & 3 \end{bmatrix} \begin{Bmatrix} 0.329 \\ 0.636 \\ 0.840 \end{Bmatrix} = 3.05$$

from which $\beta_1 = \sqrt{K_{p_1}/M_{p_1}} = 0.283$. Note that for the first two normal modes the orthogonality relationships, Equations 8-33 and 8-34, are verified as follows.

$$\{\tilde{N}_1\}[K]\{N_2\} = [0.329 \quad 0.636 \quad 0.840] \begin{bmatrix} 2 & -1 & 0 \\ -1 & 2 & -1 \\ 0 & -1 & 1 \end{bmatrix} \begin{Bmatrix} -0.450 \\ -0.506 \\ 0.315 \end{Bmatrix} = 0$$

$$\{\tilde{N}_1\}[M]\{N_2\} = [0.329 \quad 0.636 \quad 0.840] \begin{bmatrix} 1 & 0 & 0 \\ 0 & 2 & 0 \\ 0 & 0 & 3 \end{bmatrix} \begin{Bmatrix} -0.450 \\ -0.506 \\ 0.315 \end{Bmatrix} = 0$$

If a force of 2 lb were applied to the second mass, the generalized force in Mode 1, calculated with Equation 8-40, is

$$Q_{p_1} = [0.329 \quad 0.636 \quad 0.840] \begin{Bmatrix} 0 \\ 2 \\ 0 \end{Bmatrix} = 1.272 \text{ lb}$$

If this were a suddenly applied, constant force, the response of principal coordinate y_1 would be

$$y_1 = \frac{Q_{p_1}}{K_{p_1}}(1 - \cos \beta_1 t) = 5.21(1 - \cos 0.283t)$$

Corresponding to this coordinate, the three masses move as follows; (from $\{x\} \doteq [N]\{y\}$)

$$x_1 = 5.21 \times 0.329(1 - \cos 0.283t) = 1.715(1 - \cos 0.283t)$$

$$x_2 = 5.21 \times 0.636(1 - \cos 0.283t) = 3.32(1 - \cos 0.283t)$$

$$x_3 = 5.21 \times 0.840(1 - \cos 0.283t) = 4.38(1 - \cos 0.283t)$$

The other two modes are similarly excited, so that the complete response of the three masses is

$$x_1 = 2.0 - 1.715 \cos 0.283t - 0.518 \cos 0.935t + 0.248 \cos 1.54t$$

$$x_2 = 4.0 - 3.32 \cos 0.283t - 0.582 \cos 0.935t - 0.0955 \cos 1.54t$$

$$x_3 = 4.0 - 4.38 \cos 0.283t + 0.362 \cos 0.935t + 0.0155 \cos 1.54t$$

For Example 8-5 a different normalization causes the first mode solution vector to be

$$\begin{Bmatrix} 0.395 \\ 0.759 \\ 1.000 \end{Bmatrix}$$

whence

$$Q_{p_1} = 1.518$$

$$K_{p_1} = 0.347$$

$$M_{p_1} = 4.31$$

$$\beta_1 = \sqrt{\frac{0.347}{4.31}} = 0.284$$

Note that the value of the generalized quantities are different for different normalizations, but, of course, the frequency remains the same, and responses x_1, x_2 and x_3 also would not change from the values computed with the other normalization.

If the generalized coordinates were not principal coordinates, a single equivalent spring or mass for each mode which would represent all the potential or kinetic energy associated with that mode could not be determined. However, an illustration may be useful in clarifying concepts. Consider the same physical setup, but let ordinary coordinates be defined as the amount by which each spring stretches rather than the deflection of each mass from a fixed equilibrium position. In terms of these coordinates, an analysis by Lagrange equations leads to matrix equations, as follows.

$$T = \frac{1}{2} M_1\dot{x}_1^2 + \frac{1}{2} M_2(\dot{x}_1 + \dot{x}_2)^2 + \frac{1}{2} M_3(\dot{x}_1 + \dot{x}_2 + \dot{x}_3)^2$$

$$V = \frac{1}{2} k_1x_1^2 + \frac{1}{2} k_2x_2^2 + \frac{1}{2} k_3x_3^2$$

Let forces on the three masses be f_a, f_b, and f_c. The rate of work is then $f_a\dot{x}_1 + f_b(\dot{x}_1 + \dot{x}_2) + f_c(\dot{x}_1 + \dot{x}_2 + \dot{x}_3)$, and three equations obtained from Lagrange's equation reduce to the following matrix equation.

$$[M]\{\ddot{x}\} + [K]\{x\} = \{Q\}$$

where

$$[M] = \begin{bmatrix} 6 & 5 & 3 \\ 5 & 5 & 3 \\ 3 & 3 & 3 \end{bmatrix} \quad [K] = \begin{bmatrix} 1 & 0 & 0 \\ 0 & 1 & 0 \\ 0 & 0 & 1 \end{bmatrix} \quad \{Q\} = \begin{Bmatrix} (f_a + f_b + f_c) \\ (f_b + f_c) \\ f_c \end{Bmatrix} = \begin{Bmatrix} Q_1 \\ Q_2 \\ Q_3 \end{Bmatrix}$$

Note that with these coordinates Q_1, Q_2, and Q_3 are not simply individual forces, but various combinations of individual forces.

Now let "generalized" coordinates, $\{q\}$, be defined which prescribe the deflection of each mass from its equilibrium position. (These are the same as the "ordinary" coordinates as used heretofore in this example, except that now they are designated as $\{q\}$.) The matrix transformation between these coordinate systems is (since $x_1 = q_1$, $x_2 = q_2 - q_1$, $x_3 = q_3 - q_2$)

$$\{x\} = [G]\{q\} \qquad \text{where} \quad [G] = \begin{bmatrix} 1 & 0 & 0 \\ -1 & 1 & 0 \\ 0 & -1 & 1 \end{bmatrix}$$

Use of Equations 8-29 and 8-39 results in

$$[M_q]\{\ddot{q}\} + [K_q]\{q\} = \{f\}$$

where

$$[M_q] = \begin{bmatrix} 1 & 0 & 0 \\ 0 & 2 & 0 \\ 0 & 0 & 3 \end{bmatrix} \qquad [K_q] = \begin{bmatrix} 2 & -1 & 0 \\ -1 & 2 & -1 \\ 0 & -1 & 1 \end{bmatrix} \qquad \{f\} = \begin{Bmatrix} Q_1 - Q_2 \\ Q_2 - Q_3 \\ f_3 \end{Bmatrix} = \begin{Bmatrix} f_a \\ f_b \\ f_c \end{Bmatrix}$$

These are the expected matrices, which are the same as those of Equation 8-1 but with forces included. No simplification is observed from this transformation, of course, since the new coordinates are not principal coordinates and are still coupled.

Elimination of Lower Modes in Matrix Iteration Procedure. The procedure for eliminating a mode using the Duncan and Collar iteration procedure (Example 8-5) can be understood with the help of the orthogonality relationship (Equation 8-34). The deflected configuration of a system is determined by the values of all the coordinates. If all of the principal coordinates are nonzero, then Equation 8-26 states that the values of the ordinary coordinates may be obtained from

$$\{x\} = \{N_1\}y_1 + \{N_2\}y_2 + \{N_3\}y_3 + \cdots$$

The column $\{x\}$ is seen to be composed of various combinations of the modal columns, and it is clear that the multiplication $\{\tilde{N}_1\}[M]\{x\}$ would not be zero because part of $\{x\}$ is $\{\tilde{N}_1\}y_1$ and $\{\tilde{N}_1\}[M]\{N_1\} \neq 0$. However, principal coordinate y_1 can be arbitrarily set equal to zero by requiring that the multiplication $\{\tilde{N}_1\}[M]\{x\} = 0$, since this multiplication is then some combination of $\{\tilde{N}_1\}[M]\{N_2\}$, $\{\tilde{N}_1\}[M]\{N_3\}$, etc. and these are zero according to Equation 8-34. Therefore, if $\{\tilde{N}_1\}[M]\{x\} = 0$, the coordinates $\{x\}$ must be some combination of the other modal columns, $\{N_2\}$, $\{N_3\}$, etc. but containing none of column $\{N_1\}$. That is, the coordinates are constrained in such manner that the first mode is eliminated.

The first equation of $[S]$ of Example 8-5 expresses this relationship. That is, if $[B] = \{\tilde{N}_1\}[M]$, then $[B]\{x\} = 0$ results in

$$B_1x_1 + B_2x_2 + \cdots = 0$$

or

$$x_1 = -\frac{B_1}{B_1}x_2 - \frac{B_3}{B_1}x_3 - \cdots$$

If then $x_2 = x_2$, $x_3 = x_3$, etc., the relationship $\{x\} = [S]\{x\}$ expresses the restriction that the first mode shall not be a component of $\{x\}$. When this column $\{x\}$ is used on the right side of the equation $\{x\} = \beta^2[U]\{x\}$, the result is $\{x\} = \beta^2[U][S]\{x\}$ and the new dynamic matrix is $[U]_2 = [U][S]$ as indicated in Example 8-5.

CHAPTER 9

Multiple Degree Systems with Significant Damping

9.1 The Characteristic Equation

A method of estimating the effect of light damping was described in Example 8-7. If the damping is significant, the coupling between the normal undamped modes cannot be neglected. The damped normal modes may differ appreciably from the undamped modes. A satisfactory way to determine the natural modes and frequencies for a heavily damped system (or for negatively damped systems) is to make use of the characteristic equation, as in Section 8.4, Example 8-6. However, the damping causes certain complications which require numerical techniques different from those of Example 8-6.

The transformed equations of motion will be similar to Equations 8-17, but for more generality can be written in the following form.

$$\begin{aligned}
&(A_{11} + B_{11}s + C_{11}s^2)X_1 + (A_{12} + B_{12}s + C_{12}s^2)X_2 + \cdots \\
&\qquad + (A_{1m} + B_{1m}s + C_{1m}s^2)X_m = F_1(s) \\
&(A_{21} + B_{21}s + C_{21}s^2)X_1 + (A_{22} + B_{22}s + C_{22}s^2)X_2 + \cdots \\
&\qquad + (A_{2m} + B_{2m}s + C_{2m}s^2)X_m = F_2(s) \qquad (9\text{-}1) \\
&\cdots\cdots\cdots\cdots\cdots\cdots\cdots\cdots \\
&(A_{m1} + B_{m1}s + C_{m1}s^2)X_1 + (A_{m2} + B_{m2}s + C_{m2}s^2)X_2 + \cdots \\
&\qquad + (A_{mm} + B_{mm}s + C_{mm}s^2)X_m = F_m(s)
\end{aligned}$$

The functions on the right in these equations would result from forcing functions or initial conditions or both. Any of the transforms, X_1, X_2, ... X_m, could be obtained from the ratio of two determinants, the denominator being the same for any of the variables. This denominator is a polynomial, the expansion of the following determinant.

$$\begin{vmatrix} (A_{11} + B_{11}s + C_{11}s^2)(A_{12} + B_{12}s + C_{12}s^2)\cdots(A_{1m} + B_{1m}s + C_{1m}s^2) \\ (A_{21} + B_{21}s + C_{21}s^2)(A_{22} + B_{22}s + C_{22}s^2)\cdots(A_{2m} + B_{2m}s + C_{2m}s^2) \\ \cdot\quad\cdot\quad\cdot\quad\cdot\quad\cdot\quad\cdot\quad\cdot\quad\cdot\quad\cdot\quad\cdot\quad\cdot\quad\cdot \\ (A_{m1} + B_{m1}s + C_{m1}s^2)(A_{m2} + B_{m2}s + C_{m2}s^2)\cdots(A_{mm} + B_{mm}s + C_{mm}s^2) \end{vmatrix} \tag{9-2}$$

In order to apply the methods of Appendix 1 to the problem of determining the inverse transforms of $X_1, X_2, \ldots X_m$, it is necessary for this polynomial to be in factored form. The polynomial set equal to zero is the characteristic equation and the roots of the characteristic equation are the "eigenvalues" or characteristic values of s. The negatives of the roots are used to form the required factors of the polynomial.

The efficient expansion by digital computer of a high order determinant of quadratics of the form shown in Equation 9-2 is an exercise in logic. A program for accomplishing this is given in Reference 1. It is worth noting that this can be useful in the solution of any set of simultaneous linear differential equations, even with higher order elements than the quadratics of Equations 9-1, since additional variables can be introduced to reduce the order of the elements and increase the number of equations. For example, the two simultaneous differential equations represented by the transformed equations,

$$(s^4 + 2s^3 + s + 1)X + (s^3 + 3)Y = 0$$

$$(s^2 - 1)X + (s^3 + s + 1)Y = 0$$

could be changed by introducing two more variables $u = d^2x/dt^2$ and $v = d^2y/dt^2$ to the transformed set of four second order equations shown below.

$$(s + 1)X + 3Y + (s^2 + 2s)U + sV = 0$$

$$(s^2 - 1)X + (s + 1)Y + 0U + s^2V = 0$$

$$s^2X + 0Y - 1U + 0V = 0$$

$$0X + s^2Y + 0U - 1V = 0$$

For the vibration problem under study, however, the quadratic elements of Equations 9-1 and 9-2 are sufficient without modification. It is entirely possible that many of the coefficients of 9-2 would be zero, but the degree of the polynomial would not exceed $2m$ in any event. When damping is present, the odd powers of s in the characteristic equation will not be absent (as they were in Example 8-6 for zero damping). The roots of the polynomial will not be pure imaginaries. It is necessary to have a method for solving the general polynomial equation of order n, where $n \leqq 2m$,

$$s^n + a_1s^{n-1} + \cdots + a_{n-1}s + a_n = 0 \tag{9-3}$$

For convenience and also so that the subscripts will have the same values as the exponents, the equation will be divided through by a_n (if it should happen that $a_n = 0$, then an s would simply be factored out and the constants redefined). Therefore, the equation which is considered is the following

$$1 + C_1s + C_2s^2 + \cdots + C_{n-1}s^{n-1} + C_ns^n = 0 \tag{9-4}$$

If this equation is a quadratic there is no problem in finding its roots. If it is a cubic there must be one real root which can easily be found by trial and error or by synthetic division, and after it is found it can be divided out so that only the quadratic is left. If the characteristic equation is a quartic, it may be that all the roots are complex, in which case trial and error becomes a tedious process, since both the real and imaginary parts of the root must be assumed. For quintics and all odd-power polynomials there is at least one real root which can be found by trial and error or by synthetic division, after which a polynomial of even degree remains to be solved. Accordingly, a method for solution of a quartic and then higher polynomials of even degree will be developed.

9.2 Quadratic Factors of a Quartic

The procedure is essentially one of determining quadratic factors. Thus, a quartic can be considered as the product of two quadratics. This is true regardless of whether the roots are real or complex, of course, and consequently this method applies equally well to the determination of real roots. If the product of two quadratics is set equal to the quartic,

$$(1 + A_1 s + A_2 s^2)(1 + B_1 s + B_2 s^2) = 1 + C_1 s + C_2 s^2 + C_2 s^3 + C_4 s^4$$

$$1 + (A_1 + B_1)s + (A_2 + A_1 B_1 + B_2)s^2 + (A_1 B_2 + A_2 B_1)s^3 + A_2 B_2 s^4 = 1 + C_1 s + C_2 s^2 + C_3 s^3 + C_4 s^4$$

If the coefficients of the powers of s are equated, the following four equations result.

$$\begin{aligned} A_1 + B_1 &= C_1 \\ A_2 + A_1 B_1 + B_2 &= C_2 \\ A_1 B_2 + A_2 B_1 &= C_3 \\ A_2 B_2 &= C_4 \end{aligned} \tag{9-5}$$

If the first and third of these equations are solved simultaneously in order to obtain A_1 in terms of A_2 and B_2, Equations 9-5 can be replaced with Equations 9-6 as follows.

$$\begin{aligned} A_2 B_2 &= C_4 \\ A_1 &= \frac{C_3 - A_2 C_1}{B_2 - A_2} \\ B_1 &= C_1 - A_1 \\ A_2 + A_1 B_1 + B_2 &= C_2 \end{aligned} \tag{9-6}$$

Now a trial-and-error solution is easily applied. Assume B_2, calculate A_2 from the first equation, A_1 from the second, B_1 from the third and check to find if the fourth is satisfied.

In the process of assuming B_2 and calculating A_2 in this procedure, it is possible that A_2 could be equal to B_2, so that A_1 could not be calculated from the second of Equations 9-6. In this event, Equations 9-7 may be used, proof of which is left to the reader. If $A_2 = B_2$, and also $C_3/C_1 = A_2$ and $C_1^2 + 8A_2 \geq 4C_2$, then A_1 and B_1 can be computed from the third and fourth equations.

$$A_2 = B_2$$

If

$$\frac{C_3}{C_1} = A_2 \text{ and } C_1^2 + 8A_2 \geqq 4C_2 \text{ (checks)}$$

$$A_1 = C_1 + \frac{\sqrt{C_1^2 - 4\left(C_2 - \dfrac{2C_3}{C_1}\right)}}{2} \tag{9-7}$$

$$B_1 = C_1 - A_1$$

Example 9-1. Demonstrate trial and error solution of quartic. If two known quadratics are used to form the quartic, it will be possible to check the results. Let the two quadratics be $(1 + s + s^2)$ and $(1 + 2s + 4s^2)$, for which the quartic is

$$1 + 3s + 7s^2 + 6s^3 + 4s^4 = 0$$

Assuming this to be the original problem, then $C_1 = 3$, $C_2 = 7$, $C_3 = 6$, $C_4 = 4$ for use in Equations 9-6. Assuming $B_2 = 3$, Equations 9-6 yield $A_2 = \frac{4}{3}$, $A_1 = \frac{6}{5}$, $B_1 = \frac{9}{5}$, $A_2 + A_1B_1 + B_2 = \frac{22}{5}$ not 4 as required. It is necessary to make a new assumption for B_2. Try $B_2 = 2$. Then $A_2 = 2$, and since $A_2 = B_2$, Equation 9-5 must be used instead of Equation 9-6. Accordingly, the checks $C_3/C_1 = A_2$ and $C_1^2 + 8A_2 \geqq 4C_2$ are investigated, and although the first of these is satisfied, the second is not, so another assumption for B_2 must be tried. Eventually, of course, either $B_2 = 1$ or $B_2 = 4$ would be tried, which would cause the last of Equations 9-6 to be satisfied, resulting in the factored equation,

$$(1 + s + s^2)(1 + 2s + 4s^2) = 0$$

If such an equation resulted from a physical problem, the natural frequencies (undamped) would be 1.0 and 0.5 rad/sec, both damping factors 0.5, and the damped natural frequencies 0.867 and 0.453 rad/sec, respectively.

9.3 Quadratic Factors of Higher Order Polynomials

For sixth-degree equations or higher the matter is not quite so simple. If the procedure used for the fourth-degree equation is applied, it becomes necessary to assume two different quantities rather than one. However, another way suggests itself at that point, so the method used for the fourth-degree equation will be applied for the higher-degree equations

$$(1 + A_1s + A_2s^2)(1 + B_1s + \cdots + B_{n-3}s^{n-3} + B_{n-2}s^{n-2}) = 1 + C_1s + \cdots + C_ns^n$$

Equating like powers of s on each side of the equation results in relationships between the coefficients as follows:

$$\begin{aligned}
B_1 &= C_1 - A_1 \\
B_2 &= C_2 - A_2 - A_1B_1 \\
B_3 &= C_3 - A_2B_1 - A_1B_2 \\
B_4 &= C_4 - A_2B_2 - A_1B_3 \\
B_k &= C_k - A_2B_{k-2} - A_1B_{k-1} \quad \text{for } 3 \leqq k \leqq (n-1) \\
B_{n-1} &= f_1(A_1, A_2) = 0 \\
C_n - A_2B_{n-2} &= f_2(A_1, A_2) = 0
\end{aligned} \tag{9-8}$$

Both of the final two equations must be satisfied by a proper choice of A_1 and A_2. It would seem as if the simultaneous solution of these two equations for A_1 and A_2 would yield the desired values of A_1 and A_2. The trouble is that both of the last two equations are polynomials involving various powers of A_1 and A_2 so that an explicit equation for A_1 in terms of A_2 (or vice versa) cannot be obtained. If it could be, it would then be an easy matter to assume one, calculate the other, and check the result in the other equation. As it is, however, a trial-and-error solution involves assuming both A_1 and A_2 and testing both of the final equations. This might be done by assuming a value for A_2, varying A_1 until one of the equations is satisfied, calculating the left side of the other equation, and then repeating the process with other assumed values of A_2 until both equations are satisfied. A more practical method is the following.

In general, when A_1 and A_2 are assumed, the functions $f_1(A_1, A_2)$ and $f_2(A_1, A_2)$ are not zero. If it were supposed that only a small change in A_1 and A_2 would be sufficient to reduce these functions to zero, and that Δf_1 and Δf_2 are the changes in f_1 and f_2 caused by ΔA_1 and ΔA_2, then

$$f_1 + \Delta f_1 = 0 \qquad \text{and} \qquad f_2 + \Delta f_2 = 0$$

$$\frac{\partial f_1}{\partial A_1}\Delta A_1 + \frac{\partial f_1}{\partial A_2}\Delta A_2 = -f_1 \tag{9-9}$$

$$\frac{\partial f_2}{\partial A_1}\Delta A_1 + \frac{\partial f_2}{\partial A_2}\Delta A_2 = -f_2$$

If A_1 and A_2 are assumed, the foregoing partial derivatives may be calculated and Equations 9-9 can be solved simultaneously for the ΔA_1 and ΔA_2, which when added to A_1 and A_2 should satisfy the equations, or at least be a more accurate estimate for another trial. Accordingly, expressions for the partial derivatives are required.

$$\frac{\partial f_1}{\partial A_1} = \frac{\partial B_{n-1}}{\partial A_1} \qquad \frac{\partial f_1}{\partial A_2} = \frac{\partial B_{n-1}}{\partial A_2}$$

$$\frac{\partial f_2}{\partial A_1} = -A_2\frac{\partial B_{n-2}}{\partial A_1} \qquad \frac{\partial f_2}{\partial A_2} = -B_{n-2} - A_2\frac{\partial B_{n-2}}{\partial A_2} \tag{9-10}$$

The partial derivatives of Equations 9-8 are

$$\frac{\partial B_1}{\partial A_1} = -1 \qquad \frac{\partial B_1}{\partial A_2} = 0$$

$$\frac{\partial B_2}{\partial A_1} = -B_1 - A_1\frac{\partial B_1}{\partial A_1} \qquad \frac{\partial B_2}{\partial A_2} = -1$$

$$\frac{\partial B_3}{\partial A_1} = -A_2\frac{\partial B_1}{\partial A_1} - A_1\frac{\partial B_2}{\partial A_1} - B_2 \qquad \frac{\partial B_3}{\partial A_2} = -A_2\frac{\partial B_1}{\partial A_2} - A_1\frac{\partial B_2}{\partial A_2} - B_1 \tag{9-11}$$

$$\frac{\partial B_k}{\partial A_1} = -A_2\frac{\partial B_{k-2}}{\partial A_1} - A_1\frac{\partial B_{k-1}}{\partial A_1} - B_{k-1} \qquad \frac{\partial B_k}{\partial A_2} = -A_2\frac{\partial B_{k-2}}{\partial A_2} - A_1\frac{\partial B_{k-1}}{\partial A_2} - B_{k-2}$$

All the numbers required for a new assumption can be obtained from Equations 9-8 to 9-11. Sometimes it is possible to avoid part of the work of calculating the partial derivatives by using approximations. For instance, if B_{n-3} and B_{n-4} are considered constants, Equations 9-10 would become simply

$$\frac{\partial f_1}{\partial A_1} = A_1 B_{n-3} - B_{n-2} \qquad \frac{\partial f_1}{\partial A_2} = A_1 B_{n-4} - B_{n-3}$$
$$\frac{\partial f_2}{\partial A_1} = A_2 B_{n-3} \qquad \frac{\partial f_2}{\partial A_2} = A_2 B_{n-4} - B_{n-2} \tag{9-12}$$

If the calculations using these simpler equations do not converge, the more complicated set Equations 9-10 may be used. A digital computer program for doing this is given in Reference 1.

Example 9-2. Demonstrate the method of determination of quadratic factors with a sixth-degree equation. As in the last example, let the sixth-degree equation be constructed from these quadratics, $(1 + 2s + 4s^2)(1 + 5s + 10s^2)(1 + 12s + 24s^2)$. The result is $1 + 19s + 132s^2 + 496s^3 + 1096s^4 + 1440s^5 + 960s^6$. $C_0 = 1$, $C_1 = 19$, etc. To start, simply assume that $A_1 = A_2 = 0$. In this problem, $n = 6$. With $A_1 = A_2 = 0$,

$$f_1 = B_{n-1} = C_{n-1} = 1440$$

$$f_2 = C_n = 960$$

$$\frac{\partial f_1}{\partial A_1} = -B_{n-2} = C_{n-2} = -1096$$

$$\frac{\partial f_1}{\partial A_2} = -B_{n-3} = -C_{n-3} = -496$$

$$\frac{\partial f_2}{\partial A_1} = 0$$

$$\frac{\partial f_2}{\partial A_2} = -B_{n-2} = -1096$$

Application of Equation 9-9 provides values of $\Delta A_1 = 0.918$, $\Delta A_2 = 0.875$. Then the assumptions for the next trial are

$$A_1 = 0 + 0.918 = 0.918$$

$$A_2 = 0 + 0.875 = 0.875$$

These values used in Equations 9-8 result in

$$B_1 = 18.08, \quad B_2 = 114.5, \quad B_3 = 375, \quad B_4 = 652, \quad B_5 = 513$$

$$f_1 = B_5 = 513$$

$$f_2 = C_6 - A_2 B_4 = 490$$

Neither f_1 nor f_2 is zero, but they are closer this time than last. To find the next assumption for A_1 and A_2 either Equations 9-11 or 9-12 could be used. The simpler equations, 9-12 with 9-9 yield

$$\frac{\partial f_1}{\partial A_1} = -308 \qquad \frac{\partial f_1}{\partial A_2} = -269.7$$

$$\frac{\partial f_2}{\partial A_1} = 328 \qquad \frac{\partial f_2}{\partial A_2} = -552$$

$$\Delta A_1 = 0.190 \qquad \Delta A_2 = 1.79$$

New values of A_1 and A_2 are

$$A_1 = 0.918 + 0.190 = 1.108 \qquad A_2 = 0.875 + 1.79 = 2.665$$

For comparison, the longer equations, (Equations 9-11 with 9-10 and 9-9) with the old values of A_1 and A_2, yield

$$\frac{\partial B_1}{\partial A_1} = -1$$

$$\frac{\partial B_2}{\partial A_1} = -B_1 + A_1 = -18.08 + 0.918 = -17.16$$

$$\frac{\partial B_3}{\partial A_1} = -A_2 \frac{\partial B_2}{\partial A_1} - A_1 \frac{\partial B_2}{\partial A_1} - B_2 = -0.875(-1) - 0.918(-17.16) - 114.5 = -97.9$$

until

$$\frac{\partial B_4}{\partial A_1} = -270, \quad \frac{\partial B_5}{\partial A_1} = -319, \quad \frac{\partial B_4}{\partial A_2} = -97.9, \quad \frac{\partial B_5}{\partial A_2} = -270.2$$

$$\frac{\partial f_1}{\partial A_1} = -319 \qquad \frac{\partial f_1}{\partial A_2} = -270.2$$

$$\frac{\partial f_2}{\partial A_1} = 237 \qquad \frac{\partial f_2}{\partial A_2} = -566$$

$$\Delta A_1 = 0.758 \qquad \Delta A_2 = 1.005$$

New values of A_1 and A_2 are

$$A_1 = 0.918 + 0.758 = 1.676 \qquad A_2 = 0.875 + 1.005 = 1.880$$

The differences in the two methods at this stage are not very great. Evidently the figures are converging on the factor $(1 + 2s + 4s^2)$ and it is seen what progress has been made in two trials. While the foregoing example was worked with a slide rule, more significant figures should be carried, and for higher degree polynomials than six, a digital computor is a necessity. Using a digital computer and the more exact method (Equations 9-11), the coefficients of the quadratic are correct to one part in 10^8 after eight passes.

9.4 Modal Columns for Highly Damped Systems

After the quadratic factors have been determined, the modes corresponding to the various quadratic factors can be determined by substituting the quadratic factors back into the equations in a manner similar to that of Example 8-6 for conservative systems. This is equivalent to expressing each of the transformed equations in terms of the ratios of variables and then solving any $(n - 1)$ of the n equations simultaneously for the ratios, as follows. Assume the general form

$$(a_{11}s^2 + b_{11}s + c_{11})X_1 + (a_{12}s^2 + b_{12}s + c_{12})X_2 + \cdots + (a_{1n}s^2 + b_{1n}s + c_{1n})X_n = 0$$

$$(a_{21}s^2 + b_{21}s + c_{21})X_1 + (a_{22}s^2 + b_{22}s + c_{22})X_2 + \cdots + (a_{2n}s^2 + b_{2n}s + c_{2n})X_n = 0$$

$$\cdots$$

$$(a_{n1}s^2 + b_{n1}s + c_{n1})X_1 + (a_{n2}s^2 + b_{n2}s + c_{n2})X_2 + \cdots + (a_{nn}s^2 + b_{nn}s + c_{nn})X_n = 0$$

If the equations are divided by X_n and $s = -\zeta\beta + i\beta\sqrt{1 - \zeta^2}$ (or $s^2 + A_1s + A_2 = 0$) is substituted into the resulting equations n equations are obtained in terms of

X_1/X_n, X_2/X_n, ... X_{n-1}/X_n. Any $(n - 1)$ of these may be solved simultaneously for the ratios. The set of equations is

$$(f_{11} + ig_{11})\frac{X_1}{X_n} + (f_{12} + ig_{12})\frac{X_2}{X_n} + \cdots + (f_{1(n-1)} + ig_{1(n-1)})\frac{X_{n-1}}{X_n} = -f_{1n} - ig_{1n}$$

$$(f_{21} + ig_{21})\frac{X_1}{X_n} + (f_{22} + ig_{22})\frac{X_2}{X_n} + \cdots + (f_{2(n-1)} + ig_{2(n-1)})\frac{X_{n-1}}{X_n} = -f_{2n} - ig_{2n}$$

$$\cdot \quad \cdot \quad \cdot \quad \cdot \quad \cdot \quad \cdot \quad \cdot \quad \cdot \quad \cdot \quad \cdot \quad \cdot \quad \cdot$$

$$(f_{n1} + ig_{n1})\frac{X_1}{X_n} + (f_{n2} + ig_{n2})\frac{X_2}{X_n} + \cdots + (f_{n(n-1)} + ig_{n(n-1)})\frac{X_{n-1}}{X_n} = -f_{nn} - ig_{nn} \tag{9-13}$$

where

$$f_{jk} = \beta^2(2\zeta^2 - 1)a_{jk} - \zeta\beta b_{jk} + c_{jk}$$

$$g_{jk} = -2\zeta\beta^2\sqrt{1 - \zeta^2}\, a_{jk} + \beta\sqrt{1 - \zeta^2}\, b_{jk}$$

Solution of these equations will result in ratios for each of the variables, but these ratios are complex numbers such as $x_1/x_n = X_1/X_n = 0.7 - 0.2i$, $x_2/x_n = X_2/X_n =$

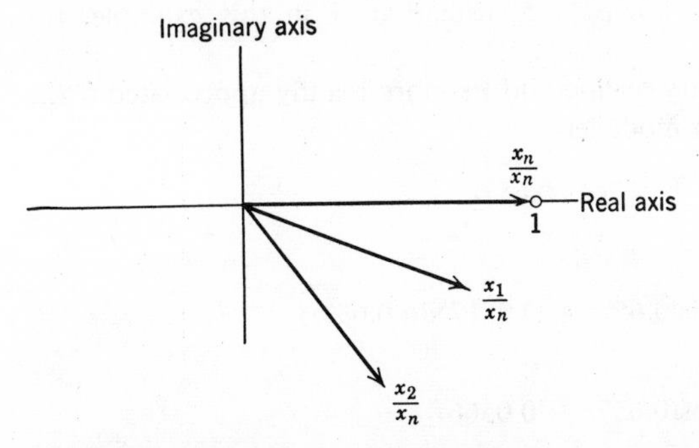

Fig. 9-1 Relationship between coordinates in a natural mode for system with significant damping

$0.3 - 0.4i$, etc. The significance of the complex numbers is that the coordinates are not exactly in phase or out of phase as they are in the undamped problem. The angle by which x_1 lags x_n in the previous instance would be $\tan^{-1} 0.2/0.7$, for example. On the complex plane the relationships between the variables would be indicated by the positions of the vectors (Fig. 9-1).

Example 9-3. Determine modes of vibration for a heavily damped system.

This example will make use of a two-degree system instead of a three-degree system in order to save work. The system of Example 6-1 will be used since the numerical work for that example is already available. The two equations are

$$\ddot{x}_1 + 2\dot{x}_1 + 6x_1 - \dot{x}_2 - 5x_2 = 0$$

$$-\dot{x}_1 - 5x_1 + \ddot{x}_2 + \dot{x}_2 + 5x_2 = 0$$

The factors $s^2 + 0.463s + 0.483$ and $s^2 + 2.53s + 10.35$ satisfy the characteristic equation, and oscillation occurs at frequencies of 0.657 and 2.96 rad/sec and damping factors of

0.333 and 0.393. If the variables are then normalized on x_2 as was done for the zero damping example, the ratio, x_1/x_2, can be found for both frequencies. For convenience, the imaginary exponent is used rather than the trignometric form.

$$x_2 = 1\, e^{-0.333(0.696)t}\, e^{i0.657t}$$

From the first or second of the previous equations (use both as a check),

$$x_1 = (0.915 - 0.0515i)\, e^{-0.232t}\, e^{i0.657t}$$

$$x_1 = (0.913 - 0.0518i)\, e^{-0.232t}\, e^{i0.657t}$$

Therefore $x_1/x_2 = 0.914 - 0.0517i$. The slight discrepancy indicates the accuracy obtainable with the slide rule. A similar calculation for the second mode yields

$$\frac{x_1}{x_2} = -1.15 - 0.305i$$

The presence of the imaginary term in each case indicates that the motion of the masses are not exactly in phase or 180° out of phase as they are when there is no damping. In fact the first mass lags about $3\frac{1}{4}°$ behind the second mass for the first mode and about 15 degrees less than 180 degrees behind for the second mode. If there had been three degrees of freedom the phase angles would in general be different for all the coordinates and all the modes. (However, damped systems with coordinates either in phase or 180° out of phase, like undamped systems, also can exist—use $c_2 = 5$ instead of 1 in this example, for instance.)

Perhaps the significance of the imaginary term could be more readily appreciated if the trignometric form were used. For the first mode let

$$x_2 = 1\, e^{-0.232t} \cos 0.657t$$

Then, solving for x_1

$$x_1 = e^{-0.232t}(0.914 \cos 0.657t + 0.0517 \sin 0.657t)$$

or

$$x_1 = e^{-0.232t}[0.914 \cos(0.657t - 0.0566)]$$

Clearly x_1 is lagging x_2 by 0.0566 rad, and the ratio $x_1/x_2 = 0.914 + 0.0517 \tan 0.657t$ is not a constant in the same sense as for the zero damping example.

Equations 9-13 could have been used directly. Then for the first mode, $\beta_1 = 0.696$, $\zeta_1 = 0.333$

$$a_{11} = 1,\ b_{11} = 2,\ c_{11} = 6,\ a_{12} = 0,\ b_{12} = -1,\ c_{12} = -5$$

$$a_{12} = 0,\ b_{21} = -1,\ c_{21} = -5,\ a_{22} = 1,\ b_{22} = 1,\ c_{22} = 5$$

$$f_{11} = 5.16,\quad g_{11} = 1.006,\quad f_{12} = -4.768,\quad g_{12} = -0.655$$

$$f_{21} = -4.768,\quad g_{21} = -0.655,\quad f_{22} = 4.391,\quad g_{22} = 0.351$$

These lead to substantially the same results as before,

$$\frac{x_1}{x_2} = 0.914 - 0.0517i$$

It is interesting to compare the results of this damped system with the same system without damping and with the approximate analysis described in Example 8-7. The following summary of significant items shows that even rather heavy damping may not materially affect the conclusions that would be reached by the approximation procedure.

	Undamped System		Damped System Exact Analysis		Damped System Approximate Analysis	
	Mode 1	Mode 2	Mode 1	Mode 2	Mode 1	Mode 2
Natural Frequency	0.690	3.25	0.657	2.96	0.652	3.01
Damping Factor	0	0	0.333	0.393	0.330	0.385
Mode Description (x_1/x_2)	0.905	-1.105	$0.914 - 0.052i$	$-1.150 - 0.305i$	0.905	-1.105

CHAPTER 10

Forced Vibration of Multiple Degree Systems

10.1 Frequency Response from the Transfer Function

In a linear system composed of a finite number of lumped parameters (discrete masses, springs, and dampers), the transfer function relating any two of the time-dependent variables can be reduced to a fraction in which the numerator and denominator are both polynomials in s. These polynomials can be factored to yield a transfer function of the general form of Equation 10-1.

$$\frac{X}{F} = \frac{K(s + A_1)(s + A_2)\cdots(s^2 + B_1 s + C_1)(s^2 + B_2 s + C_2)\cdots}{(s + E_1)(s + E_2)\cdots(s^2 + G_1 s + H_1)(s^2 + G_2 s + H_2)\cdots} \tag{10-1}$$

(The quadratic factors are only those which cannot be factored into additional real linear factors.) It is also possible that some of the factors could be repeated (or raised to some integer power), but as far as forced vibration is concerned this possibility does not require special treatment and Equation 10-1 is sufficiently general.

The transfer function is ordinarily written as the ratio of an "output" variable to an "input" variable. That is, in Equation 10-1 F is the transform of a force which varies according to some arbitrary time function, and X is the transform of a displacement which varies with time in response to the input force. Clearly, there would be many instances where variables other than force and displacement would be of interest, so the transfer function might represent the relation between an input displacement and an output force, or an input displacement and an output displacement, or between input displacement and output acceleration, or any other input and output variables of interest, but for discussion purposes let the input and output be force and displacement as implied by Equation 10-1.

The Harmonic Forcing Function. If the forcing function, $f(t)$, is selected, its transform, $F(s)$, is fixed; therefore, $X(s)$ and $x(t)$ are also fixed. If the forcing function, $f(t)$, is a harmonic function, $f_0 \sin \omega t$, $f_0 \cos \omega t$, or $f_0 e^{i\omega t}$, then $F(s)$ becomes

$$f_0 \frac{\omega}{s^2 + \omega^2}, \quad f_0 \frac{s}{s^2 + \omega^2}, \quad f_0 \frac{1}{s - i\omega}$$

and $X(s)$ is the right side of Equation 10-1 multiplied by the appropriate one of these three expressions. It is perhaps most convenient to use

$$f(t) = f_0 \, e^{i\omega t}$$

or

$$F(s) = f_0 \frac{1}{s - i\omega}$$

so that

$$X = f_0 K \frac{(s + A_1)(s + A_2)\cdots(s^2 + B_1 s + C_1)(s^2 + B_2 s + C_2)}{(s - i\omega)(s + E_1)(s + E_2)\cdots(s^2 + G_1 s + H_1)(s^2 + G_2 s + H_2)} \quad \text{(10-2)}$$

There would be factors in the inverse transform corresponding to each of the factors in the denominator of Equation 10-2. However, if the E's and G's of these factors are all positive, all of the factors except $(s - i\omega)$ will result in terms which decrease exponentially with time and may be ignored as far as forced or steady state vibration is concerned. If even one of the E's or G's is negative, terms in the inverse transform which increase exponentially with time will result so that the "steady state" component has no practical significance. Therefore, it is assumed that the E's and G's are all positive for any case where forced vibration is of interest. Consequently, the only effective term in $x(t)$ for large values of t is the one corresponding to $(s - i\omega)$ in Equation 10-2, or therefore as shown in Equation 10-3.

$$x(t) = \left[\frac{K(s + A_1)(s + A_2)\cdots(s^2 + B_1 s + C_1)(s^2 + B_2 s + C_2)}{(s + E_1)(s + E_2)\cdots(s^2 + G_1 s + H_1)(s^2 + G_2 s + G_2)}\right]_{s = i\omega} f_0 \, e^{i\omega t} \quad \text{(10-3)}$$

Response to the Harmonic Function. The real part of Equation 10-3 is the response to the cosine forcing function and the imaginary part is the response to the sine forcing function, but it is more convenient to continue with the complex form and write

$$\left.\begin{aligned} x(t) &= x_0 \, e^{i(\omega t + \psi)} \\ \frac{x_0}{f_0} &= \sqrt{\phi_r^2 + \phi_i^2} \\ \psi &= \tan^{-1} \frac{\phi_i}{\phi_r} \\ \phi_r + i\phi_i &= K \left[\frac{(s + A_1)(s + A_2)\cdots(s^2 + B_1 s + C_1)(s^2 + B_2 s + C_2)}{(s + E_1)(s + E_2)\cdots(s^2 + G_1 s + H_1)(s^2 + G_2 s + H_2)}\right]_{s = i\omega} \end{aligned}\right\} \quad \text{(10-4)}$$

In this form, x_0 is the amplitude of the steady state oscillation, and ψ is the phase angle relative to the input forcing function. Usually, the amplitude is of major interest, and it is seen that the ratio of amplitude of response to amplitude of forcing function can be obtained by taking the absolute value of the complex number resulting when $i\omega$ is substituted for s in the transfer function, Equation 10-1. If there were no damping in the system, none of the linear factors in the denominator of the transfer function would be present, and all of the G's would be zero. Actually, a practical system would contain some slight damping, so that the G's would have some small value, and extraneous transient terms could be ignored in the investigation of forced vibration. Nevertheless, for such systems, the small damping is often ignored and the G's indicated as zero. It is clear that when this is done there are certain forcing frequencies, ω, for which the denominator of the transfer function becomes zero. These are the resonant frequencies, $\omega_1 = \sqrt{H_1}$, $\omega_2 = \sqrt{H_2}$, etc. With slight unavoidable damping, the resonant frequencies are not altered appreciably from these values. When significant damping is present, either unavoidably or purposely to limit resonant response, the resonant frequencies may be considerably different from these, but will be near the damped natural frequencies determined from converting the quadratic factors in the denominator of Equation 10-1 to the familiar form, $s^2 + 2\zeta_n\beta_n s + \beta_n^2$, and computing the corresponding damped natural frequencies from $\beta_n\sqrt{1 - \zeta_n^2}$.

If the damping is slight (or even zero) and the forcing frequency is not equal to the resonant frequency, the response amplitude is limited. A plot of the ratio of output to input amplitude (and often phase angle between output and input) as a function of frequency, usually to logarithmic scales, is called a "frequency response" or Bode* plot. Such plots are similar to those of Fig. 3-1 to 3-14 for single-degree systems, and in addition to the convenient display of information afforded, they provide a valuable vehicle for increased understanding of linear vibration and control system theory (Reference 1). Although ordinary coordinates and forces are implied in the previous discussion, it applies equally well to transfer functions between principal coordinates and the corresponding generalized forces as demonstrated in Example 10-1.

There are several resonance frequencies for a multiple degree system, as can be determined either physically from the number of degrees of freedom or mathematically from the denominator of the transfer function. The forcing function may also contain harmonic terms having different frequencies (see Fourier Series in Appendix 1). Therefore numerous possibilities for resonance or near resonance operation may occur. These must be kept in mind when analyzing a system and several pertinent facts are illustrated in Example 10-1.

10.2 Impedance and Mobility

The transfer function of Equation 10-1 can be derived by any convenient method. Some of these have already been discussed. This section will briefly describe the use of "mobility" and "impedance" in the development of a transfer function for a complex system from the combination of a number of simpler transfer functions.

Elementary Transfer Functions. The three simplest elements are mass, spring, and damper, and the two variables which are often of most interest are force and displacement, although velocity, acceleration, or other derivatives or integrals of displacement may be of interest. Figure 10-1 represents these three elements with their corresponding transfer functions, considering either variable as input or output and using both displacement and velocity. The zero indicated for the mass is a fixed reference point in space. The transfer functions are easily obtained from the differential equations between force and displacement or force and velocity for the three elements. The differential equations relating force and velocity are exactly like the equations relating voltage and current in elements of an electrical system. Consequently, electrical circuit analysis techniques are easily applied to complex mechanical systems. The analogies

* After H. W. Bode, whose name is prominently associated with the use of such plots in linear control system theory.

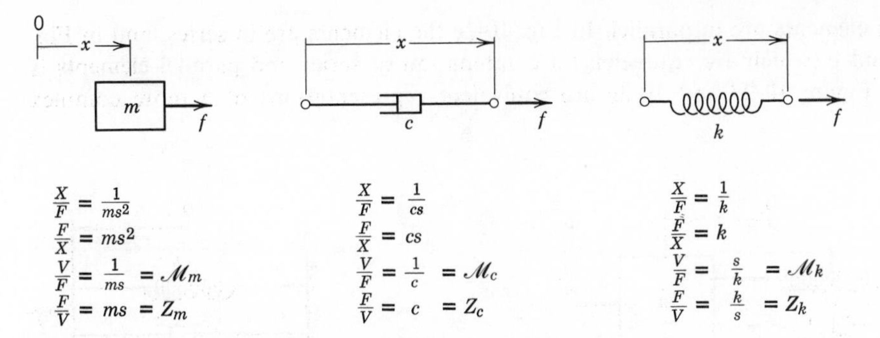

Fig. 10-1 Mechanical elements and significant transforms

between the two systems are indicated in Table 10-1. (A "parallel" electrical analogy is also available, but neither analogy will be used further in this text.)

Table 10-1

Mechanical system		Electrical system	
Element or variable	Transfer function	Element or variable	Transfer function
Force, F	$\frac{F}{V} \sim$ Impedance	Voltage, E	$\frac{E}{I} \sim$ Impedance
Velocity, V	$\frac{V}{F} \sim$ Mobility	Current, I	$\frac{I}{E} \sim$ Admittance
Mass, m	$\frac{V}{F} = \frac{1}{ms}$ $\frac{F}{V} = ms$	Inductor, L	$\frac{I}{E} = \frac{1}{Ls}$ $\frac{E}{I} = Ls$
Damper, c	$\frac{V}{F} = \frac{1}{c}$ $\frac{F}{V} = c$	Resistor, R	$\frac{I}{E} = \frac{1}{R}$ $\frac{E}{I} = R$
Spring, k	$\frac{V}{F} = \frac{s}{k}$ $\frac{F}{V} = \frac{k}{s}$	Capacitor, C	$\frac{I}{E} = Cs$ $\frac{E}{I} = \frac{1}{Cs}$

It is noted that the ratio F/V or E/I is called "impedance" in either system while the reciprocals of these are "mobility" in the mechanical system or "admittance" in the electrical system. "Mobility" may also be used to describe the ratio of displacement or acceleration to force. The definition in use must be determined from the context.

Impedance and Mobility of Elements in Combination. Figure 10-2 shows several possible combinations of spring, mass, and damper. Figure 10-2*a* and 10-2*b* are equivalent and the elements are in parallel. In Fig. 10-2*c* the elements are in series, and in Fig. 10-2*d* and *e* (which are equivalent) a combination of series and parallel elements is shown. Figure 10-2*f* and 10-2*g* are equivalent representations of a more complex system.

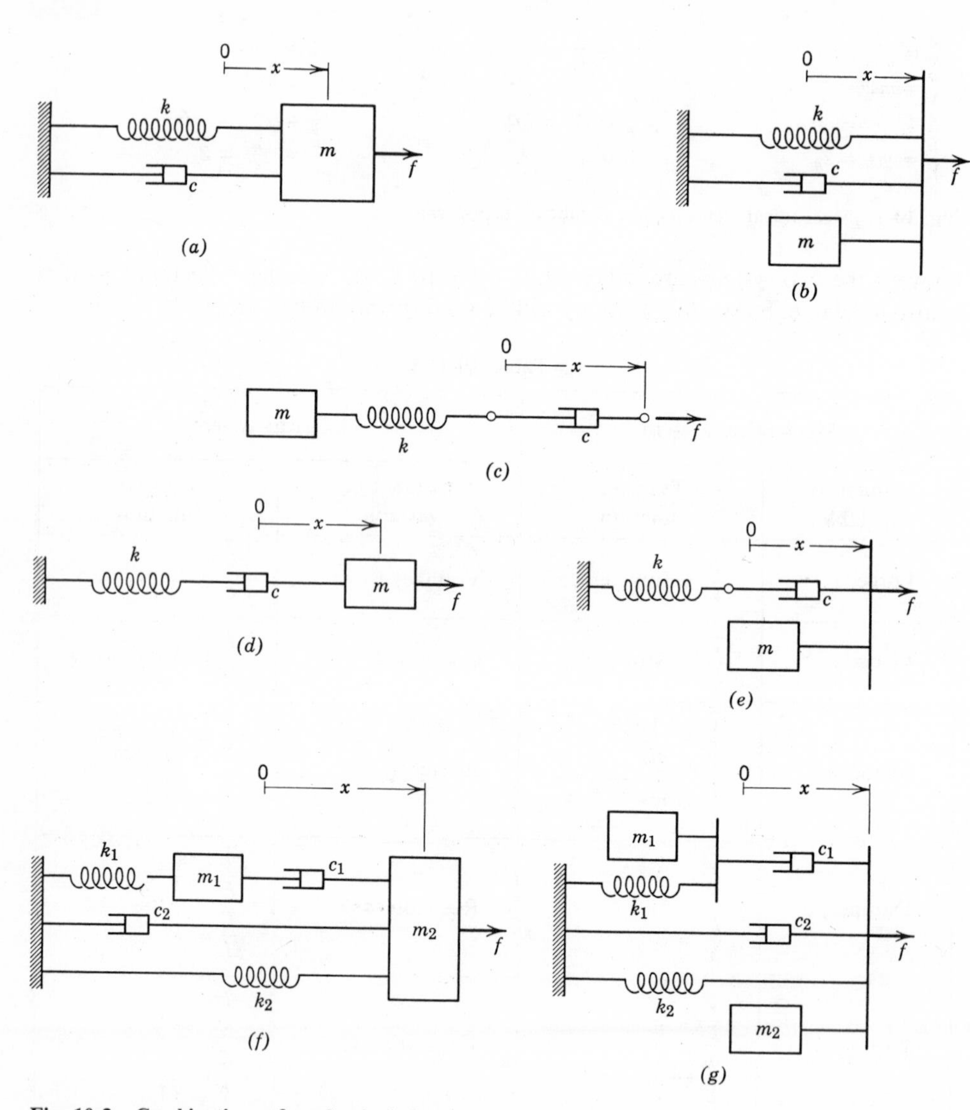

Fig. 10-2 Combinations of mechanical elements

For Fig. 10-2*a* and 10-2*b* the velocity is common to all of the elements and the force is the sum of the forces required for each element, so it is convenient to compute the impedance of the system from the sum of the individual impedances. That is,

$$Z = \frac{F}{V} = \frac{F_m + F_c + F_k}{V} = ms + c + \frac{k}{s}$$

The mobility is the inverse of this or

$$\mathcal{M} = \frac{V}{F} = \frac{1}{ms + c + \dfrac{k}{s}}$$

The familiar transfer function relating displacement and force is easily computed using $V = sX$.

$$\frac{X}{F} = \frac{1}{ms^2 + cs + k}$$

In general, the equivalent impedance and mobility for mechanical elements in parallel is given by Equations 10-5 and 10-6.

$$Z = Z_1 + Z_2 \tag{10-5}$$

$$\mathcal{M} = \frac{1}{\dfrac{1}{\mathcal{M}_1} + \dfrac{1}{\mathcal{M}_2}} \tag{10-6}$$

For Fig. 10-2*c* the force is common to all elements and the velocity is the sum of the individual velocities, so it is convenient to compute the mobility of the system from the sum of the individual mobilities.

$$\mathcal{M} = \frac{V}{F} = \frac{V_m + V_c + V_k}{F} = \frac{1}{ms} + \frac{1}{c} + \frac{s}{k}$$

The impedance of the system is the inverse of this or

$$Z = \frac{F}{V} = \frac{mcks}{mcs^2 + mks + kc}$$

In general, the equivalent impedance and mobility for mechanical elements in series is given by Equations 10-7 and 10-8.

$$Z = \frac{1}{\dfrac{1}{Z_1} + \dfrac{1}{Z_2}} \tag{10-7}$$

$$\mathcal{M} = \mathcal{M}_1 + \mathcal{M}_2 \tag{10-8}$$

Figure 10-2*d* and *e* represent a system having elements both in parallel and in series. The spring and damper are in series and this combination is in parallel with the mass. Therefore, the mobility for the spring-damper combination is the sum of the individual mobilities and the impedance of the entire system is the sum of the impedances of the mass and the spring-damper combination.

$$\mathcal{M}_{k,c} = \frac{1}{c} + \frac{s}{k}$$

$$Z_{k,c} = \frac{1}{\dfrac{1}{c} + \dfrac{s}{k}} = \frac{ck}{k + cs}$$

$$Z = Z_m + Z_{k,c} = ms + \frac{ck}{k + cs} = \frac{kms + cms^2 + ck}{k + cs}$$

$$\frac{F}{V} = \frac{mcs^2 + mks + ck}{cs + k} \quad (= Z)$$

$$\frac{V}{F} = \frac{cs + k}{mcs^2 + mks + ck} \quad (= \mathcal{M})$$

System f and g of Fig. 10-2 can be analyzed as follows. Since m_2, c_2, and k_2 are in parallel, the impedance for these elements in combination is

$$Z_2 = m_2 s + c_2 + \frac{k_2}{s}$$

Elements m_1 and k_1 are in parallel and this combination in series with c_1. The mobility of these three elements is

$$\mathcal{M}_1 = \mathcal{M}_{c_1} = \frac{1}{Z_{m_1} + Z_{k_1}} = \frac{1}{c_1} + \frac{1}{m_1 s + \dfrac{k_1}{s}}$$

Subsystem 1 is in parallel with Subsystem 2, so the overall impedance is

$$Z = Z_1 + Z_2 = \frac{1}{\dfrac{1}{c_1} + \dfrac{1}{m_1 s + \dfrac{k_1}{s}}} + m_2 s + c_2 + \frac{k_2}{s}$$

After simplification,

$$Z = \frac{m_1 m_2 s^4 + (m_1 c_2 + m_2 c_1 + m_1 c_1)s^3 + (m_1 k_1 + m_2 k_2 + c_1 c_2)s^2 + (c_1 k_2 + c_2 k_1 + c_1 k_1)s + k_1 k_2}{s(m_1 s^2 + c_1 s + k_1)}$$

Finally, if the force is the input and displacement the output,

$$\frac{X}{F} = \frac{1}{sZ} = \frac{m_1 s^2 + c_1 s + k_1}{m_1 m_2 s^4 + (m_1 c_1 + m_1 c_2 + m_2 c_1)s^3 + (m_1 k_1 + m_2 k_2 + c_1 c_2)s^2 + (c_1 k_1 + c_1 k_2 + c_2 k_1)s + k_1 k_2}$$

In summary, the mobility or impedance for individual elements are computed on the basis that the velocity is the relative velocity of the two ends of the spring or damper but the absolute velocity (relative to fixed space) of the mass. Individual impedances may be added for mechanical elements or subsystems in parallel and individual mobilities may be added for mechanical elements or subsystems in series. The final result is a transfer function relating an input and output quantity. If the input function of time is known, the output function of time may be computed. As a special case, if the input is a harmonic function of time, the steady state response of the output can be determined by substitution of $i\omega$ for s in the transfer function.

10.3 Forced Vibration of a Three-Degree System—An Example

The significant points of the preceding sections are illustrated for the moderately complex three-degree system of earlier chapters in the following example.

Example 10-1 Investigate the system represented by Fig. 10-3a for steady-state response to a harmonic applied force.

If the coordinate of interest is x_3, the transfer function X_3/F is required. It is easier to determine this transfer function from Fig. 10-3b. where the combinations of elements in series and parallel are more easily recognized.

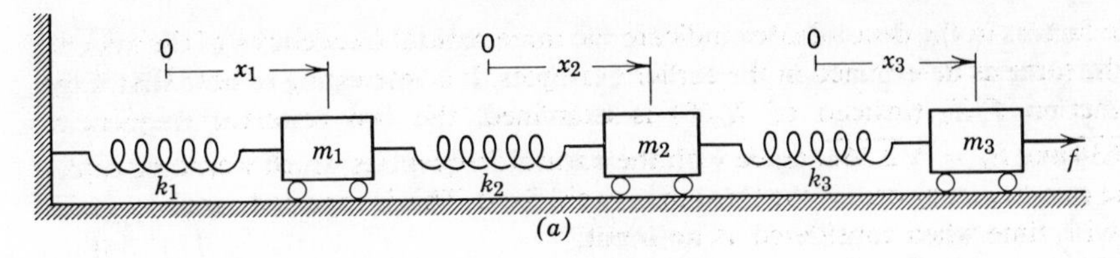

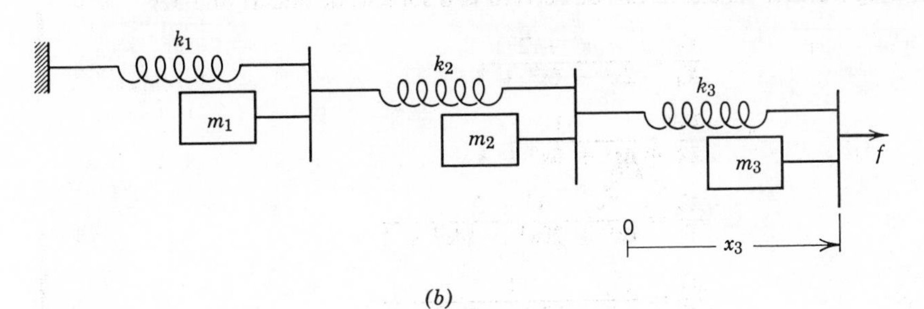

Fig. 10-3

$$\frac{X_3}{F} = \frac{1}{s}\,\frac{V_3}{F}$$

and

$$\frac{V_3}{F} = \mathscr{M}_3$$

where

$$\mathscr{M}_3 = \frac{1}{z_3}$$

$$z_3 = z_{m_3} + z_a$$

$$z_a = \frac{1}{\mathscr{M}_a}$$

$$\mathscr{M}_a = \mathscr{M}_{k_3} + \mathscr{M}_b$$

$$\mathscr{M}_b = \frac{1}{z_b}$$

$$z_b = z_{m_2} + z_c$$

$$z_c = \frac{1}{\mathscr{M}_c}$$

$$\mathscr{M}_c = \mathscr{M}_{k_2} + \mathscr{M}_d$$

$$\mathscr{M}_d = \frac{1}{z_d}$$

$$z_d = z_{m_1} + z_{k_1}$$

$$\frac{V_3}{F} = \cfrac{1}{m_3 s + \cfrac{1}{\cfrac{s}{k_3} + \cfrac{1}{\cfrac{s}{k_2} + \cfrac{1}{m_1 s + \cfrac{k_1}{s}}}}}$$

Letting $k_1 = k_2 = k_3 = 1$ and $m_1 = 1$, $m_2 = 2$, $m_3 = 3$, in order to compare with and make use of the results of Example 8-1 and others, and simplifying.

$$\frac{X_3}{F} = \frac{1}{s}\,\frac{V_3}{F} = \frac{2s^4 + 6s^2 + 3}{6s^6 + 20s^4 + 14s^2 + 1}$$

$$\frac{X_3}{F} = \frac{\frac{1}{3}(s^2 + 0.6340)(s^2 + 2.3660)}{(s^2 + 0.08045)(s^2 + 0.86902)(s^2 + 2.3836)}$$

The three factors in the denominator indicate the three natural frequencies of the system, which are the same as determined in the earlier examples. It is interesting to note that if the transfer function F/X_3 (instead of X_3/F) is examined, the two resonant frequencies ($\beta_1 = \sqrt{0.634}$ and $\beta_2 = \sqrt{2.366}$) agree with the natural frequencies which would be calculated for the two-degree system if the third mass were fixed. This is expected, since x_3 varies arbitrarily with time when considered as an input.

The following transfer functions can be derived in a somewhat similar manner.

$$\frac{X_2}{X_3} = \frac{s^2 + 2}{2s^4 + 6s^2 + 3}$$

$$\frac{X_1}{X_3} = \frac{1}{2s^4 + 6s^2 + 3}$$

$$\frac{X_2}{F} = \frac{s^2 + 2}{6s^6 + 20s^4 + 14s^2 + 1}$$

$$\frac{X_1}{F} = \frac{1}{6s^6 + 20s^4 + 14s^2 + 1}$$

If the forcing function is harmonic, the s in these transfer functions can be replaced with $i\omega$ and the resulting equations plotted as a function of ω. These plots often use logarithmic coordinates, but for this discussion it is convenient to use rectilinear coordinates. Figure 10-4*a* shows the ratio of.response amplitude to applied force amplitude, and Fig. 10-4*b* the ratio of response amplitude to applied displacement amplitude. Negative values on these figures indicate that the response is 180 degrees out of phase with the forcing function.

Figure 10-4*a* displays the three resonant frequencies expected when the force excites the vibration and Fig. 10-4*b* shows the two resonant frequencies expected when displacement of the third mass excites the vibration. Also illustrated are the increasing sharpness of the resonance peaks for the higher modes, changes of phase as the resonance points are passed, and certain frequencies for which the displacement of one of the masses is zero, a phenomenon associated with multiple degree systems which is sometimes utilized in so-called "vibration absorbers" or "inertia dampers."

The characteristic modal relationship for natural vibration of the three-mass system can be found on Fig. 10-4*b* at the resonant frequencies of Fig. 10-4*a*. For instance, at $\omega = 0.284$ (first mode natural frequency), $x_1/x_3 = 0.40$ and $x_2/x_3 = 0.76$, in agreement with Example 8-1. (This is true because at the natural frequencies the amplitudes can be finite even for zero applied force.)

At a specific applied frequency, 0.9 for example, the ratio of displacement to force for the three masses is -2.46, -2.92, and 1.34, obtained either from Fig. 10-4*a* or from the appropriate equations. It is instructive to obtain these by use of generalized quantities associated with the three modes. The following normal modes and frequencies were determined in Example 8-1.

Mode 1	*Mode 2*	*Mode 3*
$\frac{\partial x_1}{\partial y_1} = 0.39522$	$\frac{\partial x_1}{\partial y_2} = -1.4210$	$\frac{\partial x_1}{\partial y_3} = 16.025$
$\frac{\partial x_2}{\partial y_1} = 0.75864$	$\frac{\partial x_2}{\partial y_2} = -1.6071$	$\frac{\partial x_2}{\partial y_3} = -6.151$
$\frac{\partial x_3}{\partial y_1} = 1.0000$	$\frac{\partial x_3}{\partial y_2} = 1.0000$	$\frac{\partial x_3}{\partial y_3} = 1.0000$
$\beta_1^2 = 0.08045$	$\beta_2^2 = 0.8690$	$\beta_3^2 = 2.3836$

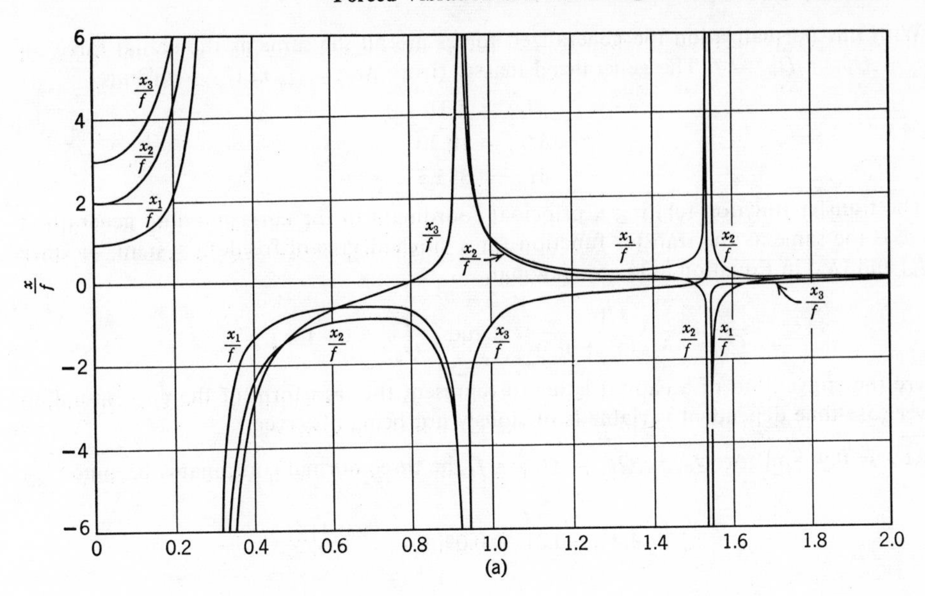
6
4
2
0
−2
−4
−6
x/f
x3/f
x2/f
x1/f
x3/f
x2/f
x1/f
x2/f
x3/f
x1/f
x2/f
x3/f
x2/f
x1/f
0
0.2
0.4
0.6
0.8
1.0
1.2
1.4
1.6
1.8
2.0
(a)

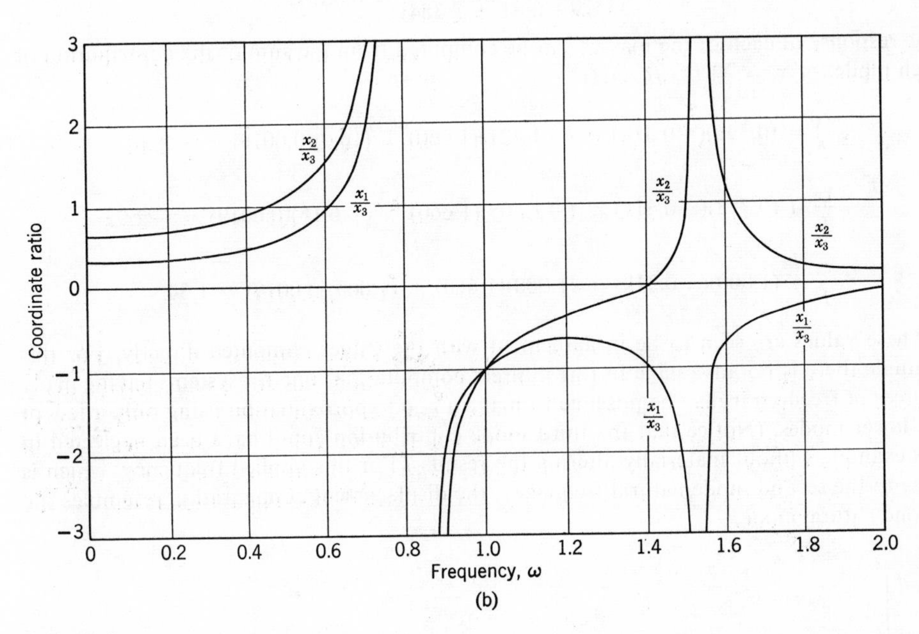
3
2
1
0
−1
−2
−3
Coordinate ratio
x2/x3
x1/x3
x2/x3
x2/x3
x1/x3
x1/x3
0
0.2
0.4
0.6
0.8
1.0
1.2
1.4
1.6
1.8
2.0
Frequency, ω
(b)

Fig. 10-4

With this normalization the generalized forces are all the same as the actual force, or $Q_{p_1} = Q_{p_2} = Q_{p_3} = f$. The generalized masses (from $M_{p_i} = \sum_k m_k(\partial x_k/\partial q_i)^2$) are

$$M_{p_1} = 4.31$$
$$M_{p_2} = 10.20$$
$$M_{p_3} = 335.5$$

The transfer function relating a principal coordinate to the corresponding generalized force is the same as the transfer function for a single-degree-of-freedom system, or since $[M_p]$ and $[K_p]$ in Equation 8-24 are diagonal,

$$\frac{Y_i}{Q_{p_i}} = \frac{1}{M_{p_i}(s^2 + \beta_i^2)} \quad \text{and} \quad \frac{Y_i}{Q_{p_j}} = 0 \quad \text{for } i \neq j$$

(Here the convention of a capital letter to represent the transform of the corresponding lower case time dependent variable is obviously not being observed.)

At $s = 0.9i$ and for $Q_{p_1} = Q_{p_2} = Q_{p_3} = f$, the three normal coordinates become

$$y_1 = \frac{f}{4.31(-0.81 + 0.0805)} = -0.318f$$

$$y_2 = \frac{f}{10.20(-0.81 + 0.8690)} = 1.660f$$

$$y_3 = \frac{f}{335.5(-0.81 + 2.384)} = 0.0019f$$

The response of each of the masses can be computed from the sum of the contribution of each mode, or $x_i = \sum_k (\partial x_i/\partial y_k)y_k$.

$$\frac{x_1}{f} = (0.395)(-0.318) + (-1.421)(1.660) + (16.0)(0.0019) = -2.46$$

$$\frac{x_2}{f} = (0.758)(-0.318) + (-1.607)(1.660) + (-6.15)(0.0019) = -2.92$$

$$\frac{x_3}{f} = (1.000)(-0.318) + (1.000)(1.660) + (1.000)(0.0019) = 1.34$$

These values are seen to be in agreement with the values computed directly. For this example there is no advantage in this indirect computation, but for systems having many degrees of freedom it may be possible to make a good approximation using only a few of the lower modes. (Notice that the third mode contribution could have been neglected in this example without materially altering the results.) For this applied frequency, which is close to the second mode natural frequency, the displacement configuration resembles the second natural mode.

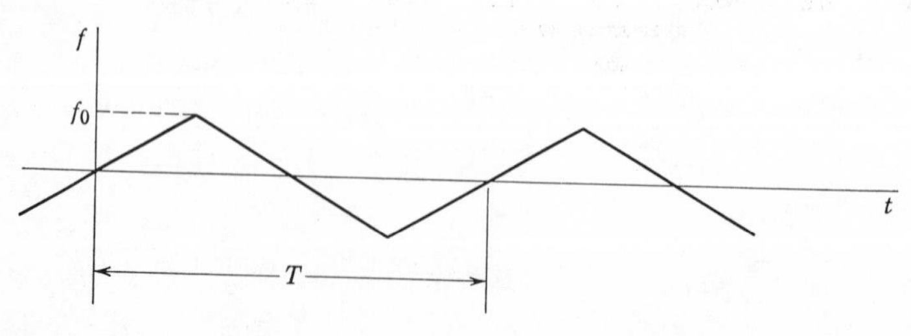

Fig. 10-5

This example will close with a short analysis of the response to be expected when the forcing function is not a pure sinusoid. For illustration, assume that the applied force varies as indicated in Fig. 10-5.

This function can be represented by the Fourier series

$$f = f_0 \frac{8}{\pi^2}\left(\frac{\sin \omega t}{1^2} - \frac{\sin 3\omega t}{3^2} + \frac{\sin 5\omega t}{5^2} - \cdots\right)$$

where

$$\omega = \frac{2\pi}{T}$$

Because of the linearity of the system, each of the individual terms in this series can be considered to be exciting the system, the response of the system consisting of the summation of the responses to the individual terms. It is seen that a possibility of resonance exists whenever any of the frequencies, ω, 3ω, 5ω, etc., coincides with one of the three natural frequencies. If the lowest of these frequencies, ω, is greater than about 1.6 rad/sec for this system, then no resonance can occur. However, if $\omega = 0.186$, for example, none of the frequencies in the above series coincides with a natural frequency except the frequency $5\omega = 0.930$, which coincides with the second mode natural frequency, indicating a resonant response of this mode.

The response, either of generalized coordinates, or of the ordinary coordinates can be obtained by superposition, as explained previously. For instance, suppose $\omega_1 = 0.2$, and the response, x_3, is desired. Then, by reference to Fig. 10-4*a*,

$$x_3 = \frac{8}{\pi^2} f_0 \left[6.0 \sin 0.2t - \frac{(-0.6)}{9} \sin 0.6t + \frac{(-1.0)}{25} \sin 1.0t - \frac{(-0.2)}{36} \sin 1.4t + \frac{(-0.1)}{49} \sin 1.8t - \cdots\right]$$

The first term of this series is dominant, so the response is nearly a pure sine function at the fundamental frequency.

CHAPTER 11

Continuous Systems—Classical Methods

11.1 Derivation of the Wave Equation

The preceding chapters have dealt with systems having lumped parameters—systems with discrete masses, springs, or dampers. Most physical systems actually possess smoothly distributed masses, springs, or dampers, and the lumped parameter systems are often convenient (but adequate) approximations of these continuous systems. Some simple distributed systems can be analyzed by methods appropriate to the solution of linear partial differential equations. An understanding of these methods is of value in formulating suitable lumped-parameter approximations for more complex distributed systems. This chapter describes the classical techniques for solving vibration problems associated with several elementary continuous systems.

The Partial Differential Equation. Perhaps the easiest of the continuous systems to understand is the stretched string or wire. The string or wire is assumed to be so thin that it is perfectly flexible so far as bending is concerned, and able to resist only a tensile force. Figure 11-1 shows a string with tension, T, throughout its length. Figure 11-1a shows it in the rest position, Fig. 11-1b in a possible deflected position at some instant, indicating the definitions of x and y, and Fig. 11-1c shows a small element of the string enlarged. While the distance, x, is shown as the distance from a wall, this is only a convenience and x could be the distance along the string from any particular point in space. The deflection, y, of a point from the position it would have at rest is considered to be small enough so that the tension in the string is not significantly altered as a result of the increased distance along the arc of the string as compared with the distance when the string is at rest. If this were not assumed, the tension in the string would be a function of displacement, and the problem would be greatly complicated. As a result of the assumption, however, the tension in the string is constant and also the local angle which the string makes with the position when the string is at rest is small. In this respect, Fig. 11-1c is exaggerated. In addition to these assumptions, gravity forces on the string are neglected, and also any dissipative forces which may be present are neglected. The partial differential equation which governs the motion can now be derived without difficulty.

The element shown in Fig. 11-1c must be slightly curved so that the angles which the string makes at the left and right ends of the element are slightly different. If this were not so, the element would be in equilibrium and would not move. The slope of the left end is $(\partial y/\partial x)_x$ and at the right end is $(\partial y/\partial_x)_{x+dx}$. (Partial derivatives are used because y varies both with time and x.) Often it is possible after a little experience to be able to neglect higher order infinitesimals at the outset, but in order to demonstrate the procedure for instances in which it is not immediately clear how to do this, the derivation here will proceed more cautiously than usual, and the acceleration of the element in the upward direction will be designated as $(\partial^2 y/\partial t^2)_{x+dx/2}$, the acceleration of the

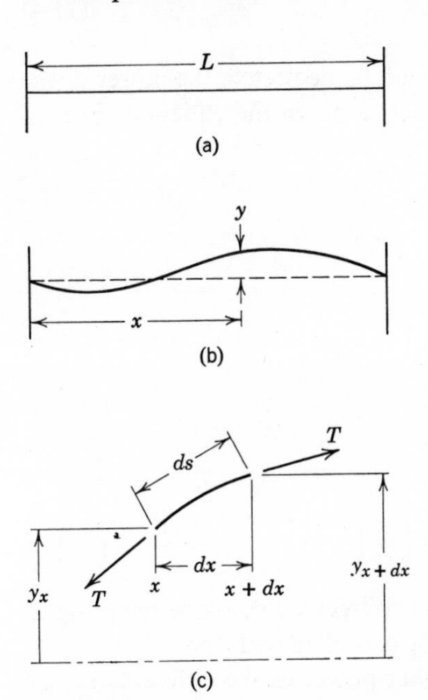

Fig. 11-1 String under tension

midpoint of the element, rather than just $(\partial^2 y/\partial t^2)$. Since the mass times the acceleration in a given direction is equal to the force in that direction,

$$(\rho A\, ds)\left(\frac{\partial^2 y}{\partial t^2}\right)_{x+dx/2} = T\left(\frac{\partial y}{\partial x}\right)_{x+dx} - T\left(\frac{\partial y}{\partial x}\right)_x \tag{11-1}$$

where ρ is the mass density and A the cross-section area. Since the slopes are small, ds can be replaced with dx. The difference between the slopes at the left and right ends depends on the rate of change of slope, as follows:

$$\left(\frac{\partial y}{\partial x}\right)_{x+dx} - \left(\frac{\partial y}{\partial x}\right)_x = \left[\frac{\partial}{\partial x}\left(\frac{\partial y}{\partial x}\right)\right]_{x+dx/2} dx$$

Equation 11-1 thus becomes

$$\begin{aligned}(\rho A\, dx)\left(\frac{\partial^2 y}{\partial t^2}\right)_{x+dx/2} &= T\left[\left(\frac{\partial y}{\partial x}\right)_x + \left(\frac{\partial^2 y}{\partial x^2}\right)_{x+dx/2} dx - \left(\frac{\partial y}{\partial x}\right)_x\right] \\ &= T\left(\frac{\partial^2 y}{\partial x^2}\right)_{x+dx/2} dx\end{aligned} \tag{11-2}$$

As dx approaches zero this becomes

$$\rho A\left(\frac{\partial^2 y}{\partial t^2}\right)_x = T\left(\frac{\partial^2 y}{\partial x^2}\right)_x$$

or, dropping the subscript, since it is no longer needed for clarity,

$$\frac{\partial^2 y}{\partial t^2} = a^2\frac{\partial^2 y}{\partial x^2} \qquad (11\text{-}3)$$

where

$$a^2 = \frac{T}{\rho A} \qquad (11\text{-}4)$$

Whenever there is any doubt about whether a term can be neglected, the power of the differential is examined and compared with the other terms in the equation. For instance, $(\partial^2 y/\partial t^2)_{x+dx/2}$ might have been written as

$$\left(\frac{\partial^2 y}{\partial t^2}\right)_x + \left[\frac{\partial}{\partial x}\left(\frac{\partial^2 y}{\partial t^2}\right)\right]_{x+dx/4}\frac{dx}{2}$$

and a similar term for

$$\left(\frac{\partial^2 y}{\partial x^2}\right)_{x+dx/2}$$

so that Equation 11-2 might have appeared as

$$\rho A\left\{\left(\frac{\partial^2 y}{\partial t^2}\right)_x dx + \left[\frac{\partial}{\partial x}\left(\frac{\partial^2 y}{\partial t^2}\right)\right]_{x+dx/4}\frac{(dx)^2}{2}\right\}$$

$$= T\left\{\left(\frac{\partial y}{\partial x}\right)_x + \left(\frac{\partial^2 y}{\partial x^2}\right)_x dx + \left[\frac{\partial}{\partial x}\left(\frac{\partial^2 y}{\partial x^2}\right)\right]_{x+dx/4}\frac{(dx)^2}{2} - \left(\frac{\partial y}{\partial x}\right)_x\right\}$$

The term with the lowest power of the differential is $(\partial y/\partial x)$ so it might be tempting to drop all terms but this one. However, it is identically cancelled with the $-(\partial y/\partial x)_x$ so that the result would simply be $0 = 0$. The next higher power of the differential is dx and it is necessary to retain all of these terms. However, the terms involving dx^2 can be dropped as negligible since the dx terms do not cancel out identically.

Wave Equation by Minimizing the Lagrangian. Equation 11-3 is known as the "wave equation," because it governs the propagation of a wave along the string. It is now derived by minimizing the Lagrangian in order to demonstrate this method for systems having two independent variables, x and t, and one dependent variable, y. Previously it was seen how it applied to systems having one independent variable, t, and several dependent variables, x_1, x_2, x_3, etc. At a given instant the kinetic energy is

$$\text{K.E.} = \int_{x=0}^{L}\frac{1}{2}\left(\rho A\, dx\right)\left(\frac{\partial y}{\partial t}\right)^2$$

At this same instant the string is deflected into some shape, y, a function of x. The amount of work it would take to get it into this shape would be the potential energy stored in the string. The potential energy stored in the element, dx, would be the tension load times the amount the element stretches.

$$V = \int_{x=0}^{L} T(ds - dx)$$

Since

$$ds = \sqrt{dy^2 + dx^2} = dx\sqrt{1 + \left(\frac{dy}{dx}\right)^2} \simeq dx\left[1 + \frac{1}{2}\left(\frac{dy}{dx}\right)^2\right]$$

for small slopes, and using $\partial y/\partial x$ since y varies with t as well as x,

$$V = \int_{x=0}^{L} \frac{T}{2}\left(\frac{\partial y}{\partial x}\right)^2 dx$$

$$L = \int_{x=0}^{L} \left[\frac{\rho A}{2}\left(\frac{\partial y}{\partial t}\right)^2 - \frac{T}{2}\left(\frac{\partial y}{\partial x}\right)^2\right] dx \tag{11-5}$$

From the calculus of variations (see Appendix 1), if

$$I = \int_{t_1}^{t_2}\int_{x_1}^{x_2} F(y, x, t, y_t, y_x, y_{tt}, y_{xt}, y_{xx} \cdots)\, dx\, dt \tag{11-6}$$

where

$$y_t = \frac{\partial y}{\partial t},\ y_x = \frac{\partial y}{\partial x},\ y_{tt} = \frac{\partial^2 y}{\partial t^2},\ y_{xt} = \frac{\partial^2 y}{\partial x \partial t},\ y_{xx} = \frac{\partial^2 y}{\partial x^2}$$

then I will be a minimum or maximum if

$$\frac{\partial F}{\partial y} - \frac{\partial}{\partial t}\left(\frac{\partial F}{\partial y_t}\right) - \frac{\partial}{\partial x}\left(\frac{\partial F}{\partial y_x}\right) + \frac{\partial^2}{\partial t^2}\left(\frac{\partial F}{\partial y_{tt}}\right) + \frac{\partial^2}{\partial x\, \partial t}\left(\frac{\partial F}{\partial y_{xt}}\right) + \frac{\partial^2}{\partial x^2}\left(\frac{\partial F}{\partial y_{xx}}\right) - \cdots = 0 \tag{11-7}$$

It is obvious that $\int_{t_1}^{t_2} L\, dt$, where L is given by Equation 11-5, is an integral of the type specified by Equation 11-6 (although only y_t and y_x appear in the integrand), and so can be minimized by application of Equation 11-7.

$$-\frac{\partial}{\partial t}\left(\frac{\rho A}{2} 2y_t\right) + \frac{\partial}{\partial x}\left(\frac{T}{2} 2y_x\right) = 0$$

This is easily converted to Equation 11-3.

11.2 D'Alembert Solution of the Wave Equation

Formulation of the Solution. Several solutions of Equation 11-3 will be discussed, the first of which is the D'Alembert solution. Any homogeneous linear partial differential equation of the form

$$a_1 \frac{\partial^n y}{\partial t^n} + \alpha_2 \frac{\partial^n y}{\partial t^{n-1}\, \partial x} + \cdots + \alpha_{n-1} \frac{\partial^n y}{\partial t\, \partial x^{n-1}} + \alpha_n \frac{\partial^n y}{\partial x^n} = 0 \tag{11-8}$$

can be rewritten in the form

$$(D_t + \beta_1 D_x)(D_t + \beta_2 D_x)\cdots(D_t + \beta_n D_x)y = 0$$

where the operators are defined as

$$D_t = \frac{\partial}{\partial t},\quad D_x = \frac{\partial}{\partial x} \tag{11-9}$$

Each solution of $(D_t + \beta_k D_x)y = 0$ is a solution of the original equation and all such solutions must be added together. Examination of one of these reveals that any function of the binomial $(x - \beta_k t)$ will satisfy the equation. For instance

$$\frac{\partial y}{\partial t} + \beta_k \frac{\partial y}{\partial x} = 0 \quad \text{and} \quad y = (x - \beta_k t)^3, \quad \frac{\partial y}{\partial t} = 3(x - \beta_k t)^2(-\beta_k), \quad \frac{\partial y}{\partial x} = 3(x - \beta_k t)^2$$

Substitution shows that $(x - \beta_k t)^3$ is indeed a solution.

If $y = \sin(x - \beta_k t)$,

$$\frac{\partial y}{\partial t} = -\beta_k \cos(x - \beta_k t), \quad \frac{\partial y}{\partial x} = \cos(x - \beta_k t)$$

This similarly satisfies the equation.

If $y = f_k(x - \beta_k t)$,

$$\frac{\partial y}{\partial t} = -\beta_k \frac{df_k(x - \beta_k t)}{d(x - \beta_k t)}, \quad \frac{\partial y}{\partial x} = \frac{df_k(x - \beta_k t)}{d(x - \beta_k t)}$$

It is clear that any function of $(x - \beta_k t)$ will satisfy the partial differential equation. Therefore, the complete solution of the equation is

$$y = f_1(x - \beta_1 t) + f_2(x - \beta_2 t) + \cdots + f_n(x - \beta_n t) \tag{11-10}$$

Of course the functions f_1, f_2, etc., do not have to be the same functions. If it should happen that one of the factors in Equation 11-9 is repeated—that is, there is a factor $(D_t + \beta_k D_x)^m$—the corresponding term in Equation 11-10 will be

$$y = (1 + x + x^2 + \cdots + x^{m-1})f_k(x - \beta_k t) \tag{11-11}$$

However, the wave equation is of the very simple form $(D_t^2 - a^2 D_x^2)y = 0$ or $(D_t + a D_x)(D_t - a D_x)y = 0$, whose solution according to Equation 11-10 is

$$y = f_1(x - at) + f_2(x + at) \tag{11-12}$$

Before determining the specific functions, it might be well to examine this equation in order to see what it means. Suppose just the first term is considered and some specific function is assumed, say

$$f_1(x) = \cos x, \quad -\frac{\pi}{2} < x < \frac{\pi}{2}$$

$$f_1(x) = 0, \quad |x| > \frac{\pi}{2}$$

This function is shown in Fig. 11-2*a*. This is also the shape of the string at $t = 0$, since $f_1(x - at) = f_1(x)$ at $t = 0$. At $(at) = 2$, $y = f_1(x - 2)$, which means that at $(at) = 2$

$$y = \cos(x - 2) \quad \text{for} \quad -\frac{\pi}{2} < (x - 2) < \frac{\pi}{2}$$

$$= 0 \quad \text{for} \quad |x - 2| > \frac{\pi}{2}$$

This is shown in Fig. 11-2*b*. Similarly, at $(at) = 4$, the hump has moved farther to the right, centered at 4. It is evident that a wave travels along the string at the velocity, a, and having a shape determined by the function, f_1. The significance of the term $f_2(x + at)$ is, of course, that a wave of the shape f_2 travels to the left at the velocity, a.

It is necessary to know the form of the functions, f_1 and f_2. These are determined by the initial displacement and velocity of the string. Of course, the initial displacement is not just a single value, but is a function of x. So is the initial velocity. That is,

$$y_{t=0} = F(x)$$
$$\left(\frac{\partial y}{\partial t}\right)_{t=0} = G(x) \qquad (11\text{-}13)$$

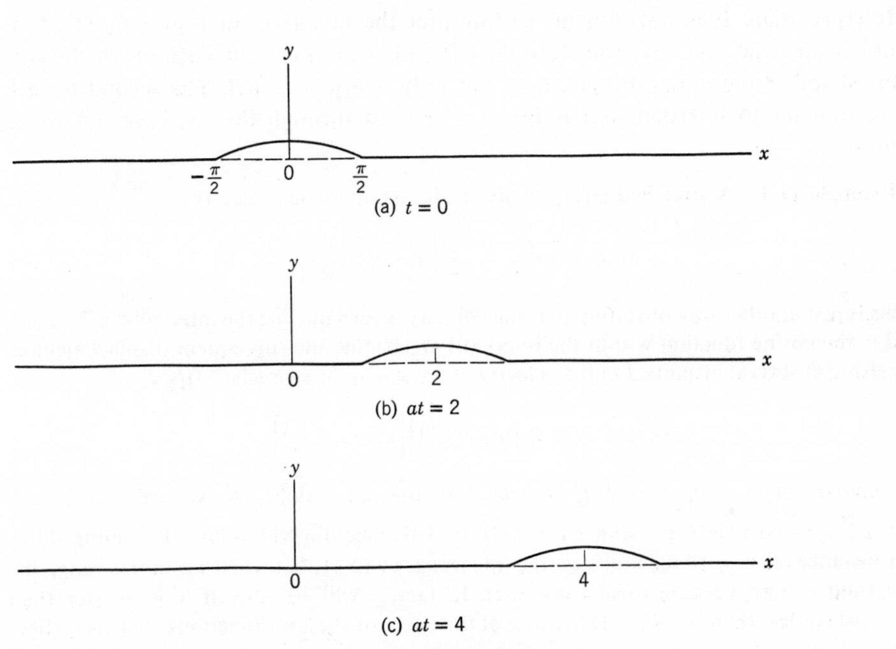

Fig. 11-2 Plot showing $f_1(x - at)$ at different instants

If Equations 11-13 are used in Equation 11-12 and also in $\partial y/\partial t$ determined from Equation 11-12, then

$$y_{t=0} = F(x) = f_1(x) + f_2(x)$$

$$\left(\frac{\partial y}{\partial t}\right)_{t=0} = G(x) = -a\frac{df_1(x)}{dx} + a\frac{df_2(x)}{dx}$$

The second of these equations can be integrated and solved simultaneously with the first to yield

$$f_1(x) = \frac{1}{2}\left[F(x) - \frac{1}{a}\int G(x)\,dx - c\right]$$

$$f_2(x) = \frac{1}{2}\left[F(x) + \frac{1}{a}\int G(x)\,dx + c\right]$$

where c is the constant arising upon integration. It is less confusing in subsequent steps if a dummy variable is used within the integral and then the variable x substituted as a limit of integration. That is, $\int G(x)\,dx = \int^{s=x} G(s)\,ds$. If x is replaced by $(x - at)$ or $(x + at)$ as required, Equation 11-12 can be written

$$y = f_1(x - at) + f_2(x + at)$$

$$= \frac{1}{2}\left[F(x - at) - \frac{1}{a}\int^{s=x-at} G(s)\,ds - c\right] + \frac{1}{2}\left[F(x + at) + \frac{1}{a}\int^{s=x+at} G(s)\,ds + c\right]$$

$$y = \frac{F(x - at) + F(x + at)}{2} + \frac{1}{2a}\int_{s=x-at}^{s=x+at} G(s)\,ds \qquad (11\text{-}14)$$

Interpretation. It is not difficult to interpret the first term in Equation 11-14; it simply states that one wave travels to the left and one to the right, each of which is the same shape as the initial displacement but only one half as tall. The second term is more difficult to interpret and is best understood through the working out of an example.

Example 11-1 A stretched string is given an instantaneous velocity

$$(\cos x)\left[u\left(x + \frac{\pi}{2}\right)\right]\left[u\left(-x + \frac{\pi}{2}\right)\right]$$

(This is just another way of stating that the velocity is zero outside the interval $-\pi/2$ to $\pi/2$, and is the cosine function within the interval.) Determine the subsequent displacement of the string at several instants. Let the velocity of a wave in the string be 2 ft/sec.

$$G(s) = (\cos s)\left[u\left(s + \frac{\pi}{2}\right)\right]\left[u\left(-s + \frac{\pi}{2}\right)\right]$$

Of course at $t = 0$, $y = \frac{1}{4}\int_x^x G(s)\,ds = 0$ for all values of x. At $t = \frac{1}{2}$ sec, $y = \frac{1}{4}\int_{s=x-1}^{s=x+1} (\cos s)u(s + \pi/2)u(-s + \pi/2)\,ds$. This has different values depending on x. For instance, at $x = 10$ the limits on the integral are 9 to 11, but when s is in this range the integrand is zero because of $u(-s + \pi/2)$. In fact, y will be zero if x is greater than $(\pi/2 + 1)$ or less than $(-\pi/2 - 1)$ because of the effect of the unit functions. Between these limits y will vary from zero at each end to a maximum at $x = 0$, where $y = \frac{1}{4}\int_{-1}^{1} \cos s\,ds = \frac{1}{2}\sin 1 = 0.421$. For values of x between $(1 - \pi/2)$ and $(\pi/2 - 1)$, y can be computed from the cosine term alone, since both unit functions are simply unity, and y can be computed from $y = \frac{1}{4}\int_{x-1}^{x+1} \cos s\,ds$. However, if x is less than $(1 - \pi/2)$ or greater than $(\pi/2 - 1)$, the upper or lower limits have to be altered to account for the unit functions. For instance, if $x = \pi/2$, $y = \frac{1}{4}\int_{s=\pi/2-1}^{s=\pi/2+1} (\cos s)u(s + \pi/2)u(-s + \pi/2)\,ds$ becomes $y = \frac{1}{4}\int_{\pi/2-1}^{\pi/2} \cos s\,ds = 0.115$.

At $t = 1$ sec
$$y = \frac{1}{4}\int_{s=x-2}^{x+2} (\cos s)u\left(s + \frac{\pi}{2}\right)u\left(-s + \frac{\pi}{2}\right)ds$$

Now, at this instant the same considerations exist as at $t = \frac{1}{2}$, but in addition there is another interesting conclusion to be drawn. At $x = 0$, $y = \frac{1}{4}\int_{-2}^{2} (\cos s)u(s + \pi/2) \times u(-s + \pi/2)$ becomes $y = \frac{1}{4}\int_{-\pi/2}^{\pi/2} \cos s\,ds = 0.500$. However, for some values of x on either side of zero the limits would be the same. For instance, at x 0.1, $y = \frac{1}{4}\int_{-1.9}^{2.1} (\cos s) \times u(-s + \pi/2)\,ds$ becomes $y = \frac{1}{4}\int_{-\pi/2}^{\pi/2} \cos s\,ds$. This condition prevails for values of x

between $(-2 + \pi/2)$ and $(2 - \pi/2)$, so that in this region the displacement of the string is constant, decreasing outside this region to zero at $x = (\pi/2 + 2)$ and $(-\pi/2 - 2)$. Of course the displacement is zero for values of x greater than $(\pi/2 + 2)$ or less than $(-\pi/2 - 2)$. The sketch shows the displacement of the string at the instants just analysed. For succeeding instants the flat top would become wider with the same shape ramp on each end, the wave travelling to the left and right at the velocity, 2 ft/sec (Fig. 11-3).

Another way of determining the function of time and distance is to make use of the following equation, the proof of which is left as an exercise for the reader. If $x_2 \geqq x_1 : b \geqq a$; $\int f(x)\,dx = F(x)$; and

$$I = \int_{x_1}^{x_2} f(x)[u(x - a)][u(b - x)]\,dx$$

then

$$I = \{[F(x_2)][u(b - x_2)] + [F(b)][u(x_2 - b)] - [F(a)][u(a - x_1)] - [F(x_1)][u(x_1 - a)]\}[u(x_2 - a)][u(b - x_1)]$$

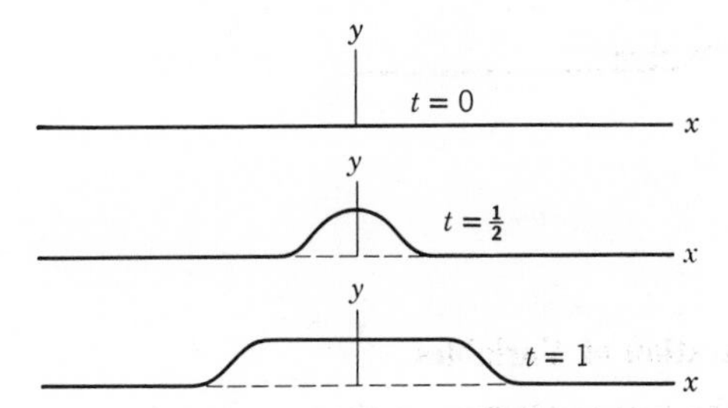

Fig. 11-3

In this example

$$f(x) = \cos x \quad F(x) = \sin x$$

$$a = -\frac{\pi}{2} \quad b = \frac{\pi}{2} \quad x_1 = (x - at) \quad x_2 = (x + at)$$

$$y = \frac{1}{2a}\left\{\left[\sin (x + at)\right]\left[u\left(\frac{\pi}{2} - x - at\right)\right] + \left[\sin \frac{\pi}{2}\right]\left[u\left(x + at - \frac{\pi}{2}\right)\right] - \left[\sin\left(-\frac{\pi}{2}\right)\right]\left[u\left(-\frac{\pi}{2} - x + at\right)\right] - \left[\sin (x - at)\right] \times \left[u\left(x - at + \frac{\pi}{2}\right)\right]\right\}\left[u\left(x + at + \frac{\pi}{2}\right)\right]\left[u\left(\frac{\pi}{2} - x + at\right)\right]$$

If the various specific values of x and t for which y was calculated in this example are substituted into this equation, the result checks the values of y previously determined.

Wave Reflection. Suppose that a string under tension is attached at each end to a support. If the support provides complete fixity for the string, a wave travelling toward the support will be reflected and will travel back along the string in the opposite direction and with the opposite sign. This can be understood by imagining that the string extends on the other side of the wall and then determining what sort of motion in this imaginary part of the string would cause zero deflection at the position of the support when superimposed upon the deflection in the real portion of the string (illustrated by Fig. 11-4). Of course a similar situation exists at the opposite end of the string. The waves in Fig. 11-4 are exaggerated for clarity.

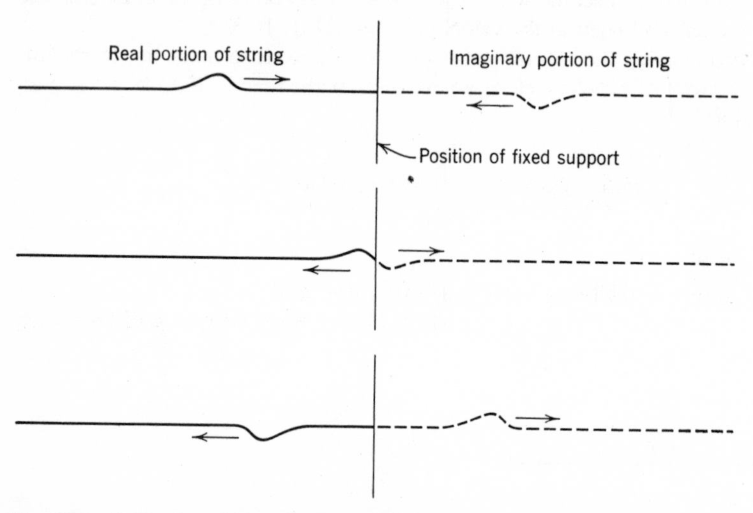

Fig. 11-4 Reflection of wave from fixed support

11.3 Solution of the Wave Equation by Separation of Variables

Perhaps the principal reason for solving the wave equation in the way just demonstrated is the insight which it affords into the wave phenomenon. Another method of solution, "separation of variables," provides a different view of the problem and is perhaps more useful because of its application to other distributed systems, such as beams.

The Product Solution. In the separation of variables method it is assumed that the partial differential equation can be satisfied by functions of the form, $X(x)T(t)$; that is, some function of x alone multiplied by some function of t alone. If such functions cannot satisfy the equation or if the resulting equation cannot be separated, then the method fails, but this becomes evident at that time and may not be apparent at the outset. It is assumed then that

$$y = XT \tag{11-15}$$

It is necessary to know $\partial^2 y/\partial x^2$ and $\partial^2 y/\partial t^2$. Since $X(x)$ contains no t's it can be considered a constant when taking the partial derivative with respect to t. Also, $\partial T/\partial t$ is the same as dT/dt since $T(t)$ contains no x's. Thus

$$\frac{\partial^2 y}{\partial t^2} = X\frac{d^2T}{dt^2} \quad \text{and} \quad \frac{\partial^2 y}{\partial x^2} = T\frac{d^2X}{dx^2}$$

Substituting these into Equation 11-3 yields

$$X\frac{d^2T}{dt^2} = a^2T\frac{d^2X}{dx^2}$$

If both sides of this equation are divided by XT, an equation results which has functions of t on one side and functions of x on the other side.

$$\frac{\left(\dfrac{d^2T}{dt^2}\right)}{T} = a^2\,\frac{\left(\dfrac{d^2X}{dx^2}\right)}{X} \tag{11-16}$$

Selection of Appropriate Common Constants. Since the left side contains no x's and the right side no t's these two expressions cannot equal each other for all values of x and t unless they are equal to some common constant, for instance C. This constant might be zero, pure real, pure imaginary, or complex, and might have any numerical value. Furthermore, since all possible values of the constant cause the partial differential equation to be satisfied, the solution must be the sum of all these solutions. The next task is to try to eliminate some of the possible solutions. First, suppose the constant C were zero. Then $(d^2T/dt^2)/T = 0$ or $T = A_0 + B_0 t$ where A_0 and B_0 are constants of integration. Since $y = TX$, if T is the foregoing function, it would have to be concluded that the deflection of the string increases positively or negatively with time or else remains at some constant value, A_0, with time. Neither of these is physically possible, so A_0 and B_0 must be zero.

Next, if a real number is tried for the constant, say C_r, then

$$\frac{d^2T}{dt^2} - C_r T = 0$$

The solution of this second-order linear equation is familiar enough to be written as either $A\,e^{\sqrt{C_r}\,t} + B\,e^{-\sqrt{C_r}\,t}$ if C_r is a positive real constant or $A \cos \sqrt{-C_r}\,t + B \sin \sqrt{-C_r}\,t$ if C_r is a negative real constant. The first possibility is eliminated by the same sort of argument that was used to eliminate A_0 and B_0 plus the fact that the system is conservative so that the motion cannot be expected to die out as would be the case if terms such as $e^{-\sqrt{C_r}\,t}$ were eligible. (This also eliminates the possibility that C could be a complex number.) Therefore, let C_r be defined as $-\beta^2$, specifying that β is a positive real number, so that

$$\frac{\left(\dfrac{d^2T}{dt^2}\right)}{T} = a^2\,\frac{\left(\dfrac{d^2X}{dx^2}\right)}{X} = -\beta^2$$

$$T = A \cos \beta t + B \sin \beta t$$

$$X = C \cos \frac{\beta}{a} x + D \sin \frac{\beta}{a} x$$

$$y = XT = (A \cos \beta t + B \sin \beta t)\left(C \cos \frac{\beta}{a} x + D \sin \frac{\beta}{a} x\right)$$

However, β can have any magnitude, so that y must be the sum of similar expressions with β taking on all possible values and the other constants taking on appropriate values. Thus

$$y = \sum_n (A_n \cos \beta_n t + B_n \sin \beta_n t)\left(C_n \cos \frac{\beta_n}{a} x + D_n \sin \frac{\beta_n}{a} x\right) \tag{11-17}$$

Normal Mode Frequency and Shape. What values of β_n actually satisfy the physical problem can be determined by considering the ends of the string which are attached to a support, presumably an inflexible support. Where $x = 0$, y must be zero for all values of t. This means that $C_n = 0$, $D_n \neq 0$ would be a satisfactory combination of constants as far as this one end condition is concerned. It might be argued that $C_n \neq 0$ could satisfy this condition if the C_n's are of such magnitude and sign as to cancel out when summed. However, even though the C_n's might cancel in this way for some specific value of t, they could not do so for all values of t, since the time functions would alter the relative effects of the constants in such a summation. Therefore, it is necessary that $C_n = 0$. With $C_n = 0$, D_n could be combined with A_n and B_n since none of these constants have yet been determined. The new constants could be called A_n' and B_n', but no particular advantage would accrue; consequently, let A_n and B_n absorb the D_n in Equation 11-17.

$$y = \sum_n (A_n \cos \beta_n t + B_n \sin \beta_n t) \sin \frac{\beta_n}{a} x \tag{11-18}$$

At the other end of the string, where $x = L$, y is also zero. This can only be true if $A_n = B_n = 0$ (trivial), or if $\sin \beta_n/a\, L = 0$; that is, if

$$\beta_n = \frac{n\pi a}{L} \qquad n = 1, 2, 3, \text{etc.} \tag{11-19}$$

Specific values of β_n are specified by Equation 11-19, and Equation 11-18 shows by its form that β_n is a frequency, so Equation 11-19 is the frequency equation. The mode shape for each frequency is the value of $X(x)$ for that particular value of β_n, or

$$X_n = \sin \frac{n\pi x}{L} \tag{11-20}$$

Thus, the normal mode of oscillation in the first (low frequency) mode is simply $\sin \pi x/L$ and the frequency in this mode is $\beta_1 = \pi a/L = \sqrt{T/\rho A}\, \pi/L$. There are an infinite number of modes, all having frequencies which are some integer times the first mode frequency. The amount of each mode present depends on the initial displacement and velocity. If the initial displacement is $F(x)$ and the initial velocity $G(x)$ as in Equation 11-13, Equation 11-18 at $t = 0$ would give

$$\begin{aligned} F(x) &= \sum_{n=1}^{\infty} A_n \sin \frac{n\pi x}{L} \\ G(x) &= \sum_{n=1}^{\infty} B_n \frac{n\pi a}{L} \sin \frac{n\pi x}{L} \end{aligned} \tag{11-21}$$

Each of these is a Fourier series, and the coefficients can be determined from (see Appendix 1)

$$\begin{aligned} A_n &= \frac{2}{L} \int_0^L F(x) \sin \frac{n\pi x}{L}\, dx \\ B_n \frac{n\pi a}{L} &= \frac{2}{L} \int_0^L G(x) \sin \frac{n\pi x}{L}\, dx \end{aligned} \tag{11-22}$$

Orthogonality of the Modes. Equation 11-22 (with Fourier series theory) shows that if one of the modes is excited by displacing the string in the exact shape of that mode, say $F(x) = \sin(m\pi x/L)$, (and the initial velocity is zero), then $A_m = 1$, but $A_n = 0$ if $n \neq m$. That is, if the string is displaced into the exact shape of one of the modes it will oscillate with only that one shape and frequency and none of the other frequencies and mode shapes will be excited. This is an important property of vibration modes, one which was observed in connection with the multiple-degree-of-freedom systems; vibration in one normal mode does not excite vibration in the other modes. This independence of the normal modes is the familiar property of orthogonality of the normal modes. The validity of this property for distributed systems can be established by extending the multiple-degree lumped systems to an infinite number of masses with their coordinates.

Example 11-2. A string is plucked by pulling the center to a displacement, δ, and then releasing the string with zero initial velocity. Determine the amplitude of the normal modes.

Since $G(x) = 0$, $B_n = 0$

$$F(x) = \delta \frac{2x}{L} \qquad \text{for} \quad 0 < x > \frac{L}{2}$$

$$= \delta\left(2 - \frac{2x}{L}\right) \qquad \text{for} \quad \frac{L}{2} < x < L$$

Because of the symmetry of $F(x)$ it is immediately seen that for A_1, A_3, A_5, etc., the integral of Equation 11-22 over the first half of the string is the same as that over the second half and therefore the integral need only be taken over the first half and then doubled. For A_2, A_4, A_6, etc., the integral over the first half is cancelled by the integral over the second half, so these coefficients are all zero.

$$A_n = 2\left(\frac{2}{L}\right)\int_0^{L/2} \delta \frac{2x}{L} \sin\frac{n\pi x}{L}\, dx \qquad \text{for} \quad n = 1, 3, 5, \text{etc.}$$

$$A_n = \frac{8}{n^2\pi^2}\,\delta$$

The motion of the string is, therefore, from Equation 11-18,

$$y = \frac{8}{\pi^2}\,\delta\left[\sin\frac{\pi x}{L}\cos\frac{\pi at}{L} + \frac{1}{9}\sin\frac{3\pi x}{L}\cos\frac{3\pi at}{L} + \frac{1}{25}\sin\frac{5\pi x}{L}\cos\frac{5\pi at}{L} + \cdots\right]$$

11.4 Laplace Transform Solution of the Wave Equation

The Laplace transform can often be used to solve the wave equation and other partial differential equations arising from the study of distributed systems. The transform must be defined carefully and its meaning kept in mind throughout. If $f(x, t)$ is a function of two independent variables as indicated, it would be possible to take the transform with respect to either variable. However, if the t variable is used, the transform can be defined as

$$\mathscr{L}[f(x, t)] = \int_{t=0}^{\infty} f(x, t)\, e^{-st}\, dt = Y(x, s)$$

The result must be a function of x and s, and it would be possible to differentiate this with respect to x, since s is merely a constant.

$$\frac{dY}{dx} = \frac{d}{dx}\left[\int_{t=0}^{\infty} f(x, t)\, e^{-st}\, dt\right]$$

The differentiation under the integral, from Liebnitz' rule, yields

$$\frac{dY}{dx} = \int_{t=0}^{\infty} \frac{\partial f}{\partial x} e^{-st}\, dt = \mathscr{L}\left(\frac{\partial f}{\partial x}\right)$$

Thus

$$\mathscr{L}\left[\frac{\partial f(x, t)}{\partial x}\right] = \frac{d[\mathscr{L}(f)]}{dx}$$

$$\mathscr{L}\left[\frac{\partial^n f(x, t)}{\partial x^n}\right] = \frac{d^n[\mathscr{L}(f)]}{dx^n} \tag{11-23}$$

This demonstrates how to transform one of the terms in the wave equation. The other term, the partial derivative with respect to t, is no different from taking the transform of a total derivative, since the x variable is considered as a constant when the partial derivative with respect to t is taken. Therefore,

$$\mathscr{L}\left[\frac{\partial f(x, t)}{\partial t}\right] = s\,\mathscr{L}(f) - [f(x, t)]_{t=0}$$

$$\mathscr{L}\left[\frac{\partial^n f(x, t)}{\partial t^n}\right] = s^n \mathscr{L}(f) - s^{n-1}[f(x, t)]_{t=0} - \cdots - \left[\frac{\partial^{n-1}}{\partial t^{n-1}} f(x, t)\right]_{t=0} \tag{11-24}$$

The only difference from previous usage is that $f_{t=0}$, $(\partial f/\partial t)_{t=0}$, etc., are functions of x instead of simple constants. If $Y = \mathscr{L}(y)$, and $F(x)$ and $G(x)$ are the initial displacement and velocity functions, the wave equation when transformed becomes

$$s^2 Y - sF(x) - G(x) = a^2 \frac{d^2 Y}{dx^2}$$

or

$$\frac{d^2 Y}{dx^2} - \left(\frac{s}{a}\right)^2 Y = -sF(x) - G(x) \tag{11-25}$$

The partial differential equation in y has become an ordinary linear differential equation in the transform of y. The solution of this equation should not be difficult, but the method is often limited in its usefulness by inability to take the inverse transform.

Example 11-3 A long string under tension is initially at rest in its equilibrium position. If the end at $x = 0$ is forced to oscillate according to $y_0 \sin \omega t$, what is the motion of the string?

Since $F(x) = G(x) = 0$, Equation 11-25 immediately yields $Y = Ae^{(s/a)x} + Be^{-(s/a)x}$. As x approaches infinity this indicates that Y would approach infinity unless $A = 0$. Y could not approach infinity unless y, the deflection, also did, but this could not occur because of the physical nature of the problem. Therefore, $A = 0$. Then at $x = 0$, $Y_{x=0} = B$, but

$$Y_{x=0} = \mathscr{L}(y_{x=0}) = \mathscr{L}(y_0 \sin \omega t) = \frac{y_0 \omega}{s^2 + \omega^2}$$

so

$$Y = \frac{y_0 \omega}{s^2 + \omega^2} e^{-(x/a)s}$$

The inverse transform of this is simply the same sine function delayed in time by the amount of time required for the wave to reach the position, x.

$$y = y_0 \left[\sin \omega \left(t - \frac{x}{a}\right)\right] u \left(t - \frac{x}{a}\right)$$

In fact, any motion performed at the left end would be repeated all along the string at the time required for the passage of the wave.

11.5 Other Problems Characterized by the Wave Equation

The wave equation characterizes many important vibration problems. One of them is the longitudinal vibration of an elastic medium of constant cross section. The equation derived for this problem is

$$\frac{\partial^2 u}{\partial t^2} = \frac{E}{\rho} \frac{\partial^2 u}{\partial x^2} \tag{11-26}$$

where E is the modulus of elasticity, ρ the mass density, and u the displacement of a point in the x direction from its position of equilibrium.

The equation for torsional displacement of a point in a cylindrical shaft is also of the wave form,

$$\frac{\partial^2 \theta}{\partial t^2} = \frac{G}{\rho} \frac{\partial^2 \theta}{\partial x^2} \tag{11-27}$$

where G is the torsional modulus of rigidity and θ is the angular displacement of the point from its equilibrium position.

Another example is the tidal wave problem, leading to

$$\frac{\partial^2 u}{\partial t^2} = gh \frac{\partial^2 u}{\partial x^2} \tag{11-28}$$

where u is the displacement of a particle of fluid in the x direction, h is the depth of water, and g the acceleration of gravity.

In the field of electricity an example of the wave equation is the passage of a voltage or current wave through a conductor having zero resistance. The equations are

$$\frac{\partial^2 e}{\partial t^2} = \frac{1}{Lc} \frac{\partial^2 e}{\partial x^2} \quad \text{or} \quad \frac{\partial^2 i}{\partial t^2} = \frac{1}{Lc} \frac{\partial^2 i}{\partial x^2} \tag{11-29}$$

where e and i are the voltage and current at a point and instant, L is the inductance of the wire per unit length, and c is the capacitance to ground per unit length.

These applications and others involving the wave equation can be solved by analogy with the string problem.

11.6 Differential Equation for the Vibrating Beam

The next continuous system to be studied is the vibrating beam (Fig. 11-5). In this derivation the mass of the beam is assumed to be concentrated along the neutral axis of the beam, and the deflection of the beam caused by shear deformation is neglected. These are the usual assumptions for relatively long thin beams. A method of analysis wherein these assumptions are not made is presented in Chapters 12 and 13.

The acceleration of the element in the upward direction is $\partial^2 y/\partial t^2$. The net force in the upward direction is $s_x - s_{x+dx}$. Since $s_{x+dx} - s_x = (\partial s/\partial x)\,dx$,

$$(\rho A\,dx)\frac{\partial^2 y}{\partial t^2} = -\frac{\partial s}{\partial x}\,dx \tag{11-30}$$

In this equation ρ is mass density and A the cross-section area, as in the string problem. If the convention for positive shear is upward on the left end of an element (or downward on the right end), and if the convention for positive moment is compression

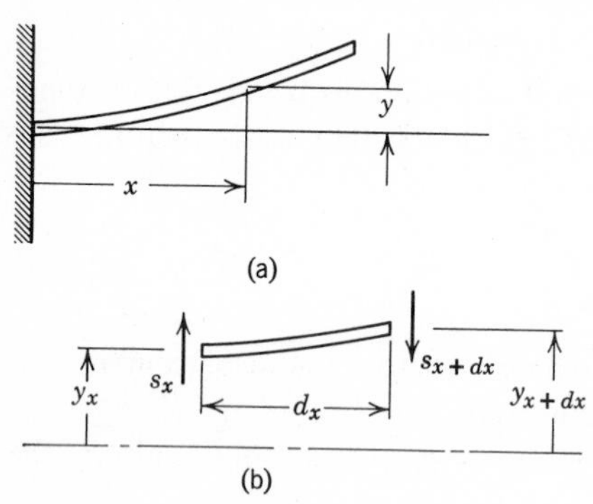

Fig. 11-5 Vibrating beam

in the upper fibers of the beam (or tension in the lower fibers) and if y is positive upward as indicated in Fig. 11-5, then the shear, moment, and deflection are related by

$$s = \frac{\partial M}{\partial x}$$
$$\frac{\partial^2 y}{\partial x^2} = \frac{M}{EI} \tag{11-31}$$

where E is the modulus of elasticity and I the area moment of inertia of the beam cross section. If these are substituted in Equation 11-30,

$$\frac{\partial^2 y}{\partial t^2} = -\frac{1}{\rho A}\frac{\partial^2}{\partial x^2}\left(EI\frac{\partial^2}{\partial x^2}\right) \tag{11-32}$$

If the area and moment of inertia are constant along the length of the beam, this becomes

$$\frac{\partial^2 y}{\partial t^2} = -a^2\frac{\partial^4 y}{\partial x^4}$$
$$a^2 = \frac{EI}{\rho A} \tag{11-33}$$

11.7 Vibrating Beam Solution by Separation of Variables

Equation 11-33 can be solved readily by the separation of variables technique. Letting $y = X(x)T(t)$,

$$\frac{\left(\dfrac{d^2T}{dt^2}\right)}{T} = -a^2\frac{\left(\dfrac{d^4X}{dx^4}\right)}{X} = C \tag{11-34}$$

As in the string problem C can be any constant, but it is soon found that it must be a negative real number, say $-\beta^2$, in order to obtain the proper kind of functions for T. Of course C must be $-\beta^2$ in the X equation too, which then becomes $d^2X/dx^4 - (\beta/a)^2X = 0$. The results are

$$T = A\cos\beta t + B\sin\beta t$$

$$X = C\cos\sqrt{\frac{\beta}{a}}\,x + D\sin\sqrt{\frac{\beta}{a}}\,x + E\cosh\sqrt{\frac{\beta}{a}}\,x + F\sinh\sqrt{\frac{\beta}{a}}\,x \qquad (11\text{-}35)$$

As in the string problem, the values of β and the various constants now depend on the beam end conditions and on initial values of deflection and velocity. For the cantilever beam indicated in Fig. 11-5, the end conditions are $y_{x=0} = 0$, $(\partial y/\partial x)_{x=0} = 0$, $(\partial^2 y/\partial x^2)_{x=L} = 0$, $(\partial^3 y/\partial x^3)_{x=L} = 0$, the last two conditions coming from the fact that the moment and shear at the free end are zero. Substituting these conditions into the Equation 11-35 results in

$$\left.\begin{aligned} C + E &= 0 \\ D + F &= 0 \\ -C\cos\sqrt{\frac{\beta}{a}}L - D\sin\sqrt{\frac{\beta}{a}}L + E\cosh\sqrt{\frac{\beta}{a}}L + F\sinh\sqrt{\frac{\beta}{a}}L &= 0 \\ C\sin\sqrt{\frac{\beta}{a}}L - D\cos\sqrt{\frac{\beta}{a}}L + E\sinh\sqrt{\frac{\beta}{a}}L + F\cosh\sqrt{\frac{\beta}{a}}L &= 0 \end{aligned}\right\} (11\text{-}36)$$

Frequency Equation. These equations can be solved simultaneously to determine β, but only the ratios of the other constants can be determined since there are five unknowns but only four equations. Equation 11-37 is the frequency equation which must be satisfied, determined from the simultaneous solutions of Equation 11-36.

$$\cos\sqrt{\frac{\beta_n}{a}}L\cosh\sqrt{\frac{\beta_n}{a}}L = -1 \qquad (11\text{-}37)$$

In this equation a subscript n has been used because there are infinitely many values of β which satisfy the equation. The values would have to be determined by trial and error. However, the approximate values can easily be determined by rewriting Equation 11-36 as

$$\cos\sqrt{\frac{\beta_n}{a}}L = -\frac{1}{\cosh\sqrt{\frac{\beta_n}{a}}L}$$

and considering the plots of the left and right sides of this equation (Fig. 11-6). From this sketch it is evident that the first solution occurs at $\sqrt{\beta/a}\,L$ somewhat greater than $\pi/2$, the second somewhat less than $3\pi/2$, and so on. For the higher frequencies, the values where the cosine curve crosses the axis might as well be used, at $(2n - 1)\pi/2$, if n is the mode number.

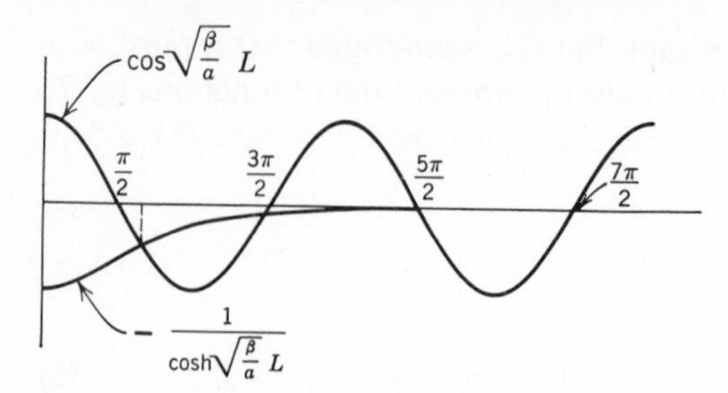

Fig. 11-6 Left and right sides of Equation 11-37

Normal Mode Equation. Now if the ratios of the constants C, D, and E to the constant F are obtained from the four equations,

$$\frac{E}{F} = -\frac{\left(\sin\sqrt{\frac{\beta}{a}}\,L + \sinh\sqrt{\frac{\beta}{a}}\,L\right)}{\left(\cos\sqrt{\frac{\beta}{a}}\,L + \cosh\sqrt{\frac{\beta}{a}}\,L\right)}$$

$$\frac{C}{F} = \frac{\left(\sin\sqrt{\frac{\beta}{a}}\,L + \sinh\sqrt{\frac{\beta}{a}}\,L\right)}{\left(\cos\sqrt{\frac{B}{a}}\,L + \cosh\sqrt{\frac{\beta}{a}}\,L\right)}$$

$$\frac{D}{F} = -1$$

If these are used in X, Equation 11-35,

$$X = \left[\frac{\sin\sqrt{\frac{\beta}{a}}\,L + \sinh\sqrt{\frac{\beta}{a}}\,L}{\cos\sqrt{\frac{\beta}{a}}\,L + \cosh\sqrt{\frac{\beta}{a}}\,L}\left(\cos\sqrt{\frac{\beta}{a}}\,x - \cosh\sqrt{\frac{\beta}{a}}\,x\right) - \sin\sqrt{\frac{\beta}{a}}\,x + \sinh\sqrt{\frac{\beta}{a}}\,x\right]F$$

This could be a satisfactory expression for the normal mode when β_n is used for β, or the expression in the bracket could be multiplied by the constant,

$$\frac{\cos\sqrt{\frac{\beta}{a}}\,L + \cosh\sqrt{\frac{\beta}{a}}\,L}{2\left(\cos\sqrt{\frac{\beta}{a}}\,L\sinh\sqrt{\frac{\beta}{a}}\,L - \sin\sqrt{\frac{\beta}{a}}\,L\cosh\sqrt{\frac{\beta}{a}}\,L\right)}$$

altering F to suit, which gives

$$X_n = \left[\frac{(\sin\sqrt{B_n/a}\,L + \sinh\sqrt{\beta_n/a}\,L)(\cos\sqrt{\beta_n/a}\,x - \cosh\sqrt{\beta_n/a}\,x) + (\cos\sqrt{\beta_n/a}\,L + \cosh\sqrt{\beta_n/a}\,L)(-\sin\sqrt{\beta_n/a}\,x + \sinh\sqrt{\beta_n/a}\,x)}{2(\cos\sqrt{\beta_n/a}\,L\sinh\sqrt{\beta_n/a}\,L - \sin\sqrt{\beta_n/a}\,L\cosh\sqrt{\beta_n/a}\,L)}\right]F_n \tag{11-38}$$

The only purpose of altering the form was so that the expression in the bracket would yield unity at $x = L$. The F_n is not necessary so far as the description of the mode shape is concerned, and can be taken as unity.

Orthogonality of Modes. These modes should of course be orthogonal, which in this instance, with no lumped masses present, means that $\int_0^L X_n X_m \, dx = 0$ if $n \neq m$. This can be seen immediately if it is recalled that vibration in one normal mode does not excite another normal mode. If the inertia forces in one mode are regarded as the generalized external force exciting another mode, this generalized force would have to be zero in order not to excite that mode. The generalized external force in the nth mode caused by vibration in the mth mode according to this view point would then be the force which would do the same amount of work, or $Q_n q_n = \int_0^L \beta_m{}^2 X_m(\rho A \, dx) X_n$ and since ρ, A, and $\beta_m{}^2$ are constants, it is clear that $\int_0^L X_n X_m \, dx = 0$. In this instance, then, as in the vibrating string, the functions which describe the normal modes are orthogonal as well as the modes. This means that the functions X_n can be manipulated like those of a Fourier series. (Additional discussion of the mathematical requirements for orthogonal functions may be found in Reference 6.)

Initial Conditions. To determine the amount of each normal mode present in a given problem, the initial conditions would have to be known, as in the vibrating-string problem. The deflection is now described by the equation

$$y = \sum_{n=1}^{\infty} (A_n \cos \beta_n t + B_n \sin \beta_n t) X_n \tag{11-39}$$

where X_n is defined by Equation (11-38) for the cantilever beam and by similar functions for other types of beams. If the initial displacement and velocity are defined as before as $y_{t=0} = F(x)$ and $(\partial y/\partial t)_{t=0} = G(x)$, then

$$\begin{aligned} F(x) &= \sum_{n=1}^{\infty} A_n X_n \\ G(x) &= \sum_{n=1}^{\infty} B_n \beta_n X_n \end{aligned} \tag{11-40}$$

and because of the orthogonality of the modes the coefficients can be determined in the same way as those of a Fourier series.

$$\begin{aligned} A_n &= \frac{\int_0^L F(x) X_n \, dx}{\int_0^L X_n{}^2 \, dx} \\ B_n \beta_n &= \frac{\int_0^L G(x) X_n \, dx}{\int_0^L X_n{}^2 \, dx} \end{aligned} \tag{11-41}$$

Example 11-4. A cantilever beam is deflected upward at the free end by a concentrated force applied there, and then released from rest. Determine the amplitude of the first and second modes present in the vibration.

As a preliminary step the first and second mode frequencies and mode shapes will be computed. Solutions of Equation 11-37 for $\sqrt{\beta/a}\,L$ slightly over $\pi/2$ and slightly under $3\pi/2$ must be found. The first occurs at $\sqrt{\beta_1/a}\,L = 1.875$ or $\beta_1 = 3.516\sqrt{EI/\rho AL^4}$ and the second at $\sqrt{\beta_2/a}\,L = 4.694$ or $\beta_2 = 22.03\sqrt{EI/\rho AL^4}$. When these values are substituted into Equation 11-38, the mode shapes are found to be

$$X_1 = -0.5000\left(\cos 1.875\frac{x}{L} - \cosh 1.875\frac{x}{L}\right) - 0.3670\left(-\sin 1.875\frac{x}{L} + \sinh 1.875\frac{x}{L}\right)$$

$$X_2 = 0.5000\left(\cos 4.694\frac{x}{L} - \cosh 4.694\frac{x}{L}\right) + 0.5092\left(-\sin 4.694\frac{x}{L} + \sinh 4.694\frac{x}{L}\right)$$

A cantilever beam with an upward load (P) at the free end (or where $x = L$) deflects into the shape

$$F(x) = \frac{PL^3}{EI}\left[\frac{1}{2}\left(\frac{x}{L}\right)^2 - \frac{1}{6}\left(\frac{x}{L}\right)^3\right]$$

When this function and the mode shapes are substituted into Equation 11-41 the results are

$$A_1 = 0.32356\frac{PL^3}{EI}$$

$$A_2 = 0.00824\frac{PL^3}{EI}$$

Similar calculations for A_3 and A_4 would result in $0.00105PL^3/EI$ and $0.00027PL^3/EI$. These results show that a concentrated load applied at the end of a cantilever beam and then released excites the first mode almost exclusively.

CHAPTER 12

Lumped Parameter Approximation for Distributed Systems

12.1 Numerical Determination of Normal Modes and Frequencies

Constant Section Beams. Most engineering problems cannot be solved by the methods of Chapter 11. The reason for this is that most structures do not possess constant cross sections, and, if they do, they may have other irregularities which cause these methods to fail or at least become impractical. Therefore, it is necessary to be able to solve such problems by numerical means. The usual method is to replace the distributed system with a system having a finite number of coordinates and discrete masses. The system then becomes similar to the multiple-degree-of-freedom systems studied in Chapters 8 to 10. The methods described therein can be used to determine the frequencies and modes. The procedure can best be illustrated by an example which can be checked by the exact methods of the last section.

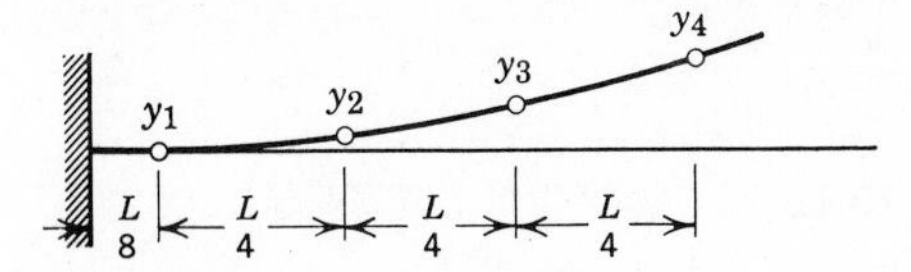

Fig. 12-1

Example 12-1. Determine the first two modes and frequencies for a cantilever beam of constant cross section.

The more coordinates used the better will be the approximation, but the numerical work will become correspondingly more tedious. Since two modes are to be calculated, there must be at least two coordinates. However, the accuracy would be rather poor with only this number of coordinates, so four will be used. In general, at least twice as many coordinates should be used as the number of modes desired. The same assumptions will be made as in Section 11.7 so that the results can be compared; that is, the mass of the beam is assumed to be concentrated along the beam neutral axis, and the shear deflection is negligible compared to the bending deflection.

The beam is now divided into four parts with the mass of each part being assumed to be concentrated at the center of gravity of each part. The problem then becomes one in which these masses are connected by a weightless beam as indicated in Fig. 12-1.

Each mass is $\rho AL/4$. The inertia matrix is

$$[M] = \frac{\rho AL}{4}\begin{bmatrix} 1 & 0 & 0 & 0 \\ 0 & 1 & 0 & 0 \\ 0 & 0 & 1 & 0 \\ 0 & 0 & 0 & 1 \end{bmatrix}$$

The flexibility matrix can be determined by the equations for a cantilever with loads applied at various points along the beam. The equation for deflection of a cantilever at x_a caused by a load at x_b, where $x_b > x_a$, is given by the following equation

$$y_a = \frac{P_b}{6EI}(x_b - x_a)^3 + \frac{P_b(x_b{}^2 x_a)}{2EI} - \frac{P_b x_b{}^3}{6EI}$$

$$= \frac{P_b L^3}{6EI}\left[\left(\frac{x_b}{L} - \frac{x_a}{L}\right)^3 + 3\left(\frac{x_b}{L}\right)^2\left(\frac{x_a}{L}\right) - \left(\frac{X_b}{L}\right)^3\right]$$

To obtain δ_{23}, the deflection at station 2 caused by unit load at 3, for example, let $Pb = 1$, $x_b/L = \frac{5}{8}$, $x_a/L = \frac{3}{8}$. Of course, $\delta_{32} = \delta_{23}$. The result of these calculations for the general element, δ_{ij} is the flexibility matrix,

$$[\delta] = \frac{L^3}{6EI}\begin{bmatrix} 0.00391 & 0.15630 & 0.02734 & 0.03906 \\ 0.01563 & 0.10547 & 0.21094 & 0.31641 \\ 0.02734 & 0.21094 & 0.48828 & 0.78125 \\ 0.03906 & 0.31641 & 0.78125 & 1.33984 \end{bmatrix}$$

Not all of the modes are to be computed; therefore, it may be advisable to use the iteration procedure described in Example 8.5. The dynamic matrix is

$$[U] = [\delta][M] = \frac{\rho AL^4}{24EI}\begin{bmatrix} 0.00391 & 0.01563 & 0.02734 & 0.03906 \\ 0.01563 & 0.10547 & 0.21094 & 0.31641 \\ 0.02734 & 0.21094 & 0.48828 & 0.78125 \\ 0.03906 & 0.31641 & 0.78125 & 1.33984 \end{bmatrix}$$

and the matrix equation is

$$\{A\} = \beta^2[U]\{A\}$$

The modal column for the first mode turns out to be

$$\{A\}_1 = \begin{Bmatrix} 0.03151 \\ 0.24868 \\ 0.59701 \\ 1.00000 \end{Bmatrix}$$

The frequency, using $\{A\}_1$ in any of the algebraic equations represented by the matrix equation, is

$$\beta_1{}^2 = 0.5302\,\frac{24EI}{\rho AL^4}$$

$$\beta_1 = 3.57\sqrt{\frac{EI}{\rho AL^4}}\ \text{rad/sec}$$

Note the comparison with the value of $3.52\sqrt{EI/\rho AL^4}$ calculated in Example 11-4.

The dynamic matrix for the second mode may be calculated as in Example 8-5.

$$B = \frac{\rho AL}{4}[0.03151\ 0.24868\ 0.59701\ 1.00000]\begin{bmatrix}1 & 0 & 0 & 0\\0 & 1 & 0 & 0\\0 & 0 & 1 & 0\\0 & 0 & 0 & 1\end{bmatrix}$$

$$[S] = \begin{bmatrix}0 & -7.892 & -18.948 & -31.736\\0 & 1 & 0 & 0\\0 & 0 & 1 & 0\\0 & 0 & 0 & 1\end{bmatrix}$$

$$[U]_2 = [U][S] = \frac{\rho AL^4}{24EI}\begin{bmatrix}0 & -0.01523 & -0.04675 & -0.08503\\0 & -0.01788 & -0.08522 & -0.17962\\0 & -0.00482 & -0.02976 & -0.08641\\0 & 0.00815 & 0.04114 & 0.10023\end{bmatrix}$$

The modal column for this mode becomes

$$\{A\}_2 = \begin{Bmatrix}-0.302\\-1.417\\-1.071\\1.000\end{Bmatrix}$$

Using this column and the original dynamic matrix, the frequency is

$$B_2{}^2 = 22.4\frac{24EI}{\rho AL^4}$$

$$\beta_2 = 23.2\sqrt{\frac{EI}{\rho AL^4}}\ \text{rad/sec}$$

This frequency compares with the correct value of $21.7\sqrt{EI/\rho AL^4}$ from Example 11.4, providing some idea of the accuracy to be expected from the assumptions made.

For comparison with the foregoing mode shapes, the correct relative deflections at the four points, from Example 11.4, in the first two modes are

$$\{A\}_1 = \begin{Bmatrix}0.0313\\0.2473\\0.5953\\1.0000\end{Bmatrix} \qquad \{A\}_2 = \begin{Bmatrix}-0.339\\-1.609\\-1.314\\1.000\end{Bmatrix}$$

If rotation of the elements were to be taken into consideration, instead of assuming the masses concentrated, four more coordinates would be added which would specify the angular rotation about the c.g of each element. The four more elements along the diagonal of the $[M]$ matrix would each be $\rho AL^3/768$ (the moments of inertia if the masses are assumed distributed along the neutral axis), while the flexibility matrix would take the following form (angular or linear deflections caused by moments or loads as explained in Example 12-3).

$$[\delta] = \frac{L^3}{6EI}\begin{bmatrix} 0.00391 & 0.01563 & 0.02734 & 0.03906 & \frac{0.04688}{L} & \frac{0.04688}{L} & \frac{0.04688}{L} & \frac{0.04688}{L} \\ 0.01563 & 0.10547 & 0.21094 & 0.31641 & \frac{0.23438}{L} & \frac{0.42188}{L} & \frac{0.42188}{L} & \frac{0.42188}{L} \\ 0.02734 & 0.21094 & 0.48828 & 0.78125 & \frac{0.42188}{L} & \frac{0.98438}{L} & \frac{1.17188}{L} & \frac{1.17188}{L} \\ 0.03906 & 0.31641 & 0.78125 & 1.33984 & \frac{0.60938}{L} & \frac{1.54688}{L} & \frac{2.10938}{L} & \frac{2.29688}{L} \\ \frac{0.04688}{L} & \frac{0.23438}{L} & \frac{0.42188}{L} & \frac{0.60938}{L} & \frac{0.75000}{L^2} & \frac{0.75000}{L^2} & \frac{0.75000}{L^2} & \frac{0.75000}{L^2} \\ \frac{0.04688}{L} & \frac{0.42188}{L} & \frac{0.98438}{L} & \frac{1.54688}{L} & \frac{0.75000}{L^2} & \frac{2.25000}{L^2} & \frac{2.25000}{L^2} & \frac{2.25000}{L^2} \\ \frac{0.04688}{L} & \frac{0.42188}{L} & \frac{1.17188}{L} & \frac{2.10938}{L} & \frac{0.75000}{L^2} & \frac{2.25000}{L^2} & \frac{3.75000}{L^2} & \frac{3.75000}{L^2} \\ \frac{0.04688}{L} & \frac{0.42188}{L} & \frac{1.17188}{L} & \frac{2.29688}{L} & \frac{0.75000}{L^2} & \frac{2.25000}{L^2} & \frac{3.75000}{L^2} & \frac{5.25000}{L^2} \end{bmatrix}$$

The matrix iteration yields the following results for the first mode:

$$\{A\} = \begin{Bmatrix} 0.0311 \\ 0.246 \\ 0.594 \\ 1.000 \\ 3.18/L \\ 3.22/L \\ 3.25/L \\ 3.26/L \end{Bmatrix} \qquad \beta^2 = 0.510\,\frac{24EI}{\rho AL^4}$$

The effect of rotation of the elements is negligible in the first mode for the assumptions made. Usually this effect is neglected unless there are elements whose masses are located quite far from the neutral axis so that their moments of inertia are large for their masses.

Complex Beam Structures. It is easy to see how this method can be extended to more difficult problems. If a beam does not have a constant cross section, the only difference is that the inertia matrix is altered to have the correct masses, and the deflections for the flexibility matrix would have to be calculated numerically because of the varying *EI*. Also, if shear deflection is to be accounted for, this is simply included in the calculation of deflections for the flexibility matrix. If the assumption that the beam masses are concentrated on the neutral axis is not sufficiently accurate, another coordinate can be added for the angular displacement of each mass. If large inflexible masses are located at points in the structure (an engine on a wing, for instance) no particular complication is involved. Coordinates for the linear and angular displacement of these masses are introduced and the analysis proceeds as before. If a structure is too complex for a trustworthy analysis of deflections, a model may be built and the flexibility matrix obtained by test. However, the flexibility matrix occupies a central position in this method of analysis. Accordingly, the next three sections are devoted to the determination of the flexibility matrix of determinate and indeterminate beams of variable section properties.

12.2 Flexibility Matrix for Variable Section Cantilever Beams

Deflections by Method of Virtual Work. As indicated in the last section, the determination of the flexibility matrix for different types of continuous structures is of great importance in the vibration analysis of such structures by numerical means. It is also useful in static-deflection problems. There are many methods for determining the deflection of a continuous structure under load. Several methods are described here. The method to be described is based on the method of virtual work and is especially adaptable to beams and frames, whether determinate or indeterminate. Flexibility matrices for beams can be computed with this method using digital computer programs provided in Reference 1. Consider first, then, the cantilever beam subjected to a concentrated load (Fig. 12-2).

If the moment at point x is designated as M and the shear as V, the total energy stored in the beam is

$$E_F = \int_0^L \left(\frac{1}{2}\frac{M^2}{EI} + \frac{1}{2}\frac{V^2Q}{GIb}\right) dx$$

where E and G are modulus of elasticity and shear modulus, Q is the first moment of area of the portion of the beam cross section above the neutral axis, I is the second moment of area of the beam cross section about the neutral axis (or moment of inertia), and b is the width of the beam cross section at the neutral axis.

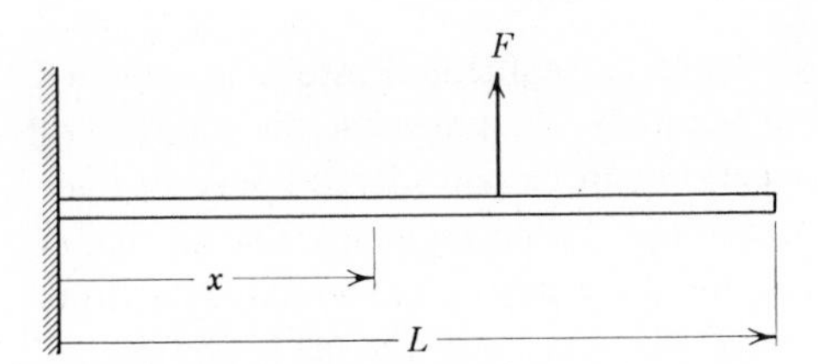

Fig. 12-2 Cantilever beam with load

Now if the actual load, F, is removed and unit force is applied at some point where the deflection, y is to be computed in the direction of the desired deflection, let the corresponding moment and shear be designated by m and v. The energy stored in the beam is

$$E_1 = \int_0^L \left(\frac{1}{2}\frac{m^2}{EI} + \frac{1}{2}\frac{v^2Q}{GIb}\right) dx$$

If the actual load and the unit load are both applied (the unit load applied earlier than the actual load) the energy stored in the beam is

$$E_{\text{total}} = \int_0^L \left(\frac{1}{2}\frac{m^2}{EI} + \frac{1}{2}\frac{v^2Q}{GIb}\right) dx + \int_0^L \left(\frac{1}{2}\frac{M^2}{EI} + \frac{1}{2}\frac{V^2Q}{GIb}\right) dx + 1y$$

(y is the additional deflection of the point where the unit load is applied. This deflection occurs when the load F is applied. The $1y$ is the additional work done by the unit load when the actual load, F is applied.) The energy stored in the beam is also determined from the total moment and shear as

$$E_{\text{total}} = \int_0^L \left[\frac{1}{2}\frac{(M+m)^2}{EI} + \frac{1}{2}\frac{(V+v)^2Q}{GIb}\right] dx$$

Equating these expressions for E yields an expression for y.

$$y = \int_0^L \left(\frac{Mm}{EI} + \frac{VvQ}{GIb}\right) dx \tag{12-1}$$

It is recalled that all of the quantities in this integral may be functions of x, although often E and G would be constants. The rotation at a point, or slope of the beam, may also be obtained the same way,

$$\theta = -\frac{VQ}{GIb} + \int_0^L \frac{Mm_r}{EI} dx$$

where m_r is the moment caused by unit pure torque applied on the beam in the direction of the desired angular deflection, θ. The term $-(VQ)/(GIb)$ may or may not be used in a given situation. It is the beam slope caused by shear at the position, x, but it does not represent rotation of the beam cross section, which the integral term does. For simplicity, and because most situations would not require its use, and because its effect is usually quite small even when legitimate, it will be omitted hereafter, so that the angular deflection equation becomes

$$\theta = \int_0^L \frac{Mm_r}{EI} dx \tag{12-2}$$

Deflections for Approximate Beam. Let the beam be segmented into a number of parts (Fig. 12-3) the more parts the better the accuracy. Assume that the number of parts is large enough so that the beam cross section can be considered constant over each segment and equal to its value at the midpoint of each segment. The segments should be chosen so that the midpoint of each segment is a position at which deflections

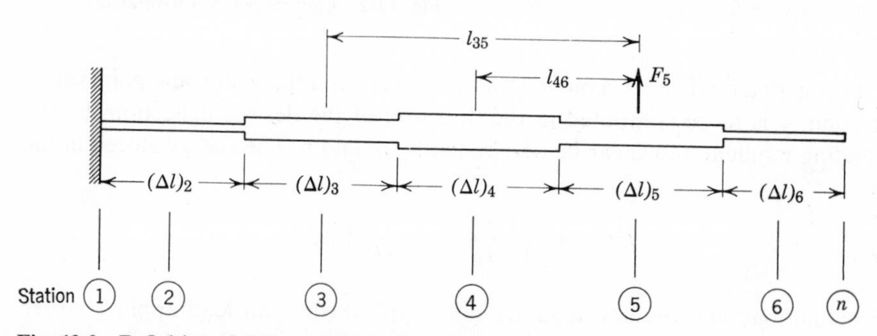

Fig. 12-3 Definition of distances for cantilever beam numerical analysis

are desired and the midpoint of one of the segments is the point at which the load is applied. Suppose it is required to calculate the deflection at 4 caused by a load at 5. A little algebra and calculus will show that

$$\int \frac{Mm}{EI} dx$$

over the first segment of the beam is

$$\frac{F_5(\Delta l)_2}{(EI)_2}\left[l_{24}l_{25} + \frac{1}{12}(\Delta l)_2{}^2\right]$$

and the integral

$$\int \frac{VvQ}{GIb}\,dx$$

over the first segment is

$$F_5(\Delta l)_2\left(\frac{Q}{GIb}\right)_2$$

The corresponding quantities for the second segment are

$$\frac{F_5(\Delta l)_3}{(EI)_3}\left[l_{34}l_{35} + \frac{1}{12}(\Delta l)_3{}^2\right]$$

and

$$F_5(\Delta l)_3\left(\frac{Q}{GIb}\right)_3$$

However, for the third segment these quantities are

$$\frac{F_5(\Delta l)_4{}^2}{8(EI)_4}\left[l_{45} + \frac{1}{3}(\Delta l)_4\right]$$

and

$$\frac{F_5(\Delta l)_4}{2}\left(\frac{Q}{GIb}\right)_4$$

Thus, the deflection at the center of the third segment caused by a load, F_5, applied at the center of the fourth segment is

$$y_{45} = \frac{F_5(\Delta l)_2}{EI_2}\left[l_{24}l_{25} + \frac{1}{12}(\Delta l)_2\right] + \frac{F_5(\Delta l)_3}{(EI)_3}\left[l_{34}l_{35} + \frac{1}{12}(\Delta l)_3{}^2\right]$$
$$+ \frac{F_5(\Delta l)_4{}^2}{8(EI)_4}\left[l_{45} + \frac{1}{3}(\Delta l)_4\right] + F_5\left(\frac{Q}{GIb}\right)_2(\Delta l)_2$$
$$+ F_5\left(\frac{Q}{GIb}\right)_3(\Delta l)_3 + \frac{1}{2}F_5\left(\frac{Q}{GIb}\right)_4(\Delta l)_4$$

Similarly, for the deflection at the center of the fourth segment

$$y_{55} = \frac{F_5(\Delta l)_2}{(EI)_2}\left[l_{25}{}^2 + \frac{1}{12}(\Delta l)_2{}^2\right] + \frac{F_5(\Delta l)_3}{(EI)_3}\left[l_{35}{}^2 + \frac{1}{12}(\Delta l)_3{}^2\right]$$
$$+ \frac{F_5(\Delta l)_4}{(EI)_4}\left[l_{45}{}^2 + \frac{1}{12}(\Delta l)_4{}^2\right] + \frac{F_5(\Delta l)_5{}^3}{24(EI)_5} + F_5\left(\frac{Q}{GIb}\right)_2(\Delta l)_2$$
$$+ F_5\left(\frac{Q}{GIb}\right)_3(\Delta l)_3 + F_5\left(\frac{Q}{GIb}\right)_4(\Delta l)_4 + \frac{1}{2}F_5\left(\frac{Q}{GIb}\right)_5(\Delta l)_5$$

If the load had been applied at the center of the third segment and the deflection at the center of the fourth segment were desired, the deflection at station 5 caused by a load at station 4 would become

$$y_{54} = \frac{F_4(\Delta l)_2}{(EI)_2}\left[l_{24}l_{25} + \frac{1}{12}(\Delta l)_2{}^2\right] + \frac{F_4(\Delta l)_3}{(EI)_3}\left[l_{34}l_{35} + \frac{1}{12}(\Delta l)_3{}^2\right]$$
$$+ \frac{F_4(\Delta l)_4{}^2}{8(EI)_4}\left[l_{45} + \frac{1}{3}(\Delta l)_4{}^2\right] + F_4\left(\frac{Q}{GIb}\right)_2(\Delta l)_2 + F_4\left(\frac{Q}{GIb}\right)_3(\Delta l)_3$$
$$+ \frac{1}{2}F_4\left(\frac{Q}{GIb}\right)_4(\Delta l)_4$$

Actually, the applied loads are supposed to be unit loads, and if F_3 and F_4 are each 1, it is seen that $y_{45} = y_{54}$. The generalization of the above pattern is,

$$y_{ij} = \frac{(\Delta l)_i^2}{8(EI)_i}\left[l_{ij} + \frac{1}{3}(\Delta l)_i\right] + \frac{1}{2}\left(\frac{Q}{GIb}\right)_i (\Delta l)_i + \sum_{k=2}^{k=(i-1)}\left[\frac{l_{ki}l_{kj} + \frac{1}{12}(\Delta l)_k^2}{(EI)_k} + \left(\frac{Q}{GIb}\right)_k\right](\Delta l)_k \qquad j \geqq i$$

$$y_{1j} = y_{i1} = 0$$

$$y_{pq} = y_{qp}$$

If $i = j = n$, y_{nn} is calculated without the first two terms, or with the summation terms only. If $i \leqq 2$, the summation terms are omitted.

j is station where unit load is applied;

i is station where deflection is calculated.

This equation can be checked with the flexibility matrix of Example 12-1 by using a constant cross-section beam divided into four segments and omitting the shear deformation terms. The results agree exactly since no approximations are required if the beam cross section is constant.

In a manner similar to the foregoing, three other sets of flexibility coefficients can be derived for the cantilever beam, which can be designated as ϵ_{ij}, θ_{ij}, and ϕ_{ij} where ϵ_{ij} means the linear deflection at i caused by unit counterclockwise moment applied at j, θ_{ij} is the angular deflection in the counterclockwise direction of the station at i caused by unit force in the y direction at j; and ϕ_{ij} is the angular deflection in the counterclockwise direction at i caused by unit pure couple in the counterclockwise direction at j.

$$\theta_{ij} = \frac{(\Delta l)_i}{2(EI)_i}\left[l_{ij} + \frac{1}{4}(\Delta l)_i\right] + \sum_{k=2}^{k=(i-1)}\frac{l_{kj}}{(EI)_k}(\Delta l)_k \qquad j \geqq i$$

$$\theta_{ij} = \frac{1}{8}\frac{(\Delta l)_j^2}{(EI)_j} + \sum_{k=2}^{k=(j-1)}\frac{l_{kj}(\Delta l)_k}{(EI)_k} \qquad j < i \tag{12-4}$$

$$\theta_{1j} = \theta_{i1} = 0$$

$$\epsilon_{ij} = \frac{1}{8}\frac{(\Delta l)_i^2}{(EI)_i} + \sum_{k=2}^{k=(i-1)}\frac{l_{ki}(\Delta l)_k}{(EI)_k} \qquad j \geqq i$$

$$\epsilon_{ij} = \frac{1}{2}\frac{(\Delta l)_j}{(EI)_j}\left[l_{ij} + \frac{1}{4}(\Delta l)_j\right] + \sum_{k=2}^{k=(j-1)}\frac{l_{ki}(\Delta l)_k}{(EI)_k} \qquad j \leqq i \tag{12-5}$$

$$\epsilon_{1j} = \epsilon_{i1} = 0$$

$$\phi_{ij} = \frac{(\Delta l)_i}{2(EI)_i} + \sum_{k=2}^{k=(i-1)}\frac{(\Delta l)_k}{(EI)_k} \qquad j \geqq i$$

$$\phi_{1j} = \phi_{i1} = 0 \tag{12-6}$$

$$\phi_{pq} = \phi_{qp}$$

In these equations $l_{ii} = l_{jj} = 0$ and for y_{2j}, θ_{2j} ϵ_{2j}, ϕ_{2j} the summation is omitted. For y_{nn}, θ_{nn}, ϵ_{nn}, and ϕ_{nn} only the terms in the summation are used. The angles are in radians. There could be another term in the equation for θ_{ij} with $j \geqq i$, the expression $(Q/GIb)_i$, but this will be omitted in accordance with the discussion of Equation (12-2). This term is the angular deflection attributable to shear deflection, and whether it should be included or not depends on the physical situation. Often, all the shear-deflection terms are neglected anyway. Even these shear deflection terms are actually only approximations and not to be depended upon near the beam ends or near sudden changes in cross section. It may be noted that $\theta_{lm} = \epsilon_{ml}$. A more comprehensive symmetrical flexibility matrix may be formed from the coefficients of Equations 12-3 to Equation 12-6 as follows:

$$[\delta] = \begin{bmatrix} y_{11} & y_{12} & \cdots & y_{1n} & \epsilon_{11} & \epsilon_{12} & \cdots & \epsilon_{1n} \\ y_{21} & y_{22} & \cdots & y_{2n} & \epsilon_{21} & \epsilon_{22} & \cdots & \epsilon_{2n} \\ \cdot & \cdot & \cdot & \cdot & \cdot & \cdot & \cdot & \cdot \\ y_{n1} & y_{n2} & \cdots & y_{nn} & \epsilon_{n1} & \epsilon_{n2} & \cdots & \epsilon_{nn} \\ \theta_{11} & \theta_{12} & \cdots & \theta_{1n} & \phi_{11} & \phi_{12} & \cdots & \phi_{1n} \\ \theta_{21} & \theta_{22} & \cdots & \theta_{2n} & \phi_{21} & \phi_{22} & \cdots & \phi_{2n} \\ \cdot & \cdot & \cdot & \cdot & \cdot & \cdot & \cdot & \cdot \\ \theta_{n1} & \theta_{n2} & \cdots & \theta_{nn} & \phi_{n1} & \phi_{n2} & \cdots & \phi_{nn} \end{bmatrix} \quad (12\text{-}7)$$

From this flexibility matrix all deflection information, both linear and angular, for any combination of loads and moments may be obtained.

12.3 Flexibility Matrix for Indeterminate Beams

It should be remembered that the objective here is to develop a method of analysis for indeterminate beams as well as determinate beams. Although the equations of Section 12.2 are applicable only to the cantilever beam, it will soon become evident that they are also useful for other beams. When an influence coefficient is computed, the unit force or moment is applied at some station. Reactions must be generated somewhere. In the cantilever beam under consideration these reactions are located at the left end of the beam. Let them be designated as R_{F_1} and R_{M_1}, the force reaction and moment reaction at the left end of the cantilever beam caused by unit force at Station j on the beam. The positive directions are upward and counterclockwise. The distance from the left reaction to the point where the load is applied is designated l_{1j}, and to the point where the deflection is measured l_{1i}.

Next, let it be assumed that instead of the beam being supported inflexibly at the left end it is supported flexibly by springs at every station (Fig. 12-4). It will be assumed that there are springs which resist translation, having spring constants k_1, k_2, etc., and springs which resist rotation, with spring rates k_{r_1}, k_{r_2}, etc. When a load is applied at Station j, all the springs are deflected and produce reactions on the beam. These are to be designated R_{F_1}, R_{F_2}, etc., for the forces which the springs exert on the beam, and R_{M_1}, R_{M_2}, etc. for the moments which the rotational springs exert on the beam. The positive direction for these reactions are upward and counterclockwise. (A reaction force is positive if it exerts a force upward on the beam, and a reaction moment is positive if it exerts a counterclockwise moment on the beam.) Let the total deflection of this beam at Station i caused by unit load at Station j be designated z_{ij}, and let the total angular deflection at i caused by the unit load at j be designated α_{ij}. The total linear deflection at i caused by unit moment at j is to be designated v_{ij} and the total angular deflection at i caused by unit moment at j is β_{ij}.

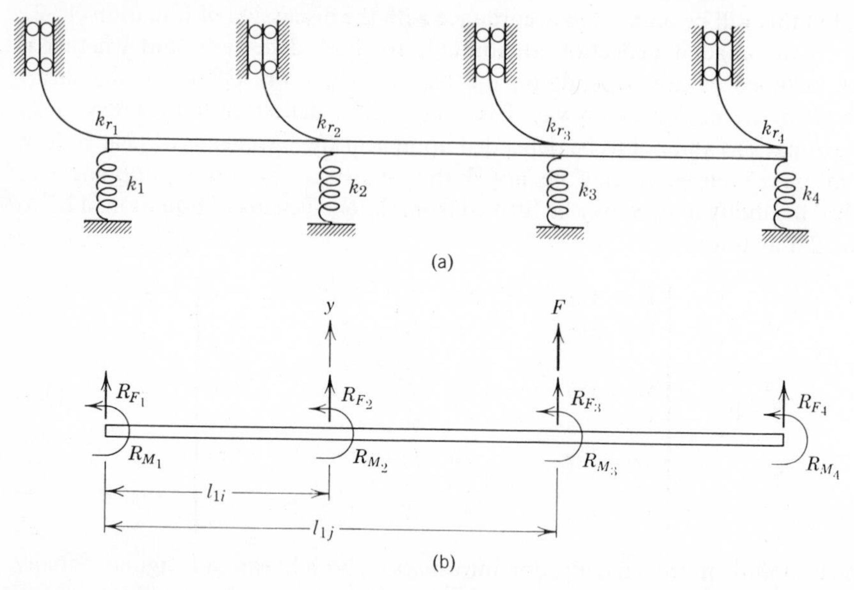

Fig. 12-4 Flexibly supported beam, with definitions of positive directions. (*a*) Schematic representation of flexibly supported beam. (*b*) Definitions of positive directions; reactions shown are forces and moments of springs *on* beam; external load, *F*, applied at station *j*; deflection, *y*, at station *i* results

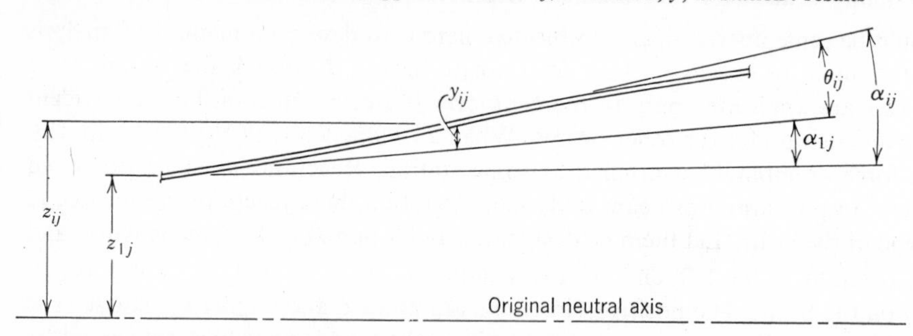

Fig. 12-5 Flexibly supported beam in deflected position

From Fig. 12-5 it is clear that

$$z_{ij} = z_{1j} + \alpha_{1j}l_{1i} + y_{ij}$$

$$\alpha_{ij} = \alpha_{1j} + \theta_{ij}$$

However, the y_{ij} and θ_{ij} are deflections caused not only by the unit load but by all the reactions acting on the beam just as if they were external loads. For instance, the deflections at Station i caused by a unit load at Station j would be

$$z_{ij} = z_{1j} + \alpha_{1j}l_{1i} + 1y_{ij} + R_{F_{1j}}y_{i1} + R_{F_{2j}}y_{i2} + \cdots + R_{F_{nj}}y_{in} + R_{M_{1j}}\epsilon_{i1} + R_{M_{2j}}\epsilon_{i2} + \cdots + R_{M_{nj}}\epsilon_{in}$$

$$\alpha_{ij} = \alpha_{1j} + \theta_{ij} + R_{F_{1j}}\theta_{i1} + R_{F_{2j}}\theta_{i2} + \cdots + R_{F_{nj}}\theta_{in} + R_{M_{1j}}\phi_{i1} + R_{M_{2j}}\phi_{i2} + \cdots + R_{M_{nj}}\phi_{in}$$

Also

$$R_{F_{1j}} = -k_1 z_{1j}, \quad R_{F_{2j}} = -k_2 z_{2j}, \quad \text{etc.}$$

$$R_{M_{1j}} = -k_{r_1}\alpha_{1j}, \quad R_{M_{2j}} = -k_{r_2}\alpha_{2j}, \quad \text{etc.}$$

and

$$R_{F_{1j}} + R_{F_{2j}} + \cdots + R_{F_{nj}} + 1 = 0$$

$$R_{M_{1j}} + R_{M_{2j}} + \cdots + R_{M_{nj}} + R_{F_{1j}}l_{11} + R_{F_{2j}}l_{12} + \cdots + R_{F_{nj}}l_{1n} + 1l_{1j} = 0$$

There are now available $2n$ equations in $2n$ unknowns for each value of j. (Let i vary from 2 to n.) These can be put into convenient matrix form as follows:

$$[\lambda]\{\Delta\} = \{\mu\} \tag{12-8}$$

Matrix $[\lambda]$ is formed from the flexibility matrix for the cantilever beam as follows:

$$[\lambda] = \begin{bmatrix} k_1 & k_2 & k_3 & \cdots & k_n & 0 & 0 & 0 & \cdots & 0 \\ (k_1y_{21}-1) & (k_2y_{22}+1) & (k_3y_{23}) & \cdots & (k_ny_{2n}) & (k_{r_1}\epsilon_{21}-l_{12}) & (k_{r_2}\epsilon_{22}) & (k_{r_3}\epsilon_{23}) & \cdots & (k_{r_n}\epsilon_{2n}) \\ (k_1y_{31}-1) & (k_2y_{32}) & (k_3y_{33}+1) & \cdots & (k_ny_{3n}) & (k_{r_1}\epsilon_{31}-l_{13}) & (k_{r_2}\epsilon_{32}) & (k_{r_3}\epsilon_{33}) & \cdots & (k_{r_n}\epsilon_{3n}) \\ \cdot & \cdot & \cdot & \cdot & \cdot & \cdot & \cdot & \cdot & \cdot & \cdot \\ (k_1y_{n1}-1) & (k_2y_{n2}) & (k_3y_{n3}) & \cdots & (k_ny_{nn}+1) & (k_{r_1}\epsilon_{n1}-l_{1n}) & (k_{r_2}\epsilon_{n2}) & (k_{r_3}\epsilon_{n3}) & \cdots & (k_{r_n}\epsilon_{nn}) \\ (k_1l_{11}) & (k_2l_{12}) & (k_3l_{13}) & \cdots & (k_nl_{1n}) & k_{r_1} & k_{r_2} & k_{r_3} & \cdots & k_{r_n} \\ (k_1\theta_{21}) & (k_2\theta_{22}) & (k_3\theta_{23}) & \cdots & (k_n\theta_{2n}) & (k_{r_1}\phi_{21}-1) & (k_{r_2}\phi_{22}+1) & (k_{r_3}\phi_{23}) & \cdots & (k_{r_n}\phi_{2n}) \\ (k_1\theta_{31}) & (k_2\theta_{32}) & (k_3\theta_{33}) & \cdots & (k_n\theta_{3n}) & (k_{r_1}\phi_{31}-1) & (k_{r_2}\phi_{32}) & (k_{r_3}\phi_{33}+1) & \cdots & (k_{r_n}\phi_{3n}) \\ \cdot & \cdot & \cdot & \cdot & \cdot & \cdot & \cdot & \cdot & \cdot & \cdot \\ (k_1\theta_{n1}) & (k_2\theta_{n2}) & (k_3\theta_{n3}) & \cdots & (k_n\theta_{nn}) & (k_{r_1}\phi_{n1}-1) & (k_{r_2}\phi_{n2}) & (k_{r_3}\phi_{n3}) & \cdots & (k_{r_n}\phi_{nn}+1) \end{bmatrix} \tag{12-9}$$

Matrix $\{\Delta\}$ is one column of the new influence coefficient matrix, defined as follows:

$$\{\Delta\} = \begin{Bmatrix} z_{1j} \\ z_{2j} \\ \cdots \\ z_{nj} \\ \alpha_{1j} \\ \alpha_{2j} \\ \cdots \\ \alpha_{nj} \end{Bmatrix} \tag{12-10}$$

Finally, matrix $\{\mu\}$ is one column of the cantilever beam flexibility matrix slightly modified.

$$\{\mu\} = \begin{Bmatrix} 1 \\ y_{2j} \\ y_{3j} \\ \cdots \\ y_{nj} \\ l_{1j} \\ \theta_{2j} \\ \theta_{3j} \\ \cdots \\ \theta_{nj} \end{Bmatrix} \tag{12-11}$$

A similar analysis for the effect of unit applied moment instead of unit force would result in the same matrix equation, Equation 12.8, with the same matrix $[\lambda]$ but with $[\Delta]$ and $[\mu]$ defined as follows (v and β defined following Equation 12.16).

$$\{\Delta\} = \begin{Bmatrix} v_{1j} \\ v_{2j} \\ \cdots \\ v_{nj} \\ \beta_{1j} \\ \beta_{2j} \\ \cdots \\ \beta_{nj} \end{Bmatrix} \tag{12-12}$$

$$\{\mu\} = \begin{Bmatrix} 0 \\ \epsilon_{2j} \\ \epsilon_{3j} \\ \cdots \\ \epsilon_{nj} \\ 1 \\ \phi_{2j} \\ \phi_{3j} \\ \cdots \\ \phi_{nj} \end{Bmatrix} \tag{12-13}$$

This entire set of matrix equations can be reduced to a single matrix equation

$$[\lambda][\Delta] = [\mu] \tag{12-14}$$

where $[\lambda]$ is defined by Equation 12-9, and $[\Delta]$ and $[\mu]$ are defined as follows:

$$[\Delta] = \begin{bmatrix} z_{11} & z_{12} & \cdots & z_{1n} & v_{11} & v_{12} & \cdots & v_{1n} \\ z_{21} & z_{22} & \cdots & z_{2n} & v_{21} & v_{22} & \cdots & v_{2n} \\ \cdot & \cdot & \cdot & \cdot & \cdot & \cdot & \cdot & \cdot \\ z_{n1} & z_{n2} & \cdots & z_{nn} & v_{n1} & v_{n2} & \cdots & v_{nn} \\ \alpha_{11} & \alpha_{12} & \cdots & \alpha_{1n} & \beta_{11} & \beta_{12} & \cdots & \beta_{1n} \\ \alpha_{21} & \alpha_{22} & \cdots & \alpha_{2n} & \beta_{21} & \beta_{22} & \cdots & \beta_{2n} \\ \cdot & \cdot & \cdot & \cdot & \cdot & \cdot & \cdot & \cdot \\ \alpha_{n1} & \alpha_{n2} & \cdots & \alpha_{nn} & \beta_{n1} & \beta_{n2} & \cdots & \beta_{nn} \end{bmatrix} \tag{12-15}$$

$$[\mu] = \begin{bmatrix} 1 & 1 & \cdots & 1 & 0 & 0 & \cdots & 0 \\ y_{21} & y_{22} & \cdots & y_{2n} & \epsilon_{21} & \epsilon_{22} & \cdots & \epsilon_{2n} \\ \cdot & \cdot & \cdot & \cdot & \cdot & \cdot & \cdot & \cdot \\ y_{n1} & y_{n2} & \cdots & y_{nn} & \epsilon_{n1} & \epsilon_{n2} & \cdots & \epsilon_{nn} \\ l_{11} & l_{12} & \cdots & l_{1n} & 1 & 1 & \cdots & 1 \\ \theta_{21} & \theta_{22} & \cdots & \theta_{2n} & \phi_{21} & \phi_{22} & \cdots & \phi_{2n} \\ \cdot & \cdot & \cdot & \cdot & \cdot & \cdot & \cdot & \cdot \\ \theta_{n1} & \theta_{n2} & \cdots & \theta_{nn} & \phi_{n1} & \phi_{n2} & \cdots & \phi_{nn} \end{bmatrix} \tag{12-16}$$

Note that $[\mu]$ is simply the flexibility matrix for the cantilever beam, $[\delta]$, modified slightly in two rows. The matrix $[\Delta]$ is the flexibility matrix for the indeterminate beam, whose elements are defined as follows along with the other coefficients:

z_{ij} = linear deflection at i caused by unit load at j,

α_{ij} = angular deflection at i caused by unit load at j,

v_{ij} = linear deflection at i caused by unit moment at j,

β_{ij} = angular deflection at i caused by unit moment at j,

y_{ij} = linear deflection at i caused by unit load at j for a cantilever beam,

θ_{ij} = angular deflection at i caused by unit load at j for a cantilever beam,

ϵ_{ij} = linear deflection at i caused by unit moment at j for a cantilever beam,

ϕ_{ij} = Angular deflection at i caused by unit moment at j for a cantilever beam.

The coefficients y_{ij}, θ_{ij}, ϵ_{ij}, ϕ_{ij} may be computed by use of Equations 12-3 through 12-6.

Modification for Rigid Support. It remains only to be seen how the foregoing matrices are modified for certain special cases. If there is no support at a station, the corresponding value of k or k_r is set to zero. If there is an infinitely rigid support at a station, either to linear or angular deflection, the corresponding spring rate becomes infinite and deflections zero. However, the product of the infinity and the zero is the reaction of the support. Hence, some of the elements of the matrices must be altered accordingly. For instance, if there is a simple support at Station 3 then $k_3 \rightarrow \infty$ and z_{3j}, v_{3j}, z_{i3}, α_{i3} all become zero (third row and column of $[\Delta]$). However, the reactions, $k_3 z_{3j}$ and $k_3 v_{3j}$, are not zero. If the elements in the third column of $[\lambda]$ are changed to

$$\begin{matrix} -1 \\ -y_{23} \\ -y_{33} \\ \cdots\cdots \\ -y_{n3} \\ -l_{13} \\ -\theta_{23} \\ -\theta_{33} \\ -\theta_{n3} \end{matrix}$$

then $[\Delta] = [\lambda]^{-1}[\mu]$ will give the proper results for all the elements of $[\Delta]$ except the third row. This row would then become the reactions at Station 3 caused by the loads or moments at the various stations, or

$$(k_3 z_{31})(k_3 z_{32}) \cdots (k_3 z_{3n})(k_3 v_{31})(k_3 v_{32}) \cdots (k_3 v_{3n})$$

In this form the matrix $[\Delta]$ would be useful in computing loads and moments in the beam, but for purposes of computing deflections—that is, as influence coefficients—the elements of the third row of $[\Delta]$ should be changed to zeros. The elements of the third column of $[\Delta]$ should come out zeros from $[\lambda]^{-1}[\mu]$ if the third column of $[\lambda]$ is changed as indicated. The modification necessary to account for a rigid rotational support is left as an exercise for the reader (Problem 12.4). The method described may be programmed for solution by digital computer. The solution of static beam-deflection or beam-stress problems is greatly facilitated by this system in addition to the usefulness of the flexibility matrix in the determination of natural modes and frequencies of vibration.

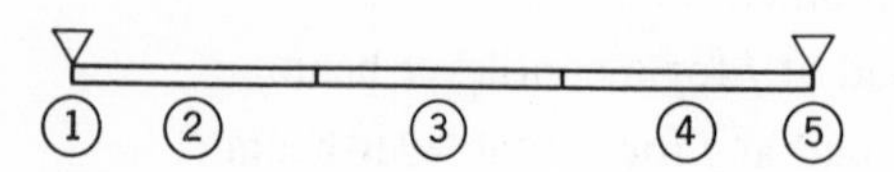

Fig. 12-6

Example 12-2. Apply the general method to the determination of the flexibility matrix of a simply supported beam of constant cross section neglecting shear deformation and using a beam divided into three equal segments (Fig. 12-6).

From Equations 12-3 through 12-7, for a cantilever beam

$$[\delta] = \frac{L}{1296EI}\begin{bmatrix} 0 & 0 & 0 & 0 & 0 & 0 & 0 & 0 & 0 & 0 \\ 0 & 2L^2 & 8L^2 & 14L^2 & 17L^2 & 0 & 18L & 18L & 18L & 18L \\ 0 & 8L^2 & 54L^2 & 108L^2 & 135L^2 & 0 & 90L & 162L & 162L & 162L \\ 0 & 14L^2 & 108L^2 & 250L^2 & 325L^2 & 0 & 162L & 378L & 450L & 450L \\ 0 & 17L^2 & 135L^2 & 325L^2 & 432L^2 & 0 & 198L & 486L & 630L & 648L \\ 0 & 0 & 0 & 0 & 0 & 0 & 0 & 0 & 0 & 0 \\ 0 & 18L & 90L & 162L & 198L & 0 & 216 & 216 & 216 & 216 \\ 0 & 18L & 162L & 378L & 486L & 0 & 216 & 648 & 648 & 648 \\ 0 & 18L & 162L & 450L & 630L & 0 & 216 & 648 & 1080 & 1080 \\ 0 & 18L & 162L & 450L & 648L & 0 & 216 & 648 & 1080 & 1296 \end{bmatrix}$$

These coefficients were obtained using

$$l_{11} = 0 \quad l_{12} = \frac{L}{6} \quad l_{13} = \frac{L}{2} \quad l_{14} = \frac{5}{6}L \quad l_{15} = L$$

$$l_{22} = 0 \quad l_{23} = \frac{1}{3}L \quad l_{24} = \frac{2}{3}L \quad l_{25} = \frac{5}{6}L$$

$$l_{33} = 0 \quad l_{34} = \frac{1}{3}L \quad l_{35} = \frac{1}{2}L$$

$$l_{44} = 0 \quad l_{45} = \frac{1}{6}L$$

$$l_{55} = 0$$

$$(\Delta l)_2 = (\Delta l)_3 = (\Delta l)_4 = \frac{1}{3}L \qquad (\Delta l)_1 = (\Delta l)_5 = 0$$

Now the matrix $[\lambda]$ can be formed, using k_1 and $k_5 \to \infty$ and the other k's and k_r's zero. Therefore, the first and fifth columns of [λ] must be modified. Equation 12-9, with the appropriate modifications to [λ], gives

$$[\lambda] = \begin{bmatrix} -1 & 0 & 0 & 0 & -1 & 0 & 0 & 0 & 0 & 0 \\ 0 & 1 & 0 & 0 & -\frac{17L^3}{1296EI} & -\frac{L}{6} & 0 & 0 & 0 & 0 \\ 0 & 0 & 1 & 0 & -\frac{135L^3}{1296EI} & -\frac{L}{2} & 0 & 0 & 0 & 0 \\ 0 & 0 & 0 & 1 & -\frac{325L^3}{1296EI} & -\frac{5}{6}L & 0 & 0 & 0 & 0 \\ 0 & 0 & 0 & 0 & -\frac{432L^3}{1296EI} & -L & 0 & 0 & 0 & 0 \\ 0 & 0 & 0 & 0 & -L & 0 & 0 & 0 & 0 & 0 \\ 0 & 0 & 0 & 0 & -\frac{198L^2}{1296EI} & -1 & 1 & 0 & 0 & 0 \\ 0 & 0 & 0 & 0 & -\frac{486L^2}{1296EI} & -1 & 0 & 1 & 0 & 0 \\ 0 & 0 & 0 & 0 & -\frac{630L^2}{1296EI} & -1 & 0 & 0 & 1 & 0 \\ 0 & 0 & 0 & 0 & -\frac{648L^2}{1296EI} & -1 & 0 & 0 & 0 & 1 \end{bmatrix}$$

The inverse of [λ] is easily calculated to be

$$[\lambda]^{-1} = \begin{bmatrix} -1 & 0 & 0 & 0 & 0 & \frac{1}{L} & 0 & 0 & 0 & 0 \\ 0 & 1 & 0 & 0 & -\frac{1}{6} & \frac{55L^2}{1296EI} & 0 & 0 & 0 & 0 \\ 0 & 0 & 1 & 0 & -\frac{1}{2} & \frac{81L^2}{1296EI} & 0 & 0 & 0 & 0 \\ 0 & 0 & 0 & 1 & -\frac{5}{6} & \frac{35L^2}{1296EI} & 0 & 0 & 0 & 0 \\ 0 & 0 & 0 & 0 & 0 & -\frac{1}{L} & 0 & 0 & 0 & 0 \\ 0 & 0 & 0 & 0 & -\frac{1}{L} & \frac{432L}{1296EI} & 0 & 0 & 0 & 0 \\ 0 & 0 & 0 & 0 & -\frac{1}{L} & \frac{234L}{1296EI} & 1 & 0 & 0 & 0 \\ 0 & 0 & 0 & 0 & -\frac{1}{L} & -\frac{54L}{1296EI} & 0 & 1 & 0 & 0 \\ 0 & 0 & 0 & 0 & -\frac{1}{L} & -\frac{198L}{1296EI} & 0 & 0 & 1 & 0 \\ 0 & 0 & 0 & 0 & -\frac{1}{L} & -\frac{216L}{1296EI} & 0 & 0 & 0 & 1 \end{bmatrix}$$

The matrix $[\mu]$ is already known, since $[\delta]$ is available.

$$[\mu] = \frac{L}{1296EI} \begin{bmatrix} \frac{1296EI}{L} & \frac{1296EI}{L} & \frac{1296EI}{L} & \frac{1296EI}{L} & \frac{1296EI}{L} & 0 & 0 & 0 & 0 & 0 \\ 0 & 2L^2 & 8L^2 & 14L^2 & 17L^2 & 0 & 18L & 18L & 18L & 18L \\ 0 & 8L^2 & 54L^2 & 108L^2 & 135L^2 & 0 & 90L & 162L & 162L & 162L \\ 0 & 14L^2 & 108L^2 & 250L^2 & 325L^2 & 0 & 162L & 378L & 450L & 450L \\ 0 & 17L^2 & 135L^2 & 325L^2 & 432L^2 & 0 & 198L & 486L & 630L & 648L \\ 0 & 216EI & 648EI & 1080EI & 1296EI & \frac{1296EI}{L} & \frac{1296EI}{L} & \frac{1296EI}{L} & \frac{1296EI}{L} & \frac{1296EI}{L} \\ 0 & 18L & 90L & 162L & 198L & 0 & 216 & 216 & 216 & 216 \\ 0 & 18L & 162L & 378L & 486L & 0 & 216 & 648 & 648 & 648 \\ 0 & 18L & 162L & 450L & 630L & 0 & 216 & 648 & 1080 & 1080 \\ 0 & 18L & 162L & 450L & 648L & 0 & 216 & 648 & 1080 & 1296 \end{bmatrix}$$

Now the matrix $[\varDelta]$ for the simple beam becomes $[\lambda]^{-1}[\mu]$

$$[\varDelta] = \frac{L}{1296EI} \begin{bmatrix} -\frac{1296EI}{L} & -\frac{1080EI}{L} & -\frac{648EI}{L} & -\frac{216EI}{L} & 0 & \frac{1296EI}{L^2} & \frac{1296EI}{L^2} & \frac{1296EI}{L^2} & \frac{1296EI}{L^2} & \frac{1296EI}{L^2} \\ 0 & \frac{25}{3}L^2 & 13L^2 & \frac{17}{3}L^2 & 0 & 55L & 40L & -8L & -32L & -35L \\ 0 & 13L^2 & 27L^2 & 13L^2 & 0 & 81L & 72L & 0 & -72L & -81L \\ 0 & \frac{17}{3}L^2 & 13L^2 & \frac{25}{3}L^2 & 0 & 35L & 32L & 8L & -40L & -55L \\ 0 & -\frac{216EI}{L} & -\frac{648EI}{L} & -\frac{1080EI}{L} & -\frac{1296EI}{L} & -\frac{1296EI}{L^2} & -\frac{1296EI}{L^2} & -\frac{1296EI}{L^2} & -\frac{1296EI}{L^2} & -\frac{1296EI}{L^2} \\ 0 & 55L & 81L & 35L & 0 & 432 & 234 & -54 & -198 & -216 \\ 0 & 40L & 72L & 32L & 0 & 234 & 252 & -36 & -180 & -198 \\ 0 & -8L & 0 & 8L & 0 & -54 & -36 & 108 & -36 & -54 \\ 0 & -32L & -72L & -40L & 0 & -198 & -180 & -36 & 252 & 234 \\ 0 & -35L & -40L & -55L & 0 & -216 & -198 & -54 & 234 & 432 \end{bmatrix}$$

However, in this matrix the elements of the first and fifth rows are the reactions at the supports caused by the various unit loads or moments. If deflections are desired, the first and fifth rows are made zero.

It is obvious that this is a hard way to compute the flexibility matrix for a simple beam. The purpose of this example was to illustrate the general method using a beam which could easily be checked by elementary means.

12.4 Free Beams

The method previously described can be used on all types of beams except free beams or beams with only one restraint. It can be modified so that these beams may be handled also. If a beam is completely unrestrained (for instance, in a free fall), there is no reaction force or moment at any point on the beam. However, if a force is applied somewhere on the beam, the beam will undergo a rigid-body translational and rotational acceleration with the beam bending superimposed. The analysis of the cantilever beam resulted in a reaction force and moment at Station 1. These reactions could be removed by applying an external moment and force at this station equal and opposite to the reactions. These new external loads must be reacted by inertia loads which can be calculated as if the beam were accelerating as a rigid body. Those new reactions must then cause additional deflections to be added to those of the cantilever.

First Correction. Assume that the mass of the beam and objects supported by it can be represented as masses whose centers of gravity are located at the various stations, each mass having a radius of gyration about its own center of gravity of ρ_k and a mass of m_k, where k is the station number. Then the new external loads which must be applied to the cantilever beam to simulate the free beam are derived as follows:

$$\left.\begin{aligned} &\text{Total mass} = M = \sum_{k=1}^{n} m_k \\ &\text{Location of the center of gravity} = l_{1\text{c.g.}} = \frac{\sum_{k=1}^{n} m_k l_{1k}}{M} \\ &\text{Moment of inertia about the center of gravity} \\ &\qquad = I_M = -Ml_{1\text{c.g.}}^2 + \sum_{k=1}^{n} m_k(l_{1k}{}^2 + \rho_k{}^2) \end{aligned}\right\} \quad (12\text{-}17)$$

For unit applied load at j,

$$\text{Linear acceleration of the center of gravity} = \frac{1}{M}$$

$$\text{Angular acceleration about the center of gravity} = \frac{1(l_{1j} - l_{1\text{c.g.}})}{I_M}$$

$$\text{Linear acceleration at } k = \frac{1}{M} + \frac{l_{1j} - l_{1\text{c.g.}}}{I_M}(l_{1k} - l_{1\text{c.g.}})$$

$$\text{Inertia force on beam at } k = -m_k\left[\frac{1}{M} + \frac{(l_{1j} - l_{1\text{c.g.}})(l_{1k} - l_{1\text{c.g.}})}{I_M}\right]$$

$$\text{Inertia moment on beam at } k = -m_k\rho_k{}^2\left(\frac{l_{1j} - l_{1\text{c.g.}}}{I_M}\right)$$

For unit applied moment at j,

$$\text{Linear acceleration of the center of gravity} = 0$$

$$\text{Angular acceleration about the center of gravity} = \frac{1}{I_M}$$

$$\text{Inertia force at } k = -m_k\frac{1}{I_M}(l_{1k} - l_{1\text{c.g.}})$$

$$\text{Inertia moment at } k = -m_k\rho_k{}^2\frac{1}{I_M}$$

Let the additional deflections be designated Δy_{ij}, $\Delta\theta_{ij}$, $\Delta\epsilon_{ij}$, $\Delta\phi_{ij}$

$$\Delta y_{ij} = -\sum_{k=1}^{n}\left\{\left[\frac{m_k}{M} + \frac{m_k(l_{1j} - l_{1\text{c.g.}})(l_{1k} - l_{1\text{c.g.}})}{I_M}\right] y_{ik} + \frac{m_k\rho_k^2}{I_M}(l_{ij} - l_{1\text{c.g.}})\epsilon_{ik}\right\}$$

$$\Delta\theta_{ij} = -\sum_{k=1}^{n}\left\{\left[\frac{m_k}{M} + \frac{m_k(l_{1j} - l_{1\text{c.g.}})(l_{1k} - l_{1\text{c.g.}})}{I_M}\right] \theta_{ik} + \frac{m_k\rho_k^2}{I_M}(l_{1j} - l_{1\text{c.g.}})\phi_{ik}\right\}$$

$$\Delta\epsilon_{ij} = -\sum_{k=1}^{n}\left\{\frac{m_k(l_{1k} - l_{1\text{c.g.}})}{I_M} y_{ik} + \frac{m_k\rho_k^2}{I_M}\epsilon_{ik}\right\} \qquad (12\text{-}18)$$

$$\Delta\phi_{ij} = -\sum_{k=1}^{n}\left\{\frac{m_k(l_{1k} - l_{1\text{c.g.}})}{I_M}\theta_{ik} + \frac{m_k\rho_k^2}{I_M}\phi_{ik}\right\}$$

Second Correction. If these deflections were to be added to those of Equations 12-3 through 12-6, the result would be correct for a free beam, except that the beam would have zero slope and deflection at station 1 (Fig. 12-7). Actually, the center of gravity of the bent beam is supposed to be at the same vertical location as that of the original straight beam, and the product of inertia of the bent beam about the center of gravity should be the same as the straight beam; that is, zero. This means that additional corrections are necessary corresponding to translation and rotation of the bent beam to

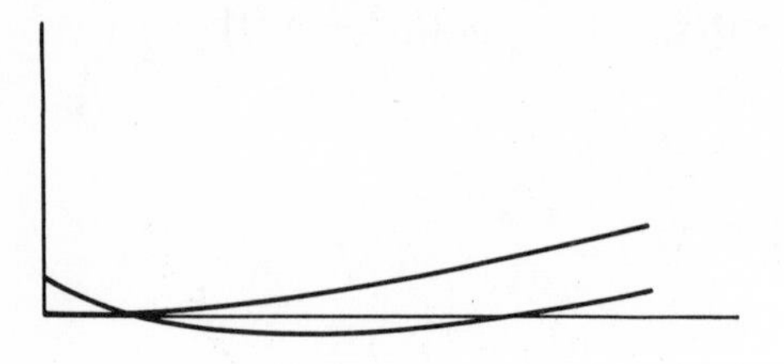

Fig. 12-7

bring about these conditions. If c_1 is the translational constant and c_2 the rotational constant, these conditions could be satisfied by

$$\sum_{k=1}^{n} m_k(y_{kj} + c_1) = 0$$

or

$$c_1 = -\frac{\sum_{k=1}^{n} m_k y_{kj}}{M}$$

$$\sum_{k=1}^{n} m_k[(y_{kj} + c_1) + c_2(l_{1k} - l_{1\text{c.g.}})](l_{1k} - l_{1\text{c.g.}}) = 0$$

or

$$c_2 = -\frac{\sum_{k=1}^{n} m_k(y_{kj} + c_1)(l_{1k} - l_{1\text{c.g.}})}{\sum_{k=1}^{n} m_k(l_{1k} - l_{1\text{c.g.}})^2}$$

Therefore, after the first corrections have been made (Equations 12-18), and the new values of y_{ij}, θ_{ij}, ϵ_{ij}, ϕ_{ij}, are known, a second set of corrections is necessary, defined as follows, using the new values of y, θ, ϵ, and ϕ.

$$\Delta_2 y_{ij} = -\frac{\sum_{k=1}^{n} m_k y_{kj}}{M} - \frac{(l_{1i} - l_{1c.g.})}{\sum_{k=1}^{n} m_k(l_{1k} - l_{1c.g.})^2} \sum_{k=1}^{n} m_k \left(y_{kj} - \frac{\sum_{k=1}^{n} m_k y_{kj}}{M} \right) (l_{1k} - l_{1c.g.})$$

$$\Delta_2 \theta_{ij} = -\frac{1}{\sum_{k=1}^{n} m_k(l_{1k} - l_{1c.g.})^2} \sum_{k=1}^{n} m_k \left(y_{kj} - \frac{\sum_{k=1}^{n} m_k y_{kj}}{M} \right) (l_{1k} - l_{1c.g.})$$

(12-19)

$$\Delta_2 \epsilon_{ij} = -\frac{\sum_{k=1}^{n} m_k \epsilon_{kj}}{M} - \frac{(l_{1i} - l_{1c.g.})}{\sum_{k=1}^{n} m_k(l_{1k} - l_{1c.g.})^2} \sum_{k=1}^{n} m_k \left(\epsilon_{kj} - \frac{\sum_{k=1}^{n} m_j \epsilon_{kj}}{M} \right) (l_{1k} - l_{1c.g.})$$

$$\Delta_2 \phi_{ij} = -\frac{1}{\sum_{k=1}^{n} m_k(l_{1k} - l_{1c.g.})^2} \sum_{k=1}^{n} m_k \left(\epsilon_{kj} - \frac{\sum_{k=1}^{n} m_k \epsilon_{kj}}{M} \right) (l_{1k} - l_{1c.g.})$$

A similar analysis can be made for a beam with one restraint.

Example 12-3. Determine the flexibility matrix for the beam of Example 12-2 if the beam is free of all external restraint. Compute only the y_{ij} coefficients.
In Example 12-2 the y_{ij} and ϵ_{ij} coefficients were calculated to be

$$[y_{ij}] = \frac{L^3}{1296EI} \begin{bmatrix} 0 & 0 & 0 & 0 & 0 \\ 0 & 2 & 8 & 14 & 17 \\ 0 & 8 & 54 & 108 & 135 \\ 0 & 14 & 108 & 250 & 325 \\ 0 & 17 & 135 & 325 & 432 \end{bmatrix} \qquad [\epsilon_{ij}] = \frac{L^2}{1296EI} \begin{bmatrix} 0 & 0 & 0 & 0 & 0 \\ 0 & 18 & 18 & 18 & 18 \\ 0 & 90 & 162 & 162 & 162 \\ 0 & 162 & 378 & 450 & 450 \\ 0 & 198 & 486 & 630 & 648 \end{bmatrix}$$

The first set of corrections is now computed.

$$m_1 = 0, \quad m_2 = m_3 = m_4 = \frac{M}{3}, \quad m_5 = 0$$

$$l_{1c.g.} = \frac{L}{2}$$

$$\rho_1^2 = 0, \quad \rho_2^2 = \rho_3^2 = \rho_4^2 = \frac{L^2}{108}, \quad \rho_5^2 = 0$$

$$I_M = -M\left(\frac{L}{2}\right)^2 + \frac{ML^2}{3}\left[\left(\frac{1}{6^2} + \frac{1}{108}\right) + \left(\frac{1}{2^2} + \frac{1}{108}\right) + \left(\frac{5^2}{6^2} + \frac{1}{108}\right)\right] = \frac{ML^2}{12}$$

The corrections become

$$\Delta y_{ij} = \frac{L^3}{11664EI} \begin{bmatrix} 0 & 0 & 0 & 0 & 0 \\ 9 & -18 & -72 & -126 & -153 \\ 159 & -64 & -510 & -956 & -1179 \\ 465 & -62 & -1116 & -2170 & -2697 \\ 636 & -53 & -1431 & -2809 & -3498 \end{bmatrix}$$

The new coefficients become

$$y_{ij} = \frac{L^3}{11664EI}\begin{bmatrix} 0 & 0 & 0 & 0 & 0 \\ 9 & 0 & 0 & 0 & 0 \\ 159 & 8 & -24 & 16 & 36 \\ 465 & 64 & -144 & 80 & 228 \\ 636 & 100 & -216 & 116 & 390 \end{bmatrix}$$

These must be corrected using Equation 12-19 and the results are

$$\Delta_2 y_{ij} = \frac{L^3}{11664EI}\begin{bmatrix} 131 & 24 & -52 & 28 & 83 \\ 17 & 8 & -16 & 8 & 26 \\ -211 & -24 & 56 & -32 & -88 \\ -439 & -56 & 128 & -72 & -202 \\ -553 & -72 & 164 & -92 & -259 \end{bmatrix}$$

from which the final corrected flexibility matrix is

$$y_{ij} = \frac{L^3}{11664EI}\begin{bmatrix} 131 & 24 & -52 & 28 & 83 \\ 26 & 8 & -16 & 8 & 26 \\ -52 & -16 & 32 & -16 & -52 \\ 26 & 8 & -16 & 8 & 26 \\ 83 & 28 & 52 & 24 & 131 \end{bmatrix}$$

12.5 Beam Stiffness Matrix

The stiffness matrix for a beam may also be used to find the flexibility matrix provided that certain precautions are taken. Since the stiffness and flexibility matrices are reciprocals, it is of course necessary that neither be singular if inverses are involved in a calculation. For instance, in Example 12-2, the matrix Δ as shown is not singular when the first and fifth rows represent reactions at the rigid supports. However, if the first and fifth rows are changed to zero to represent deflections at the rigid supports, Δ then becomes a singular matrix and the reciprocal relationship between the flexibility and stiffness matrices becomes somewhat obscure. However, the relationship may still be useful. First, it is necessary to define again the meaning of the elements of a stiffness matrix in the application to beams.

It is recalled that an element, δ_{ij}, of a flexibility matrix is the deflection at coordinate i caused by a unit load in the positive direction at coordinate j, all other loads being zero, and that an element K_{ij} of a stiffness matrix is the load required at coordinate i when a unit deflection of coordinate j occurs, all other deflections remaining zero. When this definition is applied to a beam, for which the coordinates are linear deflections and angular rotations of the various stations, the following definitions may be proposed.

f_{ij} = force required in positive direction at Station i when unit linear displacement occurs at Station j, all other linear displacements and all rotational displacements remaining zero.

p_{ij} = force required in positive direction at Station i when unit angular displacement occurs at Station j, all other angular displacements and all linear displacements remaining zero.

m_{ij} = moment required in positive direction at Station i when unit linear displacement occurs at Station j, all other linear displacements and all angular displacements remaining zero.

r_{ij} = moment required in positive direction at Station i when unit angular displacement occurs at Station j, all other angular displacements and all linear displacements remaining zero.

With these definitions a stiffness matrix can be formed from these submatrices which is the inverse of the flexibility matrix. This matrix is

$$[K] = \begin{bmatrix} f & p \\ m & r \end{bmatrix}$$

When one of the stations is located at a point of rigid support, it is then necessary to make a modification, because obviously the loads or moments required for unit deflections of such points would have to become infinite. The definition of an element corresponding to one of these points can be changed to be a load or moment caused by a unit reaction of the support rather than a unit deflection of the support. This is illustrated in Example 12-4.

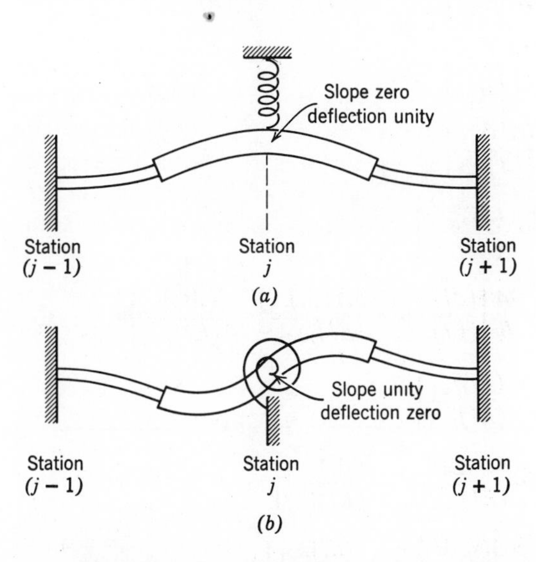

Fig. 12-8 Illustration of beam deflections for stiffness matrix elements. (a) **For elements** f_{ij} **or** m_{ij}. (b) **For elements** p_{ij} **or** r_{ij}

In terms of the definitions of Fig. 12-3, the elements of the stiffness matrix can be calculated from consideration of ordinary fixed end beams as indicated in Fig. 12-8. For Fig. 12-8 it is possible to show that if the deflection occurs at Station j, the external loads and moments required at the three stations, $(j-1)$, j, and $(j+1)$ are as follows. (At all other stations the loads and moments are zero.)

$$A = \frac{(\Delta l)_j^4}{(EI)_j^2} + \frac{4(\Delta l)_j^3(\Delta l)_{j-1}}{(EI)_j(EI)_{j-1}} + \frac{6(\Delta l)_j^2(\Delta l)_{j-1}^2}{(EI)_j(EI)_{j-1}} + \frac{4(\Delta l)_j(\Delta l)_{j-1}^3}{(EI)_j(EI)_{j-1}} + \frac{(\Delta l)_{j-1}^4}{(EI)_{j-1}^2}$$

$$B = \frac{(\Delta l)_j^4}{(EI)_j^2} + \frac{4(\Delta l)_j^3(\Delta l)_{j+1}}{(EI)_j(EI)_{j+1}} + \frac{6(\Delta l)_j^2(\Delta l)_{j+1}}{(EI)_j(EI)_{j+1}} + \frac{4(\Delta l)_j(\Delta l)_{j+1}^3}{(EI)_j(EI)_{j+1}} + \frac{(\Delta l)_{j+1}^4}{(EI)_{j+1}^2}$$

$$f_{j-1,j} = -\frac{96}{A}\left[\frac{(\Delta l)_j}{(EI)_j} + \frac{(\Delta l)_{j-1}}{(EI)_{j-1}}\right]$$

$$f_{j,j} = \frac{96}{A}\left[\frac{(\Delta l)_j}{(EI)_j} + \frac{(\Delta l)_{j-1}}{(EI)_{j-1}}\right] + \frac{96}{B}\left[\frac{(\Delta l)_j}{(EI)_j} + \frac{\Delta l)_{j+1}}{(EI)_{j+1}}\right] + k_j$$

$$f_{j+1,j} = -\frac{96}{B}\left[\frac{(\Delta l)_j}{(EI)_j} + \frac{(\Delta l)_{j+1}}{(EI)_{j+1}}\right]$$

$$m_{j-1,j} = -\frac{24}{A}\left[\frac{(\Delta l)_j^2}{(EI)_j} + \frac{2(\Delta l)_j(\Delta l)_{j-1}}{(EI)_j} + \frac{(\Delta l)_{j-1}^2}{(EI)_{j-1}}\right]$$

$$m_{j,j} = -\frac{24}{A}\left[\frac{(\Delta l)_j^2}{(EI)_j} + \frac{2(\Delta l)_j(\Delta l)_{j-1}}{(EI)_j} + \frac{(\Delta l)_{j-1}^2}{(EI)_{j-1}}\right] + \frac{24}{B}\left[\frac{(\Delta l)_j^2}{(EI)_j} + \frac{2(\Delta l)_j(\Delta l)_{j+1}}{(EI)_j} + \frac{(\Delta l)_{j+1}^2}{(EI)_{j+1}}\right]$$

$$m_{j+1,j} = \frac{24}{B}\left[\frac{(\Delta l)_j^2}{(EI)_j} + \frac{2(\Delta l)_j(\Delta l)_{j+1}}{(EI)_j} + \frac{(\Delta l)_{j+1}^2}{(EI)_{j+1}}\right] \tag{12-20}$$

$$p_{j-1,j} = \frac{24}{A}\left[\frac{(\Delta l)_j^2}{(EI)_j} + \frac{2(\Delta l)_j(\Delta l)_{j-1}}{(EI)_{j-1}} + \frac{(\Delta l)_{j-1}^2}{(EI)_{j-1}}\right]$$

$$p_{j,j} = -\frac{24}{A}\left[\frac{(\Delta l)_j^2}{(EI)_j} + \frac{2(\Delta l)_j(\Delta l)_{j-1}}{(EI)_{j-1}} + \frac{(\Delta l)_{j-1}^2}{(EI)_{j-1}}\right] + \frac{24}{B}\left[\frac{(\Delta l)_j}{(EI)_j} + \frac{2(\Delta l)_j(\Delta l)_{j+1}}{(EI)_{j+1}} + \frac{(\Delta l)_{j+1}^2}{(EI)_{j+1}}\right]$$

$$p_{j+1,j} = -\frac{24}{B}\left[\frac{(\Delta l)_j^2}{(EI)_j} + \frac{2(\Delta l)_j(\Delta l)_{j+1}}{(EI)_{j+1}} + \frac{(\Delta l)_{j+1}^2}{(EI)_{j+1}}\right]$$

$$p_{j-1,j} = \frac{4}{A}\left[\frac{(\Delta l)_j^3}{(EI)_j} + \frac{3(\Delta l)_j^2(\Delta l)_{j-1}}{(EI)_j} + \frac{3(\Delta l)_j(\Delta l)_{j-1}^2}{(EI)_{j-1}} + \frac{(\Delta l)_{j-1}^3}{(EI)_{j-1}}\right]$$

$$r_{j,j} = \frac{8}{A}\left[\frac{(\Delta l)_j^3}{(EI)_j} + \frac{3(\Delta l)_j^2(\Delta l)_{j-1}}{(EI)_{j-1}} + \frac{3(\Delta l)_j(\Delta l)_{j-1}^2}{(EI)_{j-1}} + \frac{(\Delta l)_{j-1}^3}{(EI)_{j-1}}\right] + \frac{8}{B}\left[\frac{(\Delta l)_j^3}{(EI)_j} + \frac{3(\Delta l)_j^2(\Delta l)_{j+1}}{(EI)_{j+1}} + \frac{3(\Delta l)_j(\Delta l)_{j+1}^2}{(EI)_{j+1}} + \frac{(\Delta l)_{j+1}^3}{(EI)_{j+1}}\right]$$

$$r_{j+1,j} = \frac{4}{B}\left[\frac{(\Delta l)_j^3}{(EI)_j} + \frac{3(\Delta l)_j^2(\Delta l)_{j+1}}{(EI)_j} + \frac{3(\Delta l)_j(\Delta l)_{j+1}^2}{(EI)_{j+1}} + \frac{(\Delta l)_{j+1}^3}{(EI)_{j+1}}\right]$$

If a rigid support to translation exists at a Station j, then the meaning of f_{ij} becomes the load at i necessary for a unit reaction force at j, all other deflections zero, so that $f_{ij} = 0$ if $i \neq j$ and $f_{jj} = -1$. Also, $m_{ij} = 0$ for all i. If a rigid support to rotation exists at Station j, $p_{ij} = 0$ for all i and $r_{ij} = 0$ if $i \neq j$, and $r_{jj} = -1$ (r_{ij} means the moment required at i for a unit reaction moment at j.)

Example 12-4. Form the stiffness matrix for the simply supported beam of Example 12-2. This beam has five stations and EI at all stations is the same. The beam-element lengths are $(\Delta l)_2 = (\Delta l)_3 = (\Delta l)_4 = L/3$, and $(\Delta l)_1 = (\Delta l)_5 = 0$. Use of Equations 12-20 results in the following matrix, which must still be modified to account for the end conditions.

$$[K] = \frac{6EI}{L^3}\begin{bmatrix} 432 & -432 & 0 & 0 & 0 & 36L & 36L & 0 & 0 & 0 \\ -432 & 486 & -54 & 0 & 0 & -36L & -27L & 9L & 0 & 0 \\ 0 & -54 & 108 & -54 & 0 & 0 & -9L & 0 & 9L & 0 \\ 0 & 0 & -54 & 486 & -432 & 0 & 0 & -9L & 27L & 36L \\ 0 & 0 & 0 & -432 & 432 & 0 & 0 & 0 & -36L & -36L \\ 36L & -36L & 0 & 0 & 0 & 4L^2 & 2L^2 & 0 & 0 & 0 \\ 36L & -27L & -9L & 0 & 0 & 2L^2 & 6L^2 & L^2 & 0 & 0 \\ 0 & 9L & 0 & -9L & 0 & 0 & L^2 & 4L^2 & L^2 & 0 \\ 0 & 0 & 9L & 27L & -36L & 0 & 0 & L^2 & 6L^2 & 2L^2 \\ 0 & 0 & 0 & 36L & -36L & 0 & 0 & 0 & 2L^2 & 4L^2 \end{bmatrix}$$

In forming the foregoing matrix, use of the proper Δl values will result in the elements shown, except for the elements f_{jj}, p_{jj}, m_{jj}, r_{jj} when $j = 1$ or 5. These are the end stations and, of course, the beam exists only on one side so only one of the terms in the corresponding equations is used, the contribution from the other term being zero.

Now for a simple support at Stations 1 and 5 it is necessary to modify Columns 1 and 5 to give

$$[K] = \frac{6EI}{L^3}\begin{bmatrix} \left(\frac{-L^3}{6EI}\right) & -432 & 0 & 0 & 0 & 36L & 36L & 0 & 0 & 0 \\ 0 & 486 & -54 & 0 & 0 & -36L & -27L & 9L & 0 & 0 \\ 0 & -54 & 108 & -54 & 0 & 0 & -9L & 0 & 9L & 0 \\ 0 & 0 & -54 & 486 & 0 & 0 & 0 & -9L & 27L & 36L \\ 0 & 0 & 0 & -432 & \left(\frac{-L^3}{6EI}\right) & 0 & 0 & 0 & -36L & -36L \\ 0 & -36L & 0 & 0 & 0 & 4L^2 & 2L^2 & 0 & 0 & 0 \\ 0 & -27L & -9L & 0 & 0 & 2L^2 & 6L^2 & L^2 & 0 & 0 \\ 0 & 9L & 0 & -9L & 0 & 0 & L^2 & 4L^2 & L^2 & 0 \\ 0 & 0 & 9L & 27L & 0 & 0 & 0 & L^2 & 6L^2 & 2L^2 \\ 0 & 0 & 0 & 36L & 0 & 0 & 0 & 0 & 2L^2 & 4L^2 \end{bmatrix}$$

This matrix is the inverse of $[\Delta]$ of Example 12-2. Therefore, another way of obtaining $[\Delta]$ of Example 12-2 is to form $[K]$ as just indicated and then invert it. This method can be quite useful for complex structures having many redundancies, since it is often possible to calculate loads for known deflections (unit deflections) when it is quite difficult to calculate deflections for unit loads.

CHAPTER 13

Numerical Solution of Ordinary and Partial Differential Equations

13.1 Quadratic Approximation

This chapter describes a general method for solving ordinary and partial differential equations by numerical means. This method, an adaptation of the method of finite differences, is intended for use in the determination of flexibility matrices for beams, plates, or other structures, but it can also be used to solve any linear partial or ordinary differential equation and is often applicable to nonlinear equations.

Coefficients of the Quadratic. The basis of this method is that any single-valued function can be fitted over a small interval by a polynomial.

Figure 13-1 shows a function, $f(x)$, over a portion of the x-coordinate. If there are three ordinates to be fitted with a polynomial the polynomial could be a quadratic.

$$f = A_0 + A_1 x + A_2 x^2 \tag{13-1}$$

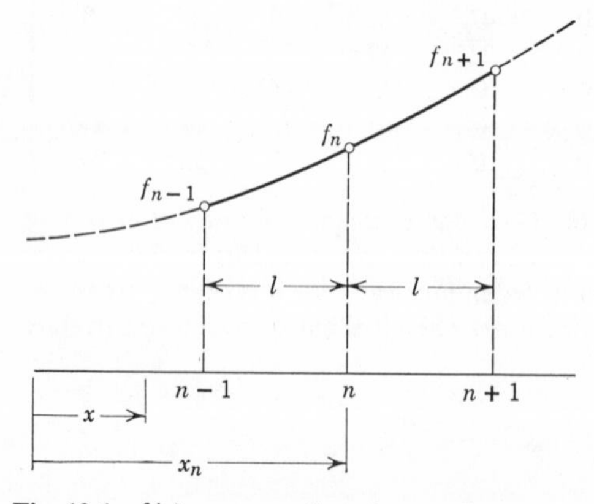

Fig. 13-1 $f(x)$ over a portion of x-coordinate

At $x = x_n - l$, x_n, and $x_n + l$, the values of the function are f_{n-1}, f_n, and f_{n+1} respectively. These three conditions are sufficient for the determination of the constants A_0, A_1, and A_2 which then become

$$A_0 = f_n - \left(\frac{f_{n+1} - f_{n-1}}{2l}\right) x_n + \left(\frac{f_{n-1} - 2f_n + f_{n+1}}{2l^2}\right) x_n^{\ 2}$$

$$A_1 = \frac{f_{n+1} - f_{n-1}}{2l} - \left(\frac{f_{n-1} - 2f_n + f_{n+1}}{l^2}\right) x_n \qquad (13\text{-}2)$$

$$A_2 = \frac{f_{n-1} - 2f_n + f_{n+1}}{2l^2}$$

Derivatives. The derivatives of Equation 13-1 are

$$\left.\begin{aligned} \frac{df}{dx} &= A_1 + 2A_2 x \\ \frac{d_2 f}{dx^2} &= 2A_2 \end{aligned}\right\} \qquad (13\text{-}3)$$

If Equations 13-2 are substituted in Equation 13-3 at $x = x_n - l$, x_n, and $x_n + l$, the derivatives become

$$\begin{aligned} \left(\frac{df}{dx}\right)_{n-1} &= \frac{-3f_{n-1} + 4f_n - f_{n+1}}{2l} \\ \left(\frac{df}{dx}\right)_{n} &= \frac{f_{n+1} - f_{n-1}}{2l} \\ \left(\frac{df}{dx}\right)_{n+1} &= \frac{f_{n-1} - 4f_n + 3f_{n+1}}{2l} \\ \left(\frac{d^2f}{dx^2}\right)_{n-1} = \left(\frac{d^2f}{dx^2}\right)_{n} = \left(\frac{d^2f}{dx^2}\right)_{n+1} &= \frac{f_{n-1} - 2f_n + f_{n+1}}{l^2} \end{aligned} \qquad (13\text{-}4)$$

Unequal Intervals. Sometimes it is necessary or convenient to have the intervals unequal or different from a standard value of l. If the intervals are βl and γl as indicated in Fig. 13-2, a similar analysis would result in the following set of equations.

$$\begin{aligned} \left(\frac{df}{dx}\right)_{n-1} &= \frac{1}{l}\left[\frac{\gamma + 2\beta}{\beta(\beta + \gamma)} f_{n-1} + \frac{\beta + \gamma}{\beta\gamma} f_n - \frac{\beta}{\gamma(\beta + \gamma)} f_{n+1}\right] \\ \left(\frac{df}{dx}\right)_{n} &= \frac{1}{l}\left[-\frac{\gamma}{\beta(\beta + \gamma)} f_{n-1} + \frac{\gamma - \beta}{\beta\gamma} f_n + \frac{\beta}{\gamma(\beta + \gamma)} f_{n+1}\right] \\ \left(\frac{df}{dx}\right)_{n+1} &= \frac{1}{l}\left[\frac{\gamma}{\beta(\beta + \gamma)} f_{n-1} - \frac{\beta + \gamma}{\beta\gamma} f_n + \frac{\beta + 2\gamma}{\gamma(\beta + \gamma)} f_{n+1}\right] \\ \left(\frac{d^2f}{dx^2}\right)_{n-1} = \left(\frac{d^2f}{dx^2}\right)_{n} = \left(\frac{d^2f}{dx^2}\right)_{n+1} &= \frac{2}{l^2}\left[\frac{f_{n-1}}{\beta(\beta + \gamma)} - \frac{f_n}{\beta\gamma} + \frac{f_{n+1}}{\gamma(\beta + \gamma)}\right] \end{aligned} \qquad (13\text{-}5)$$

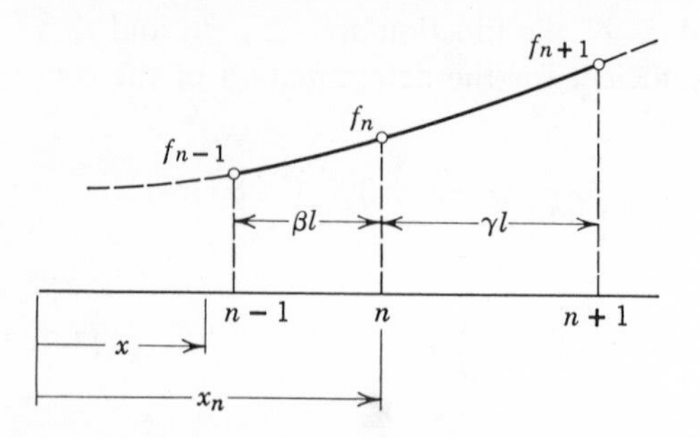

Fig. 13-2 Definitions for unequal intervals

13.2 Higher Order Derivatives

Differential equations involving derivatives higher than the second could not be solved with Equations 13-4 or 13-5 unless simultaneous equations were used. This is all right, or derivatives up to the fourth can be represented by Equations 13-6 and Appendix 2. These equations are derived in the same way as Equations 13-4 and 13-5 but a fourth degree polynomial is assumed instead of the second degree polynomial of Equation 13-1. It is also necessary to use five stations as indicated in Fig. 13-3.

For $\alpha = \beta = \gamma = \delta = 1$, Equations 13-6 result; the more general equations are found in Appendix 2.

$$
\begin{aligned}
\left(\frac{df}{dx}\right)_{n-2} &= \frac{1}{l}\left(-\frac{25}{12}f_{n-2} + 4f_{n-1} - 3f_n + \frac{4}{3}f_{n+1} - \frac{1}{4}f_{n+2}\right) \\
\left(\frac{df}{dx}\right)_{n} &= \frac{1}{l}\left(\frac{1}{12}f_{n-2} - \frac{2}{3}f_{n-1} + 0f_n + \frac{2}{3}f_{n+1} - \frac{1}{12}f_{n+2}\right) \\
\left(\frac{df}{dx}\right)_{n+2} &= \frac{1}{l}\left(\frac{1}{4}f_{n-2} - \frac{4}{3}f_{n-1} + 3f_n - 4f_{n+1} + \frac{25}{12}f_{n+2}\right) \\
\left(\frac{d^2f}{dx^2}\right)_{n-2} &= \frac{1}{l^2}\left(\frac{35}{12}f_{n-2} - \frac{26}{3}f_{n-1} + \frac{19}{2}f_n - \frac{14}{3}f_{n+1} + \frac{11}{12}f_{n+2}\right) \\
\left(\frac{d^2f}{dx^2}\right)_{n} &= \frac{1}{l^2}\left(-\frac{1}{12}f_{n-2} + \frac{4}{3}f_{n-1} - \frac{5}{2}f_n + \frac{4}{3}f_{n+1} - \frac{1}{12}f_{n+2}\right) \\
\left(\frac{d^2f}{dx^2}\right)_{n+2} &= \frac{1}{l^2}\left(\frac{11}{12}f_{n-2} - \frac{14}{3}f_{n-1} + \frac{19}{2}f_n - \frac{26}{3}f_{n+1} + \frac{35}{12}f_{n+2}\right) \\
\left(\frac{d^3f}{dx^3}\right)_{n-2} &= \frac{1}{l^3}\left(-\frac{5}{2}f_{n-2} + 9f_{n-1} - 12f_n + 7f_{n+1} - \frac{3}{2}f_{n+2}\right) \\
\left(\frac{d^3f}{dx^3}\right)_{n} &= \frac{1}{l^3}\left(-\frac{1}{2}f_{n-2} + f_{n-1} + 0f_n - f_{n+1} + \frac{1}{2}f_{n+2}\right) \\
\left(\frac{d^3f}{dx^3}\right)_{n+2} &= \frac{1}{l^3}\left(\frac{3}{2}f_{n-2} - 7f_{n-1} + 12f_n - 9f_{n+1} + \frac{5}{2}f_{n+2}\right) \\
\left(\frac{d^4f}{dx^4}\right)_{n-2} &= \left(\frac{d^4f}{dx^4}\right)_{n} = \left(\frac{d^4f}{dx^4}\right)_{n+2} = \frac{1}{l^4}(f_{n-2} - 4f_{n-1} + 6f_n - 4f_{n+1} + f_{n+2})
\end{aligned}
\tag{13-6}
$$

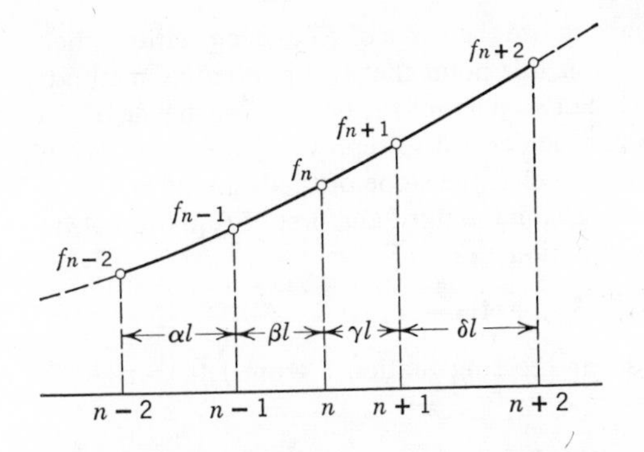

Fig. 13-3 Definitions for fourth-degree polynomial

13.3 Solution of Ordinary Differential Equations

Flexibility Matrix of a Beam. With the appropriate set of equations, an ordinary differential equation or a partial differential equation can be solved as a set of simultaneous algebraic equations, thereby lending themselves to analysis by matrix methods. The technique is best described with examples. Even though the beam problem is perhaps better solved with the method described in Chapter 12, Example 13-1 repeats part of this problem in order to illustrate this method.

Example 13-1. Determine the flexibility matrix for a fixed-hinged beam using the finite-difference method described in the text and neglecting shear deflection (Fig. 13-4).

Two alternatives will be demonstrated. First, the differential equation is required. If M is the moment in the beam and w a distributed loading in the direction of beam deflection, y, then $M = EI\, d^2y/dx^2$ and $d^2M/dx^2 = w$. These could be combined into one fourth-order equation and Equations 13-6 used, or they can be solved as simultaneous second-order equations and Equations 13-4 used. The latter method will be selected. Therefore both M and y will be considered as unknowns. Let the beam stations be selected as stations one

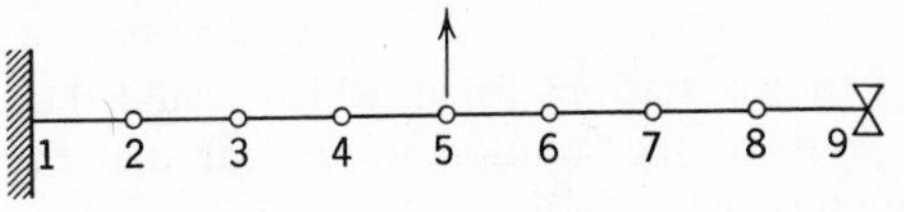

Fig. 13-4

through nine, evenly distributed along the beam, where Station one is at the fixed end (say the left end), and Station 9 is at the hinged end. There are 18 unknowns, M_i and y_i, where i is an integer from one to nine. There must be 18 simultaneous equations to be solved for these unknowns. Some of the equations must represent boundary conditions and some must represent the differential equations. Four equations can be derived immediately which represent conditions at each end of the beam. At the fixed (left) end,

$$y_1 = 0 \quad \text{and} \quad \left(\frac{dy}{dx}\right)_1 = 0$$

The equation $(dy/dx)_1 = 0$ can be expressed in terms of the y-variables by letting $n = 2$ and applying the first of Equations 13-4, $-3y_1 + 4y_2 - y_3 = 0$ (having multiplied through by $2l$). At the right, or pinned, end

$$y_9 = 0 \quad \text{and} \quad M_9 = 0$$

(Had the right end been free, $(dM/dx)_9 = 0$ could have been expressed using the third of Equations 13-4 with $n = 8$.)

Let the unit load be applied at Station 5, for example, and assume that EI is constant.

(If EI were not constant, it would be necessary to use the value of EI at each station when writing the set of equations involving EI.) It is at this point that two alternative methods may be selected. The first method is to regard the two parts of the beam on each side of the load as separate beams. The two equations can be derived to represent the conditions at the juncture of these two portions. One of these is that the slope of the beam at Station 5 must be the same for each portion of the beam. Using the third and first of Equations 13-4 with $n = 4$ and 6 respectively, results in the equation

$$y_3 - 4y_4 + 3y_5 = -3y_5 + 4y_6 - y_7$$

The other condition is that the change in shear crossing Station 5 from left to right is equal to the applied load. This means that

$$\underset{\text{right side of load}}{\left(\frac{dM}{dx}\right)_5} - \underset{\text{left side of load}}{\left(\frac{dM}{dx}\right)_5} = 1$$

In terms of the variables M_i and again using the first and third of Equations 13-4,

$$\frac{-3M_5 + 4M_6 - M_7}{2l} - \frac{M_3 - 4M_4 + 3M_5}{2l} = 1$$

(l is, of course, $L/8$ for this example, if L is the total length of the beam.)

Six of the 18 equations required for the solution have now been formulated. The other twelve equations are obtained by applying the two differential equations at successive stations along the beam; specifically, at Stations 2, 3, 4, 6, 7, 8. At Station 2, for instance, using the fourth of Equations 13-4, and letting $n = 2$,

$$M_2 = (EI)_2\left(\frac{y_1 - 2y_2 + y_3}{l^2}\right) \left(\text{for } M = EI\frac{d^2y}{dx^2}\right)$$

$M_1 - 2M_2 + M_3 = 0$ (since $w = 0$ in $\dfrac{d^2M}{dx^2} = w$, and after multiplying through by l^2)

Similar equations would be written for each of the six stations listed, which would then account for all of the eighteen equations required for the solution. It is clear that the method could be adapted to solution by digital computer.

The other alternative mentioned earlier would be to regard the unit load as a distributed load at Station 5, stretching halfway to each of the adjacent stations when writing one of the equations, as follows. The four equations representing the conditions at the ends of the beam and the twelve equations representing the differential equations at Stations 2, 3, 4, 6, 7, and 8 are unchanged. The other two equations, however, would be obtained by applying the two differential equations at Station 5,

$$M_5 = (EI)_5\frac{y_4 - 2y_5 + y_6}{l^2}$$

$$\frac{M_4 - 2M_5 + M_6}{l^2} = \frac{1}{l} \quad \left(\text{here the distributed load, } w, \text{ is } \frac{1}{l}\right)$$

The advantage of this method is that when the matrix equation representing the 18 equations is written, only one matrix inversion is required which can be applied for all positions of the load. The matrix to be inverted is a sparse matrix (that is, most of the elements are zero), and so the number of stations can be made quite large, which minimizes the error involved in representing the concentrated load as a distributed load. For purposes of illustration the matrix for a beam of constant EI divided into only four parts is formed below.

The total number of unknowns is then ten, and the matrix equation for a load applied at Station 3 is shown below. The variable Ml^2/EI replaces M.

$$\begin{bmatrix} 1 & 0 & 0 & 0 & 0 & 0 & 0 & 0 & 0 & 0 \\ -3 & 0 & 4 & 0 & -1 & 0 & 0 & 0 & 0 & 0 \\ 1 & 0 & -2 & -1 & 1 & 0 & 0 & 0 & 0 & 0 \\ 0 & 1 & 0 & -2 & 0 & 1 & 0 & 0 & 0 & 0 \\ 0 & 0 & 1 & 0 & -2 & -1 & 1 & 0 & 0 & 0 \\ 0 & 0 & 0 & 1 & 0 & -2 & 0 & 1 & 0 & 0 \\ 0 & 0 & 0 & 0 & 1 & 0 & -2 & -1 & 1 & 0 \\ 0 & 0 & 0 & 0 & 0 & 1 & 0 & -2 & 0 & 1 \\ 0 & 0 & 0 & 0 & 0 & 0 & 0 & 0 & 1 & 0 \\ 0 & 0 & 0 & 0 & 0 & 0 & 0 & 0 & & 1 \end{bmatrix} \begin{Bmatrix} y_1 \\ \left(\frac{M_1 l^2}{EI}\right) \\ y_2 \\ \left(\frac{M_2 l^2}{EI}\right) \\ y_3 \\ \left(\frac{M_3 l^2}{EI}\right) \\ y_4 \\ \left(\frac{M_4 l^2}{EI}\right) \\ y_5 \\ \left(\frac{M_5 l^2}{EI}\right) \end{Bmatrix} = \frac{l^3}{EI} \begin{Bmatrix} 0 \\ 0 \\ 0 \\ 0 \\ 0 \\ 1 \\ 0 \\ 0 \\ 0 \\ 0 \end{Bmatrix}$$

The error incurred by representing the concentrated load as a distributed load in this manner is about 3% for a beam with nine stations and about $\frac{1}{2}$% for a beam with 21 stations.

The matrix on the right would appear the same for other positions of the unit load except that the 1 would appear in different places. The two matrices on the left would remain unchanged for various positions of the load, so only the one matrix inversion would be required.

If a concentrated unit applied moment occurs at a station, all the equations except the ones involving moments at the two stations to the immediate left and right would remain unaffected. If it is assumed that the moment calculated for the station itself by this finite-difference method would really be the midpoint of the discontinuity, then the equations are so altered that the effect on the previous matrix equation is as follows. The left side would be unaltered. On the right the l^3/EI would become l^2/EI and the matrix on the right would have -1 appearing two elements above the present 1, $+1$ appearing two elements below the present 1, and the present 1 would be 0.

13.4 Solution of Partial Differential Equations

Flexibility Matrix for a Plate Example 13-2, following, describes the application of this method to the solution of partial differential equations.

Example 13-2. Demonstrate the finite-difference method described in Section 13.2 as applied to partial differential equations, by developing a method for determining the flexibility matrix of a square plate of constant thickness simply supported on all sides.

This plate is chosen because results can be checked readily with exact methods. Modifications which would apply to the calculation of plates of different shapes, boundary conditions, or variable thickness will suggest themselves.

Let the plate exist in the x–y plane and a load be applied in the z direction (Fig. 13-5). Let the deflection in the z direction be w, which is, of course, a function of x and y. If a network is laid out on the plate by drawing lines parallel with the edges at intervals, l, the intersection of these lines will establish points which can be considered stations. Suppose that the square plate is divided up so that the sides are divided into eighths. Let the deflection at each of the stations be designated as w_{ij}, where i and j can both vary by integers from 1 to 9, forming 81 lattice points, j varying in the x direction and i in the y direction.

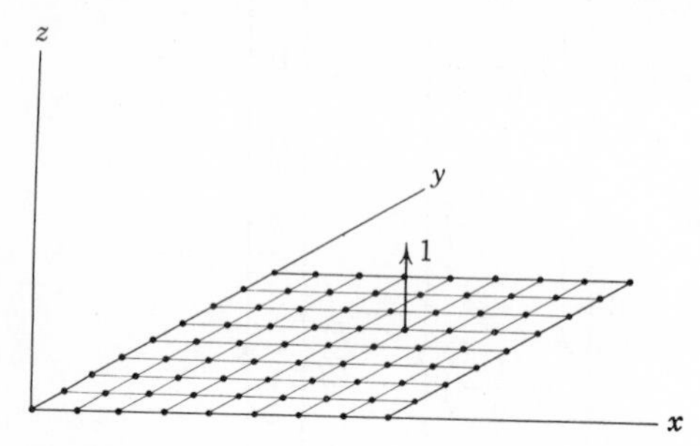

Fig. 13-5

There must be 81 equations available for simultaneous solution. Many of these equations in this example are very simple, because of the simple boundary conditions. For instance, $w_{1j} = w_{i1} = w_{9j} = w_{i9} = 0$ provides 32 equations immediately. However, if one edge had been free, say, instead of simply supported, the corresponding equations would have been slightly more complicated. The modifications will soon become apparent.

The partial differential equation which governs the deflection of a bending plate is

$$\frac{\partial^4 w}{\partial x^4} + 2\frac{\partial^4 w}{\partial x^2\, \partial y^2} + \frac{\partial^4 w}{\partial y^4} = \frac{12(1 - \mu^2)}{Et^3}\, p$$

where p is a distributed-load pressure in the z direction, pounds per square inch, E is the modulus of elasticity, μ the Poisson ratio, and t the plate thickness. Both p and t could be functions of x and y.

Since this equation is a fourth-order equation, Equations 13-6 will be used, somewhat modified of course. Considering a typical set of points somewhere out in the plate,

$$\left(\frac{\partial^4 w}{\partial x^4}\right)_{ij} = \frac{1}{l^4}(w_{i\,j-2} - 4w_{ij-1} + 6w_{i\,j} - 4w_{i\,j+1} + w_{i\,j+2})$$

$$\left(\frac{\partial^4 w}{\partial y_4}\right)_{ij} = \frac{1}{l^4}(w_{i-2\,j} - 4w_{i-1\,j} + 6w_{ij} - 4w_{i+1\,j} + w_{i+2\,j})$$

$i+2$ $j-2$	$i+2$ $j-1$	$i+2$ j	$i+2$ $j+1$	$i+2$ $j+2$
$i+1$ $j-2$	$i+1$ $j-1$	$i+1$ j	$i+1$ $j+1$	$i+1$ $j+2$
i $j-2$	i $j-1$	i j	i $j+1$	i $j+2$
$i-1$ $j-2$	$i-1$ $j-1$	$i-1$ j	$i-1$ $j+1$	$i-1$ $j+2$
$i-2$ $j-2$	$i-2$ $j-1$	$i-2$ j	$i-2$ $j+1$	$i-2$ $j+2$

However, Equations 13-6 do not indicate how to account for a term such as $\partial^4 w/\partial x^2\,\partial y^2$. This can be accomplished without difficulty, for

$$\frac{\partial^4 w}{\partial x^2\,\partial y^2} = \frac{\partial^2}{\partial x^2}\left(\frac{\partial^2 w}{\partial y^2}\right)$$

and $(\partial^2 w/\partial y^2)$ can be considered as f in Equation 13-6.

$$\left[\frac{\partial^2}{\partial x^2}\left(\frac{\partial^2 w}{\partial y^2}\right)\right]_{ij} = \frac{1}{l^2}\left[-\frac{1}{12}\left(\frac{\partial^2 w}{\partial y^2}\right)_{i\,j-2} + \frac{4}{3}\left(\frac{\partial^2 w}{\partial y^2}\right)_{i\,j-1} - \frac{5}{2}\left(\frac{\partial^2 w}{\partial y^2}\right)_{ij} + \frac{4}{3}\left(\frac{\partial^2 w}{\partial y^2}\right)_{i\,j+1} - \frac{1}{12}\left(\frac{\partial^2 w}{\partial y^2}\right)_{i\,j+2}\right]$$

Each of the terms in the bracket can also be represented by use of Equations 13-6. For instance,

$$\left(\frac{\partial^2 w}{\partial y^2}\right)_{i\,j-2} = \frac{1}{l^2}\left(-\frac{1}{12}w_{i-2\,j-2} + \frac{4}{3}w_{i-1\,j-2} - \frac{5}{2}w_{i\,j-2} + \frac{4}{3}w_{i+1\,j-2} - \frac{1}{12}w_{i+2\,j-2}\right]$$

$$\left(\frac{\partial^2 w}{\partial y^2}\right)_{i\,j-1} = \frac{1}{l^2}\left(-\frac{1}{12}w_{i-2\,j-1} + \frac{4}{3}w_{i-1\,j-1} - \frac{5}{2}w_{i\,j-1} + \frac{4}{3}w_{i+1\,j-1} - \frac{1}{12}w_{i+2\,j-1}\right]$$

Etc.

Thus,

$$\begin{aligned}\frac{\partial^4 w}{\partial x^2\,\partial y^2} = \frac{1}{l^4}\Big[&\frac{1}{144}w_{i-2\,j-2} - \frac{1}{9}w_{i-1\,j-2} + \frac{5}{24}w_{i\,j-2} - \frac{1}{9}w_{i+1\,j-2} + \frac{1}{144}w_{i+2\,j-2}\\ &- \frac{1}{9}w_{i-2\,j-1} + \frac{16}{9}w_{i-1\,j-1} - \frac{10}{3}w_{i\,j-1} + \frac{16}{9}w_{i+1\,j-1} - \frac{1}{9}w_{i+2\,j-1}\\ &+ \frac{5}{24}w_{i-2\,j} - \frac{10}{3}w_{i-1\,j} + \frac{25}{4}w_{ij} - \frac{10}{3}w_{i+1\,j} + \frac{5}{24}w_{i+2\,j}\\ &- \frac{1}{9}w_{i-2\,j+1} + \frac{16}{9}w_{i-1\,j+1} - \frac{10}{3}w_{i\,j+1} + \frac{16}{9}w_{i+1\,j+1} - \frac{1}{9}w_{i+2\,j+1}\\ &+ \frac{1}{144}w_{i-2\,j+2} - \frac{1}{9}w_{i-1\,j+2} + \frac{5}{24}w_{i\,j+2} - \frac{1}{9}w_{i+1\,j+2} + \frac{1}{144}w_{i+2\,j+2}\Big]\end{aligned}$$

Now it is possible to see how to construct all of the equations. As was mentioned earlier, there are 81 unknowns, so that 81 simultaneous equations must be available. Many of these equations must describe the boundary conditions. In fact $w_{11} = 0$, $w_{12} = 0$, etc., for the simply supported edges, provide 32 equations. The bending moment on the edges of the plate must be zero, which provides 28 more equations. Those equations may be constructed as follows.

$$M_x = \left(\frac{\partial^2 w}{\partial x^2} + \frac{\mu\partial^2 w}{\partial y^2}\right)\frac{Et^3}{12(1-\mu^2)}$$

$$M_y = \left(\frac{\partial^2 w}{\partial y^2} + \frac{\mu\partial^2 w}{\partial x^2}\right)\frac{Et^3}{12(1-\mu^2)}$$

where M_x and M_y are distributed moments on the edges of an element, positive if they put compression in the top of the plate. To apply these equations to a typical point on the edge of the sheet, consider the equation $M_x = 0$ at the point $i = 2, j = 1$. Since $\partial^2 w/\partial y^2 = 0$ here, (and all along the edge of the sheet—in fact, both M_x and M_y are zero along all edges) the equation $(\partial^2 w/\partial x^2)_{21} = 0$ will satisfy the condition. This can be stated by letting $n = 3$ in the fourth of Equations 13-6 as follows:

$$\left(\frac{\partial^2 w}{\partial x^2}\right)_{21} = 0 = \frac{1}{l^2}\left(\frac{35}{12}w_{21} - \frac{26}{3}w_{22} + \frac{19}{2}w_{23} - \frac{14}{3}w_{24} + \frac{11}{12}w_{25}\right)$$

A similar equation at Station 1, 2 for $(\partial^2 w/\partial y^2)_{12} = 0$ is

$$\left(\frac{\partial^2 w}{\partial y^2}\right)_{12} = 0 = \frac{1}{l^2}\left(\frac{35}{12} w_{12} - \frac{26}{3} w_{22} + \frac{19}{2} w_{32} - \frac{14}{3} w_{42} + \frac{11}{12} w_{52}\right)$$

So far, 60 of the 81 equations have been taken into account. Twenty-five more equations are available from the application of the differential equation itself. Here, then, four too many equations are available. It can be shown that one of the corner equations stating that the moment is zero could be derived from the others and is not independent. Therefore, one such equation at each corner should be omitted, such as $(\partial^2 w/\partial y^2)_{12} = 0$, $(\partial^2 w/\partial x^2)_{29} = 0$, $(\partial^2 w/\partial y^2)_{98} = 0$, $(\partial^2 w/\partial x^2)_{81} = 0$. The 25 equations representing the differential equation for a typical station, i, j, would be derived from the differential equation by combining the equations for $\partial^4 w/\partial x^4$, $\partial^4 w/\partial y^4$, and $\partial^4 w/\partial x^2 \partial y^2$ previously indicated to obtain

$$\left.\begin{aligned}
&\frac{1}{72} w_{i-2\,j-2} - \frac{2}{9} w_{i-2\,j-1} + \frac{17}{12} w_{i-2\,j} - \frac{2}{9} w_{i-2\,j+1} + \frac{1}{72} w_{i-2\,j+2} \\
&\quad - \frac{2}{9} w_{i-1\,j-2} + \frac{32}{9} w_{i-1\,j-1} - \frac{32}{3} w_{i-1\,j} + \frac{32}{9} w_{i-1\,j+1} - \frac{2}{9} w_{i-1\,j+2} \\
&\quad + \frac{17}{12} w_{i\,j-2} - \frac{32}{3} w_{i\,j-1} + \frac{49}{2} w_{i\,j} - \frac{32}{3} w_{i\,j+1} + \frac{17}{12} w_{i\,j+2} \\
&\quad - \frac{2}{9} w_{i+1\,j-2} + \frac{32}{9} w_{i+1\,j-1} - \frac{32}{3} w_{i+1\,j} + \frac{32}{9} w_{i+1\,j+1} - \frac{2}{9} w_{i+1\,j+2} \\
&\quad + \frac{1}{72} w_{i+2\,j-2} - \frac{2}{9} w_{i+2\,j-1} + \frac{17}{12} w_{i+2\,j} - \frac{2}{9} w_{i+2\,j+1} + \frac{1}{72} w_{i+2\,j+2}
\end{aligned}\right\} = 0$$

This equation would be applied 25 times with i and j taking on the values

3,3	3,4	3,5	3,6	3,7
4,3	4,4	4,5	4,6	4,7
5,3	5,4	5,5	5,6	5,7
6,3	6,4	6,5	6,6	6,7
7,3	7,4	7,5	7,6	7,7

However, one of the equations, the one which bears the unit load, would not have zero on the right side, but instead the quantity $12(1 - \mu^2)l^2/Et^3$ which is obtained by spreading the unit load over an area of one square unit.

Now, as in Example 13-1, only one inverse matrix is required in solving these equations simultaneously, regardless of where the unit load is applied.

If the deflection at the center of a square plate caused by unit load applied at the center is calculated with this method using ten divisions each way, the result is $w = 0.1274L^2/Et^3$, which may be compared with the "exact" value of $w = 0.1265L^2/Et^3$, an error of 0.7%.

13.5 Partial Differential Equations from Variational Calculus

It is instructive to review Example 13-2 starting at an earlier point in the development. It can be shown that if a thin plate is bent so that deflections are small compared to the thickness, the strain energy in a differential element of plate is expressed by the following equation.

$$dV = \frac{1}{2}\frac{Et^3}{12(1 - \mu^2)}\left\{\left(\frac{\partial^2 w}{\partial x^2} + \frac{\partial^2 w}{\partial y^2}\right)^2 - 2(1 - \mu)\left[\frac{\partial^2 w}{\partial x^2}\frac{\partial^2 w}{\partial y^2} - \left(\frac{\partial^2 w}{\partial x\,\partial y}\right)^2\right]\right\} dx\,dy$$

Therefore, the total strain energy in the plate would, of course, be the integral of this over the plate area. Suppose that a flat plate is clamped to a plane surface while a transverse pressure or distributed load is applied. The plate is prevented from deflecting while this load is applied, but then the restraint is slowly released so that the plate bends to the position it would naturally assume for this particular pressure load. The amount of work done by the pressure load on the external restraints would be $\iint pw\,dx\,dy - \iint dV$. It might be imagined that the deflection, w, could assume any arbitrary shape. The correct deflection would result when all external restraints are zero. It is clear that the system comprising the loads and internal strain energy stored in the plate must be at the minimum energy level when the restraints are zero or in the naturally deflected position of the plate, since any other arbitrary deflection function would require applying other external loads or restraints which would add energy to the system. Therefore, the correct deflection function, w, is that function for which the following integral is a minimum.

$$I = \int_{y_1}^{y_2} \int_{x_1}^{x_2} pw - \frac{1}{2} \frac{Et^3}{12(1-\mu^2)} \left\{ \left(\frac{\partial^2 w}{\partial x^2} + \frac{\partial^2 w}{\partial y^2} \right)^2 - 2(1-\mu) \left[\frac{\partial^2 w}{\partial x^2} \frac{\partial^2 w}{\partial y^2} - \left(\frac{\partial^2 w}{\partial x\, \partial y} \right)^2 \right] \right\} dx\, dy \quad (13\text{-}7)$$

This suggests the use of the calculus of variations to set the variation of the foregoing integral to zero. It can be shown that if

$$I = \int_{y_1}^{y_2} \int_{x_1}^{x_2} F(x, y, w, w_x, w_y, w_{xx}, w_{xy}, w_{yy})\, dx\, dy \quad (13\text{-}8)$$

then

$$\begin{aligned}
\delta I = &\int_{y_1}^{y_2} \int_{x_1}^{x_2} \left[\frac{\partial F}{\partial w} - \frac{\partial}{\partial x}\left(\frac{\partial F}{\partial w_x}\right) - \frac{\partial}{\partial y}\left(\frac{\partial F}{\partial w_y}\right) + \frac{\partial^2}{\partial x^2}\left(\frac{\partial F}{\partial w_{xx}}\right) + \frac{\partial^2}{\partial x\, \partial y}\left(\frac{\partial F}{\partial w_{xy}}\right) + \frac{\partial^2}{\partial y^2}\left(\frac{\partial F}{\partial w_{yy}}\right) \right] (\delta w)\, dx\, dy \\
&+ \int_{y_1}^{y_2} \left\{ \left[\left(\frac{\partial F}{\partial w_x}\right) - \frac{\partial}{\partial x}\left(\frac{\partial F}{\partial w_{xx}}\right) - \frac{\partial}{\partial y}\left(\frac{\partial F}{\partial w_{xy}}\right) \right] \times (\delta w) \right\}_{x=x_2} dy \\
&- \int_{y_1}^{y_2} \left\{ \left[\left(\frac{\partial F}{\partial w_x}\right) - \frac{\partial}{\partial x}\left(\frac{\partial F}{\partial w_{xx}}\right) - \frac{\partial}{\partial y}\left(\frac{\partial F}{\partial w_{xy}}\right) \right] (\delta w) \right\}_{x=x_1} dy \\
&+ \int_{x_1}^{x_2} \left\{ \left[\left(\frac{\partial F}{\partial w_y}\right) - \frac{\partial}{\partial y}\left(\frac{\partial F}{\partial w_{yy}}\right) - \frac{\partial}{\partial x}\left(\frac{\partial F}{\partial w_{xy}}\right) \right] (\delta w) \right\}_{y=y_2} dx \\
&- \int_{x_1}^{x_2} \left\{ \left[\left(\frac{\partial F}{\partial w_y}\right) - \frac{\partial}{\partial y}\left(\frac{\partial F}{\partial w_{yy}}\right) - \frac{\partial}{\partial x}\left(\frac{\partial F}{\partial w_{xy}}\right) \right] \delta w \right\}_{y=y_1} dx \qquad (13\text{-}9) \\
&+ \int_{y_1}^{y_2} \left[\left(\frac{\partial F}{\partial w_{xx}}\right)(\delta w_x) \right]_{x=x_2} dy - \int_{y_1}^{y_2} \left[\left(\frac{\partial F}{\partial w_{xx}}\right)(\delta w_x) \right]_{x=x_1} dy \\
&+ \int_{x_1}^{x_2} \left[\left(\frac{\partial F}{\partial w_{yy}}\right)(\delta w_y) \right]_{y=y_2} dx - \int_{x_1}^{x_2} \left[\left(\frac{\partial F}{\partial w_{yy}}\right)(\delta w_y) \right]_{y=y_1} dx \\
&+ \left[\left(\frac{\partial F}{\partial w_{xy}}\right)(\delta w) \right]_{\substack{x=x_2 \\ y=y_2}} + \left[\left(\frac{\partial F}{\partial w_{xy}}\right)(\delta w) \right]_{\substack{x=x_1 \\ y=y_1}} - \left[\left(\frac{\partial F}{\partial w_{xy}}\right)(\delta w) \right]_{\substack{x=x_2 \\ y=y_1}} \\
&- \left[\left(\frac{\partial F}{\partial w_{xy}}\right)(\delta w) \right]_{\substack{x=x_1 \\ y=y_2}}
\end{aligned}$$

The General Partial Differential Equation. It is possible to argue that because δw is an arbitrary function, and because δI must be zero, each of the integrals must be individually zero, and, furthermore, the integrands must be zero. Therefore, if t is constant in

$$F = pw - \frac{1}{2}\frac{Et^3}{12(1-\mu^2)}\left[(w_{xx} + w_{yy})^2 - 2(1-\mu)(w_{xx}w_{yy} - w_{xy}^2)\right]$$

(Equation 13-7) the differential equation used in Example 13-2,

$$\frac{\partial^4 w}{\partial x^4} + 2\frac{\partial^4 w}{\partial x^2\,\partial y^2} + \frac{\partial^4 w}{\partial y^4} = \frac{12(1-\mu^2)}{Et^3}p$$

will result from setting the integrand of the double integral term of Equation 13-9 equal to zero.

Boundary-Condition Partial Differential Equations. Various boundary-condition equations would result from the other integrands of Equation 13-9. For instance, suppose the edge $x = x_2$ is a simply supported edge. The second integral would be zero because (δw) would be zero so that $w = 0$ would satisfy the requirement that the second integral be zero. However, (δw_x) does not have to be zero, so that the only way that the sixth integral can become zero is if $\partial F/\partial w_{xx} = 0$. This leads to the equation

$$\left(\frac{\partial^2 w}{\partial x^2}\right)_{x=x_2} + \mu\left(\frac{\partial^2 w}{\partial y^2}\right)_{x=x_2} = 0$$

This was used in Example 13-2.

If the edge $x = x_2$ had been a free edge, then not only would this equation have to be satisfied but also, since δw would not necessarily be zero, the second integral could only be zero (as required) if

$$\frac{\partial F}{\partial w_x} - \frac{\partial}{\partial x}\left(\frac{\partial F}{\partial w_{xx}}\right) - \frac{\partial}{\partial y}\left(\frac{\partial F}{\partial w_{xy}}\right) = 0$$

along $x = x_2$. This leads to

$$\left(\frac{\partial^3 w}{\partial x^3}\right)_{x=x_2} + (2-\mu)\left(\frac{\partial^3 w}{\partial x\,\partial y^2}\right)_{x=x_2} = 0$$

which is the other boundary condition equation for a free edge.

Variable Thickness Plate. It is easy to see how to obtain a differential equation for a plate whose thickness is not constant. The fact that t is a function of x and y is simply accounted for when the various partials of F are taken. No particular difficulty is introduced in the numerical solution previously described.

Variable Geometry. A plate having an edge which is not parallel to the x or y directions could be accounted for by writing the derivatives in terms of the x- and y-coordinate system and resolving into directions parallel and perpendicular to the edge before applying the boundary-condition equations.

Lower Order Derivatives. Finally, lower order equations could be used, if desired, by working with four dependent variables, w, w_{xx}, w_{xy}, w_{yy} and utilizing four simultaneous equations. For t constant these are

$$\frac{\partial^2 w_{xx}}{\partial x^2} + 2\frac{\partial^2 w_{xy}}{\partial x\, \partial y} + \frac{\partial^2 w_{yy}}{\partial y^2} = \frac{12(1-\mu^2)}{Et^3}p$$

$$w_{xx} = \frac{\partial^2 w}{\partial x^2}$$

$$w_{xy} = \frac{\partial^2 w}{\partial x\, \partial y}$$

$$w_{yy} = \frac{\partial^2 w}{\partial y^2}$$

13.6 Minimum Energy Method

The energy relationships leading to the use of variational calculus in Section 13.5 are also useful in the direct formulation of stiffness and flexibility matrices for other structures.

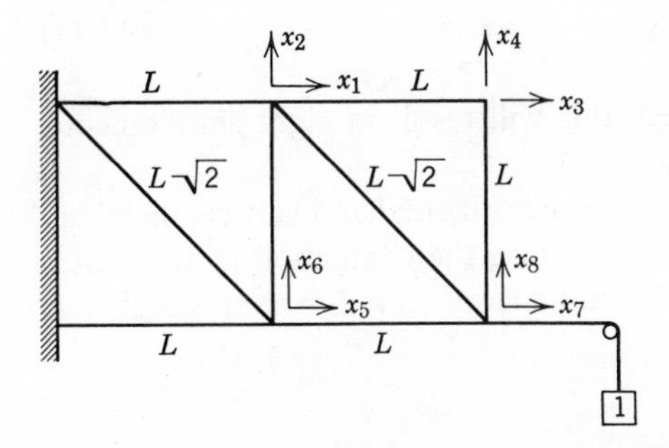

Fig. 13-6

Figure 13-6 represents a simple truss structure having a flexibility matrix that could easily be computed by elementary methods. However, for purposes of illustration, the flexibility matrix of this structure will be computed by minimizing the energy contained in the system under load. It is assumed that the truss members are all pin jointed and do not buckle or bend under load, and for simplicity that they form squares of length, L, on the side. The cross sectional area of all truss members is A. Modifications necessary for more complex structures will be apparent as the development proceeds.

If the deflections in the directions indicated in Fig. 13-6 are x_i and unit load is applied in the direction of x_7, as indicated, the results of the analysis will be the influence coefficients δ_{i7}. If the unit load were moved to the other joints and applied in the positive directions, the rest of the flexibility matrix would result.

The argument used in Section 13.5 can be applied to this structure as follows. Suppose that the unit weight were attached to the structure but supported externally so that no stress would exist in the structure. Then, let the support be gradually removed. The weight would lower by the amount x_7, and the energy lost by the weight would be $1x_7$. (One half of this energy loss would be stored as internal strain energy of the truss members and one half would do work on the external support as the weight lowered, but this is not important to the argument.) Now it can be supposed that the deflections might have any arbitrary values. By physical external force it would be possible to produce any arbitrary set of deflections specified. However, the natural deflection pattern produced by the unit weight would be that one which would require no other external forces. It is clear, therefore, that the system comprised of the truss and the weight must be in its minimum energy configuration when the deflection pattern is the natural one, since to move it into some other pattern would require the application of external forces somewhere on the system, which would then do work when the deflection to the new pattern occurred, and this work would be stored in the system. If the total energy stored in the system is U, the total strain energy stored in the truss members is V, and the work done by the constant external load as the deflection occurs is W, then

$$U = V - W \tag{13-10}$$

where in this particular instance $W = 1x_7$ (not $\frac{1}{2}x_7$).

In general, U is a function of all the variables, x_i, and in order that U be a minimum it is necessary that

$$\frac{\partial U}{\partial x_i} = 0 \tag{13-11}$$

for all variables, x_i. For the structure chosen, this will result in eight simultaneous equations in the eight variables, $x_1, x_2, \ldots x_8$.

For the structure of Fig. 13-6, the elongation of the horizontal and vertical members is easily written in terms of the variables. For instance, the elongation of the center vertical member is $(x_2 - x_6)$ and the internal strain energy stored in that member is therefore

$$\frac{1}{2}\left(\frac{EA}{L}\right)(x_2 - x_6)^2$$

The elongation of the diagonal member at the right of the figure is

$$(x_7 - x_1)\frac{\sqrt{2}}{2} + (x_2 - x_8)\frac{\sqrt{2}}{2}$$

and the energy stored in that member is then

$$\frac{1}{2}\left(\frac{EA}{2\sqrt{2}L}\right)(x_2 + x_7 - x_1 - x_8)^2$$

For structures with complex geometry, vector methods are convenient for determining these elongations. When all the strain energy is accounted for, Equation 13-10 becomes

$$U = \frac{EA}{L}\left[\frac{1}{2}x_1^2 + \frac{1}{2}x_5^2 + \frac{1}{2}\frac{1}{2\sqrt{2}}(x_5 - x_6)^2 + \frac{1}{2}(x_2 - x_6)^2 + \frac{1}{2}(x_3 - x_7)^2 \right.$$
$$\left. + \frac{1}{2}(x_7 - x_5)^2 + \frac{1}{2}(x_4 - x_8)^2 + \frac{1}{2}\frac{1}{2\sqrt{2}}(x_2 + x_7 - x_1 - x_8)^2\right] - 1x_7$$

Application of Equation 13-11 to each variable in turn results in eight simultaneous equations which can be represented by the following matrix equation.

$$\frac{EA}{L}\begin{bmatrix} \left(2+\frac{1}{2\sqrt{2}}\right) & -\frac{1}{2\sqrt{2}} & -1 & 0 & 0 & 0 & -\frac{1}{2\sqrt{2}} & \frac{1}{2\sqrt{2}} \\ -\frac{1}{2\sqrt{2}} & \left(1+\frac{1}{2\sqrt{2}}\right) & 0 & 0 & 0 & -1 & \frac{1}{2\sqrt{2}} & -\frac{1}{2\sqrt{2}} \\ -1 & 0 & 1 & 0 & 0 & 0 & 0 & 0 \\ 0 & 0 & 0 & 1 & 0 & 0 & 0 & -1 \\ 0 & 0 & 0 & 0 & \left(2+\frac{1}{2\sqrt{2}}\right) & -\frac{1}{2\sqrt{2}} & -1 & 0 \\ 0 & -1 & 0 & 0 & -\frac{1}{2\sqrt{2}} & \left(1+\frac{1}{2\sqrt{2}}\right) & 0 & 0 \\ -\frac{1}{2\sqrt{2}} & \frac{1}{2\sqrt{2}} & 0 & 0 & -1 & 0 & \left(1+\frac{1}{2\sqrt{2}}\right) & -\frac{1}{2\sqrt{2}} \\ \frac{1}{2\sqrt{2}} & -\frac{1}{2\sqrt{2}} & 0 & -1 & 0 & 0 & -\frac{1}{2\sqrt{2}} & \left(1+\frac{1}{2\sqrt{2}}\right) \end{bmatrix} \begin{Bmatrix} x_1 \\ x_2 \\ x_3 \\ x_4 \\ x_5 \\ x_6 \\ x_7 \\ x_8 \end{Bmatrix} = \begin{Bmatrix} 0 \\ 0 \\ 0 \\ 0 \\ 0 \\ 0 \\ 1 \\ 0 \end{Bmatrix} \tag{13-12}$$

It is recalled that these deflections are the deflections caused by unit load in the direction of positive x_7, and are therefore the influence coefficients δ_{i7}. The seventh element in the column at the right arises from the unit load. If the unit load were applied in the direction of x_6, the unit element in the column matrix at the right would be the sixth element, and the column matrix of x's would then be δ_{i6}. The square matrix would be unchanged. It is clear that the entire influence coefficient matrix $[\delta]$ could be formed from the columns of x's on the left with the unit matrix on the right. Therefore, the square matrix in Equation 13-12 is actually the stiffness matrix, $[K]$, and the flexibility matrix could be obtained by taking its inverse. If the process by which this square matrix was obtained from Equation 13-11 is reviewed, it is seen that any element K_{ij} of the stiffness matrix may be obtained from the following relationship

$$K_{ij} = \frac{\partial^2 V}{\partial x_i \, \partial x_j} \tag{13-13}$$

where V is the internal strain energy in the structure expressed in terms of the deflection coordinates. In the example chosen for the discussion, the internal energy was that of tension or compression in the truss members, but it is clear that bending- or shear-strain energy also must be considered when these are significant.

13.7 Iteration for Refinement of Accuracy

Many of the previous examples required the simultaneous solution of a large number of algebraic equations, which was accomplished by the use of the inverse matrix. Round-off errors which accumulate during the calculation of the inverse may spoil the results. If this occurs, it is often possible to refine the results by the Gauss-Seidel iterative procedure described in this section. In addition to the better precision afforded by this method (when applicable) it has an advantage for digital computer application when the system is characterized by a very large set of equations with only a few variables in each equation (sparse matrices). The advantage derives from the reduced memory capacity required of the computer with this method.

In many physical problems, such as the calculation of flexibility matrices by the methods of this chapter, the m simultaneous algebraic equations exhibit the property that each equation is dominated by a different variable. If this is true, then it is possible to assume any arbitrary values for the unknowns and solve each equation for the dominant variable, progressing around and around the set of equations until the desired accuracy is obtained. This is illustrated in Example 13-3.

The convergence of this procedure depends on the magnitude of the coefficient which multiplies the dominant variable. If the absolute value of the coefficient which multiplies the dominant variable in each equation is larger than the sum of the absolute values of the coefficients of all the other variables in the same equation, then the method will surely converge. This is not a necessary condition, however, and convergence will often occur for less stringent restrictions on the coefficients.

Example 13-3. If the three equations

$$2x_1 + x_2 + x_3 = 3$$

$$x_1 + 2x_2 + x_3 = 4$$

$$x_1 + x_2 + 2x_3 = 1$$

were solved simultaneously, it would be found that $x_1 = 1$, $x_2 = 2$, $x_3 = -1$. If these equations were written as follows,

$$x_1 = \frac{1}{2}(3 - x_2 - x_3)$$

$$x_2 = \frac{1}{2}(4 - x_1 - x_3)$$

$$x_3 = \frac{1}{2}(1 - x_1 - x_2)$$

and then any arbitrary values of x_1, x_2 and x_3 assumed as a start, but the newly calculated values used immediately after becoming known, the result will converge to the correct values. For instance, suppose it is assumed that $x_1 = x_2 = x_3 = 0$. Calculation of x_1 on this assumption would give $x_1 = \frac{3}{2}$. This value in the equation for x_2 produces

$$x_2 = \frac{1}{2}\left(4 - \frac{3}{2} - 0\right) = \frac{5}{4}$$

Then, if $x_1 = 3/2$, and $x_2 = 5/4$ in the equation for x_3

$$x_3 = \frac{1}{2}\left(1 - \frac{3}{2} - \frac{5}{4}\right) = -\frac{7}{8}$$

Now the newest values of x_2 and x_3 are used in the x_1 equation to obtain

$$x_1 = \frac{1}{2}\left(3 - \frac{5}{4} - \frac{7}{8}\right) = \frac{7}{16}$$

Then this value of x_1 and the newest value of x_3 are used in x_2

$$x_2 = \frac{1}{2}\left(4 - \frac{7}{16} - \frac{7}{8}\right) = \frac{43}{32}$$

The calculation continues until the new value of each variable is the same as the old value of the variable to the desired number of significant figures.

It is interesting to note that if the set of simultaneous equations had been

$$3x_1 + 2x_2 + 2x_3 = 5$$

$$2x_1 + 3x_2 + 2x_3 = 6$$

$$2x_1 + 2x_2 + 3x_3 = 3$$

the coefficients would not satisfy the restrictions mentioned for convergence (sufficient but not necessary conditions), but the iteration would nevertheless converge on the solution $x_1 = 1$, $x_2 = 2$, $x_3 = -1$.

CHAPTER 14

Use of Generalized Properties in the Analysis of Complex Systems

14.1 Free Beam Subjected to a Sudden Load

Problems are often encountered in which a continuous structure is acted upon by some external force or combination of forces. Also, several continuous systems, or continuous and lumped systems, may be coupled together in some way and acted upon by external forces. It is necessary to be able to analyze such systems with some convenient method which is easily understood and applicable to many different situations. A relatively simple problem is used to illustrate the general procedure. It will be seen that the method could be extended to more difficult problems, and several examples of applications to such problems are discussed.

Figure 14-1 depicts a beam with free ends acted upon by a force which is some function of time, specified later.

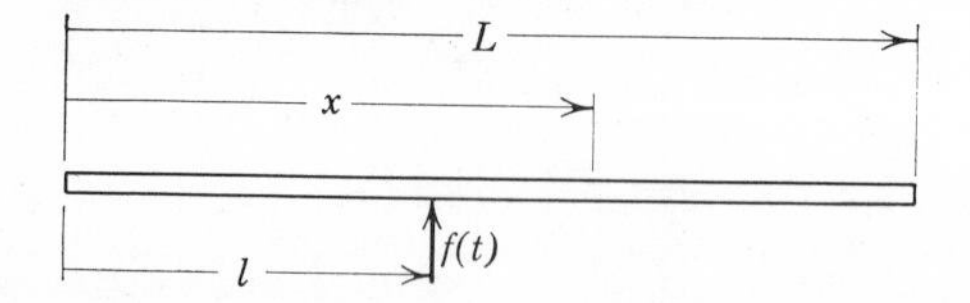

Fig. 14-1 Free beam with load

(This might represent a missile body with aerodynamic load caused by a wind gust or maneuver, for instance, although for such a structure the beam cross section would not be constant.) It is necessary to determine the natural modes and frequencies of the free beam, assuming slight or zero damping. In most structures these would have to be determined by numerical means as described in Chapters 12 and 13, although this constant cross-section beam is easily analyzed by the method of separation of variables described in Chapter 11. In order to illustrate the more general method, however, the numerical procedure will be used.

Inertia and Flexibility Matrix. Let the beam be divided into seven parts. (More divisions could be used for greater accuracy if desired.) For purposes of this analysis let the masses of the seven pieces be concentrated at their centers of gravity. Let the seven coordinates representing beam bending be the deflection of the centers of gravity from the rigid body centerline. There are also two coordinates which would define rigid body translation and rotation, but these are of no interest in this problem and can be assumed to remain zero, at least for the calculation of the bending modes and frequencies. With these assumptions, only the y_{ij} of Section 12.3 are of interest. For the constant cross-section beam, the y_{ij} values can be calculated as in Example 12-3, but the values of the deflections of the actual ends of the beam will be of no importance in this application (no concentrated masses are located there). However, coordinates for the ends are included anyway, making nine stations in all, and the mass located at Stations 1 and 9 will be set to zero. With these modifications, values to be used in Equations 12-3 are:

$$n = 9$$

$$(\Delta l)_1 = 0, \qquad (\Delta l)_i = \frac{L}{7} \quad (2 \leqq i \leqq 8), \qquad (\Delta l)_9 = 0$$

$$l_{11} = 0, \qquad l_{12} = \frac{L}{14}, \qquad l_{13} = \frac{3L}{14}, \qquad l_{14} = \frac{5L}{14}, \text{ etc.,} \qquad l_{19} = L$$

$$\left(\frac{Q}{GIb}\right)_i = 0, \qquad (EI)_i = \text{constant} = EI$$

The values to be used in Equations 12-7, 12-8, and 12-9 are

$$m_1 = 0, \qquad m_k = \frac{m}{7} \quad 2 \leqq k \leqq 8, \qquad m_9 = 0, \qquad p_k{}^2 = 0$$

When these values are used with Programs A55, given in Reference 1, the flexibility matrix is computed to be the following (only the y_{ij} elements, and only four significant figures).

$$[\delta] = \frac{0.01L^3}{EI}\begin{bmatrix} 0.9814 & 0.6039 & -0.0304 & -0.3974 & -0.4651 & -0.2794 & 0.0720 & 0.4963 & 0.7141 \\ 0.6039 & 0.3932 & -0.0022 & -0.2588 & -0.3193 & -0.1993 & 0.0439 & 0.3426 & 0.4963 \\ -0.0304 & -0.0022 & 0.0367 & 0.0062 & -0.0347 & -0.0409 & -0.0089 & 0.0439 & 0.0720 \\ -0.3974 & -0.2588 & 0.0062 & 0.1879 & 0.2013 & 0.1036 & -0.0409 & -0.1993 & -0.2794 \\ -0.4651 & -0.3193 & -0.0347 & 0.2013 & 0.3054 & 0.2013 & -0.0347 & -0.3193 & -0.4651 \\ -0.2794 & -0.1993 & -0.0409 & 0.1036 & 0.2013 & 0.1879 & 0.0062 & -0.2588 & -0.3974 \\ 0.0720 & 0.0439 & -0.0089 & -0.0409 & -0.0347 & 0.0062 & 0.0367 & -0.0022 & -0.0304 \\ 0.4963 & 0.3426 & 0.0439 & -0.1993 & -0.3193 & -0.2588 & -0.0022 & 0.3932 & 0.6039 \\ 0.7141 & 0.4963 & 0.0720 & -0.2794 & -0.4651 & -0.3974 & -0.0304 & 0.6039 & 0.9814 \end{bmatrix}$$

The inertia matrix is the following (m is the total mass of the beam).

$$[M] = m\begin{bmatrix} 0 & 0 & 0 & 0 & 0 & 0 & 0 & 0 & 0 \\ 0 & \frac{1}{7} & 0 & 0 & 0 & 0 & 0 & 0 & 0 \\ 0 & 0 & \frac{1}{7} & 0 & 0 & 0 & 0 & 0 & 0 \\ 0 & 0 & 0 & \frac{1}{7} & 0 & 0 & 0 & 0 & 0 \\ 0 & 0 & 0 & 0 & \frac{1}{7} & 0 & 0 & 0 & 0 \\ 0 & 0 & 0 & 0 & 0 & \frac{1}{7} & 0 & 0 & 0 \\ 0 & 0 & 0 & 0 & 0 & 0 & \frac{1}{7} & 0 & 0 \\ 0 & 0 & 0 & 0 & 0 & 0 & 0 & \frac{1}{7} & 0 \\ 0 & 0 & 0 & 0 & 0 & 0 & 0 & 0 & 0 \end{bmatrix}$$

Modal Properties. When these two matrices are used in Program A38NM of Reference 1, which uses the method of Duncan and Collar explained in Example 8-5, the first three normal modes and frequencies are determined to be as shown in Table 14-1.

Table 14-1. Modes and Frequencies for Free Beam

	Mode 1	Mode 2	Mode 3
Station i	$\left(\frac{\partial y_i}{\partial q_1}\right)$	$\left(\frac{\partial y_i}{\partial q_2}\right)$	$\left(\frac{\partial y_i}{\partial q_3}\right)$
1	2.068	2.141	−2.173
2	1.396	1.026	−0.712
3	0.103	−0.900	1.376
4	−0.876	−1.279	0.076
5	−1.244	0.000	−1.479
6	−0.876	1.279	0.076
7	0.103	0.900	1.376
8	1.396	−1.026	−0.712
9	2.068	−2.141	−2.173
Frequency, rad/sec	$23.11\sqrt{\frac{EI}{mL^3}}$	$65.1\sqrt{\frac{EI}{mL^3}}$	$129.7\sqrt{\frac{EI}{mL^3}}$
Generalized mass, slugs	$1.000m$	$1.000m$	$1.000m$
Generalized spring constant, lb/ft	$534\frac{EI}{L^3}$	$4240\frac{EI}{L^3}$	$16800\frac{EI}{L^3}$

The frequencies calculated for this beam, divided into seven parts, can be compared with the "exact" values of 22.4, 61.7, and 121.0, calculated by separation of variables, to give an idea of the amount of error to be expected with the assumptions made.

In Table 14-1 the columns headed $\partial y_i/\partial q_k$ are the mode shapes, or the ratios of the deflection of the various masses to the deflection of a generalized coordinate, q_k (which is also a principal coordinate). In the normalization used here there is a slight difference from that described in Example 8-5, where the normalization was such that $\partial y/\partial q$ was caused to be unity at some station. For convenience and for other reasons, a normalization of coordinates is preferred which would cause the generalized mass in each mode to have the same numerical value as the sum of the actual masses. For instance, it is clear that the column describing Mode 1 in Table 14-1 could just as well have described Mode 1 if each of the values in that column were twice as large, or any other constant multiple or fraction of the value indicated. These particular values were selected in order that the generalized mass, M_1, moving with a velocity $\dot{q}_1$ would have the same kinetic energy as the sum of the kinetic energies of the actual masses moving with their respective velocities in Mode 1, and also the values of the generalized mass would be numerically the same as the sum of the actual masses. A set of coordinate ratios, say $\partial z_i/\partial q_1$, having the correct relative values for Mode 1 but lacking the foregoing property regarding the magnitude of the generalized mass, can be transformed into the desired set of coordinate ratios by multiplying by a constant, determined as follows:

$$\frac{1}{2}M_1\dot{q}_1^2 = \sum_{i=1}^{n} \frac{1}{2}m_i\left(c\frac{\partial z_i}{\partial q_1}\dot{q}_1\right)^2$$

$$M_1 = \sum_{i=1}^{n} m_i$$

From these equations the constant c becomes

$$c = \sqrt{\frac{\sum_{i=1}^{n} m_i}{\sum_{i=1}^{n} m_i\left(\frac{\partial z_i}{\partial q_1}\right)^2}}$$

after which the desired normalized coordinate ratios may be obtained from

$$\frac{\partial y_i}{\partial q_1} = c\frac{\partial z_i}{\partial q_1}$$

The more general correction if the inertia matrix is not diagonal or not formed exclusively from mass elements is, from Equation 8-36,

$$c = \sqrt{\frac{M_1}{\widetilde{\left\{\frac{\partial y_i}{\partial q_1}\right\}}[M]\left\{\frac{\partial y_i}{\partial q_1}\right\}}}$$

where M_1 is the desired generalized mass for Mode 1.
With the generalized mass and frequency both known, the generalized spring constant shown in Table 14-1 may easily be obtained from $K_1 = \beta_1^2 M_1$. Similar calculations would be made for the other modes.

Convergence of the Matrix Iteration. It should be mentioned that the iterative method used to obtain the modes for this beam, the method described in Example 8-5, will converge if the dynamic matrix represents exactly a physical system. If the dynamic matrix is really only an approximation of a physical system, as in this example, where a lumped system is used to represent a distributed system, it may happen that the iteration will not converge. In this system, since there were seven masses assumed, it might be expected that seven modes and frequencies could be determined. However, the computation does not converge for the sixth and seventh modes. On the other hand, if the number of lumped masses representing the distributed system is increased to 21, no difficulty is experienced with convergence of the sixth and seventh modes. Another possible source of error leading to non-convergence is the accumulation of error resulting from the matrix deflation process after each successive mode determination. Also, for some complex structures, the flexibility matrix may be determined by test of a model. Unavoidable errors occur which may result in nonconvergence of the iteration process.

Beam Response. Now the original problem, represented by Fig. 14-1, can be solved rather easily, treating each mode as if it were a one-degree-of-freedom system (Fig. 14-2). For instance, suppose that the force $f(t)$ is a suddenly applied force, f_0, half way between Stations 3 and 4. Assume, then, that $\frac{1}{2}f_0$ is applied on Station 3 and $\frac{1}{2}f_0$ on Station 4. The generalized forces in Modes 1, 2, and 3 would become

$$Q_1 = \frac{1}{2}f_0(0.103) + \frac{1}{2}f_0(-0.876) = -0.387f_0$$

$$Q_2 = \frac{1}{2}f_0(-0.900) + \frac{1}{2}f_0(-1.279) = -1.089f_0$$

$$Q_3 = \frac{1}{2}f_0(1.376) + \frac{1}{2}f_0(0.076) = 0.726f_0$$

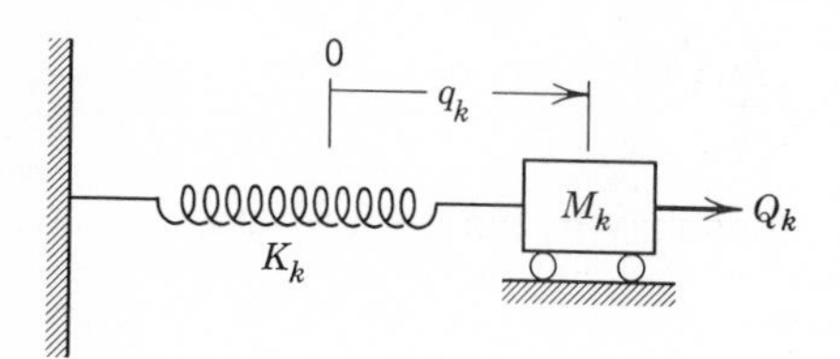

Fig. 14-2

All of these generalized forces are, of course, suddenly applied forces. Now, treating the three modes as if each were a single-degree-of-freedom system, the generalized coordinates are

$$q_1 = \frac{Q_1}{K_1}(1 - \cos \beta_1 t) = -0.725 \times 10^{-3}\frac{f_0L^3}{EI}\left(1 - \cos 23.1\sqrt{\frac{EI}{mL^3}}\,t\right)$$

$$q_2 = \frac{Q_2}{K_2}(1 - \cos \beta_2 t) = -0.257 \times 10^{-3}\frac{f_0L^3}{EI}\left(1 - \cos 65.1\sqrt{\frac{EI}{mL^3}}\,t\right)$$

$$q_3 = \frac{Q_3}{K_3}(1 - \cos \beta_3 t) = 0.0432 \times 10^{-3}\frac{f_0L^3}{EI}\left(1 - \cos 129.7\sqrt{\frac{EI}{mL^3}}\,t\right)$$

Notice that the amplitude tends to be smaller for the higher modes. The actual deflection of any one mass in a particular mode can be obtained from multiplying by the appropriate ratio from Table 14-1. Thus, the actual deflection of the center mass (Station 5) would be

$$y_5 = \left[0.902 \times 10^{-3}\left(1 - \cos 23.1\sqrt{\frac{EI}{mL^3}}\,t\right) + 0.0\left(1 - \cos 65.1\sqrt{\frac{EI}{mL^3}}\,t\right)\right.$$
$$\left. - 0.0638 \times 10^{-3}\left(1 - \cos 129.7\sqrt{\frac{EI}{mL^3}}\,t\right)\right]\frac{f_0L^3}{EI}$$

This deflection is relative to a hypothetical rigid body centerline, of course. Since the beam is free in space, the rigid body centerline would translate and rotate.

If the applied force were some other function of time, no particular difficulty would be encountered. The time dependency terms would be more complicated than $(1 - \cos \beta t)$, but whatever they would be for a single-degree-of-freedom system would simply show up in each of the terms of the summation representing each of the generalized coordinates.

14.2 Examples

In this section several examples are discussed which illustrate poi
Example 14-1 illustrates the similarity between initial displacement con
step function input and also compares the results of the exact sol
displacement with an approximate solution using four generalized coor...

Example 14-2 describes a method of obtaining natural modes and frequencies of a combined structure (crossed beams) using generalized coordinates which are principal coordinates for the component substructures.

Example 14-3 illustrates the use of generalized forces and coordinates in the stability analysis of a hypothetical missile having a simple autopilot and a flexible body. The generalized coordinates are principal coordinates for a free beam but are coupled by aerodynamic forces and the autopilot, and instability of the overall system is possible.

Example 14-1. Check the results of Example 11-4 using a step function input.

In Example 11-4 the free end of a cantilever beam was deflected by a unit force and then released. The amount of Modes 1 and 2 present in the vibration were computed.

This problem could be equally well described by the following statement. A cantilever beam is loaded with a static unit load in the positive direction at the end of the beam. Superimposed on the deflection caused by this static load is the deflection caused by unit load suddenly applied at the end of the beam in the negative direction.

The mode shapes defined in Example 11-4 are such that $X_n = 1$ at $x = L$. Since the actual deflection at $x = L$ is $q_n X_{n_{x=L}}$ (if q_n is the generalized coordinate in the nth mode), the generalized force exciting the nth mode could be obtained from

$$Q_n q_n = P_{x=L} q_n X_{n_{x=L}}$$

or $Q_n = -1$ (because $X_{n_{x=L}} = 1$ and $P_{x=L} = -1$ for the unit load in the negative direction.)

The response of a single-degree-of-freedom system to a positive step function is

$$q = \frac{Q}{K}(1 - \cos\beta t)$$

The deflection of the beam as a function of time should then be

$$y = F(x) + q_1 X_1 + q_2 X_2 + \ldots + q_n X_n$$

where $F(x)$ is the deflection of the beam under the original positive static load and X_n the various mode shapes. Therefore,

$$y = F(x) - \frac{X_1}{K_1}(1 - \cos\beta_1 t) - \frac{X_2}{K_2}(1 - \cos\beta_2 t) - \ldots - \frac{X_n}{K_n}(1 - \cos\beta_n t)$$

where the K_n's are the generalized spring constants, and the amplitudes of the vibratory components of the deflection are $1/K_1$, $1/K_2$, etc., which should agree with the values computed in Example 11-4. (These are the amplitudes of the generalized coordinates q_1, q_2, etc.).

It should also be possible to check that $F(x) = \sum_{n=1}^{\infty} X_n/K_n$, since the oscillation should occur about the undeflected beam centerline, which means that the nonoscillatory terms on the right side of the previous equation should add to zero.

To finish this example, then, the values of $1/K_n$ should be computed for several modes. It is slightly less troublesome to compute the generalized mass, instead, and obtain K_n from $\beta_n^2 M_n$. The generalized mass can be obtained from

$$\frac{1}{2} M_n \dot{q}_n^2 = \int_{x=0}^{L} \frac{1}{2}(dm)\left(\frac{\partial y}{\partial q_n}\dot{q}_n\right)^2 = \int_{x=0}^{L} \frac{1}{2}\rho A\left(\frac{\partial y}{\partial q_n}\right)^2 \dot{q}_n^2\, dx$$

Since $(\partial y/\partial q_n)$ is really X_n it is clear that

$$M_n = M \int_{x/L=0}^{1} X_n^2 \, d\left(\frac{x}{L}\right)$$

The generalized mass and spring constant for the first four modes can be computed from these equations, from which the amplitude of the vibratory portion is obtained as explained previously. The values are:

Mode, n	M_n	K_n	β_n	*Amplitude of* q_n, $\frac{1}{K_n}$
1	$0.2500m$	$3.091\frac{EI}{L^3}$	$3.516\sqrt{\frac{EI}{mL^3}}$	$0.32356\frac{L^3}{EI}$
2	$0.2500m$	$121.4\frac{EI}{L^3}$	$22.03\sqrt{\frac{EI}{mL^3}}$	$0.00824\frac{L^3}{EI}$
3	$0.2500m$	$951.7\frac{EI}{L^3}$	$61.70\sqrt{\frac{EI}{mL^3}}$	$0.00105\frac{L^3}{EI}$
4	$0.2500m$	$3654\frac{EI}{L^3}$	$120.9\sqrt{\frac{EI}{mL^3}}$	$0.00027\frac{L^3}{EI}$

A comparison between the static deflection curve, $F(x)$, and the sum $\sum_{n=1}^{4} X_n/K_n$ follows (The numbers should be multiplied by the factor PL^3/EI.)

$\frac{x}{L}$	0	0.1	0.2	0.3	0.4	0.5	0.6	0.7	0.8	0.9	1
$F(x)$	0	0.00483	0.01867	0.04050	0.06933	0.10417	0.14400	0.18783	0.23467	0.28350	0.33333
$\sum_{n=1}^{4}\frac{X_n}{K_n}$	0	0.00480	0.01861	0.04050	0.06939	0.10419	0.14394	0.18777	0.23472	0.28358	0.33312

It is evident that the sum of the first four modes very closely approximates the true deflection curve, and that all the calculations agree with those of Example 11-4.

Example 14-2. Determine the first two normal modes and frequencies of a structure composed of two free beams attached to each other to form a cross, using the first several normal bending modes of the individual beams as generalized coordinates. Use constant cross-section beams, but a numerical analysis which could be applied to more general beams.

The normal modes for a free beam divided into seven parts were calculated previously with the assumptions that the masses of the beam elements are concentrated at their centers of gravity, and that shear deflection is negligible. The results are shown in Table 14-1. Assume the structure indicated in Fig. 14-3.

With the composite structure vibrating in one of its natural modes, the deflection of the point of attachment is the same for each beam. Also, the force of one beam on the other at the point of attachment has the same magnitude, These two facts will be used in the following explanation.

Let the generalized coordinates which describe the displacement of the system be defined as follows:

q_1 = rigid body vertical displacement of the center of gravity of Beam a;
q_2 = rigid body angular displacement of Beam a about its center of gravity (right end upward for positive deflection);
q_3 = rigid body vertical displacement of the center of gravity of Beam b;

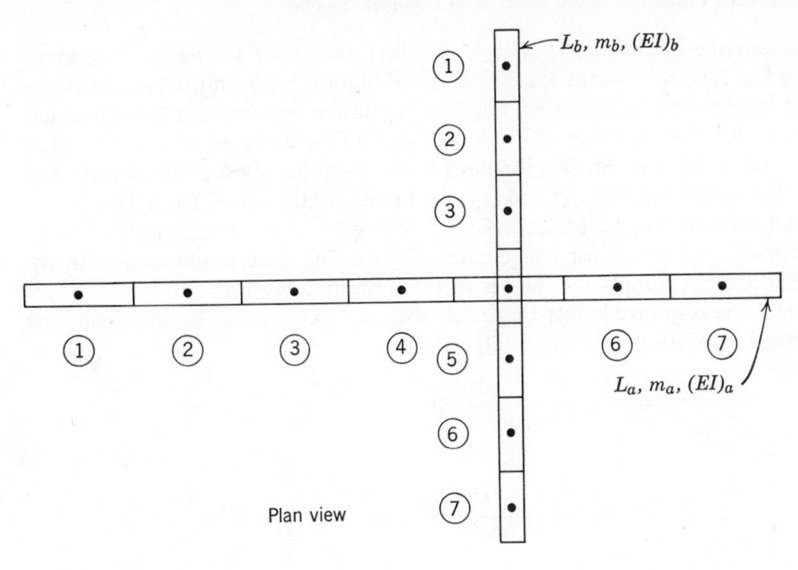

Fig. 14-3

q_4 = displacement of Beam a in its first bending mode;
q_5 = displacement of Beam a in its second bending mode;
q_6 = displacement of Beam b in its first bending mode;
q_7 = displacement of Beam b in its third bending mode.

Let the force of Beam b on Beam a in the vertical direction be $f \sin \omega_n t$ where ω_n is a natural frequency of the combined system. Then $-f \sin \omega_n t$ is the vertical force of Beam a on Beam b. The generalized forces which correspond to the foregoing generalized coordinates are then determined as follows.

(Note that the generalized forces corresponding to rotation of Beam b about its center of gravity and bending of Beam b in its second mode would be zero, which accounts for these coordinates being omitted from the list of generalized coordinates.)

$$Q_1\dot{q}_1 = (f \sin \omega_n t)\dot{q}_1 \quad \text{or} \quad Q_1 = f \sin \omega_n t$$

$$Q_2\dot{q}_2 = (f \sin \omega_n t)\dot{q}_2 \left(\frac{L_a}{7}\right) \quad \text{or} \quad Q_2 = f\frac{L_a}{7} \sin \omega_n t$$

$$Q_3\dot{q}_3 = (-f \sin \omega_n t)\dot{q}_3 \quad \text{or} \quad Q_3 = -f \sin \omega_n t$$

$$Q_4\dot{q}_4 = (f \sin \omega_n t)\dot{q}_4 \left(\frac{\partial y_5}{\partial q_1}\right)_a \quad \text{or} \quad Q_4 = f\left(\frac{\partial y_5}{\partial q_1}\right)_a \sin \omega_n t$$

$$Q_5\dot{q}_5 = (f \sin \omega_n t)\dot{q}_5 \left(\frac{\partial y_5}{\partial q_2}\right)_a \quad \text{or} \quad Q_5 = f\left(\frac{\partial y_5}{\partial q_2}\right)_a \sin \omega_n t$$

$$Q_6\dot{q}_6 = (-f \sin \omega_n t)\dot{q}_6 \left(\frac{\partial y_4}{\partial q_1}\right)_b \quad \text{or} \quad Q_6 = -f\left(\frac{\partial y_4}{\partial q_1}\right)_b \sin \omega_n t$$

$$Q_7\dot{q}_7 = (-f \sin \omega_n t)\dot{q}_7 \left(\frac{\partial y_4}{\partial q_3}\right)_b \quad \text{or} \quad Q_7 = -f\left(\frac{\partial y_4}{\partial q_3}\right)_b \sin \omega_n t$$

In these equations the quantities, $(\partial y_5/\partial q_1)$, $(\partial y_5/\partial q_2)$, etc., refer to the bending-mode shapes. For instance, $(\partial y_5/\partial q_1)$ means the deflection of Station 5 per unit deflection of the beam in the first bending mode. However, because the station numbers are defined differently for this beam than for the beam of Table 14-1 (where the first station was the end of the beam), the values to be used for $(\partial y_5/\partial q_1)$ or $(\partial y_5/\partial q_2)$ will be found under Station 6 of Table 14-1, and the values of $(\partial y_4/\partial q_1)$ and $(\partial y_4/\partial q_2)$ under Station 5 of Table 14-1.

The generalized mass of Beam a for coordinate 1 is just m_a and for coordinate 2 is I_a. The generalized mass of Beam b for coordinate 3 is m_b. The generalized masses in the various bending modes are simply the masses of the respective beams.

For coordinate 1 the response is just that of a free mass acted upon by an oscillating force or the particular solution of $M_1\ddot{q}_1 = Q_1$

$$q_1 = -\frac{f}{\omega_n^2 m_a} \sin \omega_n t$$

similarly,

$$q_2 = -\frac{fL_a}{7\omega_n^2 I_a} \sin \omega_n t$$

$$q_3 = \frac{f}{\omega_n^2 m_b} \sin \omega_n t$$

For the other coordinates the response is that of a spring-mass combination, or the particular solution of $m\ddot{q} + kq = Q$. From Table 14-1

$$q_4 = \frac{f\left(\frac{\partial y_5}{\partial q_1}\right)_a}{K_4 - M_4\omega_n^2} \sin \omega_n t = \frac{f(-0.876)}{534\left(\frac{EI}{L^3}\right)_a - m_a\omega_n^2} \sin \omega_n t$$

$$q_5 = \frac{f\left(\frac{\partial y_5}{\partial q_2}\right)_a}{K_5 - M_5\omega_n^2} \sin \omega_n t = \frac{f(1.279)}{4240\left(\frac{EI}{L^3}\right)_a - m_a\omega_n^2} \sin \omega_n t$$

$$q_6 = -\frac{f\left(\frac{\partial y_4}{\partial q_1}\right)_b}{K_6 - M_6\omega_n^2} \sin \omega_n t = \frac{-f(-1.244)}{534\left(\frac{EI}{L^3}\right)_b - m_b\omega_n^2} \sin \omega_n t$$

$$q_7 = -\frac{f\left(\frac{\partial y_4}{\partial q_3}\right)_b}{(K_7 - M_7\omega_n^2)} \sin \omega_n t = \frac{-f(-1.479)}{16800\left(\frac{EI}{L^3}\right)_b - m_b\omega_n^2} \sin \omega_n t$$

The value of ω_n can be determined by setting the displacement of Beam a equal to that of Beam b at the point of attachment.

$$q_1 + q_2\frac{L_a}{7} + q_4\left(\frac{\partial y_5}{\partial q_1}\right)_a + q_5\left(\frac{\partial y_5}{\partial q_2}\right)_a = q_3 + q_6\left(\frac{\partial y_4}{\partial q_1}\right)_b + q_7\left(\frac{\partial y_4}{\partial q_3}\right)_b$$

This equation can be satisfied if $q_1 + q_2L_a/7 = q_3$ and $q_4 = q_5 = q_6 = q_7 = 0$. This is the rigid body motion and corresponds to $\omega_n = 0$.

Now assume that the two beams are identical, or $m_a = m_b = m$ and $(EI/L^3)_a = (EI/L^3)_b = EI/L^3$. For this assumption the combination structure has all the natural frequencies of the individual beams, which for the set of coordinates used reduces to just one, the first, or $\omega = \sqrt{534EI/mL^3}$. For this frequency the two beams vibrate with their own normal modes but with a definite relationship between q_4 and q_6, while $q_1 = q_2 = q_3 = q_5 = q_7 = 0$ The force at the connection, f, is also zero for this mode. The necessary relationship between q_4 and q_6 is $q_4(\partial y_5/\partial q_1)_a = q_6(\partial y_4/\partial q_1)_b$ or $q_6 = 0.704q_4$.

The rest of the frequencies and normal modes involve coupling between the modes, and the force, f, is not zero. The frequencies and relationships between coordinates can be computed by substituting for the q's in the equation relating the deflections of the two beams at the connection. This equation then becomes

$$-\frac{f}{\omega_n^2 m_a} - \frac{f}{\omega_n^2 I_a}\left(\frac{L_a}{7}\right)^2 + \frac{(-0.876)^2 f}{534\left(\frac{EI}{L^3}\right)_a - m_a\omega_n^2} + \frac{(1.279)^2 f}{4240\left(\frac{EI}{L^3}\right)_a - m_a\omega_n^2}$$

$$= \frac{f}{\omega_n^2 m_b} - \frac{(-1.244)^2 f}{534\left(\frac{EI}{L^3}\right)_b - m_b\omega_n^2} - \frac{(-1.479)^2 f}{16800\left(\frac{EI}{L^3}\right)_b - m_b\omega_n^2}$$

which, when $m_a = m_b = m$ and $(EI/L^3)_a = (EI/L^3)_b = EI/L^3$ and $I_a = \sum_{i=1}^{7} m_i(l_i - l_{c.g.})^2$, eventually can be reduced to the solution of the following cubic in ω_n^2

$$(\omega_n^2)^3 - 16.23 \times 10^3\left(\frac{EI}{mL^3}\right)(\omega_n^2)^2 + 44.1 \times 10^6\left(\frac{EI}{mL^3}\right)^2(\omega_n^2) - 10.20 \times 10^9\left(\frac{EI}{mL^3}\right)^3 = 0$$

the roots of this equation are

$$\omega_n^2 = 254\frac{EI}{mL^3} \qquad \omega_n = 15.95\sqrt{\frac{EI}{mL^3}}$$

$$\omega_n^2 = 3110\frac{EI}{mL^3} \qquad \omega_n = 55.8\sqrt{\frac{EI}{mL^3}}$$

$$\omega_n^2 = 12870\frac{EI}{mL^3} \qquad \omega_n = 113.7\sqrt{\frac{EI}{mL^3}}$$

The frequency of the first, or lowest frequency mode, is $15.95\sqrt{EI/mL^3}$ rad/sec. The second mode is the one mentioned previously which is the same as the first mode of each beam individually, or $23.1\sqrt{EI/mL^3}$. The third mode at $55.8\sqrt{EI/mL^3}$ is not far from the second mode of the individual beams ($65.1\sqrt{EI/mL^3}$). The fourth mode of the combination structure is the one which was omitted from the computation because the beams were uncoupled. That is, Beam a would not move (or merely twist) while Beam b vibrates in its second mode at $65.1\sqrt{EI/mL^3}$. The frequency of the fifth mode of the combination structure is $113.7\sqrt{EI/mL^3}$, not far from the third mode frequency of the individual beams ($129.7\sqrt{EI/mL^3}$). The sixth mode would occur at $129.7\sqrt{EI/mL^3}$ with the beams oscillating in their third individual mode. (It should be mentioned that in most such structures the individual beams would not be identical so that the individual beam frequencies would not occur in the combination structure.)

For the modes which are coupled and different from the individual beam modes, the components of the motion and the force at the attachment can be determined by substituting the value of the frequency back into the previous equations. For example, consider the first mode. Using $\omega_n^2 = 254EI/mL^3$ in the equations for the generalized coordinates results in

$$q_1 = -0.00394\frac{fL^3}{EI}\sin 15.95\sqrt{\frac{EI}{mL^3}}\,t$$

$$q_2 = -0.00689\frac{fL^3}{EI}\sin 15.95\sqrt{\frac{EI}{mL^3}}\,t \quad \text{(This is an angle.)}$$

$$q_3 = 0.00394\frac{fL^3}{EI}\sin 15.95\sqrt{\frac{EI}{mL^3}}\,t$$

$$q_4 = -0.00312\frac{fL^3}{EI}\sin 15.95\sqrt{\frac{EI}{mL^3}}\,t$$

$$q_5 = 0.000321\frac{fL^3}{EI}\sin 15.95\sqrt{\frac{EI}{mL^3}}\,t$$

$$q_6 = 0.00445\frac{fL^3}{EI}\sin 15.95\sqrt{\frac{EI}{mL^3}}\,t$$

$$q_7 = 0.0000894\frac{fL^3}{EI}\sin 15.95\sqrt{\frac{EI}{mL^3}}\,t$$

These results show that the rigid body coordinates and the first bending-mode coordinates of the individual beams are the most important coordinates for this mode, and that Beam a is bent concave downward, whereas Beam b is concave upward in this mode, as indicated by q_4 and q_6. (Of course, the concavity changes harmonically because of the $\sin 15.95\sqrt{EI/mL^3}t$ term.)

The magnitude of the force f would depend on the magnitude of the oscillation, and could be determined from any of the equations once the q's were known.

Example. 14-3. Investigate a missile having a flexible body and autopilot making whatever simplifying assumptions seem appropriate for the purposes of an illustrative example.

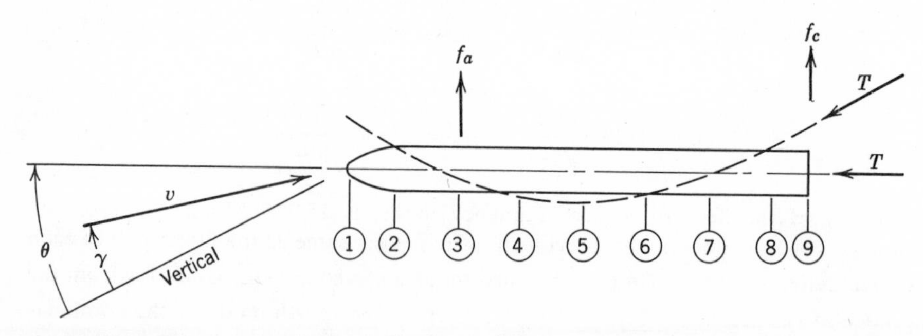

Fig. 14-4 Definitions for numerical analysis of a flexible missile with autopilot and aerodynamic coupling of generalized coordinates

Let it be supposed that a free beam with constant cross section can represent the missile body and that at a given instant during its flight its path is approximately vertically upward. An automatic pilot is supposed to maintain the missile attitude by producing transverse forces at the tail, f_c, either by the use of aerodynamic surfaces or by swiveling the thrust nozzle or auxilliary jets. Each portion of the missile body would experience aerodynamic loads, which for simplicity will be assumed to be limited to just one aerodynamic load, f_a, applied at Station 3, and which will be assumed to be proportional to the local angle of attack of Station 3, with no time delay in the load build up (Fig. 14-4).

The automatic pilot is supposed to provide stability by sensing (or sensing and calculating) the angle of the missile body in space, the angular velocity, and the angular acceleration, and then requiring a corrective force, f_c, to be produced. However, the sensing element is located at Station 2, and so the information actually applies to that station rather than the missile as a whole. If the body did not bend, then the angle at Station 2 would, of course, be the same as at all stations, but because of the flexible body this cannot be assumed. Let it be assumed that the propulsion thrust does not alter the normal modes of the free beam, and that the transfer function between the corrective force, f_c, and the corrective force commanded by the autopilot, f_{c_c}, is $F_c/F_{c_c} = \dfrac{1}{1 + 2\zeta s/\omega + s^2/\omega^2}$. Assume that the first three bending modes are sufficient to represent body bending and that each mode is damped at 2% critical damping. Consider only motion in a plane (longitudinal stability). Assume the main propulsion thrust is coincident with the local centerline at Station 9.

The equations are as follows. The rigid body acceleration perpendicular to the flight path is $v\dot{\gamma}$ if γ is the flight-path angle relative to the vertical direction in space, and v is the missile velocity. For rigid-body translation of the center of gravity perpendicular to the flight path, which is nearly vertical so that γ is a small angle,

$$mv\dot{\gamma} = f_a + f_c + mg\gamma + T[(\theta - \sigma_{91}q_1 - \sigma_{92}q_2 - \sigma_{93}q_3) - \gamma] \qquad ①$$

(For explanation of σ_{91}, σ_{92}, σ_{93} in this equation and Equations 2 to 5, see the discussion of f_a that follows.) Rigid body translation parallel to the flight path will be neglected in this example, assuming equilibrium of thrust and flight-path acceleration. For rigid-body angular acceleration about the center of gravity,

$$I\ddot{\theta} = f_a(l_{c.g.} - l_3) + (l_9 - l_{c.g.})[-f_c + T(\sigma_{91}q_1 + \sigma_{92}q_2 + \sigma_{93}q_3)] - T\left(\frac{\partial y_9}{\partial q_1}q_1 + \frac{\partial y_9}{\partial q_2}q_2 + \frac{\partial y_9}{\partial q_3}q_3\right) \qquad ②$$

In the three bending modes,

$$M_1\ddot{q}_1 + C_1\dot{q}_1 + K_1q_1 = f_a\left(\frac{\partial y_3}{\partial q_1}\right) + \frac{\partial y_9}{\partial q_1}[f_c - T(\sigma_{91}q_1 + \sigma_{92}q_2 + \sigma_{93}q_3)] \qquad ③$$

$$M_2\ddot{q}_2 + C_2\dot{q}_2 + K_2q_2 = f_a\left(\frac{\partial y_3}{\partial q_2}\right) + \frac{\partial y_9}{\partial q_2}[f_c - T(\sigma_{91}q_1 + \sigma_{92}q_2 + \sigma_{93}q_3)] \qquad ④$$

$$M_3\ddot{q}_3 + C_3\dot{q}_3 + K_3q_3 = f_a\left(\frac{\partial y_3}{\partial q_3}\right) + \frac{\partial y_9}{\partial q_3}[f_c - T(\sigma_{91}q_1 + \sigma_{92}q_2 + \sigma_{93}q_3)] \qquad ⑤$$

In these equations the generalized forces on the right side of the equation are computed using the deflections in the various modes at the stations where the loads are applied.

The force f_a is assumed to be proportional to the local angle of attack at Station 3, so $f_a = k_a\alpha$ where α is the local angle of attack. (Any possible delay in the build up of the aerodynamic forces is neglected in this example.) If the missile body were rigid and not rotating, the local angle of attack would be $(\theta - \gamma)$. Because of rigid-body rotation about the center of gravity, there is a velocity of the missile centerline at Station 3 in a direction perpendicular (or practically perpendicular) to the remote velocity, v, which would cause a decrease in the local angle of attack equal to $(\dot{\theta} - \dot{\gamma})(l_{c.g.} - l_3)/v$ radians. There would be a similar decrease of local angle of attack caused by the velocity of Station 3 which results from the bending of the beam, or

$$\frac{\dot{q}_1\left(\dfrac{\partial y_3}{\partial q_1}\right) + \dot{q}_2\left(\dfrac{\partial y_3}{\partial q_2}\right) + \dot{q}_3\left(\dfrac{\partial y_3}{\partial y_3}\right)}{v}$$

radians. There would also be a change in local angle of attack caused by the fact that the local centerline is deflected in bending. This angle is simply the negative of the slope of the bending-deflection curve in the various modes, or $-\sigma_{31}q_1 - \sigma_{32}q_2 - \sigma_{33}q_3$, where σ_{31} is the slope of the deflection curve in Mode 1 at Station 3 and similar definitions for the other coefficients. Therefore, substituting for α,

$$f_a = k_a\left[\theta - \gamma - \frac{(\dot{\theta} - \dot{\gamma})(l_{c.g.} - l_3)}{v} - \frac{\left(\frac{\partial y_3}{\partial q_1}\right)}{v}\dot{q}_1 - \frac{\left(\frac{\partial y_3}{\partial q_2}\right)}{v}\dot{q}_2 - \frac{\left(\frac{\partial y_3}{\partial q_3}\right)}{v}\dot{q}_3 - \sigma_{31}q_1 - \sigma_{32}q_2 - \sigma_{33}q_3\right] \quad (6)$$

Now consider the action of the autopilot. Let it be assumed for the purpose of this example that the job of the autopilot is to maintain a fixed attitude of the missile in space, nearly vertical, and that some guidance signal, of no present concern, would be required in order to set the correct attitude to produce a given flight path to accomplish a given mission. Let it be assumed that instruments are located at Station 2 which can detect or compute angular acceleration, velocity, or position without error. (Actually, any instrument would have a transfer function of some form which would relate the indicated quantity to the actual quantity, but in this example an "ideal" instrument is assumed.) If it is assumed that the force commanded by the autopilot is proportional to the angular position, velocity, or acceleration of the sensing instrument, and that the force commanded is in the direction to restore the rigid-body attitude to the desired value and to oppose angular velocity and acceleration, then

$$f_{c_c} = k_\theta(\theta - \theta_g - \sigma_{21}q_1 - \sigma_{22}q_2 - \sigma_{23}q_3) + k_{\dot{\theta}}(\dot{\theta} - \sigma_{21}\dot{q}_1 - \sigma_{22}\dot{q}_2 - \sigma_{23}\dot{q}_3) + k_{\ddot{\theta}}(\ddot{\theta} - \sigma_{21}\ddot{q}_1 - \sigma_{22}\ddot{q}_2 - \sigma_{23}\ddot{q}_3) \quad (7)$$

where θ_g is the desired attitude for a particular instant as determined by guidance requirements. Finally, the relationship which relates the actual corrective force to the command force might be of the following form:

$$\frac{1}{\omega^2}\frac{d^2f_c}{dt^2} + \frac{2\zeta}{\omega}\frac{df_c}{dt} + f_c = f_{c_c} \quad (8)$$

If these eight equations are transformed, the matrix equation shown on page 239 results.

For purposes of this example let it be assumed that

$$v = 3000 \text{ fps}$$

$$m = 500 \text{ slugs}$$

$$T = 50{,}000 \text{ lb}$$

$$L = 50 \text{ ft}$$

$$k_a = 50{,}000 \text{ lb/rad}$$

$$\omega = 10 \text{ rad/sec}$$

$$\zeta = 0.7$$

$$(EI) = 1 \times 10^8 \text{ lb-ft}^2$$

$$
\begin{bmatrix}
mvs + (T - mg) & -T & T\sigma_{91} & T\sigma_{92} & T\sigma_{93} & -1 & -1 & 0 \\
0 & Is^2 & -T\sigma_{91}(l_9 - l_{\text{c.g.}}) + T\dfrac{\partial y_9}{\partial q_1} & -T\sigma_{92}(l_9 - l_{\text{c.g.}}) + T\dfrac{\partial y_9}{\partial q_2} & -T\sigma_{93}(l_9 - l_{\text{c.g.}}) + T\dfrac{\partial y_9}{\partial q_3} & (l_3 - l_{\text{c.g.}}) & (l_9 - l_{\text{c.g.}}) & 0 \\
0 & 0 & M_1 s^2 + C_1 s + K_1 + \left(\dfrac{\partial y_9}{\partial q_1}\right) T\sigma_{91} & \left(\dfrac{\partial y_9}{\partial q_1}\right) T\sigma_{92} & \left(\dfrac{\partial y_9}{\partial q_1}\right) T\sigma_{93} & -\dfrac{\partial y_3}{\partial q_1} & -\dfrac{\partial y_9}{\partial q_1} & 0 \\
0 & 0 & \left(\dfrac{\partial y_9}{\partial q_2}\right) T\sigma_{91} & M_2 s^2 + C_2 s + K_2 + \left(\dfrac{\partial y_9}{\partial q_2}\right) T\sigma_{92} & \left(\dfrac{\partial y_9}{\partial q_2}\right) T\sigma_{93} & -\dfrac{\partial y_3}{\partial q_2} & -\dfrac{\partial y_9}{\partial q_2} & 0 \\
0 & 0 & \left(\dfrac{\partial y_9}{\partial q_3}\right) T\sigma_{91} & \left(\dfrac{\partial y_9}{\partial q_3}\right) T\sigma_{92} & M_3 s^2 + C_3 s + K_3 + \left(\dfrac{\partial y_9}{\partial q_3}\right) T\sigma_{93} & -\dfrac{\partial y_3}{\partial q_3} & -\dfrac{\partial y_9}{\partial q_3} & 0 \\
-\dfrac{(l_{\text{c.g.}} - l_3)}{v} s + 1 & \dfrac{(l_{\text{c.g.}} - l_3)}{v} s - 1 & \dfrac{\left(\dfrac{\partial y_3}{\partial q_1}\right) s}{v} + \sigma_{31} & \dfrac{\left(\dfrac{\partial y_3}{\partial q_2}\right) s}{v} + \sigma_{32} & \dfrac{\left(\dfrac{\partial y_3}{\partial q_3}\right) s}{v} + \sigma_{33} & \dfrac{1}{k_a} & 0 & 0 \\
0 & k_{\ddot{\theta}} s^2 + k_{\dot{\theta}} s + k_\theta & -\sigma_{21} k_{\ddot{\theta}} s^2 - \sigma_{21} k_{\dot{\theta}} s - \sigma_{21} k_\theta & -\sigma_{22} k_{\ddot{\theta}} s^2 - \sigma_{22} k_{\dot{\theta}} s - \sigma_{22} k_\theta & -\sigma_{23} k_{\ddot{\theta}} s^2 - \sigma_{23} k_{\dot{\theta}} s - \sigma_{23} k_\theta & 0 & 0 & -1 \\
0 & 0 & 0 & 0 & 0 & 0 & \dfrac{s^2}{\omega^2} + \dfrac{2\zeta s}{\omega} + 1 & -1
\end{bmatrix}
\begin{bmatrix} \gamma \\ \theta \\ q_1 \\ q_2 \\ q_3 \\ F_a \\ F_c \\ F_{c_c} \end{bmatrix}
=
\begin{bmatrix} 0 \\ 0 \\ 0 \\ 0 \\ 0 \\ 0 \\ k_\theta \theta_g \\ 0 \end{bmatrix}
$$

For the assumed beam

$$I = m\frac{L^2}{12} = 104{,}200 \text{ slug ft}^2$$

$$l_3 - l_{\text{c.g.}} = \frac{3}{14}L - \frac{L}{2} = -14.3 \text{ ft}$$

$$l_9 - l_{\text{c.g.}} = L - \frac{L}{2} = 25 \text{ ft}$$

From the normal modes calculation for the free beam,

$$\left(\frac{\partial y_3}{\partial q_1}\right) = 0.103 \quad \left(\frac{\partial y_3}{\partial q_2}\right) = -0.900 \quad \left(\frac{\partial y_3}{\partial q_3}\right) = 1.376$$

$$\left(\frac{\partial y_9}{\partial q_1}\right) = 2.068 \quad \left(\frac{\partial y_9}{\partial q_2}\right) = -2.141 \quad \left(\frac{\partial y_9}{\partial q_3}\right) = -2.173$$

$$\sigma_{21} = -0.188 \text{ rad/ft} \qquad \sigma_{31} = -0.167 \text{ rad/ft} \qquad \sigma_{91} = 0.188 \text{ rad/ft}$$

$$\sigma_{22} = -0.312 \text{ rad/ft} \qquad \sigma_{32} = -0.185 \text{ rad/ft} \qquad \sigma_{92} = -0.312 \text{ rad/ft}$$

$$\sigma_{23} = 0.405 \text{ rad/ft} \qquad \sigma_{33} = 0.060 \text{ rad/ft} \qquad \sigma_{93} = -0.405 \text{ rad/ft}$$

(Note that σ_{ij} can be computed from $\sigma_{ij} = \sum_{k=2}^{8} m_k \beta_j^2 (\partial y_k/\partial q_j)\theta_{ik}$ where θ_{ik} is an element in the flexibility matrix)

$$M_1 = m = 500 \text{ slugs} \qquad K_1 = 534\frac{EI}{L^3} = 0.427 \times 10^6 \text{ lb-ft}$$

$$M_2 = m = 500 \text{ slugs} \qquad K_2 = 4240\frac{EI}{L^3} = 3.39 \times 10^6 \text{ lb-ft}$$

$$M_3 = m = 500 \text{ slugs} \qquad K_3 = 16800\frac{EI}{L^3} = 13.45 \times 10^6 \text{ lb-ft}$$

Assume structural damping of 2% critical, so that

$$C_1 = 2(0.02)\sqrt{M_1K_1} = 586 \text{ lb/(ft/sec)}$$

$$C_2 = 2(0.02)\sqrt{M_2K_2} = 1655 \text{ lb/(ft/sec)}$$

$$C_3 = 2(0.02)\sqrt{M_3K_3} = 3150 \text{ lb/(ft/sec)}$$

Assume control constants

$$k_\theta = 48{,}000 \text{ lb/rad} \qquad k_{\dot\theta} = 18{,}000 \text{ lb/(rad/sec)} \qquad k_{\ddot\theta} = 0$$

The characteristic equation for this system will result if the determinant of the matrix is set equal to zero. A digital-computer program for determining the characteristic equation from a determinant having quadratic elements is given in Reference 1. For the constants chosen, the characteristic equation is approximately

$$1 + 4.85s + 3.63s^2 + 1.043s^3 + 0.1518s^4 + 1.306 \times 10^{-2}s^5 + 2.334 \times 10^{-4}s^6 + 1.522 \times 10^{-5}s^7 + 4.61 \times 10^{-8}s^8 + 2.406 \times 10^{-9}s^9 + 1.714 \times 10^{-12}s^{10} + 6.87 \times 10^{-14}s^{11} = 0$$

This equation can be factored by a digital computer program given in Reference 1. The roots are

$$s = -3.24 \pm 164.5i$$

$$s = -1.495 \pm 83.0i$$

$$s = -1.33 \pm 29.6i$$

$$s = -3.26 \pm 5.43i$$

$$s = -4.05$$

$$s = -2.52$$

$$s = -0.250$$

These roots all have negative real parts, so the missile is stable. This would not necessarily be true if the various constants had different values. For instance, if $k_{\dot{\theta}} = 0$, there would be roots at $s = 0.77 + 1.821$, resulting in an oscillation with increasing amplitude. Also, if the stable system values of k_{θ} and $k_{\dot{\theta}}$ used in this example were either doubled or halved, a dynamically unstable system would result.

Systematic methods exist for adjusting system parameters for satisfactory performance. These methods are described in more detail in Reference 1.

CHAPTER 15

Convolution Theorem for Transient Response

15.1 General Comments

When the relationship between a forcing function and a response is known in the form of a transfer function, and when the forcing function itself is some known transformable algebraic expression, then the response can be easily obtained by application of the rules for obtaining inverse transforms given in Appendix 1. These will not be reviewed here. It is also possible with complex linear systems to superimpose solutions of simpler systems. That is, if the structure can be represented by generalized coordinates representing deflections in the normal, vibratory modes, perhaps the first four or so modes might be adequate for a satisfactory representation of the structure. If the generalized force in each mode were known, the response in each mode would be simply the response of a single-degree system. The responses in the several modes may be superimposed to obtain the total response. This will be illustrated with an example.

One commonly used forcing function for the evaluation of transient motion is the suddenly applied constant load, or step function, used occasionally in earlier chapters. Another is the impulse function, or constant large load applied for an extremely short length of time. Each of these may be useful in experimental investigations, as well as theoretical analyses. There are also occasions when a forcing function may be known in the form of a tabular or graphical time relationship rather than as an algebraic expression. The next section explains how problems of this sort may be analyzed.

15.2 Convolution Theorem

Proof of the following theorem may be found in Reference 6 and others, and will not be repeated here. If two functions, $F(s)$ and $G(s)$, have inverse Laplace transforms, $f(t)$ and $g(t)$ respectively, the inverse transform of the product, $F(s)\,G(s)$, is given as

$$\mathscr{L}^{-1}[F(s)G(s)] = \int_{\lambda=0}^{\lambda=t} f(\lambda)g(t-\lambda)\,d\lambda \tag{15-1}$$

$$\mathscr{L}^{-1}[F(s)G(s)] = \int_{\lambda=0}^{\lambda=t} f(t-\lambda)g(\lambda)\,d\lambda \tag{15-1a}$$

Either of these forms is correct, and the choice of one or the other is strictly a matter of convenience in any given situation. The variable, λ, is merely a dummy variable in time. The character τ is often used instead of λ for this purpose.

If there is a transfer function relationship between a force and displacement, say

$$\frac{X(s)}{F(s)} = G(s) \tag{15-2}$$

it is clear that the displacement in the time domain is

$$x(t) = \mathscr{L}^{-1}[F(s)G(s)]$$

and that Equation 15-1 is applicable. If the forcing function in the time domain is not an algebraic expression, $F(s)$ is not known as an algebraic expression, but it does not matter because $f(t)$ (and therefore $f(\lambda)$ or $f(t - \lambda)$) is known either as a table or as a graph of the function and can be utilized directly in Equation 15-1 if numerical integration is used. Of course, $g(t - \lambda)$ (or else $g(\lambda)$) would have to be computed numerically in order to do this, but this is possible since $G(s)$ is presumably a known function whose inverse may be taken and evaluated at the desired intervals. Even if $G(s)$ is not known, it may be that $g(t)$ (and therefore $g(t - \lambda)$ or else $g(\lambda)$) is known from experimental observation, and the response may be obtainable by numerical integration. This is explained in more detail as follows.

Utilization of the Unit Impulse. Although either Equation 15-1 or 15-1a is acceptable, let the first form be used hereafter, because the physical meaning of this form is more easily understood.

$$x(t) = \mathscr{L}^{-1}[F(s)G(s)] = \int_{\lambda=0}^{\lambda=t} f(\lambda)g(t - \lambda)\, d\lambda \tag{15-3}$$

Now suppose that the forcing function is the unit impulse; that is, $f(t) = \delta(t)$ where $\delta(t)$ is a function (a) which is zero for all values of t except $t = 0$, (b) at $t = 0$ the function is infinitely large for an infinitesimal period, and (c) the product of the infinitely large function multiplied by the infinitesimal time period is unity. Mathematically, this could be described as

$$\delta(t) = 0 \text{ for } t \neq 0$$

$$\delta(t) = \lim_{a \to 0} \frac{1}{a} \text{ for } 0 < t < a \text{ (therefore } t \to 0)$$

The Laplace transform of the impulse function is easily shown to be unity

$$\mathscr{L}[\delta(t)] = \int_0^\infty \delta(t)e^{-st}\, dt = \int_0^a \frac{1}{a} e^{-st}\, dt = \frac{1}{as}(1 - e^{-sa}) = 1 \quad \text{if} \quad a \to 0$$

Therefore, if $f(t) = \delta(t)$, $F(s) = 1$, and the response $x(t)$ is simply the inverse of the transfer function $G(s)$, or just $g(t)$, it is clear that one possible way of approximating $g(t)$ experimentally, if it were not known analytically, would be to apply a constant, known load for a very short time and measure the displacement as a function of time. The displacement divided by the product of the force and short time interval would approximate $g(t)$. Obviously, the load should be applied at the same position and in the same direction as the variable load expected.

Interpretation. In order to help visualize the meaning of Equation 15-3, it is possible to approximate an actual force history as a succession of small impulses (not unit impulses), with a load being applied suddenly for a short time and then being removed, and another different load being applied for a short time, etc. This is indicated in the upper portion of Fig. 15-1, where λ represents time, the time at which the force has the value, f. If the deflection, x, is required at a time, t, say after the force has become

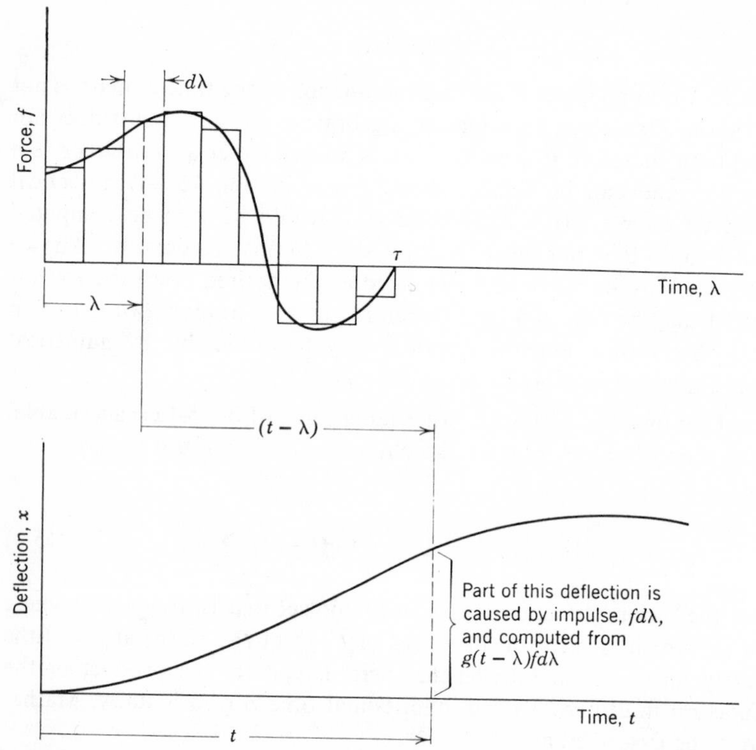

Fig. 15-1 Figure illustrating use of a series of impulses in computing response by Equation 4-3

permanently zero ($t > \tau$), it is evident that this deflection could be considered as the sum of deflections caused by the small impulses, the contribution for each impulse multiplied by the magnitude of the impulse, $f\,d\lambda$. However, the deflection caused by the unit impulse must be computed from $g(t - \lambda)$, rather than just $g(t)$ or $g(\lambda)$ because the time between the instant that the impulse occurs, λ, and the instant at which the deflection is desired, t, is $(t - \lambda)$. These relationships are indicated in Fig. 15-1. In this figure finite impulses are shown. In the limit, the time intervals become infinitesimally small and the summation becomes the integral indicated by Equation 15-3. It is clear that as far as the integration is concerned, t is a constant, the time at which the deflection is desired. If the deflection were desired at different times, different constants, t, would be used (with λ the variable in the integration) and a new integration would be required for each value of t. It is, of course, obvious that if one or more of these times at which the deflection is desired should happen to be less than τ, the time at which the force becomes permanently zero, the integration should proceed only to the time, t. The quantity $(t - \lambda)$ should never be negative. This is assured by the upper limit in Equation 15-3. Also, if $t > \tau$, the integration with respect to λ may be stopped at τ, since $f(\lambda) = 0$ for $\lambda > \tau$ (Fig. 5-1). That is, if $t > \tau$, the upper limit in Equation 15-3 can be changed from t to τ. It is readily appreciated that the numerical computations described can be greatly facilitated by use of a digital computer, since so much repetition is involved. A program for accomplishing this is given in Reference 1.

Utilization of the Unit Step Function. It is also possible to show that if $h(t)$ is the response of a system to unit step input (instead of unit impulse), the equation which would result would be

$$x(t) = f(0)h(t) + \int_{\lambda=0}^{\lambda=t} h(t - \lambda)\left(\frac{df(\lambda)}{d\lambda}\right) d\lambda \tag{15-4}$$

There is no advantage of this equation over Equation 15-3, except that it may be easier to determine $h(t)$ experimentally (if it is not known analytically) by application of a sudden, constant load, than to determine $g(t)$ by application of an impulse. The physical interpretation of Equation 15-4 is similar to the interpretation of Equation 15-3, with the following differences. The first term of Equation 15-4 represents the

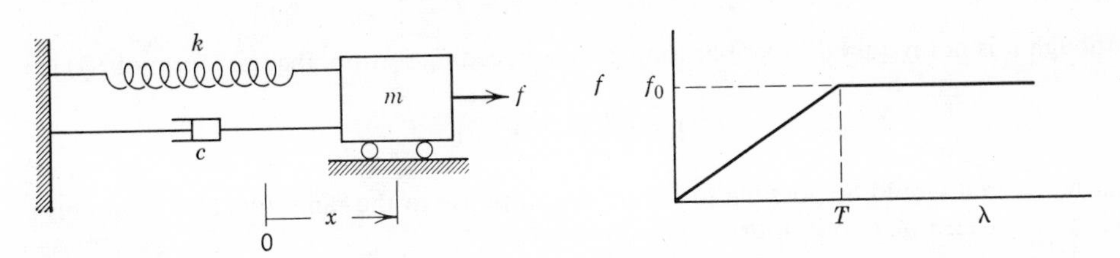

Fig. 15-2

response at time t for a constant step force, $f(0)$, applied at time zero. The integration is the summation of responses at time t caused by small step forces at time λ. (Note that $[df(\lambda)/d\lambda]\, d\lambda$ is a small step force, df.) An alternate form of Equation 15-4 is also available and is similar to the alternate form of Equation 15-1. This is

$$x(t) = f(0)h(t) + \int_{\lambda=0}^{\lambda=t} h(\lambda)\left(\frac{df(t - \lambda)}{d(t - \lambda)}\right) d\lambda \tag{15-4a}$$

With reference to Equations 15-3 and 15-4, it is possible to show that the two functions, $g(t)$ and $h(t)$, the responses to unit impulse and unit step functions respectively, are related as follows:

$$\left.\begin{aligned} g(t) &= \frac{d\,h(t)}{dt} \\ &\text{or} \\ G(s) &= sH(s) \end{aligned}\right\} \tag{15-5}$$

The following example is included in order to illustrate the use of the preceding equations.

Example 15-1. Investigate the response of a single-degree-of-freedom system to a ramp-forcing function (Fig. 15-2), using the methods of Section 15.2.

The transfer function for this system is $X/F = 1/(ms^2 + cs + k)$ or also $X/F = 1/m(s^2 + 2\zeta\beta s + \beta^2)$. If $f(t)$ were the impulse function, $\delta(t)$, then $F(s)$ would become simply unity and $X(s)$ would become $G(s)$, whose inverse is $g(t)$, the response to unit impulse.

$$g(t) = \mathscr{L}^{-1}\frac{1}{m(s^2 + 2\zeta\beta s + \beta^2)} = \frac{1}{m\beta\sqrt{1 - \zeta^2}}\, e^{-\zeta\beta t} \sin \beta \sqrt{1 - \zeta^2}t$$

Similarly, if $f(t)$ were the unit function, $u(t)$, then $F(s)$ would become $1/s$ and $X(s)$ would become $H(s)$, whose inverse is $h(t)$, the response to unit step function.

$$h(t) = \mathscr{L}^{-1}\frac{1}{ms(s^2 + 2\zeta\beta s + \beta^2)}$$

$$= \frac{1}{m\beta^2}\left[1 - e^{-\zeta\beta t}\left(\cos \beta\sqrt{1 - \zeta^2}t + \frac{\zeta}{\sqrt{1 - \zeta^2}} \sin \beta\sqrt{1 - \zeta^2 t}\right)\right]$$

Of course, the actual forcing function is the ramp function shown in the sketch. That is

$$f(t) = \frac{f_0}{T}t \quad \text{for} \quad t < T$$

$$f(t) = f_0 \quad \text{for} \quad t > T$$

Although it is not required for application of the preceding section, the transform of $f(t)$ is

$$F(s) = \frac{f_0}{Ts^2}(1 - e^{-Ts})$$

and therefore it would be possible to obtain the response to the ramp function by simply taking the inverse of $F(s)G(s)$, or

$$x(t) = \mathscr{L}^{-1}\left[\frac{f_0}{Tm}\frac{(1 - e^{-Ts})}{s^2(s^2 + 2\zeta\beta s + \beta^2)}\right]$$

However, the objective of this example is to illustrate the preceding section, which requires a different procedure.

Use of Equation 15-3 results in the following, for $t > T$.

$$x(t) = \int_{\lambda=0}^{T}\left(\frac{f_0}{T}\lambda\right)\frac{1}{m\beta\sqrt{1 - \zeta^2}}\, e^{-\zeta\beta(t-\lambda)} \sin \beta\sqrt{1 - \zeta^2}\,(t - \lambda)\, d\lambda$$

$$+ \int_{\lambda=T}^{t} f_0 \frac{1}{m\beta\sqrt{1 - \zeta^2}}\, e^{-\zeta\beta(t-\lambda)} \sin \beta\sqrt{1 - \zeta^2}\,(t - \lambda)\, d\lambda$$

Even though this equation could be integrated analytically, even with $\zeta \neq 0$, for purposes of this example let it be assumed that there is zero damping ($\zeta = 0$). Then

$$x(t) = \frac{f_0}{Tm\beta}\left[\int_0^T \lambda \sin \beta(t - \lambda)\, d\lambda + \int_T^t \sin \beta(t - \lambda)\, d\lambda\right]$$

$$x(t) = \frac{f_0}{m\beta^2}\left\{1 + \frac{1}{\beta T}[\sin \beta(t - T) - \sin \beta t]\right\}$$

$f_0/m\beta^2$ is the static deflection, δ_{st}, under a constant load f_0. This equation shows that if βT is large the oscillation is small, or that if the load is applied very slowly the oscillation is minimized, and the deflection is simply the static value.

The ratio of the maximum value of the deflection to the static deflection is

$$\frac{x_{max}}{\delta_{st}} = 1 + \sqrt{2}\frac{\sqrt{1 - \cos \beta T}}{\beta T}$$

If $\beta T \to 0$, this ratio approaches 2 as it should for a suddenly applied constant load and if $\beta T \to \infty$, the ratio approaches 1 as expected. It is also of interest that certain ramps will produce a ratio of unity, or no oscillation; namely, those for which $\cos \beta T = 1$, or $\beta T = n\pi$ $(n = 0, 2, 4, \ldots)$.

One other condition is of interest. If $\cos \beta T = -1$, the ratio of maximum deflection to static deflection becomes

$$\frac{x_{max}}{\delta_{st}} = 1 + \frac{2}{\beta T} = 1 + \frac{2}{n\pi} \quad (n = 1, 3, 5, \ldots)$$

This expression provides an upper limit to the possible value of this ratio, giving a quick means of evaluating the ramp time required to produce oscillations of arbitrary negligibility. For instance, if it were required that an overshoot of 5% could not be exceeded under any circumstances, the natural frequency and ramp time could be related so that $\beta T > 40$, or $n > 13$.

Suppose it were desired to use Equation 15-4 instead of Equation 15-3. Since the forcing function is a ramp, whose value at time zero is zero, or $f(0) = 0$, and whose slope, df/dt, is the constant f_0/T prior to T and zero thereafter, the use of the previously determined $h(t)$,

$$h(t) = \frac{1}{m\beta^2}\left[1 - e^{-\zeta\beta t}\left(\cos \beta\sqrt{1 - \zeta^2}t + \frac{\zeta}{\sqrt{1 - \zeta^2}} \sin \beta\sqrt{1 - \zeta^2}t\right)\right]$$

in Equation 15-4 results in

$$x(t) = \int_{\lambda=0}^{T} \left(\frac{f_0}{T}\right)\frac{1}{m\beta^2}\left\{1 - e^{-\zeta\beta(t-\lambda)}\left[\cos \beta\sqrt{1 - \zeta^2}\,(t - \lambda) + \frac{\zeta}{\sqrt{1 - \zeta^2}} \sin \beta\sqrt{1 - \zeta^2}\,(t - \lambda)\right]\right\}$$

This equation applies if $t \geqq T$. If the time t at which the deflection is required is less than T, the upper limit in the equation must be changed to t. For the zero-damping condition previously investigated and for $t \geqq T$, the integral results in the same solution.

$$x(t) = \frac{f_0}{m\beta^2}\left\{1 + \frac{1}{\beta T}[\sin \beta(t - T) - \sin \beta t]\right\}$$

Heretofore, the computations could all be accomplished analytically. Now, for purposes of illustration, let it be assumed that both the ramp forcing function and the response to unit impulse are experimental curves rather than algebraic expressions, and let $\beta = T = \delta_{st} = 1$. Table 15-1 shows a possible listing of "experimental" variables.

Although values of $f(t)$ and $g(t)$ are known at 0.2 intervals, it might be advisable to use increments $d\lambda = 0.1$, say, or any other value, in Equation 15-3. If 0.1 is used for $d\lambda$, then values of $f(\lambda)$ and $g(t - \lambda)$ will have to be interpolated for values not appearing in the table. (Linear interpolation is used in the following.) Assume that the deflection at time $t = 2$ is required. Table 15-2 could be constructed, using Equation 15-3.

Use of the trapezoidal rule for integration of $\int_0^t f(\lambda)g(t - \lambda)\,d\lambda$ where $d\lambda = 0.1$ and $f(\lambda)g(t - \lambda)$ is taken from the previous table, results in

$$x(t) = 0.929 \text{ ft} \quad \text{for} \quad t = 2$$

Table 15-1

Time, sec	Forcing Function, lbs	Response to Unit Impulse, ft
0	0	0
0.2	0.2	0.1988
0.4	0.4	0.390
0.6	0.6	0.565
0.8	0.8	0.718
1.0	1.0	0.842
1.2	1.0	0.933
1.4	1.0	0.988
1.6	1.0	0.999
1.8	1.0	0.975
2.0	1.0	0.910
2.2	1.0	0.809
2.4	1.0	0.675
2.6	etc.	etc.

Table 15-2

λ	$(t-\lambda)$	$f(\lambda)$	$g(t-\lambda)$	$f(\lambda)g(t-\lambda)$
0.0	2.0	0	0.91	0
0.1	1.9	0.1	0.943	0.094
0.2	1.8	0.2	0.975	0.195
0.3	1.7	0.3	0.987	0.296
0.4	1.6	0.4	0.999	0.400
0.5	1.5	0.5	0.993	0.497
0.6	1.4	0.6	0.988	0.593
0.7	1.3	0.7	0.960	0.672
0.8	1.2	0.8	0.933	0.747
0.9	1.1	0.9	0.887	0.798
1.0	1.0	1.0	0.842	0.842
1.1	0.9	1.0	0.780	0.780
1.2	0.8	1.0	0.718	0.718
1.3	0.7	1.0	0.641	0.641
1.4	0.6	1.0	0.565	0.565
1.5	0.5	1.0	0.472	0.472
1.6	0.4	1.0	0.390	0.390
1.7	0.3	1.0	0.2944	0.294
1.8	0.2	1.0	0.1988	0.199
1.9	0.1	1.0	0.0994	0.099
2.0	0	1.0	0	0

This compares with the exact value of

$$x(t) = 1 + [\sin (2 - 1) - \sin 2] = 0.932 \text{ ft} \quad \text{for} \quad t = 2$$

The computation has been carried out for only one instant. The entire computation would normally be repeated for other values of t in order to obtain a history for x.

If either $f(t)$ or $g(t)$ were known in the form of an algebraic expression, then $f(\lambda)$ or $g(t - \lambda)$ would be computed instead of taken from a table. Some improvement in accuracy could be made by using a quadratic interpolation instead of linear interpolation. It is necessary to choose small enough increments of λ so that both $f(\lambda)$ and $g(t - \lambda)$ are well described. In this example $d\lambda = 2$, for instance, would be much too coarse.

Example 15-2. Determine if the estimates of Example 4-1 are satisfactory.

It is recalled that in Example 4-1 an accelerometer was subjected to a ramp acceleration, 100 g/sec, to a maximum of 10 g, and it was required to estimate satisfactory values of spring, mass, and damper so that the indication of acceleration would not be greatly in error during the ramp portion of the acceleration. The configuration selected in Example 4-1 will now be checked accurately to determine the error.

The transfer function relating the relative displacement of the suspended mass with respect to the accelerometer housing to the acceleration of the housing is

$$\frac{X_r\beta^2}{s^2 Y} = -\frac{1}{1 + \dfrac{2\zeta}{\beta} s + \dfrac{s^2}{\beta^2}}$$

By applying the limit theorem it is possible to see that after a long time the value of $x_r\beta^2$ would have the same magnitude as the acceleration if the acceleration were constant. Therefore it is the value of $x_r\beta^2$ which indicates the acceleration.

If the acceleration increases linearly to a value a_T at time T, then the transform of the acceleration during this period is

$$s^2 Y = \frac{a_T}{Ts^2}$$

and the transform of the indication of acceleration is

$$X_r\beta^2 = \frac{a_T/T}{s^2\left(1 + \dfrac{2\zeta}{\beta} s + \dfrac{s^2}{\beta^2}\right)}$$

The transform of the error of indication of acceleration is then

$$X_r\beta^2 - s^2 Y = \frac{a_T}{Ts^2}\left(\frac{1}{1 + \dfrac{2\zeta}{\beta} s + \dfrac{s^2}{\beta^2}} - 1\right) = -\frac{a_T}{Ts}\left(\frac{2\zeta/\beta + s/\beta^2}{1 + \dfrac{2\zeta}{\beta} s + \dfrac{s^2}{\beta^2}}\right)$$

Application of the limit theorem to this expression shows that the error approaches zero at time zero, as it should. However, the *percentage* error in the vicinity of time zero should approach 100%, since the rate of change of the acceleration curve is constant and the rate of change of the relative deflection curve is zero near time zero. Therefore, the limitation of small percentage error cannot be true in the neighborhood of time zero. The percentage error at an instant, t, is

$$\frac{\%\text{ error}}{100} = \frac{\mathscr{L}^{-1}(X_r\beta^2 - s^2 Y)}{(a_T/T)t} = \frac{-\mathscr{L}^{-1}\left[\dfrac{s + 2\zeta\beta}{s(s^2 + 2\zeta\beta s + \beta^2)}\right]}{t}$$

$$= \frac{1}{\beta t}\left\{-2\zeta - e^{-\zeta\beta t}\left[-2\zeta \cos \beta\sqrt{1 - \zeta^2}\, t + \frac{(1 - 2\zeta^2)}{\sqrt{1 - \zeta^2}} \sin \beta\sqrt{1 - \zeta^2}\, t\right]\right\}$$

For the values selected in Example 4-1, $\zeta = 1/\sqrt{2}$ and $\beta = 600$, this becomes

$$\frac{\%\text{ error}}{100} = \frac{\sqrt{2}}{600t}\left[-1 + e^{-(600/\sqrt{2})t}\cos\frac{600}{\sqrt{2}}t\right]$$

At $t = 0$ this indeterminate fraction becomes -1 so that the error approaches 100% as expected. A plot of per cent error as a function of time is illustrated in Fig. 15-3. It is

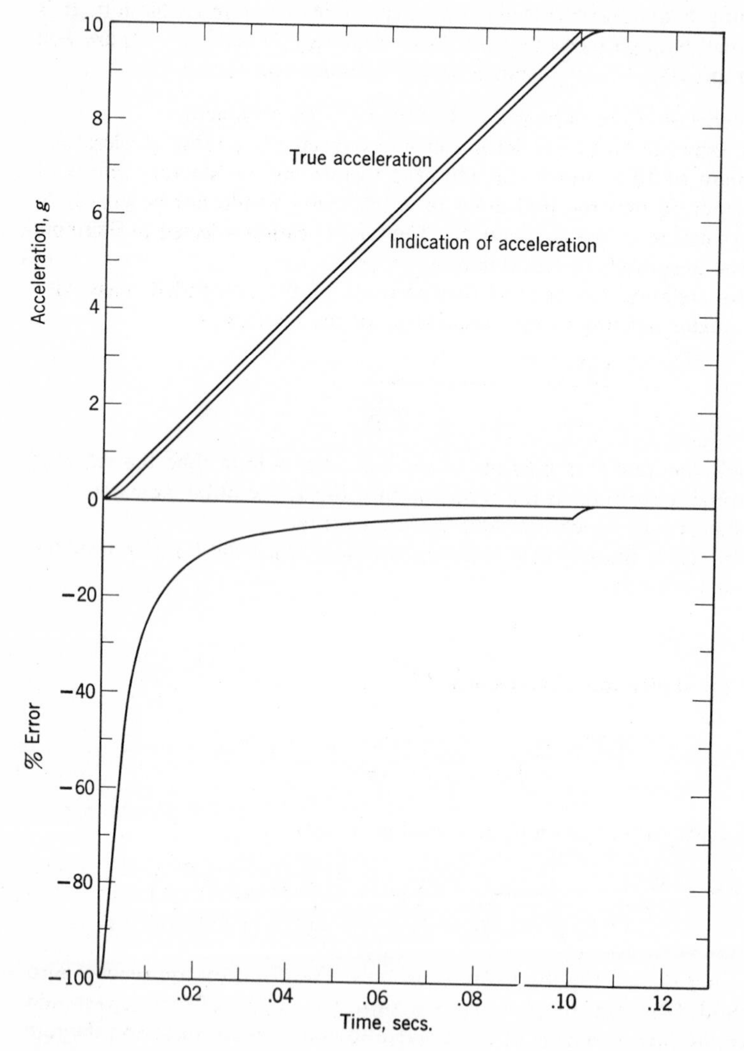

Fig. 15-3

noteworthy that one half the ramp time elapses before the error falls to 5%. However, it is easily shown that the error itself (not per cent error) approaches a constant value of $-2\, a_T\zeta/\beta T$ in a time of about $3/\zeta\beta$. For this example, then, the error itself would be only -0.23 g after about 0.004 sec. This is probably satisfactory for most applications.

This example did not make use of the convolution theorem because of the elementary nature of the transfer functions involved.

15.3 Equations for Numerical Computation of Transient Response, General Conditions

This section provides equations for numerical computation of the transient response under very general conditions. The forcing function is assumed to be a tabular function with linear interpolation between tabulated points. The transfer function, $G(s)$, relating the response and forcing functions, is of general form and may have poles of any order. Although the equations shown may be used for manual computations, this is impractical unless the system is quite elementary. However, the method is easily programmed for digital computer use, and such a program is provided in Reference 1.

The equations to be developed are based on the convolution theorem in the form of Equation 15-3. It is assumed that the transfer function, $G(s)$, having poles of any order, is known, and that the inverse of this function has been computed by the method explained in Appendix 1 and summarized by Equations A1-19 to A1-28. The forcing function, $f(t)$, must be single valued, except that finite discontinuities are allowed. This forcing function is then approximated by a series of straight line segments and the exact value of the integral required in Equation 15-3 is computed using the straight line approximation for $f(t)$.

The response of the system to unit impulse is $g(t) = \mathscr{L}^{-1}[G(s)]$. As shown in Appendix 1, $g(t)$ is composed of the sum of terms as indicated in Equation 15-6,

$$g(t) = \sum_{i=1}^{m} \left[e^{a_i t} \sum_{k=1}^{q} t^{k-1}(A_{i,k} \cos p_k t + B_{i,k} \sin p_k t) \right] \tag{15-6}$$

Linear factors in the denominator of $G(s)$ lead to terms such as $C_{i,k}\, e^{a_i t}\, t^{k-1}$, but these can be handled by letting $p_k = 0$ in the functions of Equation 15-6. Application of Equation 15-3 (using τ for λ) will then require the evaluation of terms such as

$$\begin{aligned} &\int_0^t f(\tau)(t-\tau)^n e^{a(t-\tau)} \cos p(t-\tau)\, d\tau \\ &\int_0^t f(\tau)(t-\tau)^n e^{a(t-\tau)} \sin p(t-\tau)\, d\tau \end{aligned} \tag{15-7}$$

If the forcing function could be represented by a graph composed of a series of straight lines, then the contribution to these integrals corresponding to the portion of the forcing function between two values of time, τ_1 and τ_2, could be obtained by replacing $f(\tau)$ in Equation 15-7 with

$$f(\tau) = c_1 + c_2\tau \tag{15-8}$$

where

$$\begin{aligned} c_1 &= \frac{\tau_2 f(\tau_2) - \tau_1 f(\tau_1)}{\tau_2 - \tau_1} \\ c_2 &= \frac{f(\tau_2) - f(\tau_1)}{\tau_2 - \tau_1} \end{aligned} \tag{15-9}$$

(At a finite discontinuity in $f(\tau)$, where $\tau_2 = \tau_1$, there is no contribution to the integral, and Equation 15-9 will not be used.)

When Equation 15-8 is used in Equation 15-7 it is convenient to evaluate these integrals by taking the real and imaginary parts of

$$\int_{\tau_1}^{\tau_2} (c_1 + c_2\tau)(t-\tau)^n e^{a(t-\tau)} e^{ip(t-\tau)}\, d\tau \tag{15-10}$$

The expression, $e^{(a+ip)t}$ can be removed from the integral, and $(t - \tau)^n$ can be expanded by the binomial theorem, yielding

$$(t - \tau)^n = \sum_{k=1}^{n+1} (-1)^{k-1} \frac{n!t^{n-k+1}}{(n - k + 1)!(k - 1)!} \tau^{k-1} \tag{15-11}$$

(The index k in Equation 15-11 must not be confused with the same index in Equation 15-6 when programming the equations.) Further manipulation of the integrand of Equation 15-10 results in the expression 15-12 which must still be integrated with respect to τ between τ_1 and τ_2.

$$e^{(a+ip)t} e^{-(a+ip)\tau}\left[c_1 t^n + (-1)^n c_2 \tau^{n+1} + \sum_{k=2}^{n+1} c_k \tau^{k-1}\right] \tag{15-12}$$

where

$$c_k = (-1)^{k-1} \frac{n!t^{n-k+1}}{(n - k + 1)!(k - 1)!}\left[c_1 - \frac{c_2(k - 1)t}{n - k + 2}\right] \tag{15-13}$$

(Note that if $n = 0$ the summation in 15-12 is omitted.)

Since the integral of 15-12 is required, it is necessary to evaluate integrals of the form

$$\int \tau^q e^{-(a+ip)\tau} d\tau$$

where q must not be confused with the index of Equation 15-6. The preceding expression can be integrated by successive integration by parts, stepping the exponent of τ down each time until it reaches zero. The result is Equation 15-14.

$$\int \tau^q e^{-(a+ip)\tau} d\tau = e^{-(a+ip)\tau} \sum_{l=1}^{q+1} \frac{q!}{(q - l + 1)!} \frac{1}{(a + ip)^l} \tau^{q-l+1} \tag{15-14}$$

Within the summation of Equation 15-14 is the expression $1/(a + ip)^l$. The denominator is evaluated by the binomial equation. The result is

$$\left.\begin{aligned}
\frac{1}{(a + ip)^l} &= c_{3_r} + ic_{3_i} = \frac{c_{2_r}}{c_{2_r}{}^2 + c_{2_i}{}^2} - i\frac{c_{2i}}{c_{2_r}{}^2 + c_{2_i}{}^2} \\
\text{where} \qquad & \\
c_{2_r} &= \sum_{m=1}^{(l+2)/2} (-1)^{m-1} \frac{l!a^{l-2m+2}p^{2m-2}}{(2m - 2)!(l - 2m + 2)!} \\
c_{2_i} &= \sum_{m=1}^{(l+1)/2} (-1)^{m-1} \frac{l!a^{l-2m+1}p^{2m-1}}{(2m - 1)!(l - 2m + 1)!}
\end{aligned}\right\} \tag{15-15}$$

The upper limits on the summations of Equation 15-15 must be rounded *downward* to the nearest integer if they are not integers. Also, if either a or p is zero, the quantity 0^0 must be evaluated as 1 if it occurs. If both a and p are zero, Equation 15-15 is not used and the integral of Equation 15-14 is elementary.

$$\int \tau^q dq = \frac{1}{q + 1} \tau^{q+1} \tag{15-16}$$

Equations 15-6 to 15-16 provide means for obtaining the contribution of one segment of the forcing function curve to the integral of Equation 15-3 (where τ replaces λ in that equation). Contributions of all segments up to the time, t (the time for which the response is being computed), must be summed. If $\tau_1 = \tau_2$ (a discontinuity of f), there is no contribution of the segment to the integral, and if $t < \tau_2$ for one of the segments, then τ_2 must be changed to t for that segment. If $t < \tau_1$, the segment makes no contribution to the integral.

Everything necessary for the evaluation of the transient response by the use of Equation 15-3 (where τ replaces λ in that equation) is now available. However, careful bookkeeping is required when all these equations are combined in the digital-computer program. It is evident from the development that the only approximation involved in the computation is the approximation of the forcing function with a series of straight-line segments. This computation therefore does not require closely spaced intervals for the numerical integration except as needed to represent the forcing function.

15.4 Distributed Systems Subjected to Arbitrary Forcing Functions

Complex structures subjected to arbitrary loads can be analyzed by an extension of the method described in Section 15.2. The procedure is perhaps most easily described by means of an example dealing with a relatively simple structure.

Example 15-3. Investigate the response of a simple beam to a concentrated load, P applied suddenly at the center of the beam (Fig. 15-4).

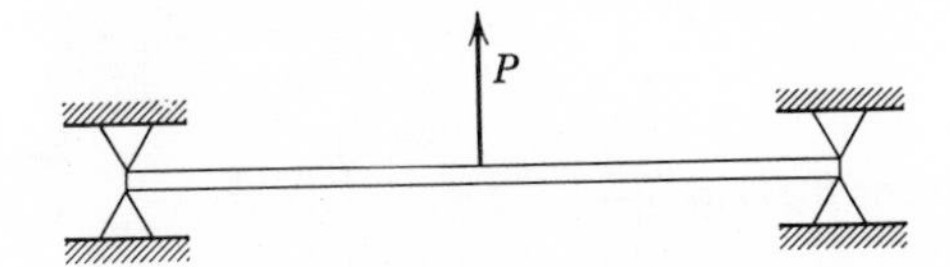

Fig. 15-4

Although a numerical solution would normally be required for most structures, this one can easily be analyzed analytically, and in fact was chosen because of this, in order to illustrate some interesting limitations of this method.

The natural modes and frequencies of a simply supported beam of constant cross section, neglecting shear deformation, can be computed using the methods of Section 11.3.

$$\beta_n = \frac{\pi^2 n^2 a}{L^2} \text{ (natural frequency)}$$

$$X_n = \sin \sqrt{\frac{\beta_n}{a}}\, x = \sin \frac{n\pi x}{L} \text{ (natural mode description)}$$

where n is an integer and $a = \sqrt{EI/\rho A}$ (see Section 11.3).

The simply supported beam natural mode is described by a much simpler expression than beams with other restraints, as is evident from the foregoing equation for X_n. This makes it attractive for an illustrative example, since numerical complications are avoided. The procedure can be applied to structures having more complicated mode descriptions.

Now each individual mode can be treated as if it were a one-degree-of-freedom system (Fig. 15-5), having generalized mass M_n, generalized spring constant, K_n, and generalized force, Q_n, suddenly applied. It is necessary to compute these quantities. Since the force is applied at $x = L/2$, the generalized force in the nth mode which would have the same rate of work as the actual force is

$$Q_n = P \sin \frac{n\pi}{2}$$

The kinetic energy of the generalized mass will be the same as the distributed mass if

$$M_n = \int_0^L (\rho A\, dx)\left(\sin \frac{n\pi x}{L}\right)^2 = \frac{\rho AL}{2} = \frac{m}{2}, \quad m = \text{mass of beam}$$

$$K_n = M_n \beta_n^2 = \frac{m}{2}\frac{\pi^4 n^4}{L^4}\frac{EI}{\rho A} = \frac{\pi^4 n^4 EI}{2L^3}$$

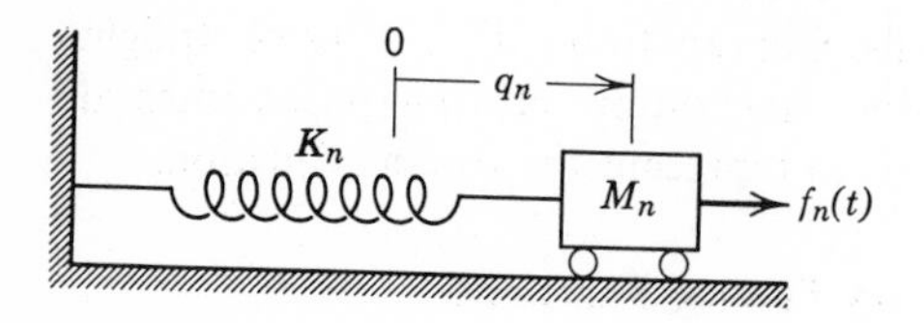

Fig. 15-5

For a suddenly applied force the displacement is

$$q_n = \frac{Q_n}{K_n}(1 - \cos \beta_n t) = \frac{2PL^3 \sin \frac{n\pi}{2}}{\pi^4 n^4 EI}(1 - \cos \beta_n t)$$

The displacement of any point on the beam would be the sum of the displacement in all modes.

$$y = \frac{2PL^3}{\pi^4 EI}\sum_{n=1}^{\infty} \frac{\sin \frac{n\pi}{2}}{n^4}(1 - \cos \beta_n t)\sin \frac{n\pi x}{L}$$

The summations can be separated into two summations, one which does not involve the time variable and one which does, originating with the two terms of the factor, $(1 - \cos \beta_n t)$. The series which does not involve time can be shown to represent the Fourier series description of the deflection of a simple beam under a concentrated, static load. The other series describes the vibration which is started. The $\sin n\pi/2$ term shows that the even-numbered modes are absent, as expected. At the center of the beam ($x = L/2$) the sign of each term in the series is the same, and since the higher mode frequencies are exact multiples of the fundamental (9, 25, 49, etc.), there would be an instant at which the deflections would all add together, or $\cos \beta_n t = -1$ at that instant for all n odd. This then shows that at the beam center there are times at which the total deflection is twice the static deflection. The n^4 in the denominator of each term in the series indicates that the higher modes contribute very little to the deflection pattern. However, the series for the bending moment, which is proportional to $\partial^2 y/\partial x^2$, possesses terms which decrease according to n^2 in the denominator, and more modes are required to accurately represent the bending moment.

There are occasions when the acceleration of a point on a beam is of interest. If the series for y is differentiated twice with respect to time,

$$\frac{\partial^2 y}{\partial t^2} = \frac{2PL^3}{\pi^4 EI}\sum_{n=1}^{\infty} \frac{\sin n\pi/2}{n^4}\beta_n^2 \cos \beta_n t \sin \frac{n\pi x}{L}$$

$$= \frac{2P}{M}\sum \sin \frac{n\pi}{2}\cos \beta_n t \sin \frac{n\pi x}{L}$$

The interesting point here is that this series does not converge, since the n^4 term in the denominator is exactly cancelled by a similar term from β_n^2. Thus it appears that at the center of the beam every term would add together at certain times (one of these being time zero) to produce an infinite acceleration. While this may seem an unreasonable result at first glance, a review of the assumptions will quickly indicate the source of the trouble. It was assumed that the force was concentrated at a point but that the mass of the beam was distributed. Therefore, at the very first instant the finite force must be acting on an infinitesimally small mass just under the concentrated force. At that instant the acceleration at that isolated point should be infinite, mathematically, with such an assumption. Of course a real force, even if "concentrated," would have to be spread over a finite portion of the beam, so that there would be a finite mass under this distributed force to limit the initial acceleration. Also, the force was assumed to be "suddenly" applied, meaning instantaneously as far as the mathematics is concerned. A real force would have to be generated as some form of ramp, even if steep, which would have the effect of eliminating the contribution of higher frequency modes, as can be seen from Example 15-1. Finally, it was assumed that the beam was undamped. Structural damping in a real beam would have the effect of attenuating the higher frequency modes for all of the instants at which the terms of the series are in phase except the time zero instant.

Example 15-4. Example 15-3 made use of a forcing function having an algebraic form, a constant. If the forcing function were a table of force as a function of time, the numerical method described in Section 15.2 and Example 15-1 could be used, with each mode having a different transfer function. The ramp-forcing function of Example 15-1 could be described analytically, of course, so that the numerical method would not be necessary. However, for illustrative purposes, let it be assumed that the beam is excited with the ramp forcing function of Example 15-1, applied as a concentrated force at the beam midpoint, and that the first four beam bending modes are sufficient to describe the response of the beam. Determine the beam configuration at time $t = 2.0$.

For each of the four bending modes, the equivalent picture is that of Fig. 15-5, for which the transfer function and its inverse follow.

$$G_n(s) = \left(\frac{Q_n}{F_n}\right) = \frac{1}{M_n(s^2 + \beta_n^2)}$$

$$g_n(t) = \frac{1}{M_n\beta_n} \sin \beta_n t$$

A table of generalized forces in the first four modes corresponding to the actual force description of Example 15-1 is shown in Table 15-1. This is determined by using the equation previously shown to be

$$f_n = P \sin \frac{n\pi}{2}$$

where $P = 1$ and the time dependence is that of Example 15-3.

Let it be assumed again that the condition of the beam at $t = 2$ sec is required. In order to proceed with the numerical investigation it is necessary to know some beam properties. Assume the beam is a steel rod $\frac{1}{2}$ inch in diameter and 20 ft long, for which

$$a = 173 \text{ ft}^2/\text{sec}$$

$$\beta_n = 4.28n^2$$

$$M_n = \frac{m}{2} = 0.208 \text{ slugs}$$

Table 15-3

Time, sec	Generalized Forces, f, lb			
	$n = 1$	$n = 2$	$n = 3$	$n = 4$
0	0	0	0	0
0.2	0.2	0	−0.2	0
0.4	0.4	0	−0.4	0
0.6	0.6	0	−0.6	0
0.8	0.8	0	−0.8	0
1.0	1.0	0	−1.0	0
1.2	1.0	0	−1.0	0
1.4	1.0	0	−1.0	0
etc.	etc.	etc.	etc.	etc.

At $t = 2$ the displacement in each mode is (Equation 15-3)

$$q_n = \int_0^{2.0} f_n(\lambda) \frac{1}{M_n \beta_n} \sin \beta_n(2.0 - \lambda)\, d\lambda$$

$$q_n = \frac{1.127}{n^2} \int_0^{2.0} f_n(\lambda) \sin [4.28n^2(2.0 - \lambda)]\, d\lambda$$

For $n = 2$ and $n = 4$, $f_n = 0$, so only $n = 1$ and $n = 3$ need be considered. For $n = 3$, $d\lambda = 0.0136$ sec corresponds to 30° increments in $4.28n^2\, d\lambda$. Therefore let $d\lambda = 0.01$ for a relatively accurate numerical approximation for the amount of the third mode present in the response. However, since the response at $t = 2$ sec is desired, 200 values of λ are required. A partial table of values of the integrands for the previous integral at 0.01-sec increments is shown in Table 15-4. The values of f_n are obtained by interpolation.

Table 15-4

① λ	② $4.28n^2(2 - \lambda)$				③ sin ②		④ f_n		⑤ ③ × ④	
	$n = 1$		$n = 3$		$n = 1$	$n = 3$	$n = 1$	$n = 3$	$n = 1$	$n = 3$
0	8.560	490.5	77.04	4414.4	0.761	0.997	0	0	0	0
0.01	8.517	488.0	76.65	4392.3	0.789	0.954	0.01	−0.01	0.0079	−0.0095
0.02	8.474	485.6	76.27	4370.2	0.814	0.769	0.02	−0.02	0.0163	−0.0154
0.03	8.432	483.1	75.88	4348.1	0.838	0.471	0.03	−0.03	0.0251	−0.0141

The integration of Column 5 of Table 15-4 by trapezoidal rule shows that at $t = 2$ sec the displacements of the generalized coordinates for the first and third modes are as follows

$$q_1 = 0.15 \text{ ft}$$

$$q_3 = 0.0041 \text{ ft}$$

The correct values of q_1 and q_3 are 0.16 and 0.0032 ft respectively, giving an indication of the magnitude of error resulting from the assumption of increments of λ of 0.01 sec. The error is practically eliminated by taking increments of λ of 0.001 sec, and could be entirely eliminated by using the method described in Section 15.3.

The deflection of the beam at any point for this instant can be obtained from the mode descriptions,

$$y = 0.15 \sin \frac{\pi x}{20} + 0.0041 \sin \frac{3\pi x}{20}, \text{ ft}$$

and the bending moment at any point from $EI\ \partial^2 y/\partial x^2$

$$m = -32.9 \sin \frac{\pi x}{20} - 8.1 \sin \frac{3\pi x}{20}, \text{ lb-ft}$$

In a practical problem the mode descriptions would be given as a numerical table rather than as the simple sine functions of this example, so that the deflection and moment descriptions would be determined numerically.

CHAPTER 16

Shock Spectrum

16.1 General Comments

If a complex system having many degrees of freedom is analyzed by the method of superimposing the solutions of equivalent single degree systems, as described in earlier chapters, there is some advantage to describing a shock (or transient forcing function) in terms of the effect it has on a single degree system rather than simply a time history of the forcing function. This view holds that any complex system may be considered to be a collection of single-degree systems and that a shock will excite all of these systems. Therefore, an understanding of the response of these systems (having different natural frequencies) to an impressed shock should be of more significance than a time history of the shock itself.

The shock spectrum furnishes this understanding and also provides the additional advantage that the effect of a shock having a specific time history can be simulated in shock testing apparatus by an equivalent shock with a different time history but having a nearly identical spectrum. This is useful for several reasons: It may be that the specific history of an applied shock is only an estimation so that some other history would be equally significant; it might be difficult to generate a specific shock with laboratory equipment available, but some easily generated shock could yield essentially equivalent information about the effects of the shock; for comparison of performance of equipment subjected to shock, the use of some "standard" shock, instead of a specific shock, could produce more significant results.

When an instrument or piece of equipment is subjected to a sudden acceleration, or shock, there are numerous masses contained within the instrument which must be accelerated by whatever structure supports these masses. This structure is flexible, and so vibration is excited. This flexible structure which supports and accelerates the masses is therefore subjected to loads proportional to the acceleration of the individual masses rather than the instrument as a whole. These loads could cause failure of the supporting structure. In general, there are so many individual masses that an analysis of a multiple degree system with coupling between coordinates, as described in previous chapters, may become impractical (with exceptions, of course, which must be left to judgment). If it is assumed that the complex structure is a collection of single degree systems having natural frequencies ranging from zero to infinity, then the effect of an acceleration on all possible single degree systems would be of significance even if the actual specific individual single degree systems are not known for the structure. Testing of the instrument could be performed so as to subject the unknown single degree systems to accelerations which would be more realistic than might otherwise be expected.

Accordingly, the peak acceleration of a spring-suspended mass when the suspension point is subjected to an arbitrary, specified acceleration is of interest. This peak acceleration of the mass corresponds to the peak load required of the spring and therefore to the most likelihood of damage or failure. If this peak acceleration is plotted as a function of the natural frequency of the single degree system for a specific

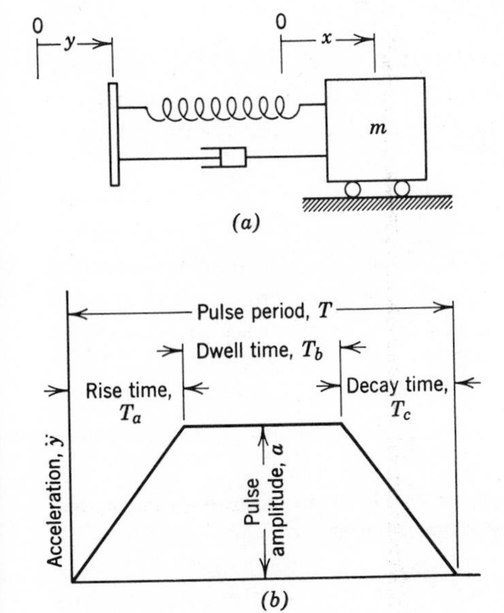

Fig. 16-1 Single-degree system subject to transient acceleration pulse, $\ddot{y}$

acceleration history of the suspension point, the curve is known as a "shock spectrum" or "response spectrum" Fig. 16-1 shows the problem to be investigated, (a) the physical problem and (b) a typical input acceleration history or pulse. Figs. 16-4 to 16-8 are examples of shock spectra resulting from shocks of the general form of Fig. 16-1.

16.2 Equations for Simple Shocks

In terms of the physical problem defined in Fig. 16-1, the input acceleration is $\ddot{y}$ and the response acceleration is $\ddot{x}$, which can be computed by use of the convolution theorem, Equation 15-3 or 15-4. The value of $\ddot{x}$ can be computed at various times in order to determine the maximum value of $\ddot{x}$ for a single-degree system having a natural frequency, β, and subjected to the input acceleration history, $\ddot{y}$. Then this same computation can be repeated using different values of β so that a plot of maximum response acceleration as a function of natural frequency ($\ddot{x}_{max}$ versus β) can be constructed, which is the shock spectrum for the particular input shock history, $\ddot{y}$, being investigated. The shock spectra of Figs. 16-4 to 16-8 are presented in terms of dimensionless parameters. (The $\ddot{x}$ indicated on these figures is the maximum or peak value of the response acceleration, and β is in cycles per second rather than radians per second.)

The transfer function for this system is

$$\frac{X}{Y} = \frac{2\zeta\beta s + \beta^2}{s^2 + 2\zeta\beta s + \beta^2}$$

Since accelerations are desired, a more useful form is

$$\frac{s^2 X}{s^2 Y} = \frac{2\zeta\beta s + \beta^2}{s^2 + 2\zeta\beta s + \beta^2}$$

The time history of the acceleration of the mass will then become

$$\ddot{x} = \mathscr{L}^{-1}\left[\frac{2\zeta\beta s + \beta^2}{s^2 + 2\zeta\beta s + \beta^2}(s^2 Y)\right] \tag{16-1}$$

where $(s^2 Y)$ is the transform of the applied acceleration which forces the response. For illustration, the shock spectrum will be computed for a shock whose time history is shown in Fig. 16-2 for which $T_a = T_c = \frac{1}{2}T$, and $T_b = 0$. Also, the damping factor, ζ, for the single degree system will be zero.

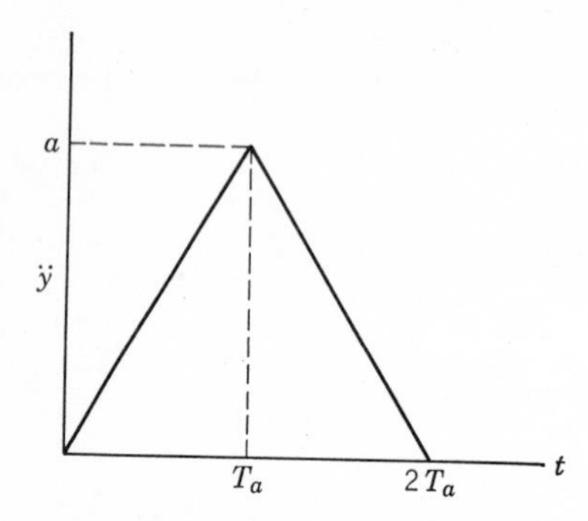

Fig. 16-2 Shock for illustrative computation of shock spectrum

It is slightly more convenient to use Equation 15-4 than 15-3 for the computation. Accordingly, let

$$h(t) = \mathscr{L}^{-1}\frac{\beta^2}{s(s^2 + \beta^2)} = 1 - \cos\beta t$$

$$f(t) = \mathscr{L}^{-1}(s^2 Y) = \frac{a}{T_a}t - \frac{2a}{T_a}(t - T_a)u(t - T_a) + \frac{a}{T_a}(t - 2T_a)u(t - 2T_a)$$

$$\frac{df(t)}{dt} = \frac{a}{T_a} - 2\frac{a}{T_a}u(t - T_a) + \frac{a}{T_a}u(t - 2T_a)$$

Substitution in Equation 15-4 and solution yields

$$\begin{aligned}
\ddot{x} &= a\left(\frac{t}{T_a} - \frac{1}{\beta T_a}\sin\beta T_a\frac{t}{T_a}\right), \quad \frac{t}{T_a} \lesseqgtr 1 \\
&= a\left[2 - \frac{t}{T_a} + \frac{2}{\beta T_a}\sin\beta T_a\left(\frac{t}{T_a} - 1\right) - \frac{1}{\beta T_a}\sin\beta T_a\frac{t}{T_a}\right], \quad 1 \lesseqgtr \frac{t}{T_a} \lesseqgtr 2 \\
&= \frac{a}{\beta T_a}\left[-\sin\beta T_a\frac{t}{T_a} + 2\sin\beta T_a\left(\frac{t}{T_a} - 1\right) - \sin\beta T_a\left(\frac{t}{T_a} - 2\right)\right], \quad \frac{t}{T_a} \gtreqless 2
\end{aligned} \tag{16-2}$$

16.3 Primary and Residual Shock

The first of Equations 16-2 describes the acceleration of the mass in the time interval during which the shock or applied acceleration of the support point is still in existence. The third equation describes the acceleration of the mass after this time

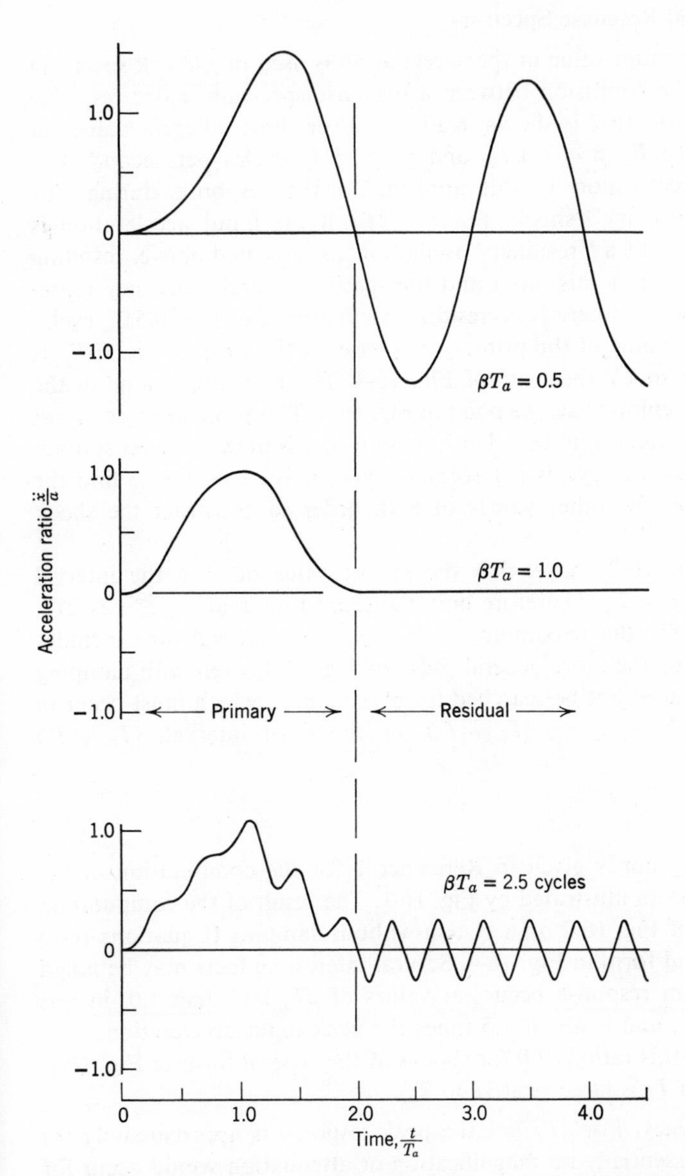

Fig. 16-3 Time history of acceleration response to input acceleration of Fig. 16-2

provided that the acceleration of the platform is restrained to be exactly zero. This would require a force on the support point, which might or might not be realistic for a given situation, depending on the physical configuration. If the support point is restrained to zero acceleration after the end of the pulse, the mass will oscillate so as to produce both positive and negative acceleration peaks. This phase is referred to as "residual" shock. It may be useful to know both the primary shock spectrum and the residual spectrum, and so both are often plotted.

16.4 Response History and Response Spectrum

Although only the maximum value of the acceleration is used in a shock spectrum computation, there may be confusion between a response spectrum and a response history. A plot of Equation 16-2 is shown in Fig. 16-3 for three different values of natural frequency, $\beta = 0.5/T_a$, $\beta = 1.0/T_a$, and $\beta = 2.5/T_a$ cycles per second. For $t < 2T_a$, the forcing acceleration is still applied, so the response during this interval is designated "primary" shock. For $t > 2T_a$, if the input acceleration is forced to be zero, there will be a "residual" oscillation, as indicated above, resulting in the accelerations shown. For this input and the specific natural frequency represented by $\beta = 1.0/T_a$, however, there is no residual oscillation. For $\beta = 0.5/T_a$ cycles per second, the maximum value of the primary response, at the time $t = 1.210T_a$, is used as one point on the shock spectrum of Fig. 16-4. The maximum value of the residual acceleration is also plotted as one point in Fig. 16-4. This peak value occurs at the times $t = 2.5T_a$, $3.5T_a$, etc. (Note that β in Equation 16-2 is in radians per second, but in Fig. 16-3 to 16-8 β is in cycles per second.) Now it is necessary to find the peak value of acceleration for other values of β in order to construct the shock spectrum of Fig. 16-4.

Inspection of Equations 16-2 shows that the largest value of $\ddot{x}$ in the interval $0 \leqq t \leqq T_a$ occurs where $t = T_a$. Therefore only the second interval, $T_a \leqq t \leqq 2T_a$, needs to be investigated for the maximum value, since this interval also includes $t = T_a$. This is also true for the more general pulse of Fig. 16-1, even with damping present. The first interval need not be searched for maximum $\ddot{x}$, which must occur in either the second interval, $T_a \leqq t \leqq (T_a + T_b)$, or the third interval, $(T_a + T_b) \leqq t \leqq (T_a + T_b + T_c)$.

16.5 Discussion

A digital computer program is given in Reference 1 for the computation of the shock spectrum for the system illustrated by Fig. 16-1. The result of the computation for the specialized shock of Fig. 16-2 on a system without damping (Equations 16-2) is shown in nondimensional form in Fig. 16-4. Several interesting facts may be noted in this plot. The maximum response occurs at values of βT_a less than 1.0, in this instance at 0.5 revolutions, and is about 1.5 times the peak input acceleration. (The theoretical upper limit for this ratio is 2.0 for shocks of the general form of Fig. 16-1, which is approached when T_b is large relative to T_a).

Effect of Natural Frequency. For $\beta T_a \geqq 1$ the peak response is approximately the same as the peak input. Essentially no magnification or attenuation would occur for systems having natural frequencies greater than $1/T_a$ cycles per second.

If the purpose of a suspension system is to reduce the shock intensity, it will be necessary to provide values of βT_a less than about 0.2 cycles. That is, the maximum natural frequency should be less than $0.2/T_a$ cycles per second, the smaller the better as far as shock attenuation is concerned, limited by practical considerations of course.

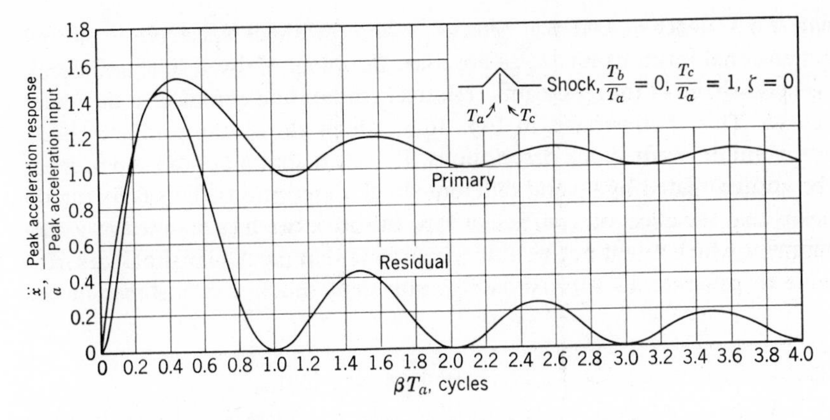

Fig. 16-4 Shock spectrum

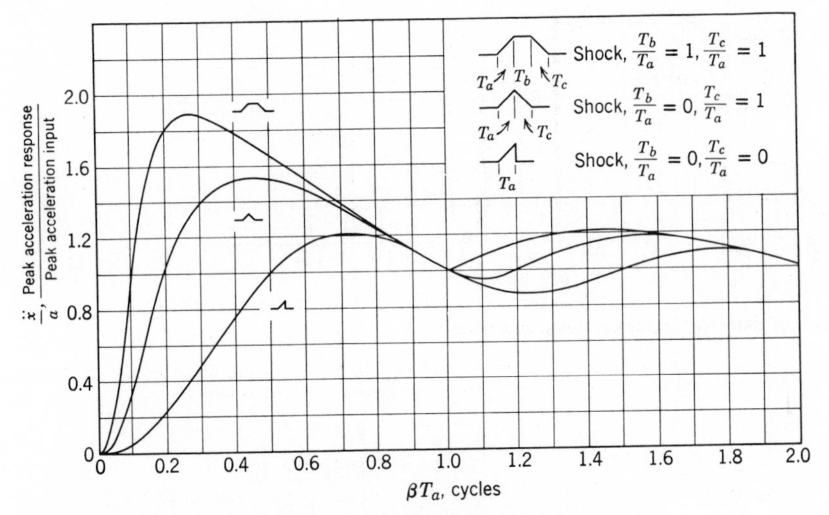

Fig. 16-5 Effect of shock history on primary shock spectrum

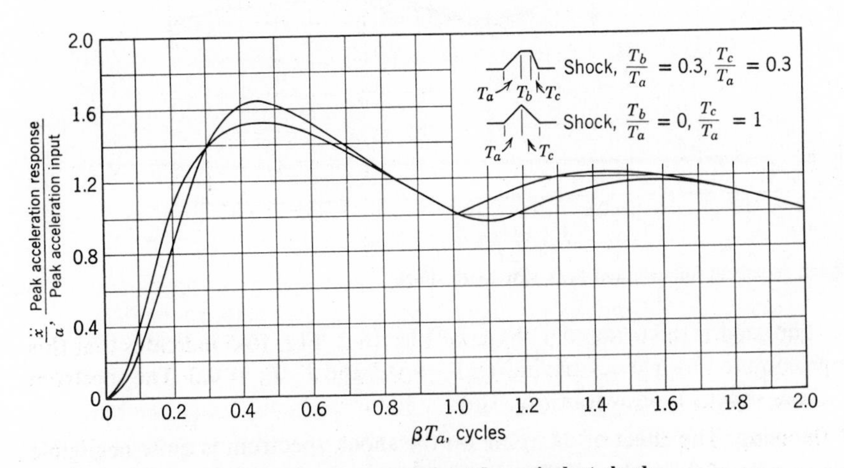

Fig. 16-6 Primary spectrum for two approximately equivalent shocks

Approximate Equivalence of Different Shocks. When the shock spectrum is plotted in this nondimensional form, using βT_a as abscissa, the effect of dwell time and decay time on the general shape of the spectrum is relatively minor and confined to the lower end of the curve. This is illustrated in Fig. 16-5, which shows the primary shock spectrum for several different shock descriptions. It is clear that a desired shock spectrum could be approximated by several different shock descriptions. This is fortunate because it means that the effect of a particular type of shock can be simulated by available test equipment which might not be able to generate that particular shock description but is able to generate an approximately equivalent shock. For instance, if the

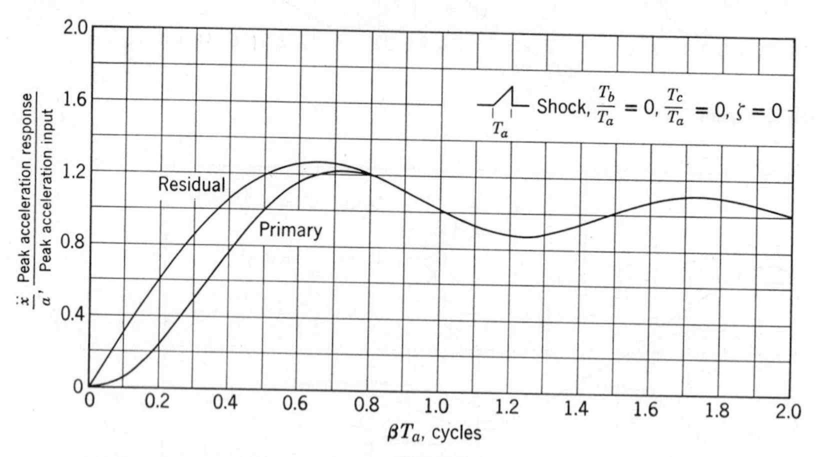

Fig. 16-7 Effect of damping factor on shock spectrum

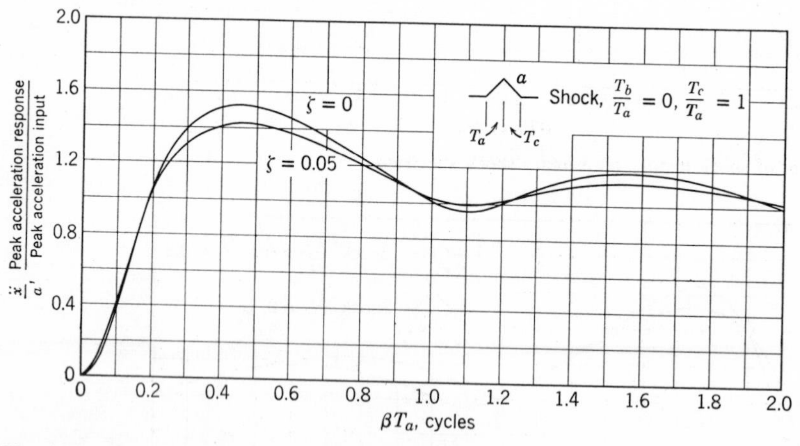

Fig. 16-8 Shock spectrum for terminal peak saw-tooth shock

shock to be simulated is the triangular shape of Fig. 16-2, Fig. 16-5 indicates that this could be approximated by a shock having $T_b/T_a = 0.3$ and $T_c/T_a = 0.3$. The spectrum for each of these shocks is shown in Fig. 16-6.

Effect of Damping. The effect of damping on the shock spectrum is quite negligible for damping factors of the order of 2% of critical. Since structural damping is of this order, it is usually unnecessary to include the effect of damping in the spectrum. Figure 16-7 shows the effect of 5% damping for a triangular shock like that of Fig. 16-2.

Terminal Peak Sawtooth Shock. A "terminal-peak-sawtooth" shock is considered by some authorities to be a desirable type of shock for testing purposes, for practical reasons, and because the response is relatively constant over the entire spectrum. Also, the residual shock spectrum does not differ appreciably from the primary spectrum except at low natural frequencies. Figure 16-8 illustrates this property.

Complex Shock. The foregoing discussion applies to shocks whose description can be represented or at least approximated by Fig. 16-2. For shocks of this type the limiting peak response acceleration is twice the magnitude of the input acceleration (the value expected for shocks approaching a step function). Of course, it is possible that the input acceleration might not have a description of this simple form. For instance, it might have negative as well as positive values and might have more than just one pulse. For such "complex" shocks, the peak response could exceed the above limitation of twice the peak input acceleration for certain natural frequencies (similar to a resonance phenomenon), and the period of primary shock could contain negative as well as positive response accelerations. Problem 16.3 suggests a method of computation which is somewhat more convenient than the convolution integral for such shocks if they can be described, or at least approximated, by an acceleration history composed of straight line segments.

Concluding Remarks. The discussion of this chapter has been intended to clarify the method of shock description known as the shock spectrum. The principal advantages of this description over the simple description of the pulse as a function of time are: (1) a somewhat broader understanding of the effect of shock on single degree systems may be achieved through this description, and (2) approximately equivalent pulses can be used in shock testing apparatus.

CHAPTER 17

Transient Response by Fourier Transforms

17.1 Fourier Integral and Fourier Transform

In Chapter 16 the response of systems subject to transient forcing functions was described in terms of the response to unit step or impulse functions. The transient function was considered to be composed of a series of small impulses and the responses to this series superimposed to determine the response to the actual forcing function. It is also possible to define a forcing function in terms of an infinite number of sine or cosine functions of infinitesimal amplitude. Then the response to these may be superimposed to determine the response to the actual forcing function. The description of the transient forcing function in terms of its harmonic components is accomplished by means of the Fourier integral.

Fourier Integral and Laplace Transforms. The development of the Fourier integral method of representing a function is described in Reference 6 and others and will not be repeated here. Briefly, however, the function to be represented must be single valued (except that it may have a finite number of finite discontinuities in a finite interval), it must not have infinite discontinuities ($\tan t$ is unacceptable, for instance), and it must approach zero as the independent variable approaches infinity in either the positive or negative direction (t^2 or e^t or e^{-t} are unacceptable for instance, unless "cut-off"). The function must also exhibit only a finite number of maximum or minimum points in a finite interval ($\sin 1/t$ is unacceptable, for instance). For transient analyses nearly any forcing function of practical interest would obey these requirements and so be a possible subject for a Fourier analysis.

The Fourier integral equation is shown in the complex exponential form in Equation 17-1, in which ω should be regarded as a parameter, rather than frequency, since it may assume negative values.

$$f(t) = \frac{1}{2\pi} \int_{\omega=-\infty}^{+\infty} e^{it\omega} \left[\int_{t=-\infty}^{+\infty} f(t)\, e^{-i\omega t}\, dt \right] d\omega \tag{17-1}$$

The $f(t)$ inside the integral is the same function as that at the left side. However, the function inside the integral might be described by several different expressions, each valid for a different range of the variable, t. After it is operated on as indicated by Equation 17-1, the left side describes the same function but with a single expression valid for all values of t. A similar expression relating the Laplace transform with its inverse is Equation 17-2.

$$f(t) = \frac{1}{2\pi i}\int_{s=a-i\infty}^{a+i\infty} e^{ts}\left[\int_{t=0}^{\infty} f(t)\, e^{-st}\, dt\right] ds \tag{17-2}$$

Fourier Transform. Although Equation 17-2 is often derived from Equation 17-1 in the development of theory pertaining to the Laplace transform, the extensive use of the Laplace transform perhaps has caused it to become more familiar to most readers, and so it is convenient to consider Equation 17-1 as analogous to Equation 17-2 rather than the reverse. This suggests that the same transform relationship might be useful and accordingly Equation 17-1 can be conveniently expressed as

$$\begin{aligned} g(\omega) &= \int_{t=-\infty}^{+\infty} f(t)\, e^{-i\omega t}\, dt \equiv F[f(t)] \\ f(t) &= \frac{1}{2\pi}\int_{\omega=-\infty}^{+\infty} g(\omega)\, e^{it\omega}\, d\omega \equiv F^{-1}[g(\omega)] \end{aligned} \tag{17-3}$$

where $g(\omega)$ or $F[f(t)]$ is the Fourier transform of $f(t)$ and $f(t)$ or $F^{-1}[g(\omega)]$ is the inverse Fourier transform of $g(\omega)$. These definitions are not the only ones in use, and therefore whenever a table of Fourier transforms is consulted, it is wise to ascertain the definitions used in the table.

Fourier Transforms of Even or Odd Functions. If $f(t)$ is an even function or an odd function, Equations 17-3 can be modified to Equations 17-4.

$$\begin{aligned} &\left.\begin{aligned} g(\omega) &= \int_{t=0}^{\infty} f(t)\cos \omega t\, dt \\ f(t) &= \frac{2}{\pi}\int_{\omega=0}^{\infty} g(\omega)\cos t\omega\, d\omega \end{aligned}\right\} f(t) \text{ even} \\ &\left.\begin{aligned} g(\omega) &= \int_{t=0}^{\infty} f(t)\sin \omega t\, dt \\ f(t) &= \frac{2}{\pi}\int_{\omega=0}^{\infty} g(\omega)\sin t\omega\, d\omega \end{aligned}\right\} f(t) \text{ odd} \end{aligned} \tag{17-4}$$

Any real function can be considered as the sum of an even function and an odd function, where these functions may be determined as indicated in Equations 17-5.

$$\left.\begin{aligned} f(t) &= f_e(t) + f_o(t) \\ f_e(t) &= \frac{f(t) + f(-t)}{2} \\ f_o(t) &= \frac{f(t) - f(-t)}{2} \end{aligned}\right\} \tag{17-5}$$

If these even and odd functions are used in Equation 17-3, the real and imaginary parts of the Fourier transform can be shown to be even and odd functions respectively (of ω), and therefore the integration involved in obtaining the inverse transform need only go from limits of 0 to infinity, as summarized in Equations 17-6. Of course, the imaginary part of this inverse is zero since $f(t)$ in Equation 17-5 is a real function. (This is manifested as an integration from $-\infty$ to $+\infty$ of an odd function in the calculation of the inverse.)

$$\left.\begin{aligned} g(\omega) &= g_r(\omega) + ig_i(\omega) \\ g_r(\omega) &= 2\int_{t=0}^{\infty} f_e(t)\cos\omega t\,dt \\ g_i(\omega) &= -2\int_{t=0}^{\infty} f_o(t)\sin\omega t\,dt \\ &g_r(\omega) \text{ is an even function of } \omega \\ &g_i(\omega) \text{ is an odd function of } \omega \\ f(t) &= \frac{1}{\pi}\int_{\omega=0}^{\infty} [g_r(\omega)\cos t\omega - g_i(\omega)\sin t\omega]\,d\omega \end{aligned}\right\} \tag{17-6}$$

In Equations 17-1 and 17-3 ω may have negative values and so must be considered a parameter rather than a frequency. However, in Equation 17-6 the use of negative values of ω is not required, so ω can properly be considered a frequency.

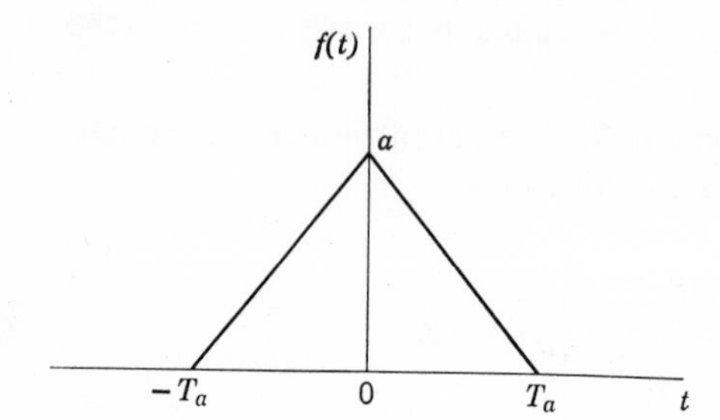

Fig. 17-1

Systems Quiescent Prior to Zero Time. If it is known that the function, $f(t)$, is identically zero for $t < 0$, then the last equation can be simplified somewhat, as follows.

$$f(-t) = 0 = \frac{1}{\pi}\int_{\omega=0}^{\infty} [g_r(\omega)\cos(-t\omega) - g_i(\omega)\sin(-t\omega)]\,d\omega$$

Since $\cos(-t\omega) = \cos(t\omega)$ and $\sin(-t\omega) = -\sin(t\omega)$

$$\frac{1}{\pi}\int_{\omega=0}^{\infty} g_i(\omega)\sin(t\omega)\,d\omega = -\frac{1}{\pi}\int_{\omega=0}^{\infty} g_r(\omega)\cos(t\omega)\,d\omega$$

When this relation is used in the last of Equations 17-6,

$$f(t) = \frac{2}{\pi}\int_{\omega=0}^{\infty} g_r(\omega)\cos t\omega\,d\omega \tag{17-7}$$

Equation 17-7 is valid only if $f(t) = 0$ for $t < 0$.

Example 17-1. Discuss the pulse defined in Fig. 17-1, using the Fourier Integral.

Since this is an even function, a convenient form of the Fourier transform is that of Equation 17-4.

$$F[f(t)] = g(\omega) = \int_{t=0}^{\infty} f(t) \cos \omega t \, dt$$

$$g(\omega) = \int_{t=0}^{T_a} a\left(1 - \frac{t}{T_a}\right) \cos \omega t \, dt = \frac{a}{\omega^2 T_a}(1 - \cos \omega T_a)$$

Here the upper limit has been changed from ∞ to T_a because $f(t) = 0$ for $t > T_a$. A plot of $g(\omega)$, but in the dimensionless form, is indicated by Fig. 17-2, to an approximate scale. (The indeterminate fraction at $\omega \to 0$ is readily evaluated by L'Hospital's rule.)

For purposes of discussion, let a and T_a be unity. Another interpretation of the plot in Fig. 17-2 is as follows. If a set of cosine functions ($A \cos \omega t$) having *relative* amplitudes as indicated by the ordinate were constructed for frequencies as indicated by the abscissa (not just integer values of the frequency, but all values of this continuously varying parameter), the sum of all this infinity of curves would add up to a figure having the straight-line pulse shape of Fig. 17-1, except that the amplitude of the pulse would be infinite if the amplitudes of the individual cosine curves were finite. In order to reproduce the finite pulse, the individual amplitudes must be infinitesimal, but their relative magnitudes are given by the plot, and it is seen that low-frequency components are important. One result of this observation is that instruments for registering or recording pulses (such as seismographs

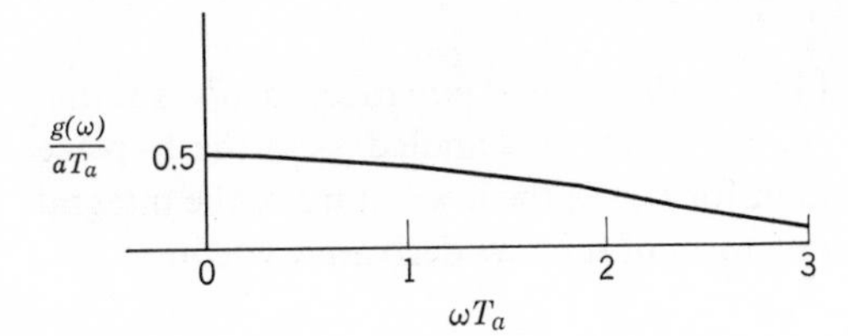

Fig. 17-2

and accelerometers) may be required to reproduce low-frequency components accurately.

To obtain the function of time having the Fourier transform,

$$g(\omega) = (a/\omega^2 T_a)(1 - \cos \omega T_a)$$

it is necessary to take the inverse transform, or from Equation 17-4

$$F^{-1}[g(\omega)] = \frac{2}{\pi}\int_{\omega=0}^{\infty} g(\omega) \cos t\omega \, d\omega = \frac{2}{\pi}\int_{\omega=0}^{\infty} \frac{a}{\omega^2 T_a}(1 - \cos T_a\omega) \cos t\omega \, d\omega$$

(Note that the above expression is equivalent to summing all cosine curves having sign and infinitesimal amplitudes determined by $[(2/\pi)g(\omega)\, d\omega]$.)

This may be integrated numerically for each value of t of interest. The result is the isosceles triangle pulse of Fig. 17-1. Although this expression for the pulse is somewhat disappointing, because of some difficulty encountered in performing the integration, it has the property of being a valid representation of the original function for all values of t, and as such could be used in whatever way might be convenient in any analysis using the pulse.

17.2 Solution of Differential Equations by Fourier Transforms

As might be expected, linear differential equations may be solved by use of the Fourier transform in a manner similar to the Laplace transform. In order to do this, it is useful to be able to express the transform of the derivative in terms of the transform of the variable, so that the differential equation can be converted to an algebraic equation.

Fourier Transform of Derivatives. It is desired to determine an expression for the transform of derivatives of $f(t)$. Start with the first derivative.

$$F\left[\frac{df(t)}{dt}\right] = \int_{t=-\infty}^{+\infty} \frac{df(t)}{dt} e^{-i\omega t}\, dt$$

Integrate by parts, $\int u\, dv = uv - \int v\, du$, where $u = e^{-i\omega t}$ and $dv = df/dt\, dt = df$, so $v = f$

$$F\left[\frac{df(t)}{dt}\right] = f(t)\, e^{-i\omega t}\Big|_{t=-\infty}^{+\infty} + (i\omega) \int_{t=-\infty}^{+\infty} f(t)\, e^{-i\omega t}\, dt$$

Since $f(t) \to 0$ for $t \to \pm\infty$

$$F\left[\frac{df(t)}{dt}\right] = (i\omega) F[f(t)]$$

In general, for higher derivatives,

$$F\left[\frac{d^n f(t)}{dt^n}\right] = (i\omega)^n F[f(t)] \tag{17-8}$$

In the event that the system represented by the differential equation involves initial conditions at $t = 0$ rather than at $t \to -\infty$, these may be handled as in the Laplace transform; that is, since the system is quiescent for $t < 0$, the lower limit of the integral can be changed from $-\infty$ to 0. Then the transform of the first derivative becomes

$$F\left[\frac{df(t)}{dt}\right] = f(t)\, e^{-i\omega t}\Big]_{t=0}^{\infty} + i\omega \int_{t=0}^{\infty} f(t)\, e^{-i\omega t}\, dt$$

$$= -f(0) + i\omega F[f(t)]$$

Similarly, if $f(t) = 0$ for $t < 0$.

$$F\left[\frac{d^n f(t)}{dt^n}\right] = (i\omega)^n F[f(t)] - [(i\omega)^{(n-1)} f(0) + (i\omega)^{(n-2)} f'(0) + \cdots + f^{n-1}(0)] \tag{17-9}$$

The inverse transforms are not affected by this modification and are still as indicated in Equations 17-3, 17-4, 17-5, or 17-6.

Response of a Simple System to a Pulse. As an illustration of some of the points brought out in this section, let the response of the damped single degree of freedom system of Chapter 16 be computed using the Fourier transform method of solution. The system is quiescent previous to the time $t = -1$. The differential equation is

$$\frac{d^2x}{dt^2} + 2\zeta\beta\left(\frac{dx}{dt} - \frac{dy}{dt}\right) + \beta^2(x - y) = 0$$

If the Fourier transform of this equation is taken, where X = transform of $x(t)$ and Y = transform of $y(t)$, $(i\omega)^2 X + 2\zeta\beta(i\omega)X + \beta^2 X = 2\zeta\beta(i\omega)Y + \beta^2 Y$

$$\frac{X}{Y} = \frac{2\zeta\beta(i\omega) + \beta^2}{(i\omega)^2 + 2\zeta\beta(i\omega) + \beta^2}$$

If the accelerations are of principal interest

$$\ddot{x} = F^{-1}\left\{\frac{2\zeta\beta(i\omega) + \beta^2}{(i\omega)^2 + 2\zeta\beta(i\omega) + \beta^2}[F(\ddot{y})]\right\} \tag{17-10}$$

Numerical Analysis. It is possible to solve this problem without resort to numerical analysis, but it is instructive to consider the problem from a numerical point of view, treating $\ddot{y}$ as a graph or table rather than as an algebraic expression. Therefore, even though the function of Fig. 15-5 can be expressed algebraically, let it be considered as a graph which could not be expressed analytically. Its Fourier transform could also be expressed in graphical form as a function of ω. That is, since

$$F(\ddot{y}) = \int_{t=-\infty}^{+\infty} e^{-i\omega t}\, \ddot{y}\, dt$$

$$= \int_{t=-\infty}^{+\infty} \ddot{y} \cos \omega t\, dt - i\int_{t=-\infty}^{+\infty} \ddot{y} \sin \omega t\, dt$$

it would be possible to assume different values of ω from $-\infty$ to $+\infty$ and at each ω an integration over t from $-\infty$ to $+\infty$ would result in a single complex number. A plot of the real and imaginary parts as functions of ω could then be made. This would represent $F(\ddot{y})$ in Equation 17-10. Then at each ω, if ζ and β are known, a real and imaginary part of the right side of Equation 17-10 can be obtained and plotted. This would represent the Fourier transform of $\ddot{x}$ in graphical form. The value of $\ddot{x}$ at any instant could then be obtained by a numerical integration with respect to ω in the following equation, in which t is a constant during the integration.

$$\ddot{x}(t) = \frac{1}{2\pi}\int_{t=-\infty}^{+\infty} \ddot{X}(\omega)\, e^{it\omega}\, d\omega \tag{17-11}$$

(Here the symbol $\ddot{X}$ means the Fourier transform of $\ddot{x}$.) These operations are shown in Fig. 17-3, for specific numerical values of $\beta = 1$, $\zeta = 0.5$.

Figure 17-3a shows the input triangular acceleration pulse, a function of time. The Fourier transform of this pulse, $F[\ddot{y}(t)] = g(\omega) = \int_{t=-\infty}^{+\infty} \ddot{x}(t)\, e^{-i\omega t}\, dt$ is shown in Fig. 17-3b. At different constant values of ω the foregoing integral is evaluated. The limits of the integral become -1 to $+1$ since $\ddot{y}(t)$ is zero outside this range. Normally, there would be a real and imaginary part of this integral, but because of the symmetry of $\ddot{y}(t)$, the imaginary part is zero. Note that ω must assume values ranging from $-\infty$ to $+\infty$, so some judgment is required as to the finite value of ω which approximates infinity. For the calculation shown, $\omega = \pm 5$ was assumed for these limits. (The wider the limits, the better the accuracy, of course.) Figure 17-3*c* is obtained from Fig. 17-3*b* by multiplying by

$$\frac{2\zeta\beta(i\omega) + \beta^2}{(i\omega)^2 + 2\zeta\beta(i\omega) + \beta^2}$$

where $\beta = 1$ and $\zeta = 0.5$. This is now the transform of $\ddot{x}$, the quantity within the braces of Equation 17-10. It is clear from Fig. 17-3*c* that the assumed range of ω from -5 to $+5$ is sufficient for ordinary accuracy requirements, since $F(\ddot{x}) \approx 0$ outside this

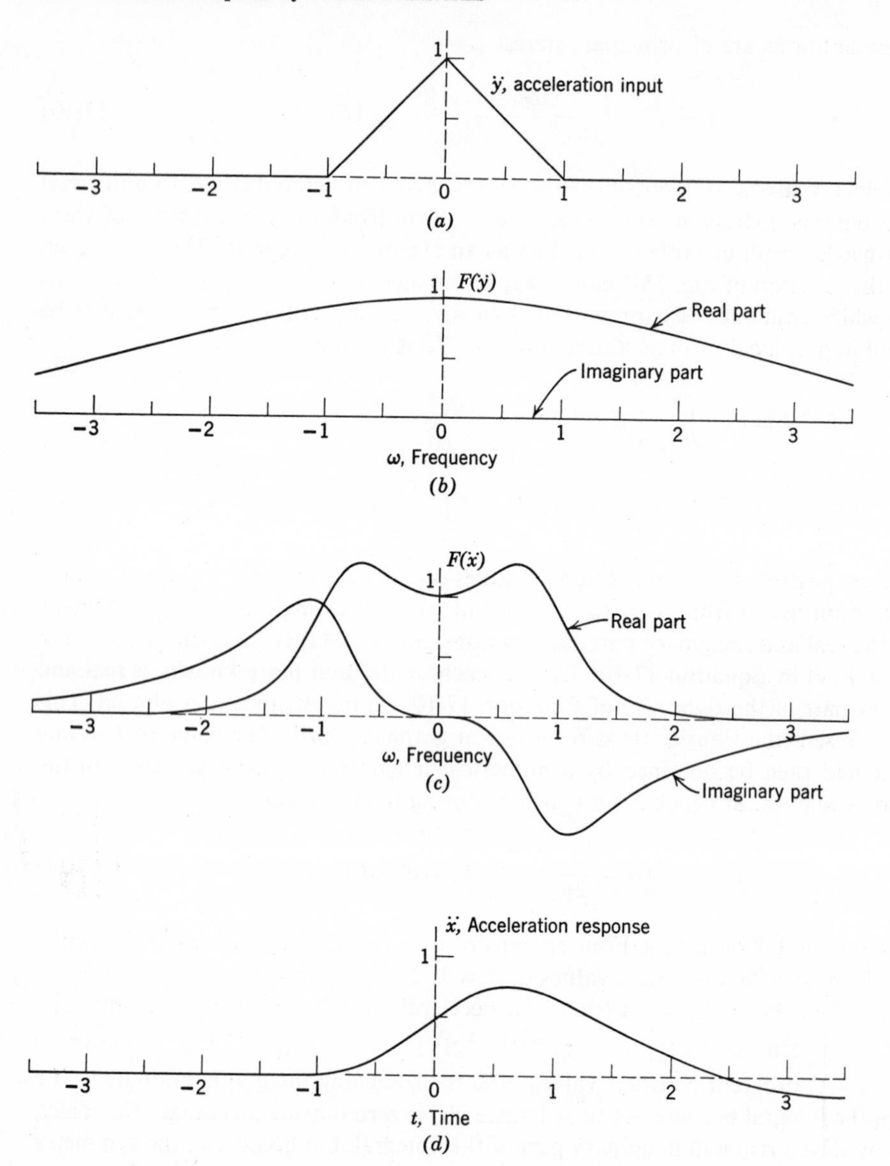

Fig. 17-3 Illustration of numerical analysis by Fourier transform

range. In order to obtain the function, $\ddot{x}$, the inverse transform, must be computed. Thus, at different values of t of interest the integral

$$\ddot{x} = \frac{1}{2\pi} \int_{\omega=-\infty}^{+\infty} \ddot{X}(\omega)\, e^{it\omega}\, d\omega$$

is made numerically to determine the graph of Fig. 17-3*d*. Note that although the imaginary part of $\ddot{x}(t)$ is zero (as it should be), the imaginary part of $\ddot{X}(\omega)$ is not zero and must not be neglected or assumed to be zero, since it contributes to the real part of $\ddot{x}$. Also note that the real part of $\ddot{X}$ (the transform of $\ddot{x}$) is even and the imaginary part odd as expected.

17.3 Analytic Solution Using Fourier Transforms

The numerical procedure illustrated in the previous section leads to a better appreciation of the physical meaning of the Fourier transform and inverse transform, and also provides one form of numerical solution for response to transient forcing functions. Example 17-2, following, illustrates certain interesting aspects of an analytical solution of a similar problem.

Example 17-2. Investigate the use of Fourier transform analysis for a spring supported mass subjected to a force, f_0, which remains constant for $-a < t < +a$, and zero outside this range.

In order to investigate this, it will be convenient to consider a slight amount of damping in the system and then determine what happens when the damping approaches zero. The differential equation is

$$\frac{d^2x}{dt^2} + 2\zeta\beta\frac{dx}{dt} + \beta^2 x = \frac{f_0}{k}\beta^2[u(t + a) - u(t - a)]$$

For zero damping and the pulse starting at time $t = 0$ instead of $t = -a$, the solution is easily found using Laplace transforms. If the time is then shifted to agree with the problem proposed above, it is found that the desired result for zero damping is

$$x = \frac{f_0}{k}[1 - \cos\beta(t + a)] \qquad \text{for} \quad -a < t < +a$$

$$x = \frac{f_0}{k}[\cos\beta(t - a) - \cos\beta(t + a)] \quad \text{for} \quad t > +a$$

Now can these results be obtained using Fourier transform analysis?

The Fourier transfer function of the differential equation, including damping, is readily obtained, using Equation 17-8.

$$\frac{X}{F} = \frac{\beta^2}{k}\frac{1}{\beta^2 - \omega^2 + i2\zeta\beta\omega}$$

and the Fourier transform of the pulse is $(f_0/i\omega)(e^{i\omega a} - e^{-i\omega a})$

$$X = -\frac{f_0\beta^2}{ki}\frac{e^{i\omega a} - e^{-i\omega a}}{\omega(\omega^2 - \beta^2 - i2\zeta\beta\omega)}$$

The inverse transform of this is

$$x = -\frac{f_0\beta^2}{2\pi ki}\int_{\omega=-\infty}^{+\infty}\frac{(e^{i\omega a} - e^{-i\omega a})e^{it\omega}}{\omega(\omega^2 - \beta^2 - i2\zeta\beta\omega)}\,d\omega$$

Note that $\omega = 0$ is not a pole of the integrand since

$$\lim_{\omega\to 0}\frac{e^{i\omega a} - e^{-i\omega a}}{i\omega} = \lim_{\omega\to 0}\frac{2\sin\omega a}{\omega} = 2a$$

The poles are

$$\omega = \beta\sqrt{1 - \zeta^2} + i\zeta\beta \quad \text{and} \quad \omega = -\beta\sqrt{1 - \zeta^2} + i\zeta\beta$$

Both of these poles are in the upper half plane.

If $t > a$, it would be possible to obtain the desired integral by integrating the complex variable, ω, around a closed curve consisting of the real axis and a semicircle of infinite radius enclosing the upper half plane, since the integral along the infinite semi-circle is zero. (See Appendix 1 for additional discussion of a similar problem.) Therefore, the desired integral becomes $2\pi i$ times the sum of the residues at the two poles. This results in

$$x = \frac{f_0}{k}\left\{e^{-\zeta\beta(t-a)}\left[\cos\beta\sqrt{1-\zeta^2}(t-a) + \frac{\zeta}{\sqrt{1-\zeta^2}}\sin\beta\sqrt{1-\zeta^2}(t-a)\right]\right.$$

$$\left. - e^{-\zeta\beta(t+a)}\left[\cos\beta\sqrt{1-\zeta^2}(t+a) + \frac{\zeta}{\sqrt{1-\zeta^2}}\sin\beta\sqrt{1-\zeta^2}(t+a)\right]\right\} t > a$$

which is the correct result, and when $\zeta = 0$ becomes

$$x = \frac{f_0}{k}[\cos\beta(t-a) - \cos\beta(t+a)], \qquad t > +a$$

as anticipated.

For $-a < t < +a$ the integral may be performed in two parts. (See Appendix 1 for a more detailed discussion of this point.)

$$x = -\frac{f_0\beta^2}{2\pi k i}\left\{\int_{\omega=-\infty}^{+\infty}\frac{e^{i(t+a)\omega}\,d\omega}{\omega(\omega^2-\beta^2-i2\zeta\beta\omega)} - \int_{\omega=-\infty}^{+\infty}\frac{e^{i(t-a)\omega}\,d\omega}{\omega(\omega^2-\beta^2-i2\zeta\beta\omega)}\right\}$$

The contour for the first integral will be about the upper half-plane, and the second about the lower half-plane, both indented to avoid the apparent pole at $\omega = 0$, as described in Appendix 1. Thus there will be no contribution from the second integral, and the contribution from the first will be obtained from $2\pi i$ times the sum of residues at $\omega = 0$ and the two poles, $\beta\sqrt{1-\zeta^2} + i\zeta\beta$ and $-\beta\sqrt{1-\zeta^2} + i\zeta\beta$. The result is the correct equation

$$x = \frac{f_0}{k}\left\{1 - e^{-\zeta\beta(t+a)}\left[\cos\beta\sqrt{1-\zeta^2}(t+a) + \frac{\zeta}{\sqrt{1-\zeta^2}}\sin\beta\sqrt{1-\zeta^2}(t+a)\right]\right\}$$

or for $\zeta = 0$

$$x = \frac{f_0}{k}[1 - \cos\beta(t+a)], \qquad -a < t < +a$$

It is seen that the correct results can be achieved by inserting some damping into the system prior to the analysis by Fourier transform.

It is interesting to attempt this with zero damping right from the beginning. Then

$$X = -\frac{f_0\beta^2\, e^{i\omega a} - e^{-i\omega a}}{ki\;\omega(\omega^2-\beta^2)}$$

$$x = -\frac{f_0\beta^2}{2\pi k i}\int_{\omega=-\infty}^{+\infty}\frac{e^{i(t+a)\omega} - e^{i(t-a)\omega}}{\omega(\omega^2-\beta^2)}\,d\omega$$

Now, as before, if $t > a$, the integral could be evaluated by obtaining the line integral of a complex variable around the upper half plane. However, the poles at β and $-\beta$ lie on the path of integration, and so the integral can be shown to be πi times the sum of the residues at these two poles, instead of $2\pi i$ times the sum of the residues. (See Appendix 1 for discussion of a similar problem.) This leads to the result

$$x = \frac{f_0}{2k}[\cos\beta(t-a) - \cos\beta(t+a)], \qquad t > a$$

which is half the correct value, unless $\beta a = n\pi$, n an integer. In this instance $x = 0$ is the correct result.

For the interval, $-a < t < +a$, the integral may be evaluated in two parts, using the appropriate contours, as before, with the following result.

$$x = \frac{f_0}{k}\left[1 - \frac{1}{2}\cos\beta(t + a) - \frac{1}{2}\cos\beta(t - a)\right]$$

This is erroneous except for $\beta a = n\pi$, in which instance

$$x = \frac{f_0}{k}[1 - \cos\beta(t + a)]$$

is the correct result.

The reason that the result is erroneous is that with zero damping an oscillation does not die out, and therefore x is not a function approaching zero as $t \to \infty$ and so cannot have a Fourier transform, except for the conditions, $\beta a = n\pi$. For these values of β there is no residual oscillation, so x is zero for $t \to \infty$ and does have a Fourier transform. Consequently, the correct expression results from a Fourier analysis.

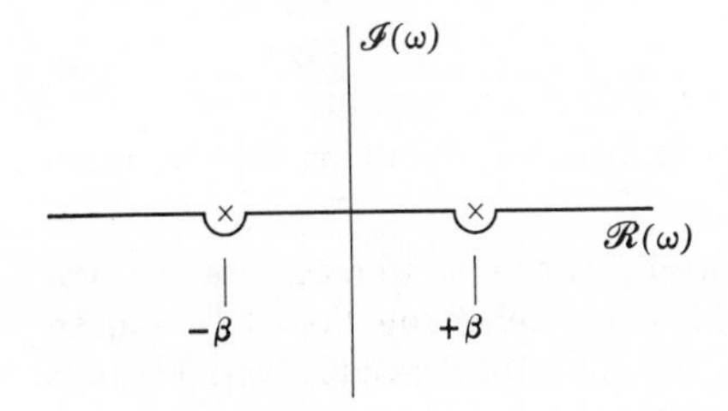

Fig. 17-4

However, from this discussion it is easily seen that a Fourier analysis could be used even with zero damping, for any forcing function having a Fourier transform, simply by following the contour along the real axis indicated in Fig. 17-4. This causes the two poles to have the same effect as if damping were used and allowed to approach zero; that is, the contribution to the integral would be $2\pi i$ times the sum of the appropriate residues rather than πi times this sum. A numerical method using the Fourier transform should also make use of such a contour if poles of the transfer function lie on the real axis.

17.4 Concluding Remarks

The Fourier integral and transform method of analysis has no advantage over the Laplace transform method for the type of problems investigated in this chapter. It is useful in the analysis of random vibration, a subject not included in this text, and also in any problem for which boundary conditions are specified at positive and negative infinity rather than at finite values of the independent variable, or where the forcing function falls off to zero gradually in the negative direction so that no zero values of the independent variable can be selected for which the effect of events at values more negative than this can be neglected. Since the Laplace transform has the effect of disregarding events which occur at values of the independent variable less than zero. it cannot be used unless some artifice is introduced so that effects of events occurring prior to zero are suitably simulated or approximated.

Digital computer programs are provided in Reference 1 for numerically calculating Fourier transforms and inverse transforms as described in this Chapter.

APPENDIX 1

Review of Mathematics

A1.1 Linear Differential Equations

In this section methods of solution of ordinary differential equations with constant coefficients are reviewed.

Linear and Nonlinear Equations. First, it is important to be able to recognize this type of equation, and not to try to apply techniques for solving linear equations to nonlinear systems. A linear equation with constant coefficients, where x is the dependent variable and t the independent variable, is one which can be represented as follows:

$$\frac{d^n x}{dt^n} + a_1 \frac{d^{n-1}x}{dt^{n-1}} + \cdots + a_{n-1}\frac{dx}{dt} + a_n x = f(t) \tag{A1-1}$$

where a_1, a_2, etc. are constants (some of which could be zero), and $f(t)$ is a function of t exclusively. (It is convenient to regard x as displacement and t as time, although obviously the techniques used are just as applicable for variables having some other significance.) The important feature of a linear equation is that the dependent variable, x, and all of its derivatives appear with an exponent of 1, and there are no terms involving the products or quotients of derivatives, or of derivatives with x. Examples of nonlinear equations follow.

$$\frac{d^2x}{dt^2} + \sin x = t^2 \qquad \frac{\left(\dfrac{d^2x}{dt^2}\right)}{\left(\dfrac{dx}{dt}\right)} + x = t$$

$$\left(\frac{d^2x}{dt^2}\right)\left(\frac{dx}{dt}\right) + 2x = \sin t \qquad \frac{d^2x}{dt^2} + 3x^2 = 0$$

$$\frac{d^2x}{dt^2} + 2\frac{dx}{dt} + 3x = x^2 t \qquad \frac{d^2x}{dt^2} + 2\left(\frac{dx}{dt}\right)^2 + x = t$$

$$2x\frac{d^2x}{dt^2} + \frac{dx}{dt} = t \qquad \frac{1}{x}\left(\frac{d^2x}{dt^2}\right) + \frac{dx}{dt} + x = t$$

Auxiliary Equation and Complementary Solution. An equation of the form of Equation A1-2 can be written as

$$D^n x + a_1 D^{n-1}x + \cdots + a_{n-1} Dx + a_n x = f(t) \tag{A1-2}$$

where D is an operator, d/dt. It is possible to treat this operator like an algebraic quantity, and x can be factored out, and also the resulting polynomial in D can be factored, to give the following equation, if there are no repeated factors.

$$(D - r_1)(D - r_2)\cdots(D - r_n)x = f(t) \tag{A1-3}$$

where r_1, r_2, etc., are roots of the equation

$$D^n + a_1 D^{n-1} + \cdots + a_{n-1} D + a_n = 0 \tag{A1-4}$$

For linear equations it is possible to solve an equation such as Equation A1-3 by solving the same equation with $f(t)$ set equal to zero, and then adding to this a particular solution which reduces to the $f(t)$ when substituted in the differential equation. The equation,

$$(D - r_1)(D - r_2)\cdots(D - r_n)x = 0 \tag{A1-5}$$

is called the "auxiliary equation" or "related homogeneous equation," and has the solution, called the "complementary solution," as follows:

$$x_c = A_1 e^{r_1 t} + A_2 e^{r_2 t} + \cdots + A_n e^{r_n t} \tag{A1-6}$$

where A_1, A_2, etc., are arbitrary independent constants. There are as many of these arbitrary constants as the order of the differential equation. Each of the terms in Equation A1-6 individually satisfies Equation A1-1 with right side zero, or Equation A1-4 or A1-5, as is easily shown by substitution.

If the auxiliary equation has one or more repeated roots, such as the following,

$$(D - r_1)^2(D - r_2)^3(D - r_3)\cdots(D - r_n)x = 0 \tag{A1-7}$$

then the solution can be shown to be

$$x_c = (A_1 + B_1 t) e^{r_1 t} + (A_2 + B_2 t + c_2 t^2) e^{r_2 t} + A_3 e^{r_3 t} + \cdots + A_n e^{r_n t} \tag{A1-8}$$

where the B's and C's are also arbitrary constants, and again the total number of these constants is equal to the order of the original differential equation.

Particular Solution by Method of Undetermined Coefficients. The particular solution of an equation such as Equation A1-3 is usually most easily determined by the "method of undetermined coefficients," which is now described. The $f(t)$ appearing on the right of Equation A1-3 is examined and a tentative solution is formed which contains terms similar to all the terms comprising the $f(t)$, and also all derivatives of these terms which result in expressions having different mathematical forms. (Complications arise if there are an infinite number of these different terms—see Example A1-6. Each term is assigned an unknown coefficient. This tentative solution is then compared with the complementary solution. If there is no term in the tentative particular solution which has the same mathematical form as one of the terms in the complementary solution, then the tentative particular solution is satisfactory and it is safe to proceed. If there is a duplication of some term, then a change must be made in the particular solution. This is best illustrated with the examples that follow. After a satisfactory form for the particular solution has been determined, the unknown coefficients are evaluated by substitution in the original differential equation and selecting the coefficients so that the resulting equation is consistent. Let this result be designated x_p.

The General Solution and Evaluation of Constants. Once the complementary and particular solutions are available, the "general" or "complete" solution is the sum of the two.

$$x = x_c + x_p \tag{A1-9}$$

The constants in this general solution (coming from x_c) must be evaluated by making the general equation hold true for known conditions often referred to as "boundary conditions." These constants are not evaluated until after the particular solution is determined and added to the complementary solution to form the general solution. The following examples illustrate this method of solution of differential equations.

Example A1-1.

$$\frac{d^2x}{dt^2} - 6\frac{dx}{dt} + 5x = e^{4t} \quad \text{and} \quad x = 0, \frac{dx}{dt} = 0, \quad \text{when} \quad t = 0$$

In operational form, this is

$$(D^2 - 6\,D + 5)x = e^{4t}$$

The auxiliary equation is

$$(D^2 - 6\,D + 5)x = 0$$

or

$$(D - 5)(D - 1)x = 0$$

The complementary solution is, since $r_1 = 5, r_2 = 1$,

$$x_c = A_1\,e^{5t} + A_2\,e^t$$

The tentative particular solution, since the various derivatives of e^{4t} are also of the same form, is

$$x_p = A\,e^{4t}$$

Here the constant A is the unknown coefficient and not one of the arbitrary constants in the complementary solution. Since the function e^{4t} is not like any term in the x_c, it is not necessary to make a change. If x is e^{4t}, then $dx/dt = 4\,e^{4t}$, and $d^2x/dt^2 = 16\,e^{4t}$. When these are substituted in the differential equation,

$$16A\,e^{4t} - 24A\,e^{4t} + 5A\,e^{4t} = e^{4t}$$

In order for this equation to be true

$$(16 - 24 + 5)A = 1 \qquad \text{or} \quad A = -\frac{1}{3}$$

Therefore,

$$x_p = -\frac{1}{3}\,e^{4t}$$

The general solution is $x_c + x_p$

$$x = A_1\,e^{5t} + A_2\,e^t - \frac{1}{3}\,e^{4t}$$

If a check were desired, this could be substituted in the original differential equation to see if an identity results. Since it does, and two arbitrary constants are present, this is the complete solution. It is now possible to determine the numerical values of the constants, A_1 and A_2, by the use of the initial conditions. Notice that these constants are not determined from the complementary solution alone, but from the general solution, which includes the particular solution. Since $x = 0$ when $t = 0$,

$$0 = A_1 + A_2 - \frac{1}{3}$$

Also since $dx/dt = 0$ when $t = 0$, it is necessary to obtain

$$\frac{dx}{dt} = 5A_1\,e^{5t} + A_2\,e^t - \frac{4}{3}\,e^{4t}$$

$$0 = 5A_1 + A_2 - \frac{4}{3}$$

From the simultaneous solution of the two equations involving A_1 and A_2 the values of $A_1 = \frac{1}{4}$ and $A_2 = \frac{1}{12}$ are obtained. Finally, then, the solution is

$$x = \frac{1}{4} e^{5t} + \frac{1}{12} e^{t} - \frac{1}{3} e^{4t}$$

Example A1-2.

$$(D + 1)^2(D - 2)x = t$$

or

$$(D^3 - 3\,D - 2)x = t$$

Since one of the roots is repeated, the complementary solution is

$$x_c = (A_1 + B_1 t)\, e^{-t} + A_2\, e^{2t}$$

The tentative particular solution is

$$x_p = At + B$$

Comparing this with the complementary solution reveals no difficulty, so continuing, $dx/dt = A$, $d^2x/dt^2 = d^3x/dt^3 = 0$. The only terms in the differential equation which would need to be considered would then be the first derivative term and constant term, or $(-3\,D - 2)x = t$

$$-3A - 2(At + B) = t$$

Comparison of terms shows that $-2A = 1$ since the coefficients of t must be equal and that $-3A - 2B = 0$ since the constant terms must be equal on each side of the equation. (This is the only way that the above equation can be true for *all* values of t.) Therefore, $A = -1/2$ and $B = 3/4$.

$$x_p = -\frac{1}{2} t + \frac{3}{4}$$

The general solution is

$$x = (A_1 + B_1 t)\, e^{-t} + A_2\, e^{2t} - \frac{1}{2} t + \frac{3}{4}$$

The arbitrary constants cannot be determined with the information given. Three known conditions are necessary to solve three simultaneous equations for the three constants. These could be the value of x at three different times or the values of x, dx/dt, and d^2x/dt^2 at $t = 0$, or some other combination of three known conditions.

Example A1-3.

$$(D - 2)(D - 3)x = e^{2t} + t$$

The complementary solution is

$$x_c = A_1\, e^{2t} + A_2\, e^{3t}$$

The tentative particular solution is

$$x_p = A\, e^{2t} + Bt + C$$

However, since e^{2t} is the same function as one of the terms in the complementary solution, it is necessary to assume

$$x_p = At\, e^{2t} + Bt + C$$

Notice that the e^{2t} term was multiplied by t, but the other two terms, $Bt + C$, were not. The solution then proceeds as in the previous examples.

Example A1-4. If Example A-3 were slightly different, as follows:

$$(D - 2)^2(D - 3)x = e^{2t} + t$$

then

$$x_c = (A_1 + B_1 t)\, e^{2t} + A_2\, e^{3t}$$

and tentatively,

$$x_p = A\, e^{2t} + Bt + C$$

Now if the term e^{2t} were multiplied by t, one of the terms in the complementary solution would still be duplicated, so the assumed particular solution becomes

$$x_p = At^2\, e^{2t} + Bt + C$$

The rule is to multiply by t^n where n is a positive integer, the smallest one which will prevent duplication of a term in the complementary solution.

Example A1-5.

$$D(D - 1)x = e^{-t} + t$$

Here the complementary solution is

$$x_c = A_1\, e^{0t} + A_2\, e^t \quad \text{or} \quad x_c = A_1 + A_2\, e^t$$

and the tentative particular solution is

$$x_p = A\, e^{-t} + Bt + C$$

Since C duplicates the constant A_1, it is necessary to multiply C by t. However, both of the terms Bt and C in the tentative solution came from the term t in the differential equation Both Bt and C must be multiplied by t, so the corrected particular solution (assumed) becomes

$$x_p = A\, e^{-t} + Bt^2 + Ct$$

If one term in the tentative particular solution duplicates a term in the complementary solution, determine which term in the differential equation gave rise to the troublesome term. All of the terms in the tentative solution which are descended from this term in the differential equation must be multiplied by the lowest positive integer power of t which will prevent duplicating a term in the complementary solution.

The rest of the solution proceeds as in the previous examples.

Example A1-6.

$$\frac{dx}{dt} - x = \sqrt{t}$$

As usual,

$$x_c = A_1\, e^t$$

However, the particular solution would have to contain an infinite number of terms. It is normally required that there should be a finite number of derivatives of the function on the right side of the differential equation if the method of undetermined coefficients is to be used to find the particular solution. In this instance a satisfactory result can be obtained without this requirement being satisfied.

$$x_p = At^{1/2} + Bt^{-1/2} + ct^{-3/2} + \cdots$$

Also, taking the derivative,

$$\frac{dx}{dt} = \frac{1}{2} At^{-1/2} - \frac{1}{2} Bt^{-3/2} - \frac{3}{2} ct^{-5/2} - \cdots$$

Substituting these in the differential equation yields

$$\frac{1}{2}At^{-1/2} - \frac{1}{2}Bt^{-3/2} - \frac{3}{2}ct^{-5/2} - \cdots - At^{1/2} - Bt^{-1/2} - ct^{-3/2} - \cdots = t^{1/2}$$

In order for this equality to hold for all values of t the coefficients of each power of t must be equal on each side of the equation, or $-A = 1$, $\frac{1}{2}A - B = 0$, $-\frac{1}{2}B - C = 0$, $-\frac{3}{2}C - D = 0$, etc., or $A = -1$, $B = -\frac{1}{2}$, $C = \frac{1}{4}$, $D = -\frac{3}{8}$, $E = \frac{5}{16}$, etc. Then the complete solution is

$$x = A\,e^t - t^{1/2} - \frac{1}{2}t^{-1/2} + \frac{1}{4}t^{-3/2} - \frac{3}{8}t^{-5/2} + \frac{5}{16}t^{-7/2} - \cdots$$

It is possible to check this result by solving the first-order differential equation by another method, and obtain

$$x = C\,e^t + e^t \int t^{1/2}\,e^{-t}\,dt$$

This can be shown to result in the same series as that above. This example illustrates the sort of difficulty which occurs if the function of t on the right side of the differential equation has an infinite number of derivatives, leading to a tentative particular solution with an infinite number of terms. Sometimes this method does not result in a convergent series.

Example A1-7.

$$(D^2 + 2\,D + 5)x = \sin 2t$$

When this is written in factored form, it becomes the following (for a review of the use of complex numbers see Section A1.3):

$$(D + 1 - 2i)(D + 1 + 2i)x = \sin 2t$$

The complementary solution is then

$$x_c = A_1\,e^{(-1+2it)} + A_2\,e^{(-1-2it)}$$

Since A_1 and A_2 are arbitrary constants until they are determined by application of boundary conditions, it is possible and preferable to change this form to

$$x_c = e^{-t}(C_1 \cos 2t + C_2 \sin 2t)$$

where C_1 and C_2 are two different constants. The relationship between C_1 and C_2 and A_1 and A_2 is expressed by these equations:

$$C_1 = A_1 + A_2 \qquad C_2 = i(A_1 - A_2)$$

However, it is not necessary to make these substitutions, because instead of finding the constants A_1 and A_2 by application of boundary conditions and then converting to C_1 and C_2, it is easier to find C_1 and C_2 directly from the boundary conditions. The tentative particular solution is

$$x_p = A \sin 2t + B \cos 2t$$

Notice that we only have these two different terms. Further differentiation would lead only to more of the same two fundamental forms. There is no duplication of the terms in the complementary solution, since in that solution the terms are $e^{-t} \cos 2t$ and $e^{-t} \sin 2t$ rather than just $\cos 2t$ and $\sin 2t$. Therefore, this tentative solution is satisfactory and the rest of the solution may proceed as in previous examples.

A1.2 The Laplace Transform

In recent years a method of solution of linear differential equations has become widely used which is based on the Laplace transform. Because it is so universally used and so powerful, it is important to understand the use of this tool.

Definitions and Requirements. The Laplace transform of a function of t is defined as follows.

$$\phi(s) = \mathscr{L}[f(t)] = \int_{t=0}^{t\to\infty} f(t)\, e^{-st}\, dt \tag{A1-10}$$

In the above integration s is considered a constant, and therefore after the function is integrated and limits substituted for t, a function of s results.

Example A1-8. What is $\phi(s)$ if $f(t) = e^{-at}$ and a is a constant?

$$\phi(s) = \mathscr{L}(e^{-at}) = \int_{t=0}^{\infty} e^{-at}\, e^{-st}\, dt = \int_{t=0}^{\infty} e^{-(s+a)t}\, dt = -\frac{1}{s+a}\, e^{-(s+a)t}\Big|_{t=0}^{\infty}$$

$$\mathscr{L}(e^{-at}) = \frac{1}{s+a}$$

Example A1-9. What is $\phi(s)$ if $f(t) = t$?

$$\phi(s) = \mathscr{L}(t) = \int_{t=0}^{\infty} te^{-st}\, dt = \left(-\frac{t}{s} - \frac{1}{s^2}\right) e^{-st}\Big|_{t=0}^{\infty} = \lim_{t\to\infty} -\frac{te^{-st}}{s} + \frac{1}{s^2}$$

$$\mathscr{L}(t) = \frac{1}{s^2}$$

Not all functions have transforms. If the function, $f(t)\, e^{-st}$, when integrated over the interval $t = 0$ to $t \to \infty$ results in infinity (or is "unbounded"), instead of a function of s, then the function has no transform. Examples of functions which do not have transforms are e^{t^2}, $\tan t$, $\sin 1/t$, $1/t^n$ where $n \geqq 1$. Essentially, to have a transform, a function must be single-valued (although finite discontinuities are allowable), must have no infinite discontinuities, must have only a finite number of maximums and minimums in a finite time interval, and must be of "exponential order"; that is, when $f(t)\, e^{-st}$ is evaluated at $t \to \infty$ it must be possible to select a constant for s so that $\lim_{t\to\infty} f(t)\, e^{-st} = 0$ [consider $f(t) = e^{t^2}$ as compared with $f(t) = e^{3t}$]. A table of transforms of elementary functions (Table A1-1) appears at the end of this section.

The function $f(t)$ whose transform is $\phi(s)$ when operated upon as indicated in Equation A1-10 is called the "inverse transform" of $\phi(s)$. The inverse transform is designated with the symbol $\mathscr{L}^{-1}$; thus, if $\phi(s) = \mathscr{L}[f(t)]$, then

$$f(t) = \mathscr{L}^{-1}[\phi(s)] = \frac{1}{2\pi i}\int_{s=a-i\infty}^{s=a+i\infty} \phi(s)\, e^{st}\, ds \tag{A1-11}$$

In Equation A1-11 the last expression represents a line integral in the complex plane, and the complete explanation of its meaning will not be given here, although methods of obtaining the inverse transform will be discussed.

Solution of Differential Equations by Laplace Transform. The application of Laplace transform to differential equations is facilitated by two especially useful characteristics of this transform, which are indicated in Equations A1-12 and A1-13. In these equations, $\phi(s)$ is understood to be the transform of $f(t)$.

$$\mathscr{L}\left[\frac{d^nf(t)}{dt^n}\right] = s^n\phi(s) - s^{n-1}f(0) - s^{n-2}f^1(0) - \cdots - sf^{(n-2)}(0) - f^{(n-1)}(0) \tag{A1-12}$$

$$\mathscr{L}\left[\int_0^t\int_0^t \cdots \int_0^t f(t)\, dt^n\right] = \frac{\phi(s)}{s^n} \tag{A1-13}$$

These equations may be interpreted in their application to the solution of differential equations in the following examples.

Example A1-10. What is the solution of the equation $dx/dt + 2x + \int_0^t x\,dt = t$ when the value of x for $t = 0$ is x_0?

It is apparent that x is a function of t even though the form of the function has not yet been determined. Therefore, dx/dt and $\int_0^t x\,dt$ are also functions of t. Thus, the entire left side is a function of t, and it is possible to take its transform. Since the left side of the equation is equal to the right side, the transforms are equal, and since $\mathscr{L}(t) = 1/s^2$ from Example A1-9, we have

$$\mathscr{L}\left[\frac{dx}{dt} + 2x + \int_0^t x\,dt\right] = \frac{1}{s^2}$$

It is easily shown that the transform of the sum of functions is equal to the sum of the transforms and that the transform of a constant times a function is the constant times the transform of the function; therefore,

$$\mathscr{L}\left(\frac{dx}{dt}\right) + 2\mathscr{L}(x) + \mathscr{L}\left[\int_0^t x\,dt\right] = \frac{1}{s^2}$$

Application of Equations A1-12 and A1-13 results in

$$\mathscr{L}(x) \equiv \mathscr{L}[x(t)] = \phi(s)$$

$$\mathscr{L}\left(\frac{dx}{dt}\right) = s\phi(s) - x_0 \quad \text{[since } x(0) \text{ means the value of } x \text{ for } t = 0]$$

$$\mathscr{L}\left[\int_0^t x\,dt\right] = \frac{\phi(s)}{s}$$

Therefore, the transformed differential equation is

$$s\phi(s) - x_0 + 2\phi(s) + \frac{\phi(s)}{s} = \frac{1}{s^2}$$

or, solving for $\phi(s)$,

$$\phi(s) = \frac{1 + x_0 s^2}{s(s^2 + 2s + 1)}$$

Finally,

$$x = \mathscr{L}^{-1}\left[\frac{1 + x_0 s^2}{s(s^2 + 2s + 1)}\right]$$

If a method were available for easily obtaining the inverse transform, the solution would be at hand, with initial condition automatically accounted for.

Example A1-11. What is the solution of Equation 3-2?

$$\frac{d^2x}{dt^2} + 2\zeta\beta\frac{dx}{dt} + \beta^2 x = \frac{\beta^2}{k} f_0 \sin \omega t$$

Since the transform of $\sin \omega t$ is $\omega/(s^2 + \omega^2)$ from Table A1-1, and since x_0 and $\dot{x}_0$ are the values of x and dx/dt at $t = 0$,

$$s^2\mathscr{L}(x) - sx_0 - \dot{x}_0 + 2\zeta\beta[s\mathscr{L}(x) - x_0] + \beta^2\mathscr{L}(x) = \frac{\beta^2}{k} f_0 \frac{\omega}{s^2 + \omega^2}$$

$$(s^2 + 2\zeta\beta s + \beta^2)\mathscr{L}(x) = \frac{\beta^2}{k} f_0 \frac{\omega}{s^2 + \omega^2} + (s + 2\zeta\beta)x_0 + \dot{x}_0$$

$$x = \mathscr{L}^{-1}\left\{\frac{x_0(s + 2\zeta\beta) + \dot{x}_0}{(s + \zeta\beta^2) + \beta^2(1 - \zeta^2)} + \frac{\left(\dfrac{\beta^2 f_0 \omega}{k}\right)}{(s^2 + \omega^2)[(s + \zeta\beta)^2 + \beta^2(1 - \zeta^2)]}\right\}$$

Again, all that is needed is a method of obtaining the inverse transform.

From these examples it is seen that the use of the Laplace transform reduces a differential equation to an algebraic equation, and that the solution of the differential equation then depends on being able to obtain an inverse transform. A striking similarity between the transform variable, s, and the operator, D, of the previous section is also noted.

The Inverse Transform. Of course, a table of transforms would afford one means of obtaining the inverse transform. When such a table is readily available, and includes a function of the proper form, then the solution of a problem may be written immediately. However, most inverses may be obtained easily by the application of only a few rules, so that once these are understood it is unnecessary to rely on a table. These rules are expressed mathematically by Equations A1-14 to A1-18. First, if $\phi(s)$ is expressed as a quotient whose numerator is a polynomial in s and whose denominator is a polynomial in s of higher degree than the numerator, then

$$\mathscr{L}^{-1}[\phi(s)] = \text{sum of residues of } \phi(s)\, e^{st} \text{ at all poles} \tag{A1-14}$$

This is another expression essentially stating the same fact as Equation A1-11 and depends on an inderstanding of the theory of complex variables. For additional discussion of this subject see Section A1.4 of this appendix. If the denominator of $\phi(s)$ contains a linear factor $(s + a)$, there will be a term in $f(t)$ corresponding to this factor which can be computed from

$$f(t)_{s+a} = [(s + a)\phi(s)\, e^{st}]_{s=-a} \tag{A1-15}$$

Example A1-12. Determine $\mathscr{L}^{-1}(s + 1)/[s(s - 2)(s + 3)]$. Corresponding to the term $(s + 3)$ in the denominator, there is

$$f(t)_{s+3} = \left[\frac{(s + 3)(s + 1)\, e^{st}}{s(s - 2)(s + 3)}\right]_{s=-3} = \left[\frac{(s + 1\, e^{st}}{s(s - 2)}\right]_{s=-3} = -\frac{2}{15}\, e^{-3t}$$

Corresponding to $s - 2$ in the denominator

$$f(t)_{s-2} = \left[\frac{(s - 2)(s + 1)\, e^{st}}{s(s - 2)(s + 3)}\right]_{s=2} = \left[\frac{(s + 1)\, e^{st}}{s(s + 3)}\right]_{s=2} = \frac{3}{10}\, e^{2t}$$

Corresponding to s in the denominator, which is the same as $s + 0$,

$$f(t)_{s} = \left[\frac{s(s + 1)\, e^{st}}{s(s - 2)(s + 3)}\right]_{s=0} = \left[\frac{(s + 1)\, e^{st}}{(s - 2)(s + 3)}\right]_{s=0} = -\frac{1}{6}$$

Therefore, $f(t)$ is the sum of these terms, or

$$f(t) = \mathscr{L}^{-1}\frac{s + 1}{s(s - 2)(s + 3)} = -\frac{1}{6} + \frac{3}{10}\, e^{2t} - \frac{2}{15}\, e^{-3t}$$

If there is a factor $(s + a)^n$ in the denominator of $\phi(s)$, there will be a term in $f(t)$ corresponding to this factor which can be computed from

$$f(t)_{(s+a)^n} = \frac{1}{(n - 1)!}\left\{\frac{d^{n-1}}{ds^{n-1}}\left[(s + a)^n\phi(s)\, e^{st}\right]\right\}_{s=-a} \tag{A1-16}$$

Example A1-13. Determine $\mathscr{L}^{-1}(s + 1)/[s(s + 2)^2]$. Corresponding to the term $(s + 2)^2$ in the denominator, there is

$$f(t)_{(s+2)^2} = \frac{1}{(2 - 1)!}\left\{\frac{d}{ds}\left[(s + 2)^2\frac{(s + 1)}{s(s + 2)^2}\, e^{st}\right]\right\}_{s=-2}$$

$$f(t)_{(s+2)^2} = \left\{\frac{d}{ds}\left[\left(1 + \frac{1}{s}\right) e^{st}\right]\right\}_{s=-2} = \left[\left(1 + \frac{1}{s}\right) t\, e^{st} - \frac{1}{s^2}\, e^{st}\right]_{s=-2}$$

$$= \frac{1}{2}\, t\, e^{-2t} - \frac{1}{4}\, e^{-2t}$$

Corresponding to the term s in the denominator,

$$f(t)_s = \left[\frac{(s+1)\,e^{st}}{(s+2)^2}\right]_{s=0} = \frac{1}{4}$$

The solution is

$$f(t) = \mathscr{L}^{-1}\frac{s+1}{s(s+2)^2} = \frac{1}{4} + \frac{1}{2}\,t\,e^{-2t} - \frac{1}{4}\,e^{-2t}$$

Equations A1-15 and A1-16 can also be used if the constant, a, is complex.

Example A1-14. Determine $\mathscr{L}^{-1}\,1/(s^2+1)$. Since

$$\frac{1}{s^2+1} = \frac{1}{(s+i)(s-i)} \qquad \text{where} \quad i = \sqrt{-1}$$

$$\mathscr{L}^{-1}\frac{1}{(s+i)(s-i)} = \left[\frac{e^{st}}{s-i}\right]_{s=-i} + \left[\frac{e^{st}}{s+i}\right]_{s=+i}$$

$$= \frac{e^{-it}}{-2i} + \frac{e^{it}}{2i} = \frac{e^{it} - e^{-it}}{2i} = \sin t$$

In Example A1-14 it was necessary to convert terms with complex exponents into the equivalent trigonometric functions. This can be done for the general case, and the resulting equation is as follows.

If there is a quadratic unrepeated factor $[(s+a)^2 + b^2]$ in the denominator of $\phi(s)$, the term in $f(t)$ corresponding to this factor is

$$f(t)_{[(s+a)^2+b^2]} = \frac{e^{-at}}{b}\,[\phi_i \cos bt + \phi_r \sin bt]$$

or

$$= \frac{e^{-at}}{b}\sqrt{\phi_r^2 + \phi_i^2}\,\sin(bt + \psi) \tag{A1-17}$$

or

$$= \frac{e^{-at}}{b}\sqrt{\phi_r^2 + \phi_i^2}\,\cos(bt + \psi_1)$$

Where ϕ_r and ϕ_i are the real and imaginary parts of

$$\{[(s+a)^2 + b^2]\phi(s)\}_{s=-a+ib}$$

and

$$\psi = \tan^{-1}\frac{\phi_i}{\phi_r} = \cos^{-1}\frac{\phi_r}{\sqrt{\phi_r^2 + \phi_i^2}} = \sin^{-1}\frac{\phi_i}{\sqrt{\phi_r^2 + \phi_i^2}}$$

$$\psi_1 = \tan^{-1}\left(\frac{-\phi_r}{\phi_i}\right) = \cos^{-1}\frac{\phi_i}{\sqrt{\phi_r^2 + \phi_i^2}} = \sin^{-1}\left(\frac{-\phi_r}{\sqrt{\phi_r^2 + \phi_i^2}}\right)$$

(If the reader is not familiar with the use of complex numbers, see Section A1.3.)

Example A1-15. What is the solution of Equation 3-2? (Assume $\zeta < 1$.) Referring to Example A1-11, and making use of the fact that the inverse transform of the sum of two functions is the sum of the inverse transforms,

$$x = \mathscr{L}^{-1}\frac{x_0(s + 2\zeta\beta) + \dot{x}_0}{(s+\zeta\beta)^2 + \beta^2(1-\zeta^2)} + \mathscr{L}^{-1}\frac{\left(\dfrac{\beta^2 f_0 \omega}{k}\right)}{(s^2+\omega^2)[(s+\zeta\beta)^2 + \beta^2(1-\zeta^2)]}$$

If the above theorem relating to quadratic factors is applied, the first term above leads to

$$x_{\text{1st term}} = \frac{e^{-\zeta\beta t}}{\beta\sqrt{1-\zeta^2}}[\phi_i \cos\beta\sqrt{1-\zeta^2}\,t + \phi_r \sin\beta\sqrt{1-\zeta^2}\,t]$$

where

$$\phi_r + i\phi_i = [x_0(s + 2\zeta\beta) + \dot{x}_0]_{s=-\zeta\beta+i\beta\sqrt{1-\zeta^2}}$$

$$= (\zeta\beta x_0 + \dot{x}_0) + i(\beta\sqrt{1-\zeta^2}\,x_0)$$

If the theorem is applied to the second term (where there are two quadratic factors), two expressions result, one corresponding to the factor, $(s + \zeta\beta)^2 + \beta^2(1 - \zeta^2)$ and the other to the factor, $s^2 + \omega^2$:

$$x_{\text{2nd term}} = \frac{e^{-\zeta\beta t}}{\beta\sqrt{1-\zeta^2}}[\phi_{1_i}\cos\beta\sqrt{1-\zeta^2}\,t + \phi_{1_r}\sin\beta\sqrt{1-\zeta^2}\,t] + \frac{e^0}{\omega}[\phi_{2_i}\cos\omega t + \phi_{2_r}\sin\omega t]$$

where

$$\phi_{1_r} + i\phi_{1_i} = \left[\frac{\beta^2 f_0 \omega}{k(s^2+\omega^2)}\right]_{s=-\zeta\beta+i\beta\sqrt{1-\zeta^2}}$$

and

$$\phi_{2_r} + i\phi_{2_i} = \frac{\beta^2 f_0 \omega}{k[(s+\zeta\beta)^2 + \beta^2(1-\zeta^2)]_{s=i\omega}}$$

$$x_{\text{2nd term}} = \frac{\beta^2 f_0 \omega\, e^{-\zeta\beta t}}{k\beta\sqrt{1-\zeta^2}}\left[\frac{2\zeta\beta\sqrt{1-\zeta^2}\cos\beta\sqrt{1-\zeta^2}\,t + [\omega^2 - \beta^2(1-2\zeta^2)]\sin\beta\sqrt{1-\zeta^2}\,t}{[\omega^2 - \beta^2(1-2\zeta^2)]^2 + (2\zeta\beta^2)^2(1-\zeta^2)}\right]$$

$$+ \frac{\beta^2 f_0 \omega}{\omega k}\left[\frac{-2\zeta\beta\omega\cos\omega t + (\beta^2-\omega^2)\sin\omega t}{(\beta^2-\omega^2)^2 + (2\zeta\beta\omega)^2}\right]$$

Finally, x = sum of above terms. (The last expression can be altered slightly to present the solution in terms of the ratio ω/β as shown in Equation 3-3.)

There is another possibility which might arise in obtaining an inverse. If there is a repeated quadratic factor $[(s + a)^2 + b^2]^2$ in the denominator of $\phi(s)$, the term in $f(t)$ corresponding to this factor is

$$f(t)_{[(s+a)^2+b^2]^2} = \frac{e^{-at}}{2b^2}\left[\left(\frac{\phi_i}{b} - t\phi_r - \phi'_r\right)\cos bt + \left(\frac{\phi^r}{b} + t\phi_i + \phi'_i\right)\sin bt\right] \quad \text{(A1-18)}$$

where ϕ_r and ϕ_i are defined by

$$\phi_r + i\phi_i = \{[(s+a)^2 + b^2]^2\phi(s)\}_{s=-a+ib}$$

and ϕ'_r and ϕ'_i are defined by

$$\phi'_r + i\phi'_i = \left\{\frac{d}{ds}\{[(s+a)^2 + b^2]^2\phi(s)\}\right\}_{s=-a+ib}$$

Example A1-16. Determine $f(t)$ if

$$\phi(s) = \frac{(s+2)}{(s-1)(s^2+4s+13)^2}$$

Change the denominator to agree with the general form

$$f(t) = \mathcal{L}^{-1}\frac{(s+2)}{(s-1)[(s+2)^2+3^2]^2}$$

Then corresponding to the repeated quadratic factor in which $a = 2$, $b = 3$, we have

$$\phi_r + i\phi_i = \left\{\frac{[(s+2)^2+3^2]^2(s+2)}{(s-1)[(s+2)^2+3^2]^2}\right\}_{s=-2+3i} = \left(\frac{s+2}{s-1}\right)_{s=-2+3i}$$

$$= \frac{-2+3i+2}{-2+3i-1} = \frac{1}{2} - \frac{1}{2}i$$

$$\phi_r = \frac{1}{2} \quad \text{and} \quad \phi_i = -\frac{1}{2}$$

$$\phi'_r + i\phi'_i = \left[\frac{d}{ds}\left(\frac{s+2}{s-1}\right)\right]_{s=-2+3i} = \frac{-3}{(-2+3i-1)^2} = -\frac{1}{6}i$$

$$\phi'_r = 0, \quad \phi'_i = -\frac{1}{6}$$

Therefore, corresponding to the repeated quadratic factor is the term,

$$\frac{e^{-2t}}{2 \times 3^2}\left[\left(-\frac{1}{6} - \frac{1}{2}t - 0\right)\cos 3t + \left(\frac{1}{6} - \frac{1}{2}t - \frac{1}{6}\right)\sin 3t\right]$$

Equation A1-15, applied to the linear factor in the denominator yields the term,

$$\left\{\frac{(s-1)(s+2)\,e^{st}}{(s-1)[(s+2)^2+3^2]^2}\right\}_{s=1} = \frac{e^t}{6}$$

The desired inverse transform is the sum of these, or

$$f(t) = \frac{e^t}{6} + \frac{e^{-2t}}{18}\left[\left(-\frac{1}{6} - \frac{1}{2}t\right)\cos 3t - \frac{1}{2}t\sin 3t\right]$$

Example A1-17. Show that Equation 1-44 is the solution of Equation 1-43.

$$\frac{d^2x}{dt^2} + \beta^2 x = \frac{\beta^2 f_0}{k}\sin\beta t \quad \text{and} \quad x_0 = \dot{x}_0 = 0$$

$$(s^2+\beta^2)\mathscr{L}(x) = \frac{\beta^2 f_0}{k}\frac{\beta}{s^2+\beta^2}$$

$$x = \mathscr{L}^{-1}\frac{\beta^2 f_0}{k}\frac{\beta}{(s^2+\beta^2)^2} = \frac{\beta^3 f_0}{k}\mathscr{L}^{-1}\frac{1}{(s^2+\beta^2)^2}$$

$$\phi_r + i\phi_i = 1 \qquad \text{and} \quad \phi'_r + i\phi'_i = 0$$

Also

$$a = 0, b = \beta$$

$$x = \frac{\beta^3 f_0}{k}\frac{1}{2\beta^2}\left(-t\cos\beta t + \frac{1}{\beta}\sin\beta t\right)$$

Inverse for Multiple-Order Factors. If the denominator of the transform should contain high-order linear or quadratic factors, a digital computer program for computing the inverse is a great convenience. A method of computing inverses corresponding to such high order factors, as well as first order factors, is developed below. Let

$$G(s) = \frac{N(s)}{D(s)} = \frac{N(s)}{(s+a)^n q(s)} = \frac{\phi(s)}{(s+a)^n} \tag{A1-19}$$

This implies a pole of order n at $s = -a$ and Equation A1-16 can be used to determine the terms in the inverse corresponding to this multiple order pole. When the $(n - 1)$th derivative is taken as indicated in Equation A1-16, the result is

$$f(t) = e^{-at} \sum_{k=1}^{n} c_k t^{k-1} \tag{A1-20}$$

where

$$c_k = \frac{\phi^{(n-k)}(-a)}{(k-1)!(n-k)!} \tag{A1-21}$$

$$\left(\phi^{(n-k)}(-a) \text{ means } \left[\frac{d^{n-k}}{ds^{n-k}} \phi(s)\right]_{s=-a}\right)$$

The derivative $\phi^{(m)}$ also means $d^m/ds^m(N(s)/q(s))$. In general, the derivatives of a product of two variables are

$$(xy)' = x'y + xy'$$

$$(xy)'' = x''y + 2x'y' + xy''$$

$$(xy)''' = x'''y + 3x''y' + 3x'y'' + xy'''$$

$$(xy)^{(m)} = \sum_{l=1}^{m+1} \frac{m!x^{(m-l+1)}y^{(l-1)}}{(l-1)!(m-l+1)!}$$

where the superscripts for x and y mean derivatives. Therefore,

$$\phi^{(m)}(-a) = \sum_{l=1}^{m+1} \frac{m!N^{(m-l+1)}(-a)z^{(l-1)}(-a)}{(l-1)!(m-l+1)!} \tag{A1-22}$$

where

$$z = \frac{1}{q}$$

and the superscript for N and z indicate derivatives. The derivatives of z are required.

$$(zq) = 1 \qquad \text{or} \qquad z^{(0)} = \frac{1}{q}$$

$$(zq)' = z'q + zq' = 0 \qquad \text{or} \qquad z' = -\frac{zq'}{q}$$

$$(zq)'' = z''q + 2z'q' + zq'' = 0 \qquad \text{or} \qquad z'' = -\frac{1}{q}(q''z + 2q'z')$$

$$(zq)''' = z'''q + 3z''q' + 3z'q'' + zq''' = 0 \qquad \text{or} \qquad z''' = -\frac{1}{q}(q'''z + 3q''z' + 3q'z')$$

In general,

$$z^{(j)}(-a) = -\frac{1}{q} \sum_{r=1}^{j} \frac{j!g^{(j-r+1)}(-a)z^{(r-1)}(-a)}{(r-1)!(j-r+1)!} \tag{A1-23}$$

Note that in applying this equation $z'(-a)$ must be computed first, then used in $z''(-a)$; then both $z'(-a)$ and $z''(-a)$ are used in $z'''(-a)$ and this is continued until all of the required derivatives have been computed.

In the evaluation of C_k by Equation A1-21, s is set equal to $-a$. It is convenient to have the derivatives $q'(-a)$, $q''(-a)$, etc., evaluated in terms of $D(s)$, which is the entire denominator of the transfer function and the same for all poles, rather than $q(s)$, which is different for each pole. Now

$$D = (s + a)^n q$$

or

$$q = \frac{D}{(s + a)^n}$$

However, D itself has a zero of order n at $s = -a$, so the evaluation of $q(-a)$ is indeterminate but may be evaluated by L'Hospital's rule, or

$$q(-a) = \left[\frac{D^{(n)}(s)}{n!}\right]_{s=-a}$$

Similar evaluations are needed for $q'(-a)$, $q''(-a)$, and higher derivatives. These are also indeterminate, but may be evaluated by L'Hospital's rule. As an example, the form for the derivatives required for a third order pole of G will be developed.

$$q = \frac{D}{(s+a)^3}, \quad q(-a) = \frac{D'''(-a)}{3!}$$

$$q' = \frac{D'}{(s+a)^3} - \frac{3D}{(s+a)^4} = \frac{(s+a)D' - 3D}{(s+a)^4}$$

$$q'(-a) = \left[\frac{(s+a)D' - 3D}{(s+a)^4}\right]_{s=-a}$$

which by L'Hospital's rule becomes

$$= \left[\frac{(s+a)\,D'' - 2D'}{4(s+a)^3}\right]_{s=-a} = \left[\frac{(s+a)\,D''' - D''}{4\cdot 3(s+a)^2}\right]_{s=-a} = \left[\frac{(s+a)\,D^{\mathrm{IV}}}{4\cdot 3\cdot 2(s+a)}\right]_{s=-a}$$

$$= \left[\frac{D^{\mathrm{IV}}(s)}{4!}\right]_{s=-a} = \frac{D^{\mathrm{IV}}(-a)}{4!}$$

$$q'' = \frac{D''}{(s+a)^3} - \frac{6\,D'}{(s+a)^4} + \frac{4\cdot 3\,D}{(s+a)^5} = \frac{(s+a)^2\,D'' - 6(s+a)\,D' + 4\cdot 3\,D}{(s+a)^5}$$

Evaluating by L'Hospital's rule as was done for $q'(-a)$ results in

$$q''(-a) = \frac{2\,D^{\mathrm{V}}(-a)}{5!}$$

No higher derivatives are needed for a third-order pole.

Investigation of higher-order poles in this way results in the following general expression for the gth derivative at a pole of order n.

$$q^{(g)}(-a) = \frac{g!\,D^{(g+n)}(-a)}{(g+n)!} \tag{A1-24}$$

Now, finally, either N or D may be specified as a polynomial in s; for example,

$$D = D_1 + D_2 s + D_3 s^2 + \cdots + D_v s^{v-1}$$

The derivatives of such a polynomial of order $(v - 1)$ are calculated by the equation

$$D^{(k)}(-a) = \left[\sum_{x=k}^{v-1} \frac{x!\,D_{x+1} s^{x-k}}{(x-k)!}\right]_{s=-a} \tag{A1-25}$$

where D_{x+1} is the coefficient of s^x in the polynomial. (Note that the superscript for s in Equation A1-25 means exponent, but the superscript for D means derivative.) Similarly

$$N^{(e)}(-a) = \left[\sum_{x=e}^{u-1} \frac{x!\,N_{x+1} s^{x-e}}{(x-e)!}\right]_{s=-a} \tag{A1-26}$$

where $u - 1$ is the order of the numerator polynomial

N_{x+1} is the coefficient of s^x in the numerator polynomial

Now all quantities are available for computing the inverse, and the same logic can be employed for all poles, real or complex, and of any order. If the pole is a complex pole associated with an nth order quadratic (of the form $[(s + a)^2 + b^2]^n$), the coefficient, c_k, of Equation A1-21 will become a complex coefficient, $c_{r_k} + c_{i_k}$, and the corresponding term in the inverse transform will be

$$(c_{r_k} + ic_{i_k})t^{k-1} e^{(-a+ib)t}$$

When this term is combined with its conjugate, arising from the other complex factor in the quadratic factor, the final result is

$$f(t)_{[(s+a)^2+b^2]^n} = e^{-at} \sum_{k=1}^{n} t^{k-1}(2c_{r_k} \cos bt - 2c_{i_k} \sin bt) \qquad \text{(A1-27)}$$

where

$$c_{r_k} + ic_{i_k} = \left[\frac{\phi^{(n-k)}(s)}{(k-1)!(n-k)!}\right]_{s=-a+ib} \qquad \text{(A1-28)}$$

The same logic can be used for computing the values of c_{r_k} and c_{i_k} of Equation A1-28 as was used to compute c_k of Equation A1-21 except that complex arithmetic is used and $(-a + ib)$ is used instead of $(-a)$ in Equations A1-22 to A1-26.

A digital computer program for use of this method is provided in Reference 1.

Table A1-2 is a table of theorems often useful in obtaining transforms and inverse transforms. See Reference 6 for a discussion of these theorems.

Table A1-1. Table of Laplace Transforms

1. $\mathscr{L}[u(t)] \equiv \mathscr{L}(1) = \dfrac{1}{s}$

2. $\mathscr{L}(t^n) = \dfrac{n!}{s^{n+1}}$ (if n is a positive integer)

   $= \dfrac{\Gamma(n+1)}{s^{n+1}}$ (if $n > -1$, not necessarily an integer)

3. $\mathscr{L}(\sin \omega t) = \dfrac{\omega}{s^2 + \omega^2}$

4. $\mathscr{L}(\cos \omega t) = \dfrac{s}{s^2 + \omega^2}$

5. $\mathscr{L}(e^{-at}) = \dfrac{1}{s + a}$

6. $\mathscr{L}(e^{-at} \cos \omega t) = \dfrac{s + a}{(s + a)^2 + \omega^2}$

7. $\mathscr{L}(e^{-at} \sin \omega t) = \dfrac{\omega}{(s + a)^2 + \omega^2}$

Table A1-2. Theorems for Laplace Transforms or Inverse Transforms

	$\mathscr{L}[f(t)] = \phi(s)$	$\mathscr{L}^{-1}[\phi(s)] = f(t)$
①	$\mathscr{L}\left(\frac{df}{dt}\right) = s\mathscr{L}(f) - f(0)$ or $\mathscr{L}(f) = \frac{1}{s}\mathscr{L}\left(\frac{df}{dt}\right) + \frac{1}{s}f(0)$	$\mathscr{L}^{-1}[s\phi(s)] = \frac{d}{dt}[\mathscr{L}^{-1}(\phi)] + \mathscr{L}^{-1}\{[\mathscr{L}^{-1}(\phi)]_{t=0}\}$ or $\mathscr{L}^{-1}(\phi) = \frac{d}{dt}\left[\mathscr{L}^{-1}\left(\frac{\phi}{s}\right)\right] + \mathscr{L}^{-1}\left\{\left[\mathscr{L}^{-1}\left(\frac{\phi}{s}\right)\right]_{t=0}\right\}$ *Note.* 2nd term usually zero, but if not $\mathscr{L}^{-1}(1) = \delta(t)$
②	$\mathscr{L}\left[\int_0^t f(t)\,dt\right] = \frac{1}{s}\mathscr{L}(f)$ or $\mathscr{L}(f) = s\,\mathscr{L}\left[\int_0^t f(t)\,dt\right]$	$\mathscr{L}^{-1}\left[\frac{\phi(s)}{s}\right] = \int_0^t \{\mathscr{L}^{-1}[\phi(s)]\}\,dt$ or $\mathscr{L}^{-1}[\phi(s)] = \int_0^t \{\mathscr{L}^{-1}[s\phi(s)]\}\,dt$
③	$\mathscr{L}[f(at)] = \frac{1}{a}\{\mathscr{L}[f(t)]\}_{s\to s/a}$ or $\mathscr{L}[f(t)] = \frac{1}{a}\left\{\mathscr{L}\left[f\left(\frac{t}{a}\right)\right]\right\}_{s\to s/a}$	$\mathscr{L}^{-1}\left[\phi\left(\frac{s}{a}\right)\right] = a\{\mathscr{L}^{-1}[\phi(s)]\}_{t\to at}$ or $\mathscr{L}^{-1}[\phi(s)] = a[\mathscr{L}^{-1}\{\phi(as)\}]_{t\to at}$
④	$\mathscr{L}[e^{-at}f(t)] = \{\mathscr{L}[f(t)]\}_{s\to(s+a)}$ or $\mathscr{L}[f(t)] = \{\mathscr{L}[e^{at}f(t)]\}_{s\to(s+a)}$	$\mathscr{L}^{-1}[\phi(s+a)] = e^{-at}\mathscr{L}^{-1}[\phi(s)]$ or $\mathscr{L}^{-1}[\phi(s)] = e^{at}\mathscr{L}^{-1}[\phi(s+a)]$ or $\mathscr{L}^{-1}[\phi(s)] = e^{-at}\mathscr{L}^{-1}[\phi(s-a)]$
⑤	$\mathscr{L}[f(t-a)u(t-a)] = e^{-as}\mathscr{L}[f(t)]$ or $\mathscr{L}[f(t)u(t-a) = e^{-as}\mathscr{L}[f(t+a)]$	$\mathscr{L}^{-1}[e^{-as}\phi(s)] = u(t-a)[\mathscr{L}^{-1}\phi(s)]_{t\to(t-a)}$ or $\mathscr{L}^{-1}[\phi(s)] = [u(t-a)]\{\mathscr{L}^{-1}[e^{as}\phi(s)]\}_{t\to(t-a)}$
⑥	$\mathscr{L}[tf(t)] = -\frac{d}{ds}\{\mathscr{L}[f(t)]\}$ or $\mathscr{L}[f(t)] = -\frac{d}{ds}\left\{\mathscr{L}\frac{f(t)}{t}\right\}$	$\mathscr{L}^{-1}\left[\frac{d\phi(s)}{ds}\right] = -t\mathscr{L}^{-1}[\phi(s)]$ or $\mathscr{L}^{-1}[\phi(s)] = -\frac{1}{t}\mathscr{L}^{-1}\left[\frac{d\phi(s)}{ds}\right]$
⑦	$\mathscr{L}\left[\frac{f(t)}{t}\right] = \int_s^\infty \{\mathscr{L}[f(t)]\}\,ds$ or $\mathscr{L}[f(t)] = \int_s^\infty \{[tf(t)]\}\,ds$	$\mathscr{L}^{-1}\left[\int_s^\infty \phi(s)\,ds\right] = \frac{1}{t}\mathscr{L}^{-1}[\phi(s)]$ or $\mathscr{L}^{-1}[\phi(s)] = t\mathscr{L}^{-1}\left[\int_s^\infty \phi(s)\,ds\right]$

Limit Theorems

$$\lim_{t\to\infty} f(t) = \lim_{s\to 0} s\phi(s) \qquad \lim_{t\to 0} f(t) = \lim_{s\to\infty} s\phi(s)$$

Note. The theorems are valid only if the functions are bounded.

A1.3 Complex Numbers

Arithmetic with Complex Numbers. The symbol i (or j) is often used to designate the imaginary number, $\sqrt{-1}$. Therefore any real number multiplied by i is an imaginary number. If a number contains both a real and an imaginary part, it is a complex number. Thus the number, $2 + 3i$, is a complex number whose real part is 2 and whose imaginary part is 3. It is not possible to combine the real and imaginary parts into some equivalent real number. When complex numbers are added or subtracted, it is necessary to add or subtract the real and imaginary parts separately, as follows.

$$(2 + 3i) + (1 - 4i) = (2 + 1) + (3 - 4)i = 3 - i$$

$$(2 + 3i) - (1 - 4i) = (2 - 1) + (3 + 4)i = 1 + 7i$$

If two complex numbers are to be multiplied, it is necessary to multiply them the way that algebraic quantities are multiplied, as follows.

$$(2 + 3i)(1 - 4i) = (2 \times 1) - (2 \times 4i) + (3i \times 1) - (3i \times 4i) = 14 - 5i$$

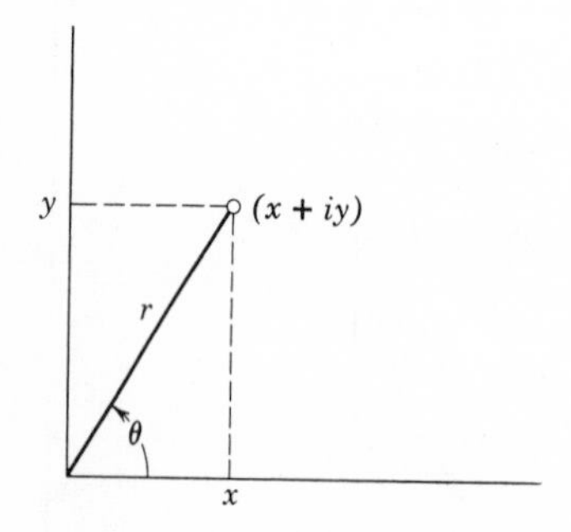

Fig. A1-1

If two complex numbers are divided, it is usually required that the final result be expressed as a single complex number. This is accomplished by clearing the denominator of imaginary numbers as follows.

$$\frac{1 - 4i}{2 + 3i} = \frac{(1 - 4i)(2 - 3i)}{(2 + 3i)(2 - 3i)} = \frac{2 - 3i - 8i - 12}{4 - 6i + 6i + 9} = -\frac{10}{13} - \frac{11}{13}i$$

This technique was used in Examples A1-15 and A1-16 to determine the real and imaginary parts of ϕ. Notice that to clear the denominator of imaginary numbers it is necessary to multiply by the same number but with the sign of the imaginary part reversed. Such a number is called the "complex conjugate." That is, the complex conjugate of $(2 + 3i)$ is $(2 - 3i)$, and the complex conjugate of $(-1 - 4i)$ is $(-1 + 4i)$.

Polar Form of a Complex Number. There is another way of representing a complex number. If the real part is plotted on the x axis and the imaginary part on the y axis of a graph, then a point on such a graph would represent a complex number. Thus a complex variable, $x + iy$, represents various complex numbers as x and y take on various values. The x, y coordinate system used in this way is referred to as the complex plane. It is also possible to represent a complex number, $x + iy$, in terms of polar coordinates as a point described by r and θ, where these are defined in Fig. A1-1. The "absolute value" or "modulus" of the complex number is r, and θ is its "angle" or "argument." By inspection, $x = r \cos \theta$ and $y = r \sin \theta$, so that

$$x + iy = r(\cos \theta + i \sin \theta) \qquad \text{(A1-29)}$$

It is possible to show by series expansion that

$$e^{i\theta} = \cos\theta + i\sin\theta$$

$$e^{-i\theta} = \cos\theta - i\sin\theta$$

$$\cos\theta = \frac{1}{2}(e^{i\theta} + e^{-i\theta}) \tag{A1-30}$$

$$\sin\theta = \frac{1}{2i}(e^{i\theta} - e^{-i\theta})$$

Using the first of Equations A1-30, the complex number $x + iy$ can be written

$$x + iy = r\,e^{i\theta} \tag{A1-31}$$

where

$$r = \sqrt{x^2 + y^2} \qquad \sin\theta = \frac{y}{r}$$

$$\cos\theta = \frac{x}{r} \qquad \tan\theta = \frac{y}{x} \tag{A1-32}$$

Equation A1-31 provides another way of multiplying or dividing complex numbers. Since $(x_1 + iy_1)(x_2 + iy_2)$ could be written $r_1\,e^{i\theta_1} r_2\,e^{i\theta_2}$, it is apparent that the product is $r_1 r_2\,e^{i(\theta_1+\theta_2)}$, and the quotient $(x_1 + iy_1)/(x_2 + iy_2)$ is $(r_1/r_2)\,e^{i(\theta_1-\theta_2)}$ Thus, since $1 + i = \sqrt{2}\,e^{i\pi/4}$ and $(-2 + 2i) = 2\sqrt{2}\,e^{i(3\pi/4)}$, the product, $(1 + i)(-2 + 2i)$, is

$$\sqrt{2}\,2\sqrt{2}\,e^{i(\pi/4+3\pi/4)} = 4\,e^{i\pi} = -4$$

(The real number -1 is equally well written $e^{i\pi}$, and the imaginary number i is the same as $e^{i(\pi/2)}$.) Also, the effect of multiplying a complex number by i is to rotate the complex number ahead by 90° in the complex plane, since $(r_1\,e^{i\theta_1})\,i = r_1\,e^{i\theta_1}\,e^{i(\pi/2)} = r_1\,e^{i(\theta_1+\pi/2)}$.

Complex Form of Harmonic Functions. It is seen that if ω is a constant and t represents time, the expression, $e^{i\omega t}$, describes a complex number having unit absolute value and an angle which increases at a constant rate or rotates with angular velocity, ω, in the complex plane. Since $e^{i\omega t} = \cos\omega t + i\sin\omega t$ (from Equation A1-30), the real part of $e^{i\omega t}$ is $\cos\omega t$ and the imaginary part is $\sin\omega t$. The use of $e^{i\omega t}$ to describe forces, displacements, velocities, or accelerations which vary harmonically with time is often preferable to the trigonometric functions.

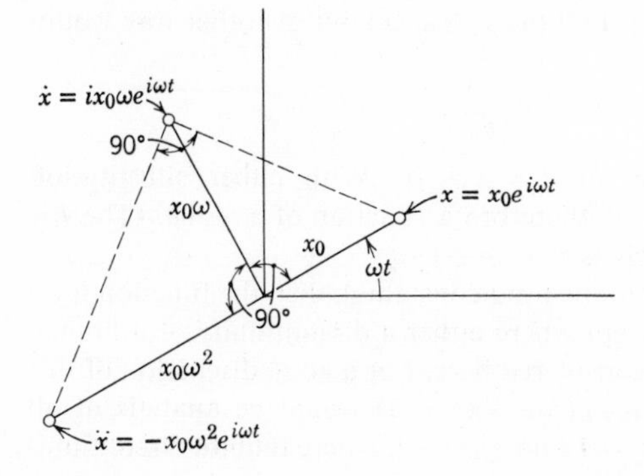

Fig. A1-2

Suppose a displacement varies according to the equation $x = x_0 \cos \omega t$. Of course the velocity is then $\dot{x} = x_0\omega \sin \omega t$ and the acceleration is $\ddot{x} = -x_0\omega^2 \cos \omega t$. A "complex displacement" can be defined, $x_0 e^{i\omega t}$, so that the actual displacement is the real part of $x_0 e^{i\omega t}$; then the velocity would be the real part of $i\omega x_0 e^{i\omega t}$ and the acceleration the real part of $i^2\omega^2 x_0 e^{i\omega t}$. A comparison with the trigonometric expressions for velocity and acceleration shows these to be equivalent forms. Also, it is evident that the complex velocity leads the displacement by 90° and the complex acceleration leads the velocity by 90°, since the effect of multiplying by i is to rotate the complex quantity 90° ahead. The actual displacements, velocities, and accelerations are the real parts of the corresponding complex quantities. Figure A1-2 shows the relationships between the complex displacement, velocity, and acceleration.

A1.4 Complex Variables

Relationships between Complex Variables. The symbol z is often used to designate a "complex variable," where $z = x + iy$ by definition, and x and y are two real variables. As x and y take on different values, the complex number z varies, and is therefore a complex variable. The symbol, w, is often used to indicate another complex variable which is some function of z, and therefore of x and y. It is conventional to use u and v to designate the real and imaginary parts of w in the same way that x and y are used to designate the real and imaginary parts of z. That is, $w = u + iv$.

An especially easy function which illustrates these relationships is the function

$$f(z) = \omega = z^2$$

Since $w = u + iv$ and $z = x + iy$, this functional relationship could be written as

$$u + iv = (x + iy)^2$$
$$u + iv = (x^2 - y^2) + i(2xy)$$

For a complex quantity to be equal to another complex quantity it is necessary that the respective real and imaginary parts be equal, so it is clear that

$$u = x^2 - y^2$$
$$v = 2xy$$

and that in general u and v are both functions of x and y, or $u = u(x, y)$ and $v = v(x, y)$.

Analytic Functions and Derivatives of a Complex Variable. It might be that a complex variable would be expressed in terms of x and y directly; for instance, consider $(3x^2y - y^3) - i(x^3 - 3xy^2)$. Then it is important to be able to determine whether such a function could be expressed in terms of the single variable z, where $z = x + iy$, without any other variables being necessary. This could be determined by substituting $x = z - iy$ into the expression and simplifying algebraically to see if all the y's cancel out. Another way would be to substitute

$$x = \frac{z + \tilde{z}}{2} \qquad y = \frac{z - \tilde{z}}{2i}$$

where $\tilde{z}$ is the complex conjugate of z, or $\tilde{z} = x - iy$. With either substitution the above number reduces to simply iz^3, and is therefore a function of z alone. (The i is simply a constant here and not a variable such as x, y, or $\tilde{z}$.)

If a function can be expressed in terms of z alone (and constants), then the function is an "analytic" function of z at all values of z except where either a discontinuity or a branch point might exist. (Branch points will not be considered here. For a good discussion of this subject, see Reference 8.) The function $(z + 1)/(z - 1)(z + 2)$ would be analytic at all values of z except at the "singular" points, $z = 1$ and $z = -2$, where infinite discontinuities occur.

An analytic function of z possesses some important properties. Perhaps the most important of these is that the real and imaginary parts of the function satisfy the Cauchy-Riemann equations.

$$\frac{\partial u}{\partial x} = \frac{\partial v}{\partial y}$$
$$\frac{\partial u}{\partial y} = -\frac{\partial v}{\partial x} \tag{A1-33}$$

By using these equations it is easy to show that the real and the imaginary parts of an analytic function both satisfy Laplace's equation; that is

$$\frac{\partial^2 u}{\partial x^2} + \frac{\partial^2 u}{\partial y^2} = 0$$
$$\frac{\partial^2 v}{\partial x^2} + \frac{\partial^2 v}{\partial y^2} = 0 \tag{A1-34}$$

It is also possible to show that the derivative of the function can be expressed in terms of the partials, as follows:

$$f'(z) = \frac{dw}{dz} = \frac{\partial u}{\partial x} + i\frac{\partial v}{\partial x}$$
$$= \frac{\partial v}{\partial y} - i\frac{\partial u}{\partial y} \tag{A1-35}$$

To illustrate these equations, consider again the simple function $w = z^2$, for which $u = x^2 - y^2$ and $v = 2xy$. Equations A1-33 and A1-34 are easily shown to be satisfied, and Equation A1-35 shows that $dw/dz = 2x + i2y$, or $2z$, which could of course be obtained by simply differentiating z^2.

However, suppose that $u = x^2 + y^2$ and $v = 2xy$. One of the Cauchy-Reimann equations is satisfied, but not the other. Therefore the function is not analytic. Also, it is not possible to determine the derivative of this function, dw/dz, because it is not unique but depends on the way in which Δz goes to zero in the defining equation

$$f'(z) = \lim_{\Delta z \to 0} \frac{f(z + \Delta z) - f(z))}{\Delta z}$$

This is also evident if an attempt is made to use Equations A1-35, where the answer obtained depends on which equation is used. Functions which are not analytic do not possess a derivative. It is also seen that u does not satisfy Equation A1-34. However, even if u and v both satisfied Equation A1-34, it would not necessarily mean that u and v are the real and imaginary parts of the same complex variable, w. In other words, although the real and imaginary parts of an analytic function satisfy Laplace's equation, functions which satisfy Laplace's equation are not necessarily the real and imaginary parts of the same complex variable. (Consider $x^3 - 3xy^2 + i2xy$, for example, where $x^3 - 3xy^2$ is the real part of z^3 and $2xy$ is the imaginary part of z^2.)

Line Integral of a Complex Variable. The line integral of a complex variable along a given path in the x,y plane (where x and y are the real and imaginary parts of z) can be evaluated by determining the line integral of two real variables, as follows.

$$\int_c w\,dz = \int_c (u + iv)(dx + i\,dy)$$
$$\int_c w\,dz = \int_c (u\,dx - v\,dy) + i\int_c (u\,dy + v\,dx) \tag{A1-36}$$

If the function is analytic everywhere within a closed curve, the line integral completely around the curve (or "contour integral") is zero (an application of Green's lemma and the Cauchy-Reimann equations) and therefore the integral of the function between two points is independent of the path and depends only on the end points.

This is not surprising. For instance,

$$\int_{z=1+i}^{z=2+3i} z^2\, dz = \frac{z^3}{3} \int_{z=1+i}^{z=2+3i}$$

Here the function to be integrated is z^2, and the result does not depend on the path, or way in which x and y vary as z goes from $1 + i$ to $2 + 3i$.

However, if the line integral is taken around a curve which encloses a singular point, or discontinuity, then the integral may not be zero even if the function is analytic everywhere else. For example, by using Equation A1-36, or else by converting to polar coordinates, it is easily shown that $\oint (dz/z)$ around a circle enclosing the origin is $2\pi i$. Therefore, in evaluating the line integral of the function $1/z$ between any two values of z, the value of the integral would depend on which side of the origin the path lies.

It is possible to show that contour integrals of functions which are analytic everywhere except at isolated points within the region can be evaluated by use of the following equations.

$$f(z_0) = \frac{1}{2\pi i}\oint \frac{f(z)}{(z - z_0)}\, dz$$

$$\left(\frac{df}{dz}\right)_{z=z_0} = \frac{1}{2\pi i}\oint \frac{f(z)}{(z - z_0)^2}\, dz \qquad \text{(A1-37)}$$

$$\left(\frac{d^n f}{dz^n}\right)_{z=z_0} = \frac{n!}{2\pi i}\oint \frac{f(z)}{(z - z_0)^{n+1}}\, dz$$

In these equations, $f(z)$ must be analytic everywhere within and on the contour, although obviously $f(z)/(z - z_0)$, $f(z)/(z - z_0)^2$, etc., are not analytic at z_0.

Example A1-18. What is $\oint (z + 1)\, dz/(z - 1)(z + 2)$ around the circle $|z - \frac{1}{2}| = 1$? The circle $|z| = 3$?

The center of the first circle (Fig. A1-3) is at $\frac{1}{2}$, but this is not the value of z_0 to be used in Equation A1-37. If $f(z)$ is selected to be $(z + 1)/(z + 2)$ and $z - z_0$ is $z - 1$, it is clear that

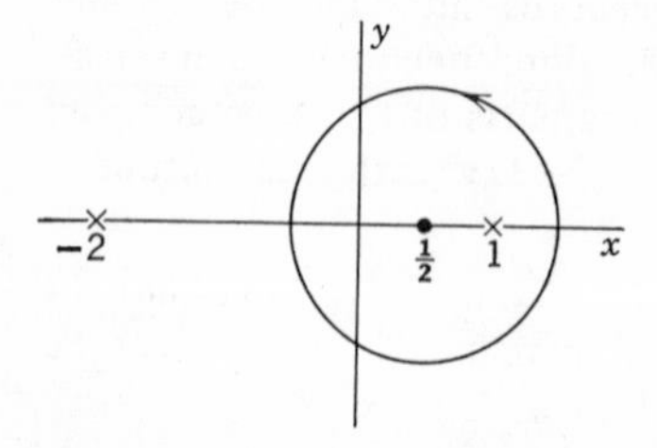

Fig. A1-3

$\oint [f(z)/(z - z_0)]$ is the desired integral and that $f(z)$ is analytic everywhere within and on the contour. Therefore z_0 is 1 and $f(z_0) = (1 + 1)/(1 + 2) = 2/3$ and the desired integral is $4\pi i/3$.

For the second path, $|z| = 3$ (Fig. A1-4), let the contour be deformed so that it touches between the two singularities. The value of the integral for this path will be the same as for the original path, since the function is analytic at all points in the region between the two paths. The line integral must therefore be the sum of the line integrals of the two paths which encircle the two singularities, and each integral can be obtained individually. One has already been determined, and the other can be determined by letting $f(z) = (z + 1)/(z - 1)$ and $z - z_0 = z + 2$ or $z_0 = -2$ so that the integral becomes $2\pi i/3$. Adding the two results gives $2\pi i$ for the path which surrounds both singularities.

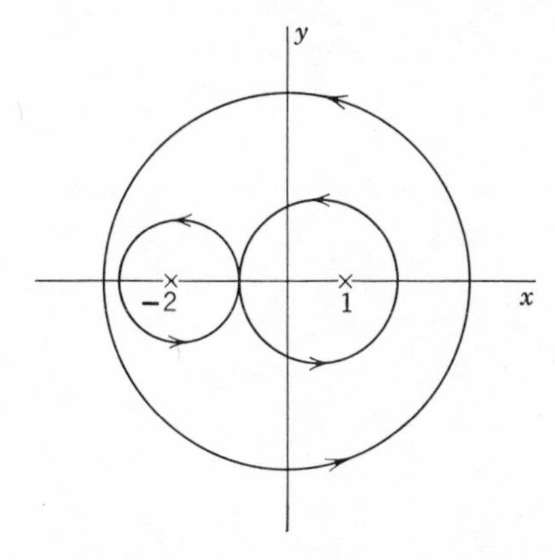

Fig. A1-4

Infinite Series. It is often useful to be able to express a function as an infinite series of the form

$$f(z) = \frac{a_{-m}}{(z - z_0)^m} + \frac{a_{-m+1}}{(z - z_0)^{m-1}} + \cdots + \frac{a_{-1}}{z - z_0} + a_0 + a_1(z - z_0) + \cdots + a_n(z - z_0)^n \quad \text{(A1-38)}$$

Such a series is called a Laurent series. If the negative powers of $(z - z_0)$ are missing, the series is called a Taylor series. Either m or n or both might approach infinity. It is often possible to determine the region of convergence for a series by examining the function which the series represents. This is most easily explained by use of an example.

Example A1-19. Determine the region of convergence for several series which represent the function $f(z) = 1/[(z^2 + 1)(z + 2)]$. This function is analytic for all values of z except the points $z = -2$, $z = +i$, $z = -i$. If it were desired to expand this function about the point $z = 0$ (or $z_0 = 0$ in Equation A1-38), there would be three different series which would be convergent, each in a different region. The regions would be found by drawing circles (Fig. A1-5) with center at the point of expansion (zero in this instance) and radii which just miss the singular points at -2 and $\pm i$. The area labeled A has no singular point anywhere in the region, and it can be shown that a Taylor series will be convergent in this region. (A Taylor series in which $z_0 = 0$ is also called a MacLaurin series.) The negative powers of z will be missing from this series. The other two areas, B and C, will be regions for which Laurent series will be convergent. The series which is convergent in B will not be convergent in C and vice versa. In each region, there will be only one series with $z_0 = 0$ which is convergent.

However, it would not be necessary to expand the function about zero. If it were chosen to write the series in terms of $(Z - 1)$, or $Z_0 = 1$, then the three regions would be circles or annuli having the center at 1. The function would again be represented by a Taylor series in A and two different Laurent series for B and C (Fig. A1-6). The coefficients of these three series would not be the same as for the first three.

If the series were written in terms of $(Z + 2)$, there would be no convergent Taylor series but two different Laurent series for Regions B and C (Fig. A1-7). The coefficients of the series may be determined by whatever method is most convenient. For a Taylor series, the coefficients may be determined from

$$a_0 = f(z_0)$$
$$a_n = \frac{1}{n!}\left(\frac{d^n f}{dz^n}\right)_{z_0} \tag{A1-39}$$

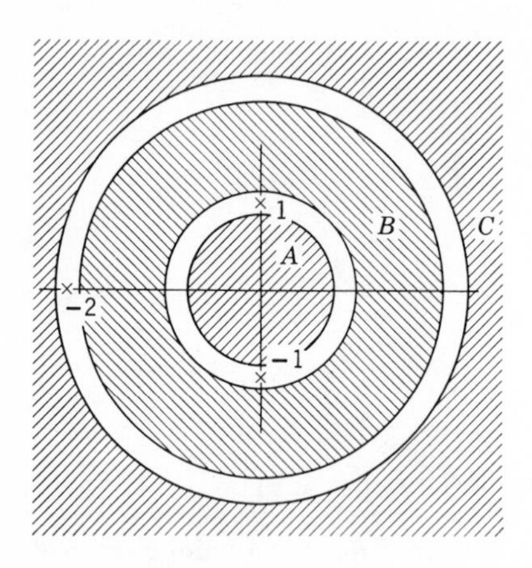

Fig. A1-5

and for the Laurent series from

$$a_n = \frac{1}{2\pi i}\oint_c \frac{f(z)\,dz}{(z - z_0)^{n+1}} \tag{A1-40}$$

where C is any curve in the annulus of convergence but encircling the inner boundary. Equation A1-40 could also be used for the Taylor series, and Equation A1-39 is simply another form of Equation A1-40 for $n \geqq 0$.

Equation A1-39 or A1-40 need not be used if the desired series can be established by some other means, which is often possible, as demonstrated in the following example.

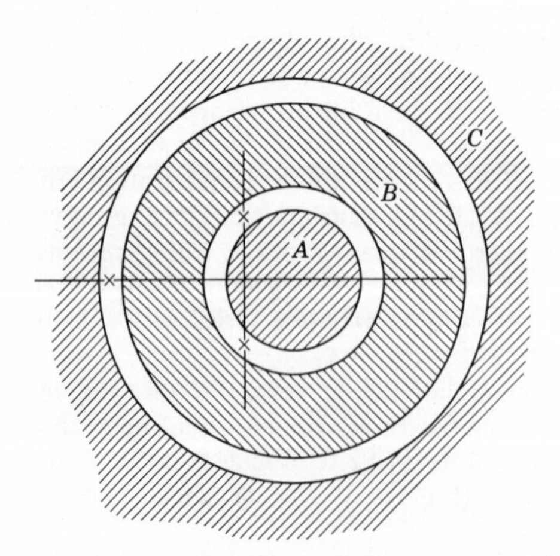

Fig. A1-6

Example A1-20. Determine the coefficients of the series for the function of Example A1-19:

$$\frac{1}{(z^2+1)(z+2)}$$

For the first set of series in Example A1-19, where $z_0 = 0$, it is convenient to split this function by the use of partial fractions so that

$$\frac{1}{(z^2+1)(z+2)} = \frac{1}{5}\left(\frac{1}{z+2} + \frac{-z+2}{z^2+1}\right)$$

By long division, or by binomial expansion, the function $1/(z+2)$ could be expressed as

$$\frac{1}{z+2} = \frac{1}{z} - \frac{1}{2z^2} + \frac{1}{4z^3} - \frac{1}{8z^4} + \cdots \tag{①}$$

or

$$\frac{1}{z+2} = \frac{1}{2} - \frac{z}{4} + \frac{z^2}{8} - \frac{z^3}{16} + \cdots \tag{②}$$

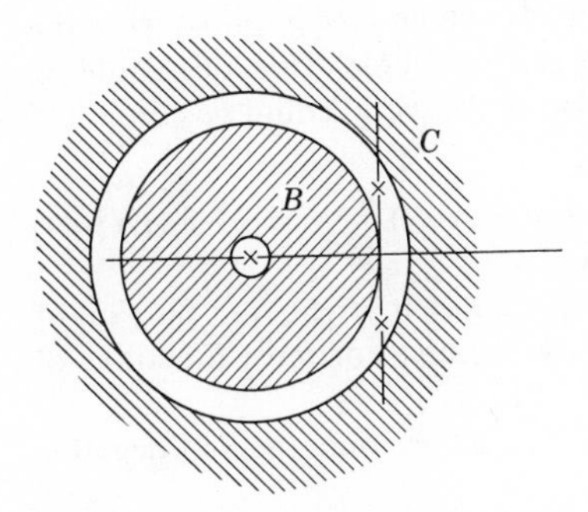

Fig. A1-7

The first of these was obtained by dividing $(z+2)$ into 1 and the second series was obtained by dividing $(2+z)$ into 1. By considering the function $1/(z+2)$ in the light of Example A1-19, it is easy to see that the second series above would be convergent for any z interior to a circle of radius 2, or $|z| < 2$, and the first series would converge for $|z| > 2$. The function $1/(z^2+1)$ could also be expressed in a series by dividing either (z^2+1) into 1 or else $(1+z^2)$ into 1. If this is done and the results multiplied by $(-z+2)$.

$$\frac{-z+2}{z^2+1} = -\frac{1}{z} + \frac{2}{z^2} + \frac{1}{z^3} - \frac{2}{z^4} - \frac{1}{z^5} + \frac{2}{z^6} \cdots \tag{③}$$

or

$$\frac{-z+2}{z^2+1} = 2 - z - 2z^2 + z^3 + 2z^4 - z^5 - 2z^6 \cdots \tag{④}$$

Series 3 is convergent for $|z| > 1$ and Series 4 for $|z| < 1$. The original function, $1/[(z^2+1)(z+2)]$, could therefore be expressed in series form by adding the appropriate series which are convergent in the different regions; that is,

$$\frac{1}{(z^2+1)(z+2)} = \frac{1}{5}(② + ④) \qquad |z| < 1$$

$$\frac{1}{(z^2+1)(z+2)} = \frac{1}{5}(② + ③) \qquad 1 < |z| < 2$$

$$\frac{1}{(z^2+1)(z+2)} = \frac{1}{5}(① + ③) \qquad |z| > 2$$

If the function were to be expanded in terms of $(z - 1)$, as in the second part of Example A1-19, it would be convenient to first substitute $w = z - 1$, or $z = w + 1$, so that the function $1/[(z^2 + 1)(z + 2)]$ would become $1/[(w^2 + 2w + 2)(w + 3)]$. Then this function could be expanded as above in terms of w, and finally $(z - 1)$ substituted for w. There would be three series for the three regions. If the function were to be expressed in powers of $(z + 2)$, as in the third part of Example A1.19, the substitution of $w = z + 2$ would result in the function $1/w(w^2 - 4w + 5)$, which could be expanded as before, resulting in two different Laurent series for the two different regions.

Residues and the Inverse Laplace Transform. Equation A1-4 shows that the coefficient a_{-1} of a Laurent series for a function expanded about a singular point is connected with the contour integral of the function about the point. This coefficient is called the "residue" of the function at the singular point or "pole" of the function, and $2\pi i$ times the residue is the contour integral of the function for any path which encloses only that one pole.

If a contour integral were to be performed along a path which encloses two poles, the path could be deformed without altering the value of the integral, because of the principle of the deformation of contours, until the path touched itself at some point, as indicated for Example A1-18, and the contour integral for the original path could be computed from the sum of the integrals for each of the paths which enclose only one pole. This idea could be extended to any number of poles enclosed, so that the contour integral could be computed from

$$\oint_c f(z)\,dz = 2\pi i(\Sigma \text{ Residues at all poles in } c) \tag{A1-41}$$

The residues could be obtained by actually determining the Laurent series, or a portion of it, for expansion of the function about the various singular points. For most functions of interest, an easier method is available which is explained below.

For a first order pole (a pole for which the Laurent expansion has only the first negative power of $z - z_0$), the residue is found by

$$a_{-1} = (z - z_0)f(z_0) \tag{A1-42}$$

This is easily seen by considering

$$f(z) = \frac{a_{-1}}{(z - z_0)} + a_0 + a_1(z - z_0) + \cdots$$

$$(z - z_0)f(z) = a_{-1} + a_0(z - z_0) + a_1(z - z_0)^2 + \cdots$$

$$(z - z_0)f(z_0) = a_{-1} + a_0(z_0 - z_0) + a_1(z_0 - z_0)^2 + \cdots = a_{-1}$$

For a higher order pole the residue can be found by

$$a_{-1} = \frac{1}{(n-1)!}\left\{\frac{d^{n-1}[(z - z_0)^n f(z)]}{dz^{n-1}}\right\}_{z=z_0} \tag{A1-43}$$

This, too, can be seen by considering a 3rd order pole for example

$$f(z) = \frac{a_{-3}}{(z - z_0)^3} + \frac{a_{-2}}{(z - z_0)^2} + \frac{a_{-1}}{(z - z_0)^1} + a_0 + \cdots$$

$$(z - z_0)^3 f(z) = a_{-3} + a_{-2}(z - z_0) + a_{-1}(z - z_0)^2 + a_0(z - z_0)^3 + \cdots$$

$$\frac{d}{dz}[(z - z_0)^3 f(z)] = a_{-2} + 2a_{-1}(z - z_0) + 3a_0(z - z_0)^2 + \cdots$$

$$\frac{d^2}{dz^2}[(z - z_0)^3 f(z)] = 2a_{-1} + 3a_0(z - z_0) + \cdots$$

$$\left\{\frac{d^2}{dz^2}[(z - z_0)^3 f(z)]\right\}_{z=z_0} = 2a_{-1} + 3a_0(z - z_0) + \cdots$$

It is clear that the method fails for an "essential" singularity, or one for which there are an infinite number of negative exponent terms in the Laurent expansion. Such an event could still be handled by resorting to the actual Laurent expansion, determining the series by whatever method suggests itself from the form of the function.

The inverse Laplace transform can be determined from Equation A1-11

$$f(t) = \mathscr{L}^{-1}[\phi(s)] = \frac{1}{2\pi i}\int_{s=a-i\infty}^{s=a+i\infty} \phi(s)\, e^{st}\, ds$$

In this equation, s is a complex variable and the line integral is carried out along a line in the complex plane parallel to the y axis, displaced by the real constant, a, which is selected so that the line is located to the right of all the singular points. Then the line integral can be evaluated by integrating around the closed contour formed by the vertical line and the semicircle of infinite radius as indicated in Fig. A1-8, provided that it can be shown that the integral along the semicircle is zero. For many functions of practical interest particularly functions of the form $\phi(s) = N(s)/D(s)$, where $N(s)$ and $D(s)$ are polynomials and the

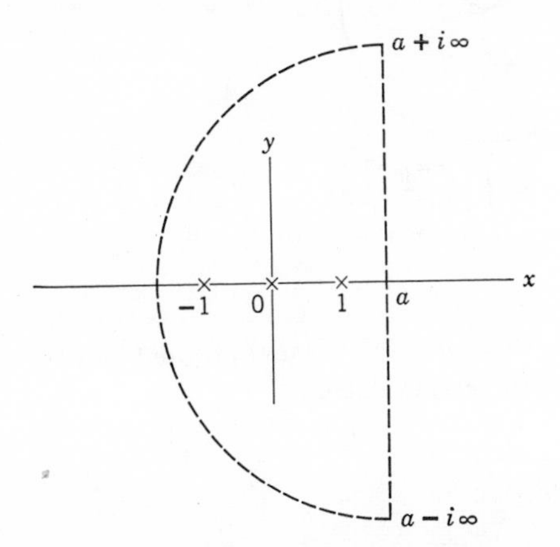

Fig. A1-8

degree of $D(s)$ is greater than the degree of $N(s)$, it is possible to show that the integral along the semicircle is zero, so the inverse transform is seen to be the sum of the residues of the function $\phi(s)e^{st}$, or $\phi(z)\, e^{zt}$ at all of the poles of $\phi(s)$, or $\phi(z)$. Examples A1-12 and A1-13 demonstrated the calculation of inverse transforms this way.

Residue Theory in the Evaluation of Definite Integrals. Residue theory is also useful in the evaluation of definite integrals. This application will not be treated extensively here. However, to illustrate some of the points which might arise, consider the definite integral $\int_{x=0}^{\infty} (\sin x)/[x(x^2 + 1)]\, dx$ where x is a real variable.

It is noted that $(\sin x)/[x(x^2 + 1)]$ is an even function and therefore the integral could be evaluated by taking half of the integral of the function from $-\infty$ to $+\infty$. This leads to the thought that a line integral of a complex variable along a closed path composed of the x axis and the infinite semicircle in the upper half-plane would give the desired result provided that the integral on the semicircle is zero. If this were true, then the integral along the x axis could be evaluated by taking $2\pi i$ times the sum of the residues at poles enclosed by the path. The only poles of $(\sin z)/[z(z^2 + 1)]$ in the finite region are the poles at $z = \pm i$. (Note that $z = 0$ is not a pole since $\lim_{z \to 0} \sin z/z = 1$.) It might seem, therefore, that the integral along the x axis could be obtained from $2\pi i$ times the residue at $z = i$, or

$$2\pi i \frac{\sin i}{i(2i)} \equiv \pi \frac{e + e^{-1}}{2}$$

However, the function, $(\sin z)/[z(z^2 + 1)]$, is not finite on the infinite semicircle, so this result is not likely to be correct.

To circumvent this difficulty, let the function be considered as

$$\frac{e^{iz} + e^{-iz}}{2iz(z^2 + 1)}$$

The difficulty arises when $z = R\,e^{i\theta} = R(\cos\theta + i\sin\theta)$ on the large semicircle and thus e^{-iz} becomes $e^{R\sin\theta}\,e^{-iR\cos\theta}$, which becomes infinite as $R \to \infty$. On the other hand e^{iz} becomes $e^{-R\sin\theta}\,e^{iR\cos\theta}$ which approaches zero as $R \to \infty$. This leads to the thought that perhaps the integral could be evaluated in two parts, one enclosing the upper half-plane

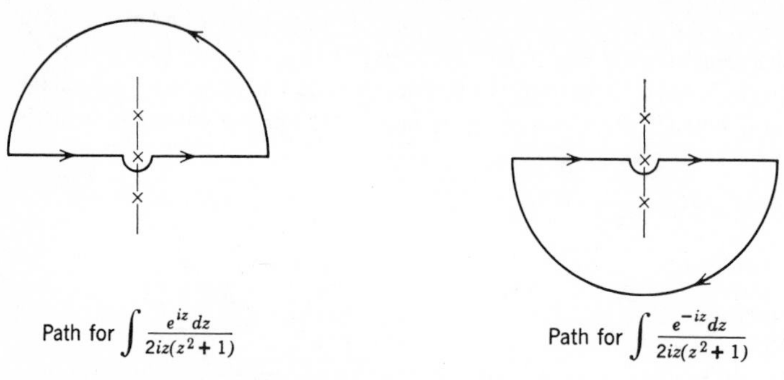

Fig. A1-9

and the other the lower half-plane. Then if $z = Re^{-i\theta} = R(\cos\theta - i\sin\theta)$ is used in e^{-iz}, the result is $e^{-R\sin\theta}\,e^{-iR\cos\theta}$, and all is well. Accordingly, evaluate

$$\int \frac{e^{iz}\,dz}{2iz(z^2 + 1)}$$

and

$$\int \frac{e^{-iz}\,dz}{2iz(z^2 + 1)}$$

separately, enclosing the upper half-plane for the first and the lower half-plane for the second. Now, however, the point $z = 0$ is a pole of each function and so the path should exclude this point. Therefore, let the paths of integration be as shown in Fig. A1-9.

The second path encircles the lower pole in the negative direction, which must be taken into account when the integrals are combined. Also, it might be argued that the integral along the infinitesimal semicircle near the origin is not necessarily the same as for the path through the origin. However, it was noted that $z = 0$ was not a pole of the original function and therefore the integral of that function (the sum of these two) along the infinitesimal semicircle is negligibly different from its integral along the x axis. Therefore, it is now seen that the original integral becomes

$$\int_{x=0}^{\infty} \frac{\sin x}{x(x^2 + 1)}\,dx = \frac{1}{2}(2\pi i)\left[\sum \text{Res. of } \frac{e^{iz}}{2iz(z^2 + 1)} \text{ at } z = 0 \text{ and } z = i \right.$$

$$\left. - \text{Res. of } \frac{e^{-iz}}{2iz(z^2 + 1)} \text{ at } z = -i\right]$$

$$= \pi i\left[\frac{1}{2i} + \frac{e^{-1}}{2i(i)(2i)} - \frac{e^{-1}}{2i(-i)(-2i)}\right]$$

$$\int_{x=0}^{\infty} \frac{\sin x}{x(x^2 + 1)}\,dx = \frac{\pi}{2}$$

An integral which illustrates a useful application is the following:

$$\int_{-\infty}^{+\infty} \frac{dx}{(x^2 - 1)(x^2 + 1)}$$

If this is attacked in the same way as the previous integral, it is seen that the path of integration passes through the two poles at ± 1. Therefore, let the integral be evaluated along three closed paths and summed, as shown in Fig. A1-10:
The sum of the integrals along these three closed paths will be the desired integral, since the integral of the function along the semicircle of infinite radius is obviously zero and the integrals along the infinitesimal semicircles cancel. The integral along c_1 is $2\pi i$ times the residue at i, or $-\pi/2$.

The integral along c_2 can be evaluated by considering the Laurent expansion of the function in the neighborhood of $z = -1$. This would result in

$$\frac{a_{-1}}{z + 1} + a_0 + a_1(z + 1) + \cdots$$

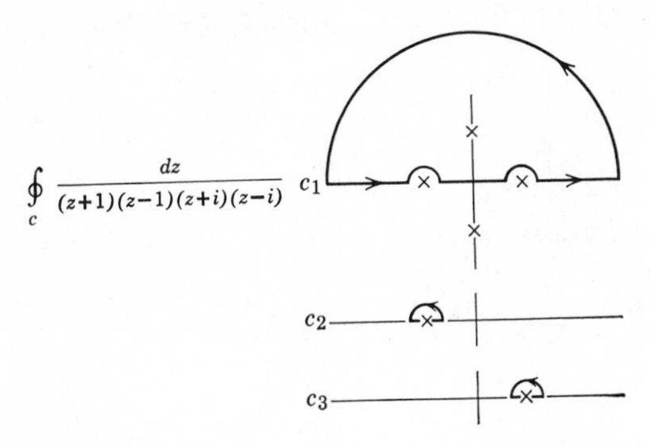

Fig. A1-10

where a_{-1} = residue of the original function at $z = -1$. The integral of all terms but the first in this series will approach zero when the radius is allowed to approach zero. It is possible to evaluate

$$a_{-1} \oint_{c_2} \frac{dz}{z + 1}$$

by summing the integral along a semicircle of radius ϵ and along the x axis from $-1 - \epsilon$ to $-1 + \epsilon$. The integral

$$\int_{-1-\varepsilon}^{-1+\varepsilon} \frac{dx}{x + 1}$$

could be replaced by

$$\int_{-\varepsilon}^{+\varepsilon} \frac{du}{u}$$

where $u = x + 1$, and it is obvious that this integral must be zero since it is an odd function. The integral along the semicircle can be evaluated by letting $z + 1 = \epsilon e^{i\theta}$, so that $dz = i\epsilon\, e^{i\theta}\, d\theta$, and the integral becomes

$$i \int_{\theta=0}^{\pi} d\theta = \pi i$$

Therefore, the integral of the original function along c_2 becomes πi times the residue at $z = -1$, or $-\pi i/4$.

Similarly, the integral along c_3 becomes πi times the residue at $z = 1$, or $\pi i/4$. The sum of the integrals along all three paths is therefore $-\pi/2 - \pi i/4 + \pi i/4$, or $-\pi/2$. This example illustrates how an integral may be evaluated even if there is one or more poles on the path.

Possible applications of evaluation of definite integrals in linear systems analysis are illustrated in Chapter 17 in connection with Fourier transforms and in the corresponding problems suggested for Chapter 17.

Conformal Transformations and Mapping of Functions. If one complex variable is a function of another, as $w = f(z)$, where $z = x + iy$ and $w = u(x, y) + iv(x, y)$, a complication arises if a graph of w for various z's were to be constructed. Since there are two different independent variables, x and y, it would be necessary to provide for the possible variation of both of these quantities. With only three dimensions, it is possible to plot only one dependent variable, either u, or v, or perhaps $|w|$, but not both u and v unless one plot for u and a different one for v were used. Even one three-dimensional plot would be inconvenient, so a different approach has been used for the problem of plotting the relationship between two complex variables. This is to construct two two-dimensional plots, one for z and the other for w, with the plot of w depending on both the value of z and the functional relationship between w and z. Then as z varies along some line in the x–y plane, w will generate

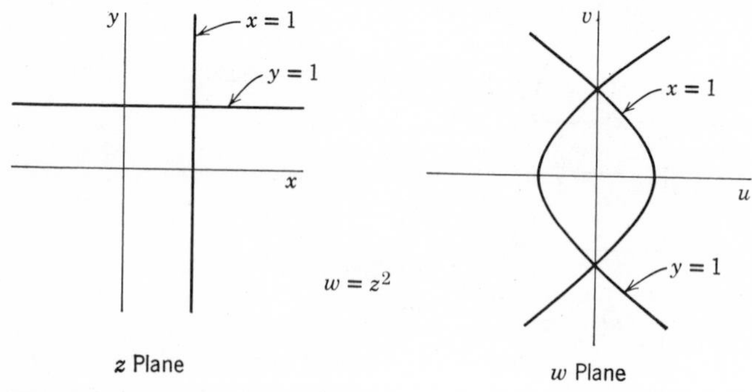

Fig. A1-11

some line in the u–v plane. A particularly easy example is the function $w = z^2$. If the straight line $x = 1$ is plotted in the w plane it is readily shown to be the parabola, $u = 1 - v^2/4$, and the straight line $y = 1$ in the z plane becomes the parabola $u = -1 + v^2/4$ in the w plane. These relationships are shown in Fig. A1-11.

Most functions are considerably more complicated than this, and it would be difficult or impossible to obtain an algebraic expression relating u and v. However, the parametric equations for u and v in terms of x and y would allow a plot of w to be constructed from values of z. Often the polar form of the variables is more convenient for this purpose, especially when the function is composed of the products and quotients of factors, such as

$$\frac{(z + 1)}{z(z + 2)(z - 3)}$$

If a figure in one plane is transformed into a figure in another plane (usually having a different shape) by making use of an analytic function of a complex variable to relate the two planes, the transformation is known as a conformal transformation. Such a transformation has the property that at all points where the function is analytic and where the derivative of the function is different from zero, corresponding angles in the figures are preserved. This is illustrated in Fig. A1-11, where it is seen that the right angle between the intersection of the lines $x = 1$ and $y = 1$ in the z plane remains a right angle in the w plane. There is only one point at which angles are not preserved for the transformation function $w = z^2$ and this is the point where $dw/dz = 0$, or at $z = 0$. At $z = 0$ it is seen that the right angle in the z plane formed by the positive segments of the two lines $x = 0$ and $y = 0$ becomes the straight angle at the origin of the w plane, so that at this one point angles are not preserved, and this is the only point for which the transformation is not conformal.

This property, and the fact that the real and imaginary parts of a complex variable are solutions of Laplace's equation, and that quantities which are governed by Laplace's equation in the x–y plane also are governed by Laplace's equation in the u–v plane if u and v are related to x and y by an analytic function, combine to make conformal transformations a useful tool in the study of many problems in engineering and science. However, these applications are not directly related to vibration analysis, so are not included here.

A1.5 Matrix Algebra

This section is intended to explain matrix algebra only to the extent necessary for an understanding of the matrix manipulations used in the text. These manipulations are all elementary.

Definitions. A "matrix" is an array of numbers or variables. The array need not have an equal number of rows and columns, but if it does, the matrix is called a "square matrix." If a matrix has only one row or column, it is called a "row matrix" or "column matrix" or "vector." In this text a column matrix is identified with braces, { }, while all other matrices are identified with brackets, [ ]. Two matrices are equal only if each of the corresponding individual numbers or "elements" of the matrices are equal. The array of numbers known as a matrix does not have some equivalent simpler form such as a determinant has. However, sometimes the determinant of a square matrix may be required, which really means the determinant of the same array as the matrix. If the determinant of a square matrix is zero, the matrix is said to be "singular"; otherwise, it is "nonsingular." A nonsingular square matrix has an "inverse" or "reciprocal matrix" which, when multiplied by the matrix in accordance with rules to be explained shortly, yields the "unit matrix." The "unit matrix" is a square matrix consisting of zeros everywhere except on the "main diagonal" (the diagonal from upper left to lower right); each of these numbers must be unity. A "diagonal matrix" is a square matrix having all its elements zero except on the main diagonal; the elements on the main diagonal may be, and usually are, different from zero. A matrix, square or not, having all zero elements is referred to as a "null matrix." A "symmetrical matrix" is symmetrical with respect to the main diagonal, or $a_{ij} = a_{ji}$ where a_{ij} is an element, the first subscript designates the row number of the element and the second subscript designates the column number of the element. The "transpose" of a matrix $[A]$ is formed by interchanging the rows and columns and is often designated $[\tilde{A}]$ or $[A]'$. Thus, if the matrix $[A]$ is formed from the elements a_{ij}, the transpose matrix $[\tilde{A}]$ is formed from the elements a_{ji}.

Matrix Addition. Matrices may be added or subtracted by adding or subtracting the individual elements. However, each matrix must have the same shape if the matrices are to be added or subtracted. Examples follow.

$$\begin{bmatrix} 1 & 2 \\ 3 & -1 \\ 5 & -3 \end{bmatrix} + \begin{bmatrix} 0 & -2 \\ 4 & 1 \\ -3 & 2 \end{bmatrix} = \begin{bmatrix} 1 & 0 \\ 7 & 0 \\ 2 & -1 \end{bmatrix}$$

$$\begin{bmatrix} 1 & 2 \\ 3 & -1 \\ 5 & -3 \end{bmatrix} - \begin{bmatrix} 0 & -2 \\ 4 & 1 \\ -3 & 2 \end{bmatrix} = \begin{bmatrix} 1 & 4 \\ -1 & -2 \\ 8 & -5 \end{bmatrix}$$

$$\begin{bmatrix} 1 & 2 \\ 3 & -1 \\ 5 & -3 \end{bmatrix} + \begin{bmatrix} 0 & -2 \\ 4 & 1 \end{bmatrix} =$$

This is not allowed. It is not permissible to add another row of zeros to the second matrix in order to make the matrices have the same shape.

Matrix Multiplication. Two elementary forms of multiplication are defined, "scalar multiplication" and "matrix multiplication." In scalar multiplication of a matrix by a number, each element in the matrix is multiplied by the number. For example,

$$2\begin{bmatrix} 1 & -2 & 3 \\ -4 & 2 & -1 \end{bmatrix} = \begin{bmatrix} 2 & -4 & 6 \\ -8 & 4 & -2 \end{bmatrix}$$

Matrix multiplication is defined only for matrices which are "conformable"; that is, the number of columns of the matrix on the left is equal to the number of rows of the matrix on the right, If $[A]$ and $[B]$ are conformable in the order $[A][B]$ and if $[C] = [A][B]$, and if the individual elements of the matrices are a_{ij}, b_{ij} and c_{ij}, then an element of the product matrix is defined as

$$c_{ij} = \sum_{k=1}^{n} a_{ik}b_{kj}$$

where n is the number of columns of $[A]$ and also rows of $[B]$. The product matrix $[C]$ should have the same number of rows as $[A]$ and the same number of columns as $[B]$. An example follows.

$$\underset{[A]}{\begin{bmatrix} 0 & 2 & 1 \\ 1 & -2 & -3 \end{bmatrix}} \underset{[B]}{\begin{bmatrix} 1 & 0 & 1 & 3 \\ -1 & 2 & -3 & -1 \\ 0 & 1 & 2 & 2 \end{bmatrix}} = \underset{[C]}{\begin{bmatrix} -2 & 5 & -4 & 0 \\ 3 & -7 & 1 & -1 \end{bmatrix}}$$

A typical element of $[C]$, say c_{13}, is formed from the first row of $[A]$ and the third column of $[B]$ as follows;

$$c_{13} = a_{11}b_{13} + a_{12}b_{23} + a_{13}b_{33} = (0)(1) + (2)(-3) + (1)(2) = -4$$

Notice that in the above example the matrices $[A]$ and $[B]$ could not have been multiplied in the reverse order because they would not be conformable in that order. (It is not permissible to simply add zeros where necessary to make the matrices conformable.) It is also probably apparent that even if the matrices were conformable in either order, the product would not necessarily be the same in either order. Since the order is important, the process of multiplication is further differentiated as "premultiplication" or "postmultiplication." In the above example $[B]$ is premultiplied by $[A]$ and also $[A]$ is postmultiplied by $[B]$.

The Inverse Matrix. Matrix division is not defined as such, but a somewhat analogous procedure to division is performed, which involves the matrix inverse. As mentioned earlier, a nonsingular square matrix has an inverse such that the product of the matrix and its inverse is the unit matrix. In this particular instance the order is unimportant, and a matrix either premultiplied or postmultiplied by its inverse yields the unit matrix. For instance, if

$$[A] = \begin{bmatrix} 1 & 2 & -1 \\ -2 & 1 & 0 \\ 0 & 1 & 2 \end{bmatrix}$$

for which the determinant of matrix $[A]$ is not zero, the inverse of $[A]$ (designated $[A]^{-1}$) will be shown later to be

$$[A]^{-1} = \frac{1}{12}\begin{bmatrix} 2 & -5 & 1 \\ 4 & 2 & 2 \\ -2 & -1 & 5 \end{bmatrix}$$

Multiplication of these matrices in either order yields the same result,

$$[A][A]^{-1} = [A]^{-1}[A] = \begin{bmatrix} 1 & 0 & 0 \\ 0 & 1 & 0 \\ 0 & 0 & 1 \end{bmatrix}$$

This allows a manipulation to be performed which is similar to ordinary division in algebra. That is, in algebra if $xy = z$, it is possible to divide each side by x and find $y = z/x$ or by y and find $x = z/y$. Similarly, if $[A][B] = [C]$, and if $[A]$ is a non singular square matrix, it would be possible to premultiply both sides by the inverse of $[A]$ to obtain

$$[A]^{-1}[A][B] = [A]^{-1}[C]$$

Since the product $[A]^{-1}[A]$ is the unit matrix and since it is easily verified that multiplication of any matrix by the unit matrix does not change the matrix, it is clear that

$$[1][B] = [A]^{-1}[C] \qquad \text{or} \quad [B] = [A]^{-1}[C]$$

It is seen that if $[A]$ and $[C]$ are known, $[B]$ can be found. Also, if $[B]$ is a nonsingular square matrix, and $[B]$ and $[C]$ are known and it is desired to find $[A]$, a similar procedure could be used as follows

$$[A][B][B]^{-1} = [C][B]^{-1} \qquad \text{or} \quad [A][1] = [C][B]^{-1} \qquad \text{or} \quad [A] = [C][B]^{-1}$$

In these examples the similarity to ordinary algebraic division is readily appreciated, as well as some of the differences. In the algebraic equation $xy = z$, it does not matter whether $y = (1/x)(z)$ or $y = (z)(1/x)$, but in the matrix equation $[A][B] = [C]$, $[B] = [A]^{-1}[C]$ is correct, but $[B] = [C][A]^{-1}$ is not. This is true because if both sides were postmultiplied by $[A]^{-1}$, the result would be $[A][B][A]^{-1} = [C][A]^{-1}$, and there is no guarantee that $[A][B][A]^{-1}$ is the same as just $[B]$. The matrices $[A]$ and $[A]^{-1}$ must be adjacent to each other if they are to be replaced by the unit matrix. It should also be emphasized that only square, nonsingular matrices have inverses. If the matrix equation, $[A]\{B\} = \{C\}$, were encountered, where $[A]$ is a square, nonsingular matrix, and $\{B\}$ and $\{C\}$ are column matrices it would be possible to solve for $\{B\}$ from $\{B\} = [A]^{-1}\{C\}$ as above, but it would not be possible to solve for $[A]$ from, say, $[A] = \{C\}\{B\}^{-1}$, because the inverse of a nonsquare matrix such as $\{B\}$ is not defined.

It is obviously important to be able to obtain the inverse of a square, nonsingular matrix. One elementary means of doing this is described below. If one starts with two matrices, the one to be inverted and the unit matrix, and premultiplies each of these by a succession of matrices until the original matrix is converted into the unit matrix, then the matrix which was originally the unit matrix will have been converted into the inverse matrix. This is clear from a consideration of the following. Say that the inverse of $[A]$ is to be obtained. Premultiply by $[B]$, $[C]$, etc.

$$\underbrace{\cdots\overbrace{[C][B]}^{[A]^{-1}}[A]}_{[1]} \qquad \Bigg| \qquad \underbrace{\cdots\overbrace{[C][B]}^{[A]^{-1}}[1]}_{[A]^{-1}}$$

If the left side eventually becomes the unit matrix, then the series of matrix multiplications, $\ldots[C][B]$, must be $[A]^{-1}$ and this must be what appears on the right side. The process of premultiplication can be shown to cause manipulation by rows. For instance, the matrix

$$\begin{bmatrix} 0 & 1 & 0 \\ 1 & 0 & 0 \\ 0 & 0 & 1 \end{bmatrix}$$

premultiplying a matrix would simply cause the interchange of the first and second rows of the matrix, and the matrix

$$\begin{bmatrix} 1 & 2 & 0 \\ 0 & 1 & 0 \\ 0 & 0 & 1 \end{bmatrix}$$

would cause twice the second row to be added to the first row. It is not necessary to determine the form of the matrix being used for the premultiplication so long as each operation is a manipulation by rows. The following example demonstrates this method for the matrix whose inverse was used earlier.

$$[A] = \begin{bmatrix} 1 & 2 & -1 \\ -2 & 1 & 0 \\ 0 & 1 & 2 \end{bmatrix}$$

$$[A] = \begin{bmatrix} 1 & 2 & -1 \\ -2 & 1 & 0 \\ 0 & 1 & 2 \end{bmatrix} \qquad [1] = \begin{bmatrix} 1 & 0 & 0 \\ 0 & 1 & 0 \\ 0 & 0 & 1 \end{bmatrix}$$

Use the first row to reduce the off-diagonal elements of the first column to zero. Multiply first row by 2 and add to second row.

$$\begin{bmatrix} 1 & 2 & -1 \\ 0 & 5 & -2 \\ 0 & 1 & 2 \end{bmatrix} \qquad \begin{bmatrix} 1 & 0 & 0 \\ 2 & 1 & 0 \\ 0 & 0 & 1 \end{bmatrix}$$

The first row must not be used again to reduce other elements to zero, because the elements in the first column would become non-zero. Use the second row to reduce off-diagonal elements of the second column to zero. Multiply second row by $\frac{1}{5}$.

$$\begin{bmatrix} 1 & 2 & -1 \\ 0 & 1 & -\frac{2}{5} \\ 0 & 1 & 2 \end{bmatrix} \qquad \begin{bmatrix} 1 & 0 & 0 \\ \frac{2}{5} & \frac{1}{5} & 0 \\ 0 & 0 & 1 \end{bmatrix}$$

Multiply second row by -1 and add to third row and multiply second row by -2 and add to first row.

$$\begin{bmatrix} 1 & 0 & -\frac{1}{5} \\ 0 & 1 & -\frac{2}{5} \\ 0 & 0 & \frac{12}{5} \end{bmatrix} \qquad \begin{bmatrix} \frac{1}{5} & -\frac{2}{5} & 0 \\ \frac{2}{5} & \frac{1}{5} & 0 \\ -\frac{2}{5} & -\frac{1}{5} & 1 \end{bmatrix}$$

Use the third row to reduce the off-diagonal elements of the third column to zero. Multiply third row by 5/12.

$$\begin{bmatrix} 1 & 0 & -\frac{1}{5} \\ 0 & 1 & -\frac{2}{5} \\ 0 & 0 & 1 \end{bmatrix} \qquad \begin{bmatrix} \frac{1}{5} & -\frac{2}{5} & 0 \\ \frac{2}{5} & \frac{1}{5} & 0 \\ -\frac{1}{6} & -\frac{1}{12} & \frac{5}{12} \end{bmatrix}$$

Multiply third row by $\frac{1}{5}$ and add to first row and multiply third row by $\frac{2}{5}$ and add to second row.

$$[1] = \begin{bmatrix} 1 & 0 & 0 \\ 0 & 1 & 0 \\ 0 & 0 & 1 \end{bmatrix} \qquad [A]^{-1} = \begin{bmatrix} \frac{1}{6} & -\frac{5}{12} & \frac{1}{12} \\ \frac{1}{3} & \frac{1}{6} & \frac{1}{6} \\ -\frac{1}{6} & -\frac{1}{12} & \frac{5}{12} \end{bmatrix}$$

Since the matrix on the left is the unit matrix, the one on the right is the inverse of $[A]$. This is the same as previously verified to be $[A]^{-1}$. The process can work equally well with columns, corresponding to postmultiplication by the intermediate matrices, and can also be modified to use an intermixing of row and column manipulation, though there is no advantage to be gained from doing this.

This method must be modified somewhat, when programmed for computer solution, in order to minimize round-off errors. Consider the following matrix for example, performing the operations in the order indicated earlier. If it is assumed that only eight significant figures are retained, then the elements in the second and third rows of the matrix on the left are lost when the first row is multiplied by -10^{10} and 10^{11} and added to the second and third rows respectively to obtain zeros in the first column.

$$[A] = \begin{bmatrix} 10^{-10} & 10^{10} & 1 \\ 1 & 2 & 1 \\ -10 & 1 & 1 \end{bmatrix} \qquad [1] = \begin{bmatrix} 1 & 0 & 0 \\ 0 & 1 & 0 \\ 0 & 0 & 1 \end{bmatrix}$$

$$\begin{bmatrix} 1 & 10^{20} & 10^{10} \\ 0 & -10^{20} & -10^{10} \\ 0 & 10^{21} & 10^{11} \end{bmatrix} \qquad \begin{bmatrix} 10^{10} & 0 & 0 \\ -10^{10} & 1 & 0 \\ 10^{11} & 0 & 1 \end{bmatrix}$$

The second and third rows of the matrix on the left are now proportional, so this matrix appears to be a singular matrix, an erroneous indication for the original matrix.

This erroneous result could have been avoided by always pivoting on the element having the largest absolute value; in this instance, the element 10^{10} instead of 10^{-10}. An easy way to do this is to move the element having the largest absolute value to the main diagonal by trading rows and then reducing the other elements in that column to zero as described previously.

$$\begin{bmatrix} 10^{-10} & 10^{10} & 1 \\ 1 & 2 & 1 \\ -10 & 1 & 1 \end{bmatrix} \qquad \begin{bmatrix} 1 & 0 & 0 \\ 0 & 1 & 0 \\ 0 & 0 & 1 \end{bmatrix}$$

$$\begin{bmatrix} 1 & 2 & 1 \\ 10^{-10} & 10^{10} & 1 \\ -10 & 1 & 1 \end{bmatrix} \qquad \begin{bmatrix} 0 & 1 & 0 \\ 1 & 0 & 0 \\ 0 & 0 & 1 \end{bmatrix}$$

$$\begin{bmatrix} 1 & 0 & 1 \\ 10^{-20} & 1 & 10^{-10} \\ -10 & 0 & 1 \end{bmatrix} \qquad \begin{bmatrix} -2 \times 10^{-10} & 1 & 0 \\ 10^{-10} & 0 & 0 \\ -10^{-10} & 0 & 1 \end{bmatrix}$$

In subsequent manipulations, the second row is never again used to reduce other elements to zero, so the second row and column (containing the pivotal element) are excluded when the matrix on the left is examined to determine the element having the largest absolute value, to be used in the next step. The element having the largest absolute value is -10. (Row 2 and Column 2 are excluded from the search.) Therefore, the next step is to trade the first and third rows in order to bring this element to the main diagonal, after which off-diagonal elements in the first column are reduced to zero, as usual. If the computation continues in this way, always using the element having the largest absolute value for the pivotal element (excluding rows and columns containing earlier pivotal elements from the search for the largest absolute value), round-off errors can be minimized.

Partitioned Matrix. Occasionally, there is advantage to be gained from partitioning large matrices into smaller submatrices. Operations with the large matrices can then be performed using the smaller submatrices. This is immediately clear for addition and subtraction. Care must be taken that the submatrices form conformable pairs when multiplication is required. For instance, the example used to illustrate matrix multiplication could be partitioned as indicated below

$$\left[\begin{array}{cc|c} 0 & 2 & 1 \\ 1 & -2 & -3 \end{array}\right] \left[\begin{array}{cc|cc} 1 & 0 & 1 & 3 \\ -1 & 2 & -3 & -1 \\ \hline 0 & 1 & 2 & 2 \end{array}\right] = [C]$$

Let

$$[D] = \begin{bmatrix} 0 & 2 \\ 1 & -2 \end{bmatrix} \qquad \{E\} = \begin{Bmatrix} 1 \\ -3 \end{Bmatrix}$$

$$[F] = \begin{bmatrix} 1 & 0 \\ -1 & 2 \end{bmatrix} \qquad [G] = \begin{bmatrix} 1 & 3 \\ -3 & -1 \end{bmatrix}$$

$$[H] = [0 \quad 1] \qquad [J] = [2 \quad 2]$$

The product matrix, $[C]$, can be formed from the individual matrices in the proper location, each "element" of the product matrix being formed in the same way as previously defined except that the multiplications involved are matrix multiplications.

$$[D \quad E]\begin{bmatrix} F & G \\ H & J \end{bmatrix} = \left[(DF + EH) \,\middle|\, (DG + EJ)\right] = \left[\begin{array}{cc|cc} -2 & 5 & -4 & 0 \\ 3 & -7 & 1 & -1 \end{array}\right]$$

The last matrix above can be verified by multiplying out

$$[D][F] + \{E\}[H] \qquad \text{and} \qquad [D][G] + \{E\}[J]$$

One is tempted to consider inversion of large matrices by partitioning. However, the inverse of a large matrix is not necessarily composed of the inverses of the smaller matrices in the appropriate positions. Even so, it is possible to use a partitioning technique, but somewhere in the process inverses of smaller submatrices will be required, and it is possible that these may be singular even though the larger matrix is nonsingular. This somewhat limits the usefulness of partitioning for the purpose of matrix inversion.

Reversal Law. The "reversal law" for the inverse and transpose matrix is sometimes useful. As applied to the inverse it states that the inverse of the product of several square, nonsingular matrices is the product of the individual inverses but in reverse order. That is, if $[A] = [B][C][D]\ldots$, where all matrices are square and nonsingular, then $[A]^{-1} = \ldots [D]^{-1}[C]^{-1}[B]^{-1}$. A similar rule applies for the transpose. That is, $[\tilde{A}] = \ldots[\tilde{D}][\tilde{C}][\tilde{B}]$. Here, however, the matrices do not have to be square or nonsingular. It should be noted, however, that whenever more than two matrices are multiplied together, every matrix must be conformable with each of the matrices immediately adjacent to it.

Solution of Simultaneous Equations. This review of matrix algebra will close with a short discussion of perhaps the most common and elementary application of matrix notation and manipulation; namely, the solution of simultaneous algebraic equations. Suppose the following set of equations were derived from a physical problem.

$$\begin{aligned} x_1 + 2x_2 - x_3 &= F_1 \\ -2x_1 + x_2 \phantom{{}- x_3} &= F_2 \\ x_2 + 2x_3 &= F_3 \end{aligned}$$

The quantities x_1, x_2, and x_3 are unknowns whose values are desired, and F_1, F_2, and F_3 are quantities which would ordinarily be known but might have different values for different problems.

A matrix equation can be formed which will express these equations. A square matrix, $[A]$, of the coefficients of the unknowns, and two column matrices, $\{x\}$ and $\{F\}$, are formed as follows.

$$[A] = \begin{bmatrix} 1 & 2 & -1 \\ -2 & 1 & 0 \\ 0 & 1 & 2 \end{bmatrix} \qquad \{x\} = \begin{Bmatrix} x_1 \\ x_2 \\ x_3 \end{Bmatrix} \qquad \{F\} = \begin{Bmatrix} F_1 \\ F_2 \\ F_3 \end{Bmatrix}$$

The matrix equation expressing the set of algebraic equations is then $[A]\{x\} = \{F\}$, as can be verified by multiplying out the two matrices on the left.

$$\begin{bmatrix} 1 & 2 & -1 \\ -2 & 1 & 0 \\ 0 & 1 & 2 \end{bmatrix} \begin{Bmatrix} x_1 \\ x_2 \\ x_3 \end{Bmatrix} = \begin{Bmatrix} F_1 \\ F_2 \\ F_3 \end{Bmatrix}$$

$$\begin{bmatrix} (x_1 + 2x_2 - x_3) \\ (-2x_1 + x_2 + 0x_3) \\ (0x_1 + x_2 + 2x_3) \end{bmatrix} = \begin{Bmatrix} F_1 \\ F_2 \\ F_3 \end{Bmatrix}$$

Two matrices are equal only if their corresponding elements are equal. Equating each of the corresponding elements of the last equation results in the three algebraic equations, showing that these algebraic equations are indeed properly expressed by the equation

$$[A]\{x\} = \{F\}$$

If the algebraic equations are all independent, the matrix $[A]$ will be nonsingular and unknowns can be solved from

$$\{x\} = [A]^{-1}\{F\}$$

For the example chosen $[A]^{-1}$ is available

$$\begin{Bmatrix} x_1 \\ x_2 \\ x_3 \end{Bmatrix} = \frac{1}{12} \begin{bmatrix} 2 & -5 & 1 \\ 4 & 2 & 2 \\ -2 & -1 & 5 \end{bmatrix} \begin{Bmatrix} F_1 \\ F_2 \\ F_3 \end{Bmatrix} = \begin{Bmatrix} \left(\frac{2}{12} F_1 - \frac{5}{12} F_2 + \frac{1}{12} F_3\right) \\ \left(\frac{4}{12} F_1 + \frac{2}{12} F_2 + \frac{2}{12} F_3\right) \\ \left(-\frac{2}{12} F_1 - \frac{1}{12} F_2 + \frac{5}{12} F_3\right) \end{Bmatrix}$$

Since F_1, F_2, and F_3 are known, x_1, x_2, and x_3 are easily obtained by setting corresponding elements equal in this last matrix equation.

Of course, the labor associated with the simultaneous solution of equations has not been avoided by use of matrices, because the matrix inversion process requires about the same amount of work. However, perhaps the "bookkeeping" is better organized with the matrix method. Also, many physical systems are characterized by equations for which the left side coefficients remain constant but the quantities F_1, F_2, F_3, take on different values for different phases of the investigation. Under such circumstances the matrix solution may offer some advantages since the inversion would only have to be performed once, the multiplication $[A]^{-1}\{F\}$ requiring relatively little effort.

The above discussion of matrix algebra should be sufficient for an understanding of the matrix equations used in the text.

A1.6 Fourier Series

Repeating Function Described by a Series. It is often convenient to be able to express a function which repeats itself periodically as a series of sine and cosine functions.

For example, a repeating force which excites a vibrating system might not be a pure sine curve, as used in Chapter 3, and elsewhere in the text. If this force were one which consistently repeated itself at intervals, as indicated in Fig. A1-12, it is possible to represent the force by the following equation, in which T is the repeat interval.

$$F(t) = A_0 + \sum_{n=1}^{\infty} A_n \cos\left(n\frac{2\pi t}{T}\right) + B_n \sin\left(n\frac{2\pi t}{T}\right) \tag{A1-44}$$

Certain conditions must be observed about the form of $F(t)$ in order that it may be represented by such a series. It must be single valued (except that finite discontinuities are allowed) must have no infinite discontinuities, and a finite number of finite discontinuities or maximum and minimum points in a finite interval.

Functions of interest as forcing functions for a vibrating system would satisfy these requirements. For such functions the series indicated by Equation A1-44 would converge and represent the function at all points, except that at discontinuities it would give a value which is the average of the values of the function immediately adjacent on each side of the discontinuity. The more uneven the function, the slower will be the convergence. This is illustrated in Example A1-21.

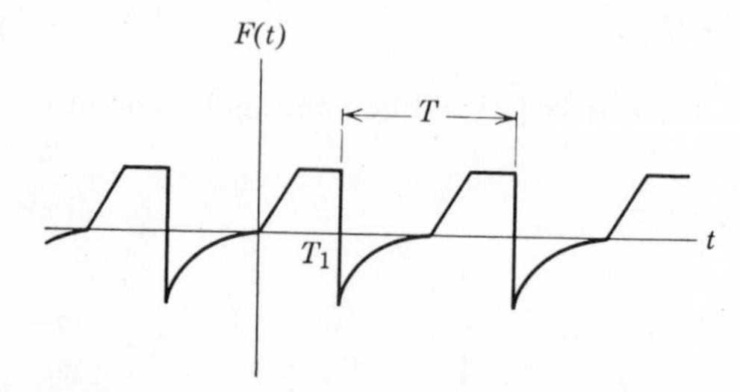

Fig. A1-12

Coefficients of the Series. The coefficients in Equation A1-44 can be determined by making use of a property of orthogonal functions which in this instance states that the product of any two of the functions integrated over the repeat interval results in zero unless the two functions are identical. Thus, if A_2 were desired, multiply left and right sides of Equation A1-34 by $\cos[2(2\pi t/T)]\,dt$ and integrate from $t = T_1$ to $t = (T_1 + T)$. All terms on the right side would be identically zero except the term

$$\int_{t=T_1}^{T+T_1} A_2 \cos\left(2\frac{2\pi t}{T}\right) \cos\left(2\frac{2\pi t}{T}\right) dt$$

On the left would be

$$\int_{t=T_1}^{T+T_1} F(t) \cos\left(2\frac{2\pi t}{T}\right) dt$$

A_2 could then be obtained without difficulty. This procedure leads to the following equation for the coefficients.

$$A_0 = \frac{1}{T}\int_{t=T_1}^{T+T_1} F(t)\,dt$$

$$A_n = \frac{2}{T}\int_{t=T_1}^{T+T_1} F(t)\cos\left(n\frac{2\pi t}{T}\right)dt \qquad \text{(A1-45)}$$

$$B_n = \frac{2}{T}\int_{t=T_1}^{T+T_1} F(t)\sin\left(n\frac{2\pi t}{T}\right)dt$$

The value of T_1, the lower end of the integration interval, may be zero, or any convenient value, not necessarily a point of discontinuity as indicated in Fig. A1-12. A digital computer program is provided in Reference 1 for the determination of the coefficients of Equation A1-45.

Some simplification occurs if the function itself is either an even function or an odd function. For even functions the sine terms are missing ($B_n = 0$ for all n) and for odd functions the cosine terms are missing ($A_n = 0$ for all n), but these results would occur automatically when Equation A1-45 is applied. However, some computational effort is saved if the time zero axis is determined so that the function can be rendered either even or odd if that is

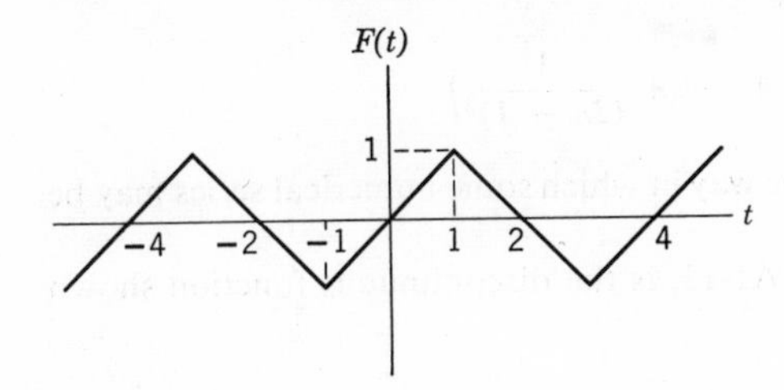

Fig. A1-13

possible for the given function. In either event, the repeat interval may then be taken as extending from $t = -T/2$ to $t = +T/2$ and because of the symmetry the integration need only go from $t = 0$ to $t = T/2$, the result then being doubled to account for the other region.

Complex Form. Another form of the series may be derived in terms of complex exponentials. The procedure is the same as that used to develop Equation A1-45 and the results are as follows.

$$F(t) = \sum_{n=-\infty}^{+\infty} c_n e^{in(2\pi t/T)}$$

$$c_n = \frac{1}{T}\int_{t=T_1}^{T+T_1} F(t)\,e^{-in(2\pi t/T)} \qquad \text{(A1-46)}$$

Example A1-21. Discuss the Fourier series representation of the function shown in Fig. A1-13.

The function is an odd function. Therefore, A_0 and $A_n = 0$. The repeat interval is 4 Therefore

$$B_n = \frac{2}{4}\int_{t=-2}^{+2} F(t)\sin\left(n\frac{2\pi t}{4}\right)dt$$

However, because of the symmetry about the $t = 0$ axis, the integration only need be performed from $t = 0$ to $t = 2$.

$$B_n = 2\left(\frac{2}{4}\right)\left[\int_{t=0}^{1} t\sin n\frac{2\pi t}{4}\,dt + \int_{t=1}^{2}(2-t)\sin n\frac{2\pi t}{4}\,dt\right]$$

Because of the further symmetry about the $t = 1$ point (for this function—not all odd functions), the contribution of each of these integrals is equal in magnitude, but for even values of n the signs are opposite. Consequently

$$B_n = 0, \; n \text{ even}$$

$$B_n = (2)(2)\left(\frac{2}{4}\right)\int_{t=0}^{1} t \sin n\frac{2\pi t}{4}\, dt$$

$$= (-1)^{(n-1)/2}\frac{8}{\pi^2 n^2}, \; n \text{ odd}$$

The Fourier series is

$$F(t) = \frac{8}{\pi^2}\left(\sin\frac{\pi t}{2} - \frac{1}{9}\sin\frac{3\pi t}{2} + \frac{1}{25}\sin\frac{5\pi t}{2} - \cdots\right)$$

Notice that the constants which multiply the successive terms decrease according to $1/n^2$. The series converges rather rapidly. If this $F(t)$ were a forcing function in a vibration problem, the possibility of a resonance exists at any of the frequencies, $\pi/2$, $3\pi/2$, $5\pi/2$, $7\pi/2$ etc. rad/sec, but the higher frequencies would not be excited very much if damping were present.

Notice that at $t = 1$ the above series should give unity, since the original function is unity at $t = 1$, so

$$1 = \frac{8}{\pi^2}\left(1 + \frac{1}{9} + \frac{1}{25} + \cdots + \frac{1}{(2n-1)^2}\right)$$

or $\sum_{n=1}^{\infty} 1/(2n-1)^2 = \pi^2/8$. This illustrates one way in which some numerical series may be evaluated by use of the Fourier series.

The derivative of the function, $f(t)$, of Fig. A1-13, is the discontinuous function shown in Fig. A1-14.

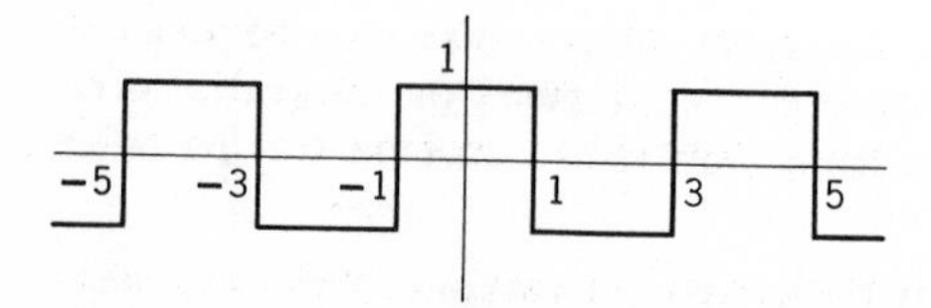

Fig. A1-14

This is an even function which could be represented by a Fourier series and the coefficients evaluated in the same way as before, except that since the function is an even function, there would be no sine terms, only cosine terms. However, it is easier to obtain the series by differentiating the series for $F(t)$ term by term, obtaining

$$F'(t) = \int_{n=1}^{\infty} (-1)^{(n-1)/2}\frac{8}{\pi^2 n^2}\frac{d}{dt}\left(\sin n\frac{2\pi t}{4}\right)$$

$$= \sum_{n=1}^{\infty} (-1)^{(n-1)/2}\frac{4}{\pi n}\cos n\frac{2\pi t}{4}, \; n \text{ odd}$$

$$= \frac{4}{\pi}\left(\cos\frac{\pi}{2}t - \frac{1}{3}\cos\frac{3\pi t}{2} + \frac{1}{5}\cos\frac{5\pi t}{2} - \cdots\right)$$

Notice that at the discontinuity ($t = 1$), the series gives zero for this function, which is the average of $+1$ and -1 immediately to each side of the discontinuity.

The series for $F'(t)$ does not converge as rapidly as for $F(t)$. The coefficients of successive terms only decrease as $1/n$ rather than $1/n^2$. If another differentiation were attempted, the new series would not converge at all, since another n would come out of the differentiation of $\cos n(2\pi t/4)$ and each term in the series would be as important as any other term. This is a characteristic of Fourier series in general. Differentiation leads to more slowly convergent series until the function which exhibits a finite discontinuity is reached. Further differentiation results in a divergent series. On the other hand, integration of the series results in a more rapidly convergent series.

To complete the discussion of Example A1.21, the complex exponential form of the series for the discontinuous function above, $F'(t)$, will be computed. From Equation A1-46,

$$c_n = \frac{1}{4}\int_{t=-2}^{+2} F'(t)\, e^{-in(2\pi t/4)}\, dt$$

$$= \frac{1}{4}\left[\int_{-2}^{-1} (-1)\, e^{-in(2\pi t/4)}\, dt + \int_{-1}^{+1} (1)\, e^{-in(2\pi t/4)}\, dt + \int_{1}^{2} (-1)\, e^{-in(2\pi t/4)}\, dt\right]$$

$$= \frac{1}{4}\left(\frac{-4}{in2\pi}\right)[-e^{in(2\pi/4)} + e^{in(2\pi 2/4)} + e^{-in(2\pi/4)} - e^{in(2\pi/4)} - e^{-in(2\pi 2/4)} + e^{-in(2\pi/4)}]$$

$$c_n = \frac{2}{\pi n}\sin\frac{n\pi}{2}$$

Therefore, the series of complex terms is

$$\sum_{n=-\infty}^{+\infty} c_n\, e^{in(2\pi t/4)}$$

or

$$F'(t) = \cdots \frac{-2}{3\pi}e^{-i(-3)(2\pi t/4)} + 0\, e^{-i(-2)(2\pi t/4)} + \frac{2}{\pi}e^{-i(-1)(2\pi t/4)} + 0\, e^{0}$$
$$+ \frac{2}{\pi}e^{i(1)(2\pi t/4)} + 0\, e^{i(2)(2\pi t/4)} - \frac{2}{3\pi}e^{i(3)(2\pi t/4)} + \cdots$$

This series is seen to be the same as the series of real terms previously computed, or

$$F'(t) = \frac{4}{\pi}\left(\cos\frac{\pi t}{2} - \frac{1}{3}\cos\frac{3\pi t}{2} + \frac{1}{5}\cos\frac{5\pi t}{2} - \cdots\right)$$

There is no advantage in using the complex form instead of the real form, but an understanding of this form makes the extension to the Fourier integral described in Chapter 17 a little easier.

A1.7 Elements of Calculus of Variations

One Dependent and One Independent Variable. In the text occasional use is made of certain aspects of the calculus of variations. The following discussion is intended to be a review of this subject. Although time is often the independent variable in dynamics problems, it is probably more convenient for conceptual purposes to use ordinary Cartesian variables, x and y, for this discussion. Suppose that x is the independent variable and y the dependent variable, and $y = y(x)$ is a "path" between two values of x, x_1 and x_2. If $F(x, y, y', y'' \ldots)$ is a function whose value is determined at x by the value of x; y, dy/dx, d^2y/dx^2, etc. as indicated, the integral of this function between limits x_1 and x_2 often is of interest.

$$I = \int_{x1}^{x_2} F(x, y, y', y'', \ldots)\, dx \qquad \text{(A1-47)}$$

To illustrate Equation A1-47 in an elementary way, determine the distance along a path in the x–y plane. A differential distance along the path is

$$ds = \sqrt{dx^2 + dy^2} = \sqrt{1 + \left(\frac{dy}{dx}\right)^2}\, dx$$

and the total length of the path between x_1 and x_2 is

$$I = \int_{x_1}^{x_2} \sqrt{1 + y'^2}\, dx \tag{A1-47a}$$

It happens that in this special example the function to be integrated, $F(x, y, y', y'' \ldots) = \sqrt{1 + y'^2}$, does not have all the possible variables in it, containing as it does only y' and not x, y, y'', etc. However, it is still a function of the type specified in Equation A1-47. Now if some $y(x)$ were selected, $y'(x)$ would be known and the integration could be completed.

Usually the problem in the calculus of variations is to determine the $y(x)$ which will make I of Equation A1-47 a maximum or minimum. This is analogous to determining the maximum or minimum point of a curve in ordinary differential calculus. In ordinary calculus this point is determined by finding a point such that the function does not change for small excursions to either side of the point. Similarly, in the calculus of variations the $y(x)$ which will maximize or minimize I is determined such that for small arbitrary changes in $y(x)$, I will not change. Therefore, it is necessary to be able to determine the "variation" of I when $y(x)$ is varied a small arbitrary amount.

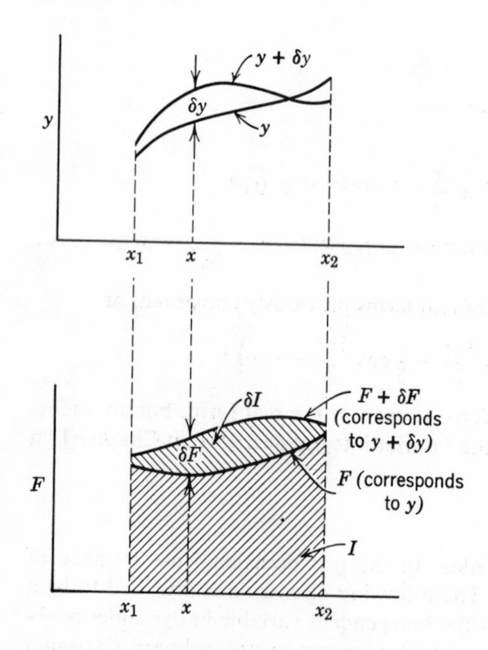

Fig. A1-15 Illustrating "varied" quantities, δy, δF, δI

The variation of $y(x)$ is itself a function of x, since the change in $y(x)$ must be specified at all values of x. Let changes caused by this variation of the function $y(x)$ be indicated with the symbol δ. δy is the variation of y and is an entire function of x. However, it is an arbitrary function; that is, it can be made any function desired, except that it is supposed to be kept very small (infinitesimal in the limit). Of course, when $y(x)$ is changed this way, the various derivatives of $y(x)$ are also changed. Let $\delta y'$, $\delta y''$, etc., indicate the variation of y', y'', etc., and these are also functions of x. Since these quantities appear in the function, F, it follows that this function is varied when y is varied, and δF indicates this variation. Again, δF must be a function of x. However, no quantity δx will exist since x is the independent variable and not subject to arbitrary change. When the function, F, is integrated between the limits, a different value of I will result and the variation of I from the original value will be indicated as δI. These relationships are indicated in Fig. A1-15.

Inspection of Fig. A1-15 indicates that

$$\delta I = \int_{x_1}^{x_2} \delta F \, dx \tag{A1-48}$$

Now since F changes whenever y, y', y'', etc. are changed, it is clear that all of these changes must be accounted for in calculating δF at any point x.

$$\delta F = \frac{\partial F}{\partial y}\delta y + \frac{\partial F}{\partial y'}\delta y' + \frac{\partial F}{\partial y''}\delta y'' + \cdots \tag{A1-49}$$

Substitute Equation A1-49 in Equation A1-48 to obtain

$$\delta I = \int_{x_1}^{x_2} \left(\frac{\partial F}{\partial y}\delta y + \frac{\partial F}{\partial y'}\delta y' + \frac{\partial F}{\partial y''}\delta y'' + \cdots\right) dx \tag{A1-50}$$

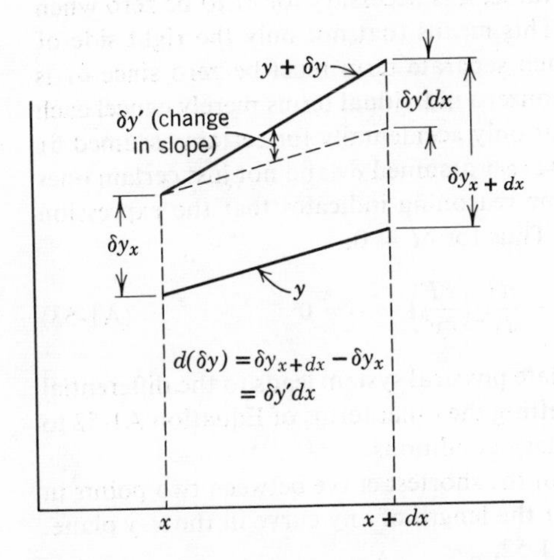

Fig. A1-16 Illustrating $\delta y' dx = d(\delta y)$

It is necessary to keep in mind that the symbol δ refers to changes resulting from changing $y(x)$ an arbitrary small amount, while the symbol d refers to changes resulting from small changes in the independent variable, x. Now examine the term

$$\int_{x_1}^{x_2} \frac{\partial F}{\partial y'}\delta y' \, dx$$

and integrate by parts, $\int u \, dv = uv - \int v \, du$, where $u = \partial F/\partial y'$ and $dv = \delta y' \, dx$.

Therefore
$$du = \frac{d}{dx}\left(\frac{\partial F}{\partial y'}\right) dx$$

and, as shown in Fig. A1-16,

$$dv = \delta y' \, dx = d(\delta y) \qquad \text{or} \quad v = \delta y$$

Therefore

$$\int_{x_1}^{x_2} \frac{\partial F}{\partial y'}\delta y' \, dx = \frac{\partial F}{\partial y'}\delta y\Big]_{x_1}^{x_2} - \int_{x_1}^{x_2}\left[\frac{d}{dx}\left(\frac{\partial F}{\partial y'}\right)\right](\delta y)\, dx \tag{A1-51}$$

Higher-order terms in Equation A1-50 can be handled in a similar way by successive integrations by parts and the results will be as indicated in Equation A1-52. Equation A1-52 shows the variation of the integral if the function F contains derivatives up to y'''. The pattern is clearly visible if F should contain even higher order terms.

$$\delta I = \int_{x_1}^{x_2} \left[\frac{\partial F}{\partial y} - \frac{d}{dx}\left(\frac{\partial F}{\partial y'}\right) + \frac{d^2}{dx^2}\left(\frac{\partial F}{\partial y''}\right) - \frac{d^3}{dx^3}\left(\frac{\partial F}{\partial y'''}\right)\right](\delta y)\,dx$$
$$+ \left\{\left[\frac{\partial F}{\partial y'} - \frac{d}{dx}\left(\frac{\partial F}{\partial y''}\right) + \frac{d^2}{dx^2}\left(\frac{\partial F}{\partial y'''}\right)\right](\delta y)\right\}_{x_1}^{x2}$$
$$+ \left\{\left[\frac{\partial F}{\partial y''} - \frac{d}{dx}\left(\frac{\partial F}{\partial y'''}\right)\right](\delta y')\right\}_{x_1}^{x_2} \qquad \text{(A1-52)}$$
$$+ \left\{\left(\frac{\partial F}{\partial y'''}\right)(\delta y'')\right\}_{x_1}^{x_2}$$

Now if I is to have a maximum or minimum value, it is necessary for δI to be zero when $y(x)$ is changed a small arbitrary amount, δy. This means that not only the right side of Equation A1-52 must be zero, but also that each separate term must be zero since δy is arbitrary, and therefore it is not sufficient that nonzero individual terms merely cancel each other, since this could not happen in general but only accidentally for certain assumed δy variations. It is necessary for δI to go to zero for *every* assumed δy and not just certain ones if I is to have its extreme value. Also, this same reasoning indicates that the expression within the bracket in the integral must be zero. Thus for $\delta I = 0$,

$$\frac{\partial F}{\partial y} - \frac{d}{dx}\left(\frac{\partial F}{\partial y'}\right) + \frac{d^2}{dx^2}\left(\frac{\partial F}{\partial y''}\right) - \frac{d^3}{dx^3}\left(\frac{\partial F}{\partial y''}\right) \cdots = 0 \qquad \text{(A1-53)}$$

Application of Equation A1-53 to an appropriate physical system leads to the differential equation of motion which governs the system. Setting the other terms of Equation A1-52 to zero yields mathematical expressions for boundary conditions.

As a simple example, determine the equation of the shortest curve between two points in the x–y plane. Equation A1-47a may be used for the length of any curve in the x–y plane. To minimize l, set $\delta l = 0$. Applying Equation A1-52,

$$\delta l = \int_{x_1}^{x_2} \left\{\frac{\partial}{\partial y}(\sqrt{1 + y'^2}) - \frac{d}{dx}\left[\frac{\partial}{\partial y'}(\sqrt{1 + y'^2})\right]\right\}(\delta y)\,dx$$
$$+ \left\{\left[\frac{\partial}{\partial y'}(\sqrt{1 - y'^2})\right](\delta y)\right\}_{x=x_2} - \left\{\left[\frac{\partial}{\partial y'}(\sqrt{1 - y'^2})\right](\delta y)\right\}_{x=x_1}$$

The first term inside the integral is zero, since y does not appear in $\sqrt{1 + y'^2}$. The differential equation for the shortest curve is therefore

$$\frac{d}{dx}\left[\frac{1}{2}(1 + y'^2)^{-1/2}2y'\right] = 0$$

or

$$\frac{y'}{\sqrt{1 + y'^2}} = c_1$$

or

$$\frac{dy}{dx} = \sqrt{\frac{c_1^2}{1 - c_1^2}} = c_2$$

whence

$$y = c_2 x + c_3$$

This is obviously the correct result for the shortest curve between two points in the x–y plane. In this instance the boundary conditions are that $\delta y_{x=x_2} = 0$ and $\delta y_{x=x_1} = 0$; that is, $y_{x=x_2} = y_2$ and $y_{x=x_1} = y_1$, since the two points are fixed and cannot be varied arbitrarily. On the other hand, if it were required to find the shortest line between two values of x, without specifying the values of y at the two points, then δy at $x = x_1$ or x_2 is not necessarily zero and it would be necessary for $\partial/\partial y'(1 - y'^2) = 0$ at x_1 and x_2. This would result in $y' = 0$ at these points, and any horizontal line would be the obviously correct result of the computation.

Example A1-22. Determine the differential equation and boundary condition equations for the deflection of a beam-column fixed at one end and free at the other, as indicated in Fig. A1-17.

When this structure is in its equilibrium deflected position any change in the deflection pattern would have to be accomplished by some additional external loads moving through deflections and therefore doing additional work on the system. Therefore, the system is in its lowest energy state when in the natural deflection pattern. The energy associated with a deflection pattern, $y(x)$, is $U = V - W$, where V is the strain energy stored in the beam fibers and W is the work done by the external loads, w and P, as the beam deflects into the

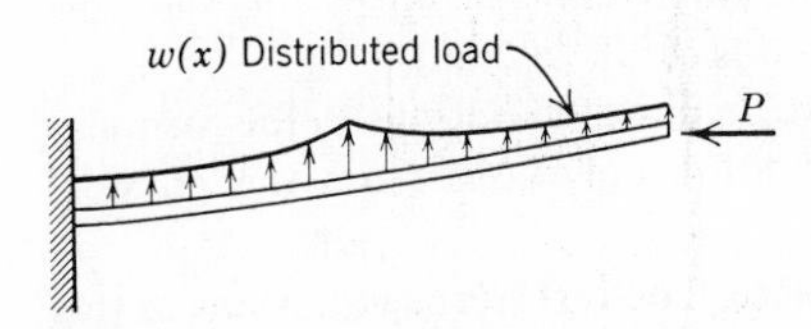

Fig. A1-17

deflection pattern. (Additional discussion of this point may be found in Chapter 13, Sections 13.5 and 13.6.)

If strain energy other than that associated with bending is neglected,

$$V = \int_0^L \frac{1}{2} EIy''^2 \, dx$$

The work done by the distributed load w is

$$W_w = \int_0^L wy \, dx$$

The work done by the load P is $P\Delta$ where

$$\Delta = \int_{x=0}^{L} \sqrt{dx^2 + dy^2} - L \doteq \int_0^L \left(1 + \frac{1}{2} y'^2\right) dx - L$$

$$\Delta = \int_0^L \frac{1}{2} y'^2 \, dx$$

$$W_p = \int_0^L \frac{1}{2} Py'^2 \, dx$$

Therefore

$$U = \int_0^L \left(-wy - \frac{1}{2} Py'^2 + \frac{1}{2} EIy''^2\right) dx$$

Now application of Equation A1-53 results in the differential equation

$$-w + P\frac{d^2y}{dx^2} + \frac{d^2}{dx^2}\left(EI\frac{d^2y}{dx^2}\right) = 0$$

This is the differential equation governing the deflection pattern, which may be confirmed by classical techniques. The other terms on the right side of Equation A1-52 must also be zero at each end of the beam, so

$$\left[\frac{\partial F}{\partial y'} - \frac{d}{dx}\left(\frac{\partial F}{\partial y''}\right)\right](\delta y) = 0$$

$$\left(\frac{\partial F}{\partial y''}\right)(\delta y') = 0$$

At the fixed end, $x = 0$, both δy and $\delta y'$ must be zero; that is, the boundary condition equations there are $y_0 = 0$ and $y_0' = 0$, or at least constants. At the free end, however, δy and $\delta y'$ may have arbitrary nonzero values. Therefore, $\partial F/\partial y'' = 0$ (which results in $EIy'' = 0$ or moment $= 0$), and

$$\frac{\partial F}{\partial y'} - \frac{d}{dx}\left(\frac{\partial F}{\partial y''}\right) = 0$$

(which results in $d(EIy'')^2/dx = -Py'$ or shear $= -P(dy/dx)$. The moment condition is not unexpected, but the fact that the shear is not zero is initially somewhat surprising until the boundary condition at the free end is reexamined with this result in mind.

This example illustrates the power and utility of the calculus of variations in the formulation of the differential equations and boundary condition equations from the physical problem.

Several Dependent Variables, One Independent Variable. The rest of the equations in this section will not be developed, but their development parallels that of the previous equations which apply to problems in which there is one dependent and one independent variable. Equations A1-54 and A1-55 apply to situations in which there are two dependent variables, y and z, and one independent variable, x, and the extension to more than two dependent variables is obvious.

$$I = \int_{x_1}^{x_2} F(x, y, z, y', z', y'', z'', \ldots)\, dx \tag{A1-54}$$

$$\begin{aligned}
\delta I = &\int_{x_1}^{x_2} \left[\frac{\partial F}{\partial y} - \frac{d}{dx}\left(\frac{\partial F}{\partial y'}\right) + \frac{d^2}{dx^2}\left(\frac{\partial F}{\partial y''}\right)\cdots\right](\delta y)\, dx \\
&+ \int_{x_1}^{x_2} \left[\frac{\partial F}{\partial z} - \frac{d}{dx}\left(\frac{\partial F}{\partial z'}\right) + \frac{d^2}{dx^2}\left(\frac{\partial F}{\partial z''}\right)\cdots\right](\delta z)\, dx \\
&+ \left\{\left[\frac{\partial F}{\partial y'} - \frac{d}{dx}\left(\frac{\partial F}{\partial y''}\right) + \cdots\right](\delta y)\right\}_{x_1}^{x_2} + \left\{\left[\frac{\partial F}{\partial y''} - \cdots\right](\delta y')\right\}_{x_1}^{x_2} + \cdots \\
&+ \left\{\left[\frac{\partial F}{\partial z'} - \frac{d}{dx}\left(\frac{\partial F}{\partial z''}\right) + \cdots\right](\delta z)\right\}_{x_1}^{x_2} + \left\{\left[\frac{\partial F}{\partial z''} - \cdots\right](\delta z')\right\}_{x_1}^{x_2} + \cdots
\end{aligned} \tag{A1-55}$$

If in this instance δI is to be zero it will be necessary for each individual term to be zero, as before. This will require that each of the terms within brackets under the integral signs be zero individually, which will lead to two ordinary differential equations which must be satisfied simultaneously. Also, the other terms will lead to appropriate boundary condition equations. Typical examples of applications of these equations may be obtained in Chapter 7 in connection with Lagrange equations for multiple-degree-of-freedom systems.

Several Independent Variables. Equations A1-56 and A1-57 apply to situations in which there are two independent variables, x and y, and one dependent variable, w. The similarity to Equations A1-47 and A1-52 is obvious. Extensions to higher derivatives and to more than two independent variables is easily made, and extension when more than one dependent variable is involved is also possible by reference to Equations A1-54 and A1-55. (This latter condition would result in simultaneous partial differential equations.) In Equations A1-56 and A1-57 the symbols w_x, w_{xx}, w_{xy} etc. mean partial derivatives. That is,

$$w_x = \frac{\partial w}{\partial x}, \quad w_{xx} = \frac{\partial^2 w}{\partial x^2}, \quad w_{xy} = \frac{\partial^2 w}{\partial x\, \partial y}, \text{ etc.}$$

Setting $\delta I = 0$ in Equation A1-57 results in a partial differential equation (when the quantity within the brackets inside the double integral is set equal to zero) and boundary condition equations (when the quantities within the brackets of the single integrals are set equal to zero). An example of the application of Equation A1-57 may be found in Chapter 13 in connection with Equation 13-9, which is the same as Equation A1-57.

This rather brief review of the elementary aspects of the variational calculus should be sufficient for an understanding of those portions of the text which make use of this subject.

$$I = \int_{x_1}^{x_2} \int_{y_1}^{y_2} F(x, y, w, w_x, w_y, w_{xx}, w_{xy}, w_{yy} \cdots)\, dy\, dx \tag{A1-56}$$

$$\begin{aligned}\delta I = \int_{x_1}^{x_2} \int_{y_1}^{y_2} \Big[\frac{\partial F}{\partial w} - \frac{\partial}{\partial x}\left(\frac{\partial F}{\partial w_x}\right) - \frac{\partial}{\partial y}\left(\frac{\partial F}{\partial w_y}\right) + \frac{\partial^2}{\partial x^2}\left(\frac{\partial F}{\partial w_{xx}}\right) \\ + \frac{\partial^2}{\partial x\, \partial y}\left(\frac{\partial F}{\partial w_{xy}}\right) + \frac{\partial^2}{\partial y^2}\left(\frac{\partial F}{\partial w_{yy}}\right) - \cdots\Big] (\delta w)\, dy\, dx \\ + \int_{y_1}^{y_2} \left\{\left[\frac{\partial F}{\partial w_x} - \frac{\partial}{\partial x}\left(\frac{\partial F}{\partial w_{xx}}\right) - \frac{\partial}{\partial y}\left(\frac{\partial F}{\partial w_{xy}}\right) + \cdots\right](\delta w)\right\}_{x=x_1}^{x=x_2} dy \\ + \int_{x_1}^{x_2} \left\{\left[\frac{\partial F}{\partial w_y} - \frac{\partial}{\partial y}\left(\frac{\partial F}{\partial w_{yy}}\right) - \frac{\partial}{\partial x}\left(\frac{\partial F}{\partial w_{xy}}\right) + \cdots\right](\delta w)\right\}_{y=y_1}^{y=y_2} dx \\ + \int_{y_1}^{y_2} \left\{\left[\frac{\partial F}{\partial w_{xx}} - \cdots\right](\delta w_x)\right\}_{x=x_1}^{x=x_2} dy + \int_{x_1}^{x_2} \left\{\left[\frac{\partial F}{\partial w_{yy}} - \cdots\left[(\delta w_y)\right\}_{y=y_1}^{y=y_2} dx \\ + \left\{\left(\frac{\partial F}{\partial w_{xy}}\right)(\delta w)\right\}_{\substack{x=x_1 \\ y=y_2}}^{\substack{x=x_2 \\ y=y_2}} + \left\{\left(\frac{\partial F}{\partial w_{xy}}\right)(\delta w)\right\}_{\substack{x=x_2 \\ y=y_1}}^{\substack{x=x_1 \\ y=y_1}}\end{aligned} \tag{A1-57}$$

APPENDIX 2

Fourth Degree Polynomial for solution of Differential Equations

The polynomial, $y = A_0 + A_1x + A_2x^2 + A_3x^3 + A_4x^4$, is assumed. This polynomial is made to fit the curve at five points not necessarily equally spaced along the x axis (Fig.

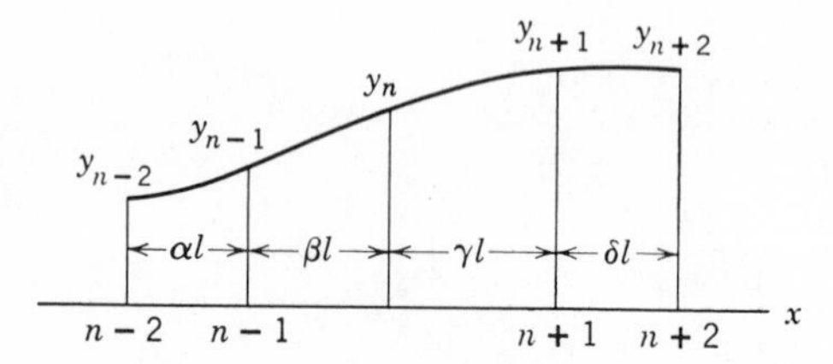

Fig. A2-1

A2-1). The nominal spacing is l, and differences from this spacing are accounted for by the factors α, β, γ, δ. The following relations are used to derive Equations A2-1 to A2-11.

$$
\begin{aligned}
\text{When} \quad x &= -(\alpha + \beta)l, & y &= y_{n-2} \\
x &= -\beta l, & y &= y_{n-1} \\
x &= 0, & y &= y_n \\
x &= \gamma l, & y &= y_{n+1} \\
x &= (\gamma + \delta)l, & y &= y_{n+2}
\end{aligned}
$$

$$y = A_0 + A_1x + A_2x^2 + A_3x^3 + A_4x^4$$

$$\frac{dx}{dy} = A_1 + 2A_2x + 3A_3x^2 + 4A_4x^3$$

$$\frac{d^2y}{dx^2} = 2A_2 + 6A_3x + 12A_4x^2$$

$$\frac{d^3y}{dx^3} = 6A_3 + 24A_4x$$

$$\frac{d^4y}{dx^4} = 24A_4$$

For the solution of differential equations with boundary conditions, all derivatives at the position n and the first three derivatives at the positions $n - 2$ and $n + 2$ are needed. These are given below.

$$\begin{aligned} d_{n-2} &= \alpha(\alpha + \beta)(\alpha + \beta + \gamma)(\alpha + \beta + \gamma + \delta) \\ d_{n-1} &= \alpha\beta(\beta + \gamma)(\beta + \gamma + \delta) \\ d_n &= \beta\gamma(\alpha + \beta)(\gamma + \delta) \\ d_{n+1} &= \gamma\delta(\beta + \gamma)(\alpha + \beta + \gamma) \\ d_{n+2} &= \delta(\gamma + \delta)(\beta + \gamma + \delta)(\alpha + \beta + \gamma + \delta) \end{aligned} \tag{A2-1}$$

$$\left(\frac{d^4y}{dx^4}\right)_n = \frac{24}{l^4}\left(\frac{y_{n-2}}{d_{n-2}} - \frac{y_{n-1}}{d_{n-1}} + \frac{y_n}{d_n} - \frac{y_{n+1}}{d_{n+1}} + \frac{y_{n+2}}{d_{n+2}}\right) \tag{A2-2}$$

$$\begin{aligned} \left(\frac{d^3y}{dx^3}\right)_{n-2} = \frac{6}{l^3}\Bigg[&-\frac{(4\alpha + 3\beta + 2\gamma + \delta)}{d_{n-2}} y_{n-2} + \frac{(3\alpha + 3\beta + 2\gamma + \delta)}{d_{n-1}} y_{n-1} \\ &- \frac{(3\alpha + 2\beta + 2\gamma + \delta)}{d_n} y_n + \frac{(3\alpha + 2\beta + \gamma + \delta)}{d_{n+1}} y_{n+1} \\ &- \frac{(3\alpha + 2\beta + \gamma)}{d_{n+2}}\Bigg] \end{aligned} \tag{A2-3}$$

$$\begin{aligned} \left(\frac{d^3y}{dx^3}\right)_n = \frac{6}{l^3}\Bigg[&\frac{(\beta - 2\gamma - \delta)}{d_{n-2}} y_{n-2} + \frac{(-\alpha - \beta + 2\gamma + \delta)}{d_{n-1}} y_{n-1} + \frac{(\alpha + 2\beta - 2\gamma - \delta)}{d_n} y_n \\ &+ \frac{(-\alpha - 2\beta + \gamma + \delta)}{d_{n+1}} y_{n+1} + \frac{(\alpha + 2\beta - \gamma)}{d_{n+2}} y_{n+2}\Bigg] \end{aligned} \tag{A2-4}$$

$$\begin{aligned} \left(\frac{d^3y}{dx^3}\right)_{n+2} = \frac{6}{l^3}\Bigg[&\frac{(\beta + 2\gamma + 3\delta)}{d_{n-2}} y_{n-2} - \frac{(\alpha + \beta + 2\gamma + 3\delta)}{d_{n-1}} y_{n-1} \\ &+ \frac{(\alpha + 2\beta + 2\gamma + 3\delta)}{d_n} y_n - \frac{(\alpha + 2\beta + 3\gamma + 3\delta)}{d_{n+1}} y_{n+1} \\ &+ \frac{(\alpha + 2\beta + 3\gamma + 4\delta)}{d_{n+2}} y_{n+2}\Bigg] \end{aligned} \tag{A2-5}$$

$$\begin{aligned} \left(\frac{d^2y}{dx^2}\right)_{n-2} = \frac{2}{l^2}\Bigg\{ &\left[\frac{\gamma(\gamma + \delta) + 3(\alpha + \beta)(2\alpha + \beta) + (2\gamma + \delta)(3\alpha + 2\beta)}{d_{n-2}}\right] y_{n-2} \\ &- \left[\frac{(\alpha + \beta)(3\alpha + 3\beta + 4\gamma + 2\delta) + \gamma(\gamma + \delta)}{d_{n-1}}\right] y_{n-1} \\ &+ \left[\frac{(\alpha + \beta)(3\alpha + \beta) + (2\alpha + \beta)(2\gamma + \delta) + \gamma(\gamma + \delta)}{d_n}\right] y_n \\ &- \left[\frac{(\alpha + \beta)(3\alpha + \beta) + (2\alpha + \beta)(\gamma + \delta)}{d_{n+1}}\right] y_{n+1} \\ &+ \left[\frac{(\alpha + \beta)(3\alpha + \beta) + \gamma(2\alpha + \beta)}{d_{n+2}}\right] y_{n+2}\Bigg\} \end{aligned} \tag{A2-6}$$

$$\begin{aligned} \left(\frac{d^2y}{dx^2}\right)_n = \frac{2}{l^2}\Bigg\{ &\left[\frac{-(\beta - \gamma)(\gamma + \delta) - \beta\gamma}{d_{n-2}}\right] y_{n-2} + \left[\frac{(\alpha + \beta)(2\gamma + \delta) - \gamma(\gamma + \delta)}{d_{n-1}}\right] y_{n-1} \\ &+ \left[\frac{(\alpha + \beta)(\beta - 2\gamma) - a\delta - (\gamma + \delta)(2\beta - \gamma)}{d_n}\right] y_n \\ &+ \left[\frac{(\alpha + 2\beta)(\gamma + \delta) - \beta(\alpha + \beta)}{d_{n+1}}\right] y_{n+1} \\ &+ \left[\frac{(\beta - \gamma)(a + \beta) - \beta\gamma}{d_{n+2}}\right] y_{n+2}\Bigg\} \end{aligned} \tag{A2-7}$$

$$\left(\frac{d^2y}{dx^2}\right)_{n+2} = \frac{2}{l^2}\left\{\left[\frac{(\gamma+\delta)(\gamma+3\delta)+\beta(\gamma+2\delta)}{d_{n-2}}\right]y_{n-2} - \left[\frac{(\alpha+\beta)(\gamma+2\delta)+(\gamma+\delta)(\gamma+3\delta)}{d_{n-1}}\right]y_{n-1} + \left[\frac{\beta(\alpha+\beta)+(\alpha+2\beta)(\gamma+2\delta)+(\gamma+3\delta)(\gamma+\delta)}{d_n}\right]y_n - \left[\frac{(\gamma+\delta)(2\alpha+4\beta+3\gamma+3\delta)+\beta(\alpha+\beta)}{d_{n+1}}\right]y_{n+1} + \left[\frac{\beta(\alpha+\beta)+(\alpha+2\beta)(2\gamma+3\delta)+3(\gamma+\delta)(\gamma+2\delta)}{d_{n+2}}\right]y_{n+2}\right\} \tag{A2-8}$$

$$\left(\frac{dy}{dx}\right)_{n-2} = \frac{1}{l}\left\{-\left[\frac{\gamma(2\alpha+\beta)(\gamma+\delta)+(4\alpha+\beta)(\alpha+\beta)^2+(\alpha+\beta)(3\alpha+\beta)(2\gamma+\delta)}{d_{n-2}}\right]y_{n-2} + \left[\frac{(\alpha+\beta)(\alpha+\beta+\gamma)(\alpha+\beta+\gamma+\delta)}{d_{n-1}}\right]y_{n-1} - \left[\frac{\alpha(\alpha+\beta+\gamma)(\alpha+\beta+\gamma+\delta)}{d_n}\right]y_n + \left[\frac{\alpha(\alpha+\beta)(\alpha+\beta+\gamma+\delta)}{d_{n+1}}\right]y_{n+1} - \left[\frac{\alpha(\alpha+\beta)(\alpha+\beta+\gamma)}{d_{n+2}}\right]y_{n+2}\right\} \tag{A2-9}$$

$$\left(\frac{dy}{dx}\right)_{n} = \frac{1}{l}\left\{\left[\frac{\beta\gamma(\gamma+\delta)}{d_{n-2}}\right]y_{n-2} - \left[\frac{\gamma(\alpha+\beta)(\gamma+\delta)}{d_{n-1}}\right]y_{n-1} + \left[\frac{\gamma(\gamma+\delta)(\alpha+2\beta)-\beta(\alpha+\beta)(2\gamma+\delta)}{d_n}\right]y_n + \left[\frac{\beta(\alpha+\beta)(\gamma+\delta)}{d_{n+1}}\right]y_{n+1} - \left[\frac{\beta\gamma(\alpha+\beta)}{d_{n+2}}\right]y_{n+2}\right\} \tag{A2-10}$$

$$\left(\frac{dy}{dx}\right)_{n+2} = \frac{1}{l}\left\{\left[\frac{\delta(\gamma+\delta)(\beta+\gamma+\delta)}{d_{n-2}}\right]y_{n-2} - \left[\frac{\delta(\gamma+\delta)(\alpha+\beta+\gamma+\delta)}{d_{n-1}}\right]y_{n-1} + \left[\frac{\delta(\beta+\gamma+\delta)(\alpha+\beta+\gamma+\delta)}{d_n}\right]y_n - \left[\frac{(\gamma+\delta)(\beta+\gamma+\delta)(\alpha+\beta+\gamma+\delta)}{d_{n+1}}\right]y_{n+1} + \left[\frac{\beta(\alpha+\beta)(\gamma+2\delta)+(\gamma+4\delta)(\gamma+\delta)^2+(\alpha+2\beta)(\gamma+3\delta)(\gamma+\delta)}{d_{n+2}}\right]y_{n+2} \tag{A2-11}$$

APPENDIX 3

Development of Equations 7-11 from 7-6

It is desired to obtain Equations 7-11 from Equations 7-6. These are shown below for convenience.

$$\frac{d}{dt}\left(\frac{\partial T}{\partial \dot{x}_1}\right) + \frac{\partial V}{\partial x_1} = 0$$

$$\frac{d}{dt}\left(\frac{\partial T}{\partial \dot{x}_2}\right) + \frac{\partial V}{\partial x_2} = 0 \qquad (7\text{-}11)$$

$$\frac{d}{dt}\left(\frac{\partial T}{\partial \dot{q}_1}\right) - \frac{\partial T}{\partial q_1} + \frac{\partial V}{\partial q_1} = 0$$

$$\frac{d}{dt}\left(\frac{\partial T}{\partial \dot{q}_2}\right) - \frac{\partial T}{\partial q_2} + \frac{\partial V}{\partial q_2} = 0 \qquad (7\text{-}6)$$

In these equations q_1 and q_2 are related to x_1 and x_2 by general functions. Let the relationships be

$$x_1 = x_1(q_1, q_2)$$

$$x_2 = x_2(q_1, q_2)$$

$$q_1 = q_1(x_1, x_2) \qquad (\text{A3-1})$$

$$q_2 = q_2(x_1, x_2)$$

It may be helpful to have some specific functions in mind in order to verify the general functions. Specific functions which adequately illustrate the general functions are the following:

$$x_1 = q_1 \cos q_2$$

$$x_2 = q_1 \sin q_2$$

$$q_1 = \sqrt{x_1^2 + x_2^2} \qquad (\text{A3-1}a)$$

$$q_2 = \sin^{-1}\left(\frac{x_2}{\sqrt{x_1^2 + x_2^2}}\right) = \cos^{-1}\left(\frac{x_1}{\sqrt{x_1^2 + x_2^2}}\right)$$

The potential energy functions, V, appearing in the Lagrange equations is a scalar function whose value depends on the configuration of the system at a given instant; that is, the potential energy stored in the elements of the system can be computed if the value of every coordinate is known. It is not necessary to know the rate of change of the coordinates, or the time, or acceleration, or any other quantities if the value of every coordinate is known. This is equivalent to stating that forces associated with, or derivable from, the potential energy function, V, are in the simplest form functions of position only. If there are other forces which are functions of velocity, time, or other variables and which cannot be converted to functions of coordinates only, the energy associated with such forces is not included in V. Therefore, terms such as

$$\frac{\partial V}{\partial \dot{x}_1}, \frac{\partial V}{\partial \dot{x}_2}, \frac{\partial V}{\partial \dot{q}_1}, \frac{\partial V}{\partial \dot{q}_2}, \frac{\partial V}{\partial t}, \frac{\partial V}{\partial \ddot{q}_2}, \text{ etc.}$$

are all zero—only terms such as

$$\frac{\partial V}{\partial x_1}, \frac{\partial V}{\partial x_2}, \frac{\partial V}{\partial q_1}, \frac{\partial V}{\partial q_2}$$

are expected. However, the kinetic energy function, T, generally may depend on both the values of the coordinates and the rate of change of the coordinates (see Example 7.1), and therefore terms such as

$$\frac{\partial T}{\partial x}, \frac{\partial T}{\partial \dot{x}}, \frac{\partial T}{\partial q}, \frac{\partial T}{\partial \dot{q}}$$

could appear. The basic expressions for these terms are now set down, using subscripts to indicate which variables in a partial derivative are to be considered constant.

$$\left.\begin{aligned}
\left(\frac{\partial T}{\partial x_1}\right)_{\dot{x}_1 x_2 \dot{x}_2} &= \left(\frac{\partial T}{\partial q_1}\right)_{\dot{q}_1 q_2 \dot{q}_2} \left(\frac{\partial q_1}{\partial x_1}\right)_{\dot{x}_1 x_2 \dot{x}_2} + \left(\frac{\partial T}{\partial q_2}\right)_{q_1 \dot{q}_1 \dot{q}_2} \left(\frac{\partial q_2}{\partial x_1}\right)_{\dot{x}_1 x_2 \dot{x}_2} \\
&\quad + \left(\frac{\partial T}{\partial \dot{q}_1}\right)_{q_1 q_2 \dot{q}_2} \left(\frac{\partial \dot{q}_1}{\partial x_1}\right)_{\dot{x}_1 x_2 \dot{x}_2} + \left(\frac{\partial T}{\partial \dot{q}_2}\right)_{q_1 \dot{q}_1 q_2} \left(\frac{\partial \dot{q}_2}{\partial x_1}\right)_{\dot{x}_1 x_2 \dot{x}_2} \\
\left(\frac{\partial T}{\partial x_2}\right)_{x_1 \dot{x}_1 \dot{x}_2} &= \left(\frac{\partial T}{\partial q_1}\right)_{\dot{q}_1 q_2 \dot{q}_2} \left(\frac{\partial q_1}{\partial x_2}\right)_{x_1 \dot{x}_1 \dot{x}_2} + \left(\frac{\partial T}{\partial q_2}\right)_{q_1 \dot{q}_1 \dot{q}_2} \left(\frac{\partial q_2}{\partial x_2}\right)_{x_1 \dot{x}_1 \dot{x}_2} \\
&\quad + \left(\frac{\partial T}{\partial \dot{q}_1}\right)_{q_1 q_2 \dot{q}_2} \left(\frac{\partial \dot{q}_1}{\partial x_2}\right)_{x_1 \dot{x}_1 \dot{x}_2} + \left(\frac{\partial T}{\partial \dot{q}_2}\right)_{q_1 \dot{q}_1 q_2} \left(\frac{\partial \dot{q}_2}{\partial x_2}\right)_{x_1 \dot{x}_1 \dot{x}_2}
\end{aligned}\right\} \quad \text{(A3-2)}$$

$$\left.\begin{aligned}
\left(\frac{\partial T}{\partial \dot{x}_1}\right)_{x_1 x_2 \dot{x}_2} &= \left(\frac{\partial T}{\partial q_1}\right)_{\dot{q}_1 q_2 \dot{q}_2} \left(\frac{\partial q_1}{\partial \dot{x}_1}\right)_{x_1 x_2 \dot{x}_2} + \left(\frac{\partial T}{\partial q_2}\right)_{q_1 \dot{q}_1 \dot{q}_2} \left(\frac{\partial q_2}{\partial \dot{x}_1}\right)_{x_1 x_2 \dot{x}_2} \\
&\quad + \left(\frac{\partial T}{\partial \dot{q}_1}\right)_{q_1 q_2 \dot{q}_2} \left(\frac{\partial \dot{q}_1}{\partial \dot{x}_1}\right)_{x_1 x_2 \dot{x}_2} + \left(\frac{\partial T}{\partial \dot{q}_2}\right)_{q_1 \dot{q}_1 q_2} \left(\frac{\partial \dot{q}_2}{\partial \dot{x}_1}\right)_{x_1 x_2 \dot{x}_2} \\
\left(\frac{\partial T}{\partial \dot{x}_2}\right)_{x_1 \dot{x}_1 x_2} &= \left(\frac{\partial T}{\partial q_1}\right)_{\dot{q}_1 q_2 \dot{q}_2} \left(\frac{\partial q_1}{\partial \dot{x}_2}\right)_{x_1 \dot{x}_1 x_2} + \left(\frac{\partial T}{\partial q_2}\right)_{q_1 \dot{q}_1 \dot{q}_2} \left(\frac{\partial q_2}{\partial \dot{x}_2}\right)_{x_1 \dot{x}_1 x_2} \\
&\quad + \left(\frac{\partial T}{\partial \dot{q}_1}\right)_{q_1 q_2 \dot{q}_2} \left(\frac{\partial \dot{q}_1}{\partial \dot{x}_2}\right)_{x_1 \dot{x}_1 x_2} + \left(\frac{\partial T}{\partial \dot{q}_2}\right)_{q_1 \dot{q}_1 q_2} \left(\frac{\partial \dot{q}_2}{\partial \dot{x}_2}\right)_{x_1 \dot{x}_1 x_2}
\end{aligned}\right\} \quad \text{(A3-3)}$$

$$\begin{aligned}
\left(\frac{\partial V}{\partial x_1}\right)_{x_2} &= \left(\frac{\partial V}{\partial q_1}\right)_{q_2} \left(\frac{\partial q_1}{\partial x_1}\right)_{x_2} + \left(\frac{\partial V}{\partial q_2}\right)_{q_1} \left(\frac{\partial q_2}{\partial x_1}\right)_{x_2} \\
\left(\frac{\partial V}{\partial x_2}\right)_{x_1} &= \left(\frac{\partial V}{\partial q_1}\right)_{q_2} \left(\frac{\partial q_1}{\partial x_2}\right)_{x_1} + \left(\frac{\partial V}{\partial q_2}\right)_{q_1} \left(\frac{\partial q_2}{\partial x_2}\right)_{x_1}
\end{aligned} \quad \text{(A3-4)}$$

Now it is necessary to prove that

$$\frac{\partial \dot{q}_i}{\partial \dot{x}_j} = \frac{\partial q_i}{\partial x_j}$$

and

$$\frac{\partial \dot{q}_i}{\partial x_j} = \frac{d}{dt}\left(\frac{\partial q_i}{\partial x_j}\right)$$

Accordingly, the derivatives of Equations A3-1 are taken, obtaining

$$\begin{aligned} \dot{q}_1 &= \left(\frac{\partial q_1}{\partial x_1}\right)_{x_2} \dot{x}_1 + \left(\frac{\partial q_1}{\partial x_2}\right)_{x_1} \dot{x}_2 \\ \dot{q}_2 &= \left(\frac{\partial q_2}{\partial x_1}\right)_{x_2} \dot{x}_1 + \left(\frac{\partial q_2}{\partial x_2}\right)_{x_1} \dot{x}_2 \end{aligned} \qquad \text{(A3-5)}$$

Since the partial derivatives above are functions of x_1 and x_2 only,

$$\begin{aligned} \left(\frac{\partial \dot{q}_1}{\partial \dot{x}_1}\right)_{x_1 x_2 \dot{x}_2} &= \left(\frac{\partial q_1}{\partial x_1}\right)_{\dot{x}_1 x_2 \dot{x}_2} & \left(\frac{\partial \dot{q}_2}{\partial \dot{x}_1}\right)_{x_1 x_2 \dot{x}_2} &= \left(\frac{\partial q_2}{\partial x_1}\right)_{\dot{x}_1 x_2 \dot{x}_2} \\ \left(\frac{\partial \dot{q}_1}{\partial \dot{x}_2}\right)_{x_1 \dot{x}_1 x_2} &= \left(\frac{\partial q_1}{\partial x_2}\right)_{x_1 \dot{x}_1 \dot{x}_2} & \left(\frac{\partial \dot{q}_2}{\partial \dot{x}_2}\right)_{x_1 \dot{x}_1 x_2} &= \left(\frac{\partial q_2}{\partial x_2}\right)_{x_1 \dot{x}_1 \dot{x}_2} \end{aligned} \qquad \text{(A3-6)}$$

Now considering a typical derivative, suppose that $(\partial q_1/\partial x_1)_{x_2} = f_1(x_1, x_2)$ and $(\partial q_1/\partial x_2)_{x_1} = f_2(x_1, x_2)$. Then the first equation of (A3-5) would become $\dot{q}_1 = f_1\dot{x}_1 + f_2\dot{x}_2$. It is clear that f_1 and f_2 contain x_1 and x_2 in their defining equation, while $\dot{x}_1$ and $\dot{x}_2$ do not, so that when the partial derivative of $\dot{q}_1 = f_1\dot{x}_1 + f_2\dot{x}_2$ is taken,

$$\left(\frac{\partial \dot{q}_1}{\partial x_1}\right)_{\dot{x}_1 x_2 \dot{x}_2} = \left(\frac{\partial f_1}{\partial x_1}\right)_{x_2} \dot{x}_1 + \left(\frac{\partial f_2}{\partial x_1}\right)_{x_2} \dot{x}_2 \equiv \left(\frac{\partial^2 q_1}{\partial x_1^2}\right)_{x_2 x_2} \dot{x}_1 + \left[\frac{\partial}{\partial x_1}\left(\frac{\partial q_1}{\partial x_2}\right)_{x_1}\right]_{x_2} \dot{x}_2$$

The derivative of $(\partial q_1/\partial x_1)_{x_2}$ with respect to time, using $f_1(x_1, x_2)$ for $(\partial q_1/\partial x_1)_{x_2}$, is

$$\frac{d}{dt}\left(\frac{\partial q_1}{\partial x_1}\right)_{x_2} = \left(\frac{\partial f_1}{\partial x_1}\right)_{x_2} \dot{x}_1 + \left(\frac{\partial f_1}{\partial x_2}\right)_{x_1} \dot{x}_2 \equiv \left(\frac{\partial^2 q_1}{\partial x_1^2}\right)_{x_2 x_2} \dot{x}_1 + \left[\frac{\partial}{\partial x_2}\left(\frac{\partial q_1}{\partial x_1}\right)_{x_2}\right]_{x_1} \dot{x}_2$$

From these two expressions and similar ones for the other variables,

$$\begin{aligned} \frac{d}{dt}\left(\frac{\partial q_1}{\partial x_1}\right)_{x_2} &= \left(\frac{\partial \dot{q}_1}{\partial x_1}\right)_{\dot{x}_1 x_2 \dot{x}_2} & \frac{d}{dt}\left(\frac{\partial q_2}{\partial x_1}\right)_{x_2} &= \left(\frac{\partial \dot{q}_2}{\partial x_1}\right)_{\dot{x}_1 x_2 \dot{x}_2} \\ \frac{d}{dt}\left(\frac{\partial q_1}{\partial x_2}\right)_{x_1} &= \left(\frac{\partial \dot{q}_1}{\partial x_2}\right)_{x_1 \dot{x}_1 \dot{x}_2} & \frac{d}{dt}\left(\frac{\partial q_2}{\partial x_2}\right)_{x_1} &= \left(\frac{\partial \dot{q}_2}{\partial x_2}\right)_{x_1 \dot{x}_1 \dot{x}_2} \end{aligned} \qquad \text{(A3-7)}$$

It is possible to verify Equations A3-6 and A3-7 with the specific functions which relate the q's and x's; namely Equations A3-1*a*. The results are

$$\begin{aligned} \left(\frac{\partial q_1}{\partial x_1}\right)_{x_2} &= \left(\frac{\partial \dot{q}_1}{\partial \dot{x}_1}\right)_{x_1 x_2 \dot{x}_2} = \cos q_2 \\ \left(\frac{\partial q_1}{\partial x_2}\right)_{x_1} &= \left(\frac{\partial \dot{q}_1}{\partial \dot{x}_2}\right)_{x_1 \dot{x}_1 x_2} = \sin q_2 \\ \left(\frac{\partial q_2}{\partial x_1}\right)_{x_2} &= \left(\frac{\partial \dot{q}_2}{\partial \dot{x}_1}\right)_{x_1 x_2 \dot{x}_2} = -\frac{\sin q_2}{q_1} \\ \left(\frac{\partial q_2}{\partial x_2}\right)_{x_1} &= \left(\frac{\partial \dot{q}_2}{\partial \dot{x}_2}\right)_{x_1 \dot{x}_1 x_2} = \frac{\cos q_2}{q_1} \end{aligned} \qquad \text{(A3-6}a\text{)}$$

$$\frac{d}{dt}\left(\frac{\partial q_1}{\partial x_1}\right)_{x_2} = \left(\frac{\partial \dot{q}_1}{\partial x_1}\right)_{\dot{x}_1 x_2 \dot{x}_2} = -\,\dot{q}_2 \sin q_2$$

$$\frac{d}{dt}\left(\frac{\partial q_1}{\partial x_2}\right)_{x_1} = \left(\frac{\partial \dot{q}_1}{\partial x_2}\right)_{x_1 \dot{x}_1 \dot{x}_2} = \dot{q}_2 \cos q_2$$

$$\frac{d}{dt}\left(\frac{\partial q_2}{\partial x_1}\right)_{x_2} = \left(\frac{\partial \dot{q}_2}{\partial x_1}\right)_{\dot{x}_1 x_2 \dot{x}_2} = \frac{\dot{q}_1 \sin q_2 - q_1\dot{q}_2 \cos q_2}{q_1^{\,2}} \tag{A3-7a}$$

$$\frac{d}{dt}\left(\frac{\partial q_2}{\partial x_2}\right)_{x_1} = \left(\frac{\partial \dot{q}_2}{\partial x_2}\right)_{x_1 \dot{x}_1 \dot{x}_2} = -\,\frac{\dot{q}_1 \cos q_2 + q_1\dot{q}_2 \sin q_2}{q_1^{\,2}}$$

The following obvious expressions (from Equations A3-1 and A3-1a) are also needed

$$\left(\frac{\partial q_1}{\partial \dot{x}_1}\right)_{x_1 x_2 \dot{x}_2} = \left(\frac{\partial q_1}{\partial \dot{x}_2}\right)_{x_1 \dot{x}_1 x_2} = \left(\frac{\partial q_2}{\partial \dot{x}_1}\right)_{x_1 x_2 \dot{x}_2} = \left(\frac{\partial q_2}{\partial \dot{x}_2}\right)_{x_1 \dot{x}_1 x_2} = 0 \tag{A3-8}$$

If Equations A3-3 are differentiated with respect to time and substituted along with Equations A3-4 in Equations 7-6 the following equations result. The subscripts are omitted in these equations but the partial derivatives have the same variables constant as in Equations A3-2, A3-3 and A3-4.

$$\left[\frac{d}{dt}\left(\frac{\partial T}{\partial \dot{q}_1}\right)\right]\left(\frac{\partial q_1}{\partial x_1}\right) + \left(\frac{\partial T}{\partial \dot{q}_1}\right)\left[\frac{d}{dt}\left(\frac{\partial q_1}{\partial x_1}\right)\right] + \left[\frac{d}{dt}\left(\frac{\partial T}{\partial \dot{q}_2}\right)\right]\left(\frac{\partial q_2}{\partial x_1}\right)$$
$$+ \left(\frac{\partial T}{\partial \dot{q}_2}\right)\left[\frac{d}{dt}\left(\frac{\partial q_2}{\partial x_1}\right)\right] + \left(\frac{\partial V}{\partial q_1}\right)\left(\frac{\partial q_1}{\partial x_1}\right) + \left(\frac{\partial V}{\partial q_2}\right)\left(\frac{\partial q_2}{\partial x_1}\right) = 0$$
$$\left[\frac{d}{dt}\left(\frac{\partial T}{\partial \dot{q}_1}\right)\right]\left(\frac{\partial q_1}{\partial x_2}\right) + \left(\frac{\partial T}{\partial \dot{q}_1}\right)\left[\frac{d}{dt}\left(\frac{\partial q_1}{\partial x_2}\right)\right] + \left[\frac{d}{dt}\left(\frac{\partial T}{\partial \dot{q}_2}\right)\right]\left(\frac{\partial q_2}{\partial x_2}\right) \tag{A3-9}$$
$$+ \left(\frac{\partial T}{\partial \dot{q}_2}\right)\left[\frac{d}{dt}\left(\frac{\partial q_2}{\partial x_2}\right)\right] + \left(\frac{\partial V}{\partial q_1}\right)\left(\frac{\partial q_1}{\partial x_2}\right) + \left(\frac{\partial V}{\partial q_2}\right)\left(\frac{\partial q_2}{\partial x_2}\right) = 0$$

If the first of these equations is multiplied by $\partial q_2/\partial x_2$ and the second by $\partial q_2/\partial x_1$ and then the second subtracted from the first, one of Equations A3-10 is obtained. The other of Equations A3-10 is obtained by multiplying the first of Equations A3-9 by $\partial q_1/\partial x_2$ and the second by $\partial q_1/\partial x_1$ and subtracting the first from the second.

$$\left[\frac{d}{dt}\left(\frac{\partial T}{\partial \dot{q}_1}\right)\right] Y + \frac{\partial V}{\partial q_1} Y + \frac{\partial T}{\partial \dot{q}_1}\left[\frac{\partial q_2}{\partial x_2}\frac{d}{dt}\left(\frac{\partial q_1}{\partial x_1}\right) - \frac{\partial q_2}{\partial x_1}\frac{d}{dt}\frac{\partial q_1}{\partial x_2}\right)\Bigg]$$
$$+ \frac{\partial T}{\partial \dot{q}_2}\left[\frac{\partial q_2}{\partial x_2}\frac{d}{dt}\left(\frac{\partial q_2}{\partial x_1}\right) - \frac{\partial q_2}{\partial x_1}\frac{d}{dt}\left(\frac{\partial q_2}{\partial x_2}\right)\right] = 0$$
$$\left[\frac{d}{dt}\left(\frac{\partial T}{\partial \dot{q}_2}\right)\right](-\,Y) + \frac{\partial V}{\partial q_2}(-\,Y) + \frac{\partial T}{\partial \dot{q}_1}\left[\frac{\partial q_1}{\partial x_2}\frac{d}{dt}\left(\frac{\partial q_1}{\partial x_1}\right) - \frac{\partial q_1}{\partial x_1}\frac{d}{dt}\left(\frac{\partial q_1}{\partial x_2}\right)\right] \tag{A3-10}$$
$$+ \frac{\partial T}{\partial \dot{q}_2}\left[\frac{\partial q_1}{\partial x_2}\frac{d}{dt}\left(\frac{\partial q_2}{\partial x_1}\right) - \frac{\partial q_1}{\partial x_1}\frac{d}{dt}\left(\frac{\partial q_2}{\partial x_2}\right)\right] = 0$$

where
$$Y = \frac{\partial q_1}{\partial x_1}\frac{\partial q_2}{\partial x_2} - \frac{\partial q_1}{\partial x_2}\frac{\partial q_2}{\partial x_1}$$

Now a comparison with the desired form (Equations 7-11) shows that if the last two terms of Equations A3-10 reduced to $-(\partial T/\partial q_1)\,Y$ in the one case and $(\partial T/\partial q_2)\,Y$ in the other, Y

could be divided out and the desired result achieved. By making use of Equations A3-2 and A3-7 it is possible to show by algebraic manipulation that

$$\frac{\partial T}{\partial x_1}\frac{\partial q_2}{\partial x_2} - \frac{\partial T}{\partial x_2}\frac{\partial q_2}{\partial x_1} = \frac{\partial T}{\partial q_1} Y \qquad + \text{ last two terms of Equation A3-10}$$

$$\frac{\partial T}{\partial x_1}\frac{\partial q_1}{\partial x_1} - \frac{\partial T}{\partial x_2}\frac{\partial q_1}{\partial x_2} = \frac{\partial T}{\partial q_2}(-Y) \quad + \text{ last two terms of Equation A3-10}$$

Since in this instance $\partial T/\partial x_1$ and $\partial T/\partial x_2$ are zero (since they do not appear in Equations 7-6) the last two terms do become $-(\partial T/\partial q_1)Y$ and $(\partial T/\partial q_2)Y$ as desired. Equations 7-11 are therefore established. It might be thought that in some other computation where perhaps equations like Equation 7-6 did contain the $-\partial T/\partial x_1$ and $-\partial T/\partial x_2$ terms, instead of these being zero, that perhaps the desired Equations 7-11 would not result. However, this case is even easier, for substitution of Equations A3-2 through A3-8 into Equation 7-6 and subsequent manipulation, as was done to obtain Equation A3-10, leads directly to the final result. Use of the particular coordinate transformations represented by Equation A3-1*a* verifies the above general results. Therefore, if it were required to shift again from the q coordinates to some other set of coordinates, say z, the same set of equations as Equations 7-11 would result only with z's replacing q's.

Problems

Chapter 1

1.1 In each of the figures shown (Fig. P1-1), spring-damper and mass-damper, develop the equation for the displacement as functions of time and initial conditions and explain the results.

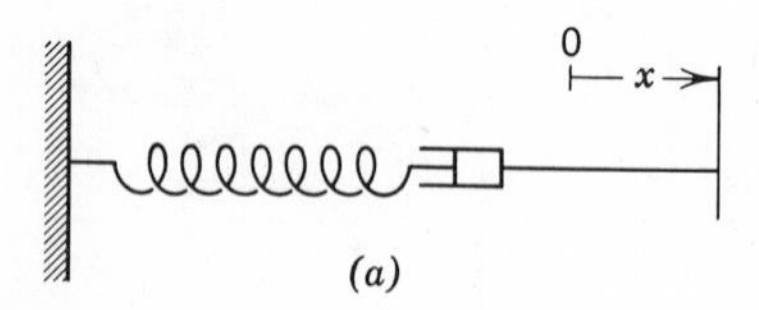

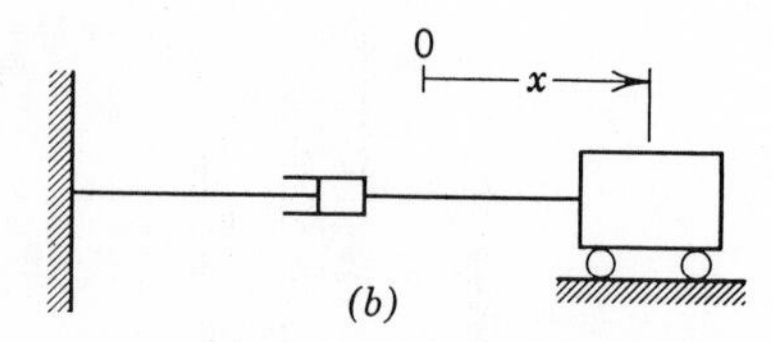

Fig. P1-1

1.2 For the systems shown in Fig. P1-2, initially quiescent, the displacement of the mass is x, the variable of interest, while the force, f, or displacement, y, forces the motion. Determine the differential equations of motion.

1.3 For the systems of Problem 1.2, determine the algebraic equations of motion in terms of the initial conditions if the forcing functions are zero, and if they are absent.

1.4 Solve Equation 1-7 using linear differential equation theory and determine if initial velocity and initial acceleration can be used to fix the values of the arbitrary constants instead of initial velocity and initial displacement. Can initial displacement and initial acceleration be used?

Chapter 2

2.1 A 10-lb mass restrained by a 20 lb/in. spring is given an initial deflection of 1 in. and an initial velocity of 10 in./sec in the direction opposite the initial deflection. Determine the frequency and amplitude of the resulting motion and the instants when the displacement, velocity, and acceleration are zero and maximum.

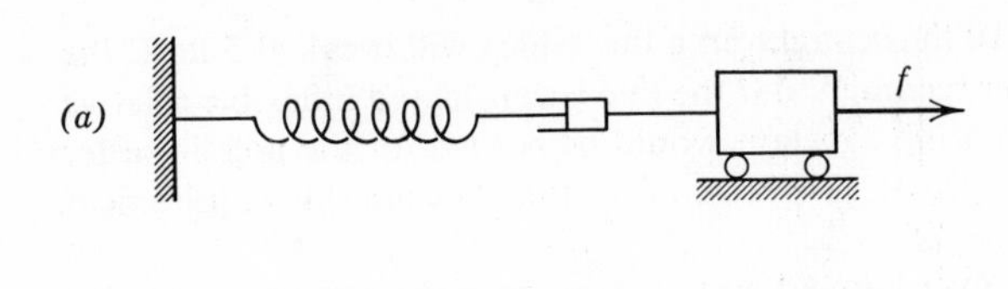

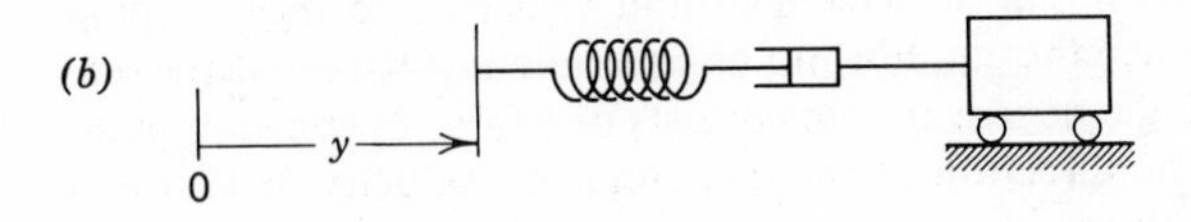

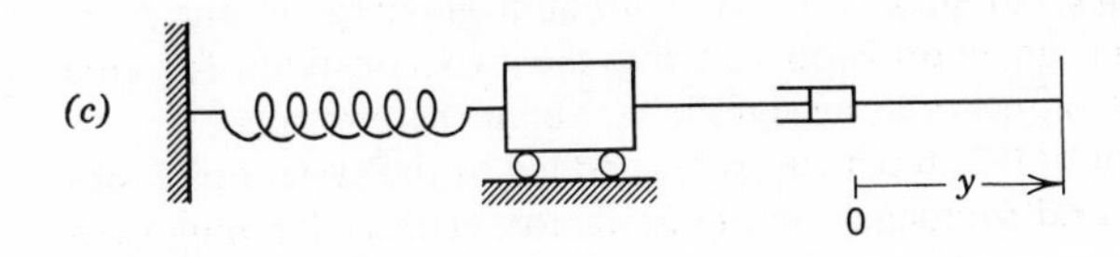

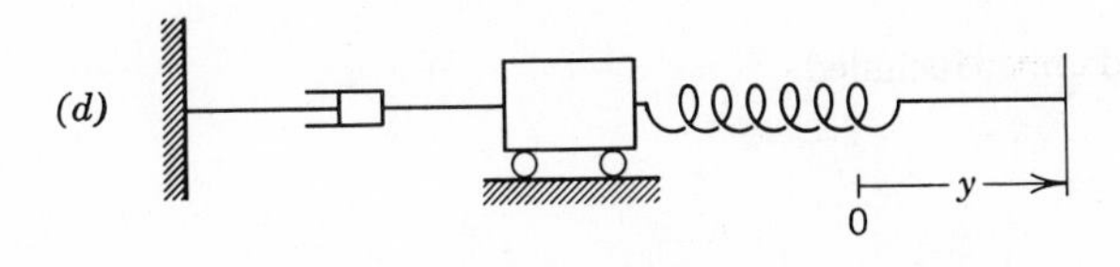

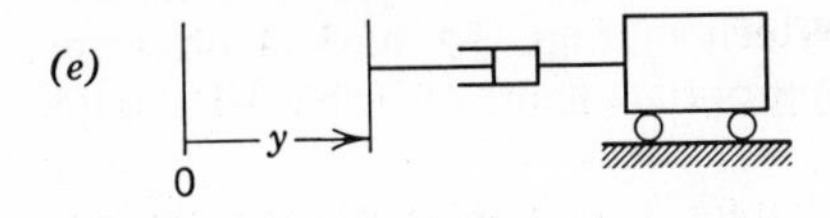

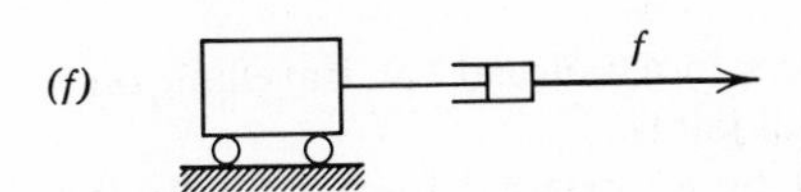

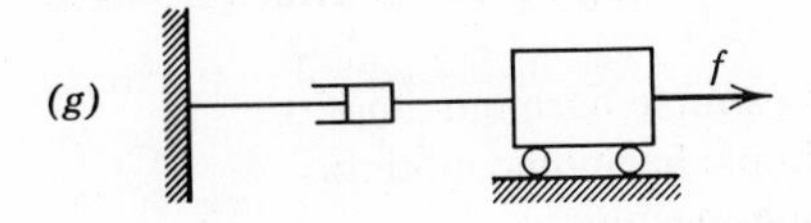

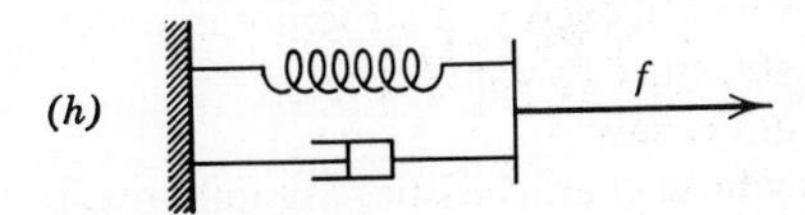

Fig. P1-2

2.2 Repeat Example 2.2 when there is an initial load of 50 lb in the spring.

2.3 Suppose that the space available to absorb the impact of the weight in Example 2.2 is limited to $\frac{1}{4}$ in. If it is desired to keep the maximum acceleration of the weight as low as possible, what relationship between spring constant and initial spring load is implied?

2.4 Assume that a fish weighing 10 lb is caught on a line which will break at 5 lb. If the fish can swim with a speed of 10 ft per second and if the line is considered inflexible relative to the pole flexibility, what effective spring constant would be needed for the pole in order to prevent the loss of the fish? What practical aspects of fishing alleviate this requirement somewhat?

2.5 Figure 2-3 indicates that an overdamped system may pass the equilibrium point once. Develop a relationship between initial displacement and velocity and the damping factor for the borderline condition where the equilibrium point would just barely be passed.

2.6 "Coulomb damping" in a single-degree system consists of a force of constant magnitude whose direction is opposite the direction of the instantaneous velocity. It is sometimes useful to be able to convert this to an equivalent viscous damping constant. If the equivalent viscous damper is one which dissipates the same amount of energy in one cycle as the Coulomb damper, determine an expression relating the two constants for free vibration, and comment on whatever appears to be significant about these results.

2.7 (a) A damper with a constant of 0.2 lb per (in./sec) is added to the system of Problem 2.1. Determine the damped natural frequency, damping factor, critical damping constant, ratio of successive peak deflections, logarithmic decrement, and number of cycles to damp to half amplitude.

(b) Repeat Problem 2.1 with the damper included.

Chapter 3

3.1 A vibrometer (displacement measuring instrument) should have a low natural frequency, while an accelerometer should have a high natural frequency, relative to the expected forcing frequencies to be measured. Why? Which of Figs. 3-1 to 3-14 illustrate this quantitatively? What physical quantity in the appropriate figure of Table 3-1 should be used to measure displacement or acceleration?

3.2 By reference to the appropriate figures of Chapter 3, indicate, with explanation, what ranges of frequency ratios and damping factors are desirable or not desirable for the following applications:

(a) Vibration isolation for the comfort of passengers in a railroad car travelling on a track with regularly occurring bumps caused by the rail joints.

(b) Vibration isolation to suppress motion caused by an external force on a flexibly mounted system.

(c) Vibration isolation to suppress the effect of a motor rotating with an unavoidable mass unbalance.

(d) An accelerometer to measure acceleration during simple harmonic motion.

(e) A vibrometer to measure displacement during simple harmonic motion.

(f) A reed tachometer for measuring speed of rotating machinery.

(g) A paint mixer, if the can of paint is part of the spring-suspended system.

(h) A variable-speed, rotating, unbalanced weight to be attached to a structure in order to determine the normal modes and frequencies of the structure by experiment.

(i) Hand sawing a flexible limb from a tree with a pruning saw.

3.3 A machine is supported flexibly by a structure whose characteristics are unknown. If a single-degree system is assumed, and a small variable speed electric motor with unbalanced weight is attached to the machine to excite the vibration, it is found that the amplitude of the motion for high frequency excitation is about half the maximum observed amplitude. What information about the support structure can be determined from this?

3.4 A spring-supported, lightly damped mass vibrates excessively in response to an oscillatory applied force. It is the acceleration of the mass which is objectionable, rather than its displacement or velocity. The forcing frequency is twice the natural frequency.

Two possibilities are suggested for reduction of the objectionable acceleration. The forcing frequency can be increased or the natural frequency decreased.

(a) Would it matter which is done, and if so which would be better?

(b) If the forcing frequency were one half of the natural frequency and the options were to decrease the forcing frequency or increase the natural frequency, what would be the conclusion?

3.5 Repeat Problem 3.4 if the vibration is caused by an unbalanced rotating weight and the amplitude is critical instead of acceleration.

3.6 A free mass is vibrated by an unbalanced motor which causes an objectionable motion. The unbalanced motor cannot conveniently be isolated from the mass by means of flexible mountings. The speed of the rotating weight is always the same (within 2%). It is suggested that the necessary ten to one reduction in amplitude of the free mass might be achieved by mounting a mass flexibly on the free mass to form a "vibration absorber."

(a) Investigate the feasibility of this suggestion.

(b) If the unbalanced motor could have been isolated by use of flexible mountings, determine a satisfactory combination of parameters for the desired purpose.

3.7 An undamped spring-supported mass vibrates in response to a periodic applied force whose characteristics are indicated in Fig. P3-7. Describe this force with a Fourier series (see Appendix 1), and then determine the steady-state vibration (displacement) of the mass in terms of a Fourier series, and plot the displacement for $\beta T = 20$ (β = natural frequency, radians per second).

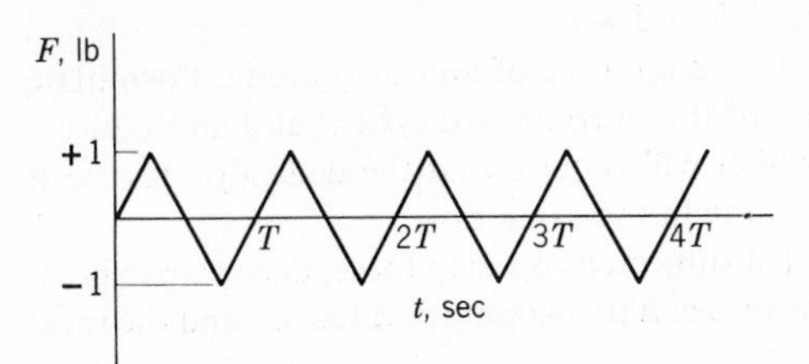

Fig. P3-7

3.8 An applied acceleration may be considered as having components of various frequencies. (See the discussion on Fourier series in Appendix 1.) Therefore, an accelerometer should indicate with little distortion accelerations having various frequencies. This implies that the accelerometer natural frequency should be as high as possible and that the damping should be either as little as possible or such that the phase angle for forced vibration increases linearly with frequency. Explain why these requirements are implied. Replot the necessary portion of the appropriate frequency response curve using rectilinear graph paper and suggest a satisfactory damping factor.

3.9 Rework Problem 2.6 for forced vibration.

(a) Use a sinusoidal input and an "exact" analysis, assuming no finite stationary intervals. Formulate a method of solution if this assumption is not made.

(b) Assume the response to the sinusoidal input is sinusoidal.

3.10 If a damping force is proportional to the square of the velocity and if the response to a sinusoidal forcing function is assumed to be sinusoidal, determine an equivalent linear damping coefficient based on equal energy dissipation.

3.11 Repeat Problem 3.10 for hysteresis damping, which causes energy dissipation approximately proportional to the square of the amplitude.

3.12 A rotating shaft simply supported by bearings carries a weight midway between the bearings. Develop an expression for the natural frequency. If the center of gravity of the weight is slightly off the shaft axis, can the response at various shaft speeds be determined from the results of Table 3-2? What if the shaft is initially slightly bowed?

3.13 If the rate of change of temperature of an object is proportional to the difference in temperature between the object and the surroundings with proportionality constant of two degrees per hour per degree, and if the temperature of the surroundings varies sinusoidally between 60° and 80°F, one cycle every three hours, how long after the surroundings reach 80° will it be when the object reaches its maximum temperature and what will be that temperature? (Assume a long time since the beginning of the sinusoidal variation.)

3.14 An accelerometer is used to measure the forced vibration of the control station of a machine. If the undamped natural frequency of the accelerometer is 100 cycles per second, the damping factor 0.7, and the acceleration as indicated by the instrument is 0.2 g (amplitude) at 40 cycles per second, would an operator stationed there be uncomfortable?

3.15 Determine equations which describe the motion occurring after a long time if the forcing functions of Problem 1.2 are sinusoidal functions.

Chapter 4

4.1 Determine the transfer functions X/F or X/Y and equations of motion if the forcing functions of Problem 1.2 are step functions. What is the nature of the motion after a long time has passed?

4.2 An accelerometer is to be designed using a damping factor of $\sqrt{2}/2$. It is required that the accelerometer indication shall reach and remain within 1% of the actual acceleration by the time T after application of a step acceleration. Formulate a requirement for the appropriate accelerometer characteristic.

4.3 Explain the relationship between Figs. 2-8 and 4-1.

4.4 An overdamped system is acted upon by a step force of unit magnitude. Formulate a relationship between appropriate parameters of the overdamped system and an "equivalent" first order system (mass is neglected) which will require that the deflection for both systems reach a specified fraction of the final value in the same time.

4.5 For an underdamped system like Fig. 1-3 subjected to a step force, derive an expression for the time required for the displacement to reach its maximum value, t_m, and the ratio of the maximum value to the final value, r.

Determine the location of the roots on the complex plane in terms of t_m and r.

Chapter 5

5.1 Determine an expression for the spring rate of a cylinder of air under compression from a piston at one end.

5.2 It is desired to obtain some information on the vibration characteristics of a mass flexibly mounted within a container with as little work as possible. The mass and spring constants are unknown. It is observed that the mass is one inch closer to one end of the container in the upright position than in the inverted position. If the purpose of the mounting is to protect the mass from damage resulting from vibration of the container, for what forcing frequencies will the mounting be (a) useful, (b) useless, and (c) harmful? Explain.

5.3 In Problem 5.2 it is suggested that some damping might be useful. Comment on the effect of damping on the conclusions of Problem 5.2

5.4 If a trailer is jacked up by jacks supporting the trailer frame, rather than the axle, it is observed that the frame must be lifted one foot before the wheels clear the ground.

(a) If this trailer were to be pulled along a "washboard" road, assumed to have a sinusoidal profile with a period of three feet and amplitude of one inch, what trailer velocity would cause resonance?

(b) If the wheels weigh 10 lb and the tires deflect one inch under the weight of the loaded trailer (1000 lb), at what trailer speed would the wheels leave the road?

(c) What is the probable cause of the washboard road?

5.5 A thin but rigid rod is suspended by four equal springs, as indicated in Fig. P5.5 Determine natural frequencies for translational and rotational motion and the condition which will cause these frequencies to be equal. Is this a single-degree system? Are single-degree equations applicable?

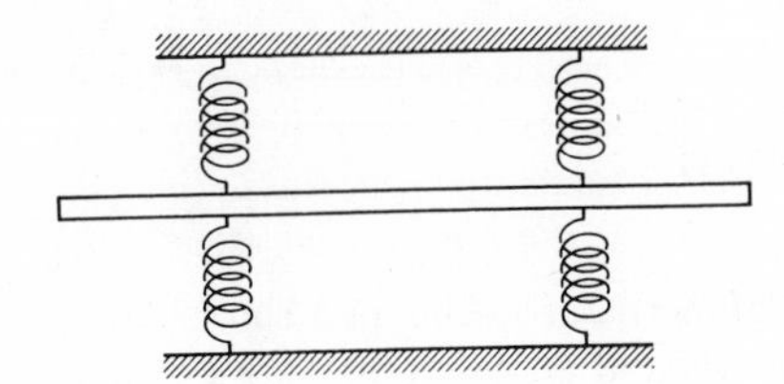

Fig. P5-5

5.6 Assume that a motor is to be mounted on a flexible mounting in order to minimize unwanted vibration transmission to the floor. Assume the four identical mountings are equally flexible for axial or transverse deflections and that the principal forcing loads or torques from the motor occur at 24 cycles per second. The motor weighs 200 lb and can be assumed to be equivalent to a homogeneous cylinder 1 ft in diameter and 2 ft long. Determine suitable spring rates and locations.

5.7 What would be the effect on the system of Fig. 5-1 if this system were mounted in a satellite instead of on the earth?

5.8 Would a pendulum clock gain or lose if its location above sea level is increased? What would be the error per thousand feet elevation?

5.9 A rigid bar of constant cross section, pivoted at its center in "teeter totter" fashion on frictionless bearings, is mounted on a shaft which rotates at constant velocity, as indicated in Fig. P5-9. Investigate the motion, neglecting aerodynamic effects.

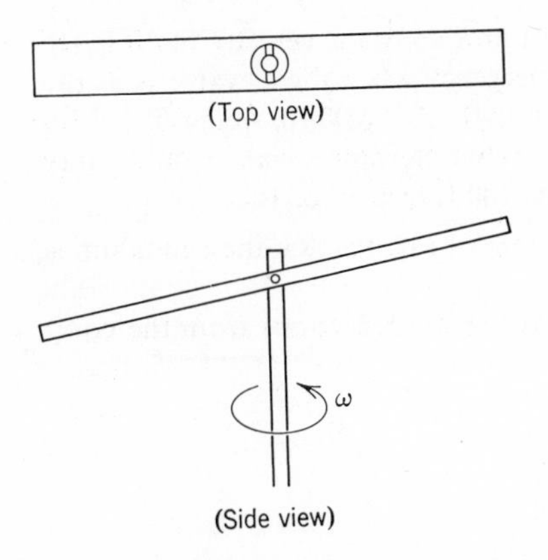

Fig. P5-9

5.10 An automobile weighing 2000 lb strikes a rigid object with the center of the bumper while moving at 2 miles per hour. If the bumper were made of steel having a proportional limit stress of 100,000 psi and rectangular cross section 8 in. wide, what thickness would be required to prevent permanent deformation of the bumper if the support points are 4 ft apart?

5.11 A flexible chain restrained by a weightless spring runs over the edge of a frictionless table as indicated in Fig. P5-11. If the chain is 10 ft long and weighs 10 lb and the spring rate is 2 lb per ft, what is the natural frequency?

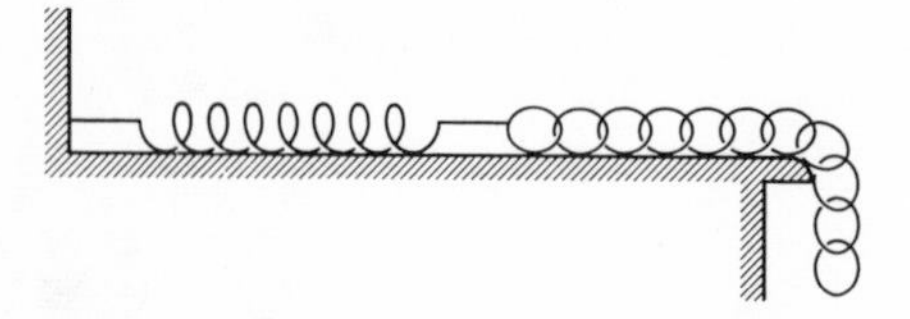

Fig. P5-11

5.12 In order to check the computed mass moment of inertia of a helicopter rotor blade, an experimental blade was suspended by two wires attached at an equal distance on each side of the center of gravity of the blade. The suspended blade was then rotated slightly about the center of gravity, released, and the period of oscillation observed. Derive an expression for the moment of inertia in terms of the appropriate parameters of the experiment. What practical difficulty might be forseen and how could it be minimized?

5.13 Determine the natural frequency of a circular disk suspended at a point which is a distance, l, from the center of the disk. What differences are expected if the pendular motion is in the plane of the disk or perpendicular to this plane?

5.14 A square table 3 ft on the side has vertical legs of $1\frac{1}{2}$ in. square cross section at its corners. If the table weighs 10 lb and is 30 in. tall, what is the lowest natural frequency? Assume modulus of elasticity for the wooden legs is 10^6 psi. What will be the effect of angling the legs outward (radially from the center of the table) at 10° from the vertical?

5.15 Determine the natural frequency for "rocking" motion of a long block of wood with square cross section and specific gravity 0.5, floating in water.

5.16 An automobile weighing 1500 lb pushes an identical automobile by contact through the bumpers. An unsteady motion having a frequency of one cycle per second is noticed. What is the effective spring rate for the bumpers?

5.17 An elevator for a mine is traveling downward at a constant velocity of 10 ft/sec when the winch is suddenly stopped because of an emergency when the elevator is at the 1000-ft level. The 5/16 in. steel cable has a breaking strength of 10,000 lb, weighs 0.173 lb. per ft and stretches 0.0015 ft per ft per 1000 lb load. What elevator weight would cause failure of the cable? What if the emergency occurred at 100 ft instead of 1000 ft?

5.18 (a) Determine the natural frequency of the system of Fig. P5-18 if the pendulum is vertical in the equilibrium position.

(b) Determine the natural frequency of the system for small deflections from the equilibrium position if the spring is removed.

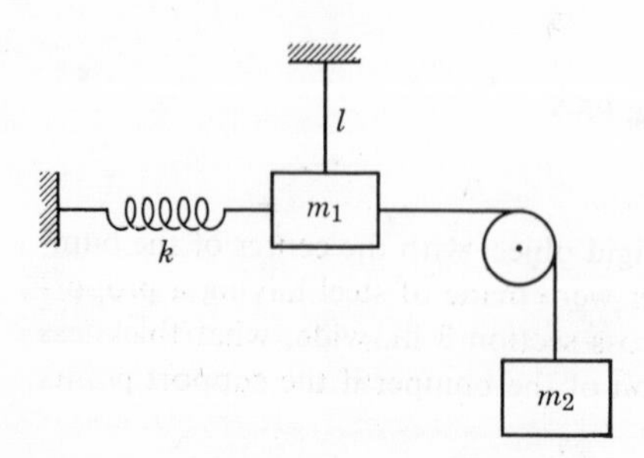

Fig. P5-18

5.19 Determine the motion of the system of Fig. P5-19 for small deflections from the neutral position.

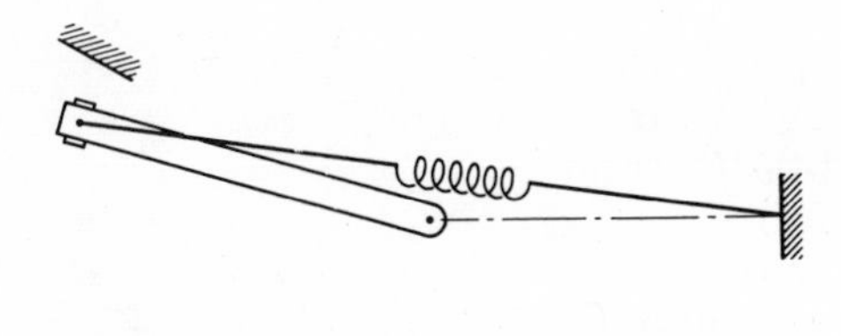

Fig. P5-19

Chapter 6

6.1 If coordinate 2 of Fig. 6-1 were defined as the amount of extension of spring 2, derive the differential equations of motion of the system.

6.2 Describe initial conditions other than those described in the text which would produce only the first or second mode vibration for an undamped two-degree system. In what respect is the damped system different?

6.3 For an undamped two-degree system like Fig. 6-1, determine a combination of springs and masses such that the natural frequency of the first mode is 4 rad/sec and there is a "beat frequency" of 1 rad/sec.

6.4 For the numerical values of Example 6-1, determine the motion of the system if the system is excited by deflecting the masses with unit load applied to the second mass followed by release from rest. How long after release could the motion of the system be described within 1% error by the low-frequency component alone?

6.5 Derive appropriate transfer functions for a two-degree system such as that of Fig. 6-1, but with no forces or dampers. Let the motion be excited by movement of the wall instead of by forces. If the wall moves with simple harmonic motion, determine expressions for the steady-state vibration of the masses. (The small amount of damping unavoidably present will eventually eliminate the transients.)

6.6 A spring-supported mass vibrates excessively because of resonance caused by an oscillatory force applied to the mass. The forcing frequency is always the same (within 5%). It is suggested that the resonance can be avoided by adding another spring-supported mass to form a tuned vibration absorber or suppressor. (It is not convenient to change the spring or mass in order to avoid the resonance.)

(a) Determine a satisfactory combination for this purpose.

(b) What differences, if any, would result if the undesired resonance is the result of an oscillating displacement of the support point rather than an oscillating force?

6.7 In Example 6-1 an equation is derived for the response to a step function, which is plotted in Fig 6-5. Derive a similar equation for x_2 which would apply if there were no damping and if the step force were applied to first one mass and then the other. Explain the differences in the expressions in terms of what intuitively would be expected from the physical system.

6.8 Equations 6-15 can be derived using vectors and matrices in a way that would facilitate extension to three dimensions. Let $\Delta\mathbf{R}$ be a displacement vector and $\Delta\mathbf{F}$ a force vector produced by the springs.

$$\Delta\mathbf{R} = i\Delta x + j\Delta y \qquad \Delta\mathbf{F} = i\Delta F_x + j\Delta F_y$$

and

$$\Delta\mathbf{R}' = i'\Delta x' + j'\Delta y' \qquad \Delta\mathbf{F}' = i'\Delta F_{x'} + j'\Delta F_{y'}$$

where i, j, i', j' are unit vectors in the x, y, x', y' directions, respectively. Let these vectors also be defined by matrices specifying their x, y and x', y' components as follows.

$$\{\Delta R\} = \begin{Bmatrix} \Delta x \\ \Delta y \end{Bmatrix} \qquad \{\Delta F\} = \begin{Bmatrix} \Delta F_x \\ \Delta F_y \end{Bmatrix}$$

$$\{\Delta R'\} = \begin{Bmatrix} \Delta x' \\ \Delta y' \end{Bmatrix} \qquad \{\Delta F'\} = \begin{Bmatrix} \Delta F_{x'} \\ \Delta F_{y'} \end{Bmatrix}$$

(a) Show that $\{\Delta R'\} = [A]\{\Delta R\}$ and $\{\Delta F'\} = [A]\{\Delta F\}$ where

$$[A] = \begin{bmatrix} (i \cdot i') & (j \cdot i') \\ (i \cdot j') & (j \cdot j') \end{bmatrix}$$

(b) If the spring constants are arranged in square matrices

$$[K] = \begin{bmatrix} k_{xx} & k_{xy} \\ k_{yx} & k_{yy} \end{bmatrix} \quad \text{and} \quad [K'] = \begin{bmatrix} k_{x'x'} & k_{x'y'} \\ k_{y'x'} & k_{y'y'} \end{bmatrix}$$

show that $[K'] = [A][K][A]^{-1}$ and use this to derive Equations 6-15 and 6-14.

(c) Describe how the analysis could be extended to motion in three dimensions.

6.9 A rigid bar of mass M and length L is bonded over half its length to a support with a flexible material such as rubber (Fig. P6-9). Define necessary spring constants and determine the various natural frequencies and mode descriptions of this system.

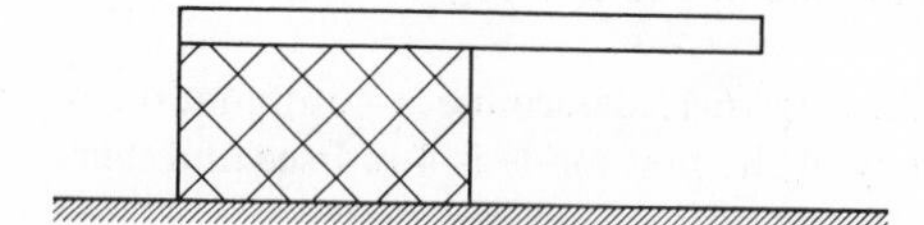

Fig. P6-9

Chapter 7

7.1 (a) Use the Rayleigh method to determine an approximate correction to be applied to a single-degree system similar to that of Fig. 1-1 if the mass of the spring is not negligible relative to the suspended mass. (Assume that the spring mass is evenly distributed between the support point and the mass, and that deflection of a point on the spring from its rest position is proportional to the distance between its rest position and the support point.)

(b) Show how to approximate the effect of the mass of the springs of a two-degree system similar to that of Fig. 6-1.

7.2 Using the Lagrange equation, determine the differential equation of motion for a mass sliding without friction on a "roller coaster" track having the shape specified by the equation $y = e^{-ax} \cos \pi x/L$.

7.3 A concentrated mass slides without friction in a circular ring which is given an initial angular velocity about a vertical axis (Fig. P7-3). Investigate the motion.

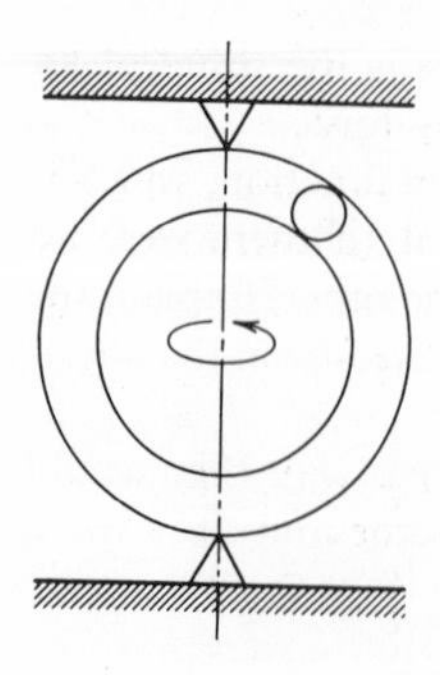

Fig. P7-3

7.4 A mass, m, slides without friction in a tube of mass, M, and length, L, suspended at one end by a frictionless bearing (Fig. P7-4). The mass is restrained by a weightless spring.

With the tube horizontal and stationary, the mass is at rest a distance "a" from the bearing. θ is not necessarily a small angle.

(a) Use Lagrange's equation to derive the differential equations of motion.

(b) What happens if the oscillations may be considered small?

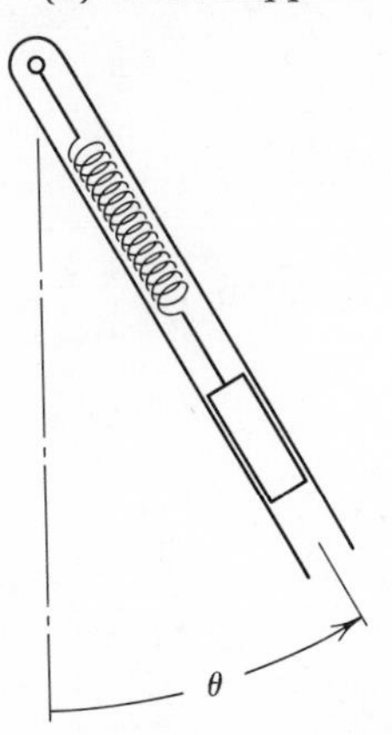

Fig. P7-4

7.5 Show that the use of coordinates which specify the center of gravity of the masses and the distance between the masses of Fig. P7.5 will lead to the same frequency and mode description for the system as the use of "ordinary" coordinates specifying the deflection of each mass.

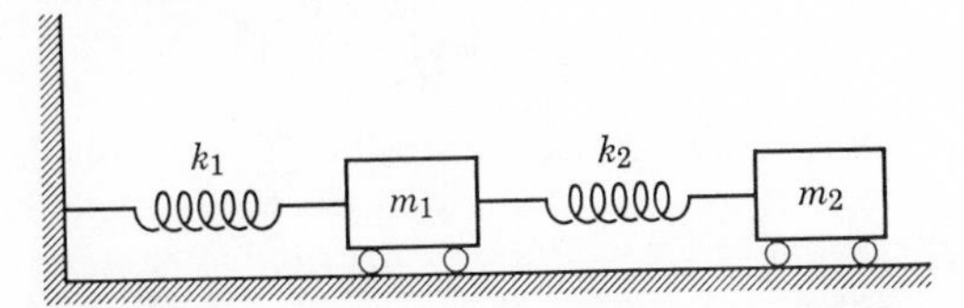

Fig. P7-5

7.6 (a) For the system of Fig. P7-5, with $k_1 = k_2 = m_1 = m_2 = 1$ and initial deflection selected to excite only the first mode, determine the time necessary for the system to reach its equilibrium configuration.

(b) Compare the integral of the Lagrangian with the same integral if the masses moved to their equilibrium position at constant velocity.

(c) Explain the result of an attempt to verify Hamilton's principle for (b) if Equation 7-18 is used instead of 7-17.

7.7 What generalized forces should be used with the coordinate system of Problem 7.5 if there are actual forces applied to the two masses?

7.8 (a) Using Newton's laws, derive differential equations for the system of Fig. P7-8, where y, f_1, and f_2 are arbitrary functions of time.

(b) Derive the differential equations of motion using the Lagrange equation.

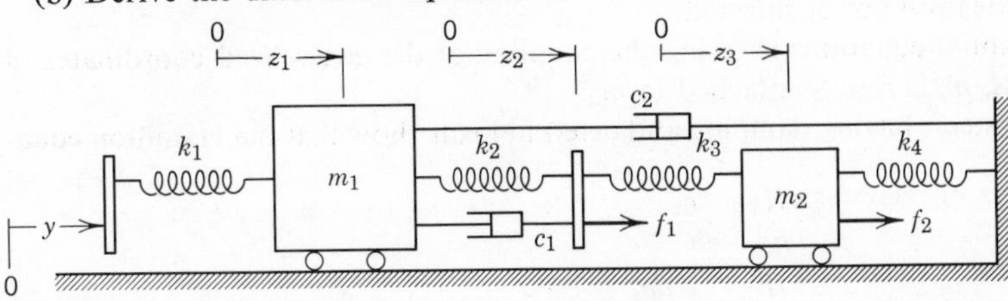

Fig. P7-8

7.9 Consider a rigid plate having a plan view as indicated in Fig. P7-9 supported at the four corners by springs and dampers. Assume that the plate is guided so that only vertical motion and angular "rocking" can exist. A force, $F(t)$, exists in the vertical direction at corner number 1, and a displacement of the support, $y(t)$, occurs at corner number 3. Let the coordinates be

$$z = \text{vertical displacement of center of gravity}$$
$$\alpha = \text{angular displacement about } x \text{ axis}$$
$$\beta = \text{angular displacement about } y \text{ axis}$$

Determine the differential equations of motion from the Lagrange equation.

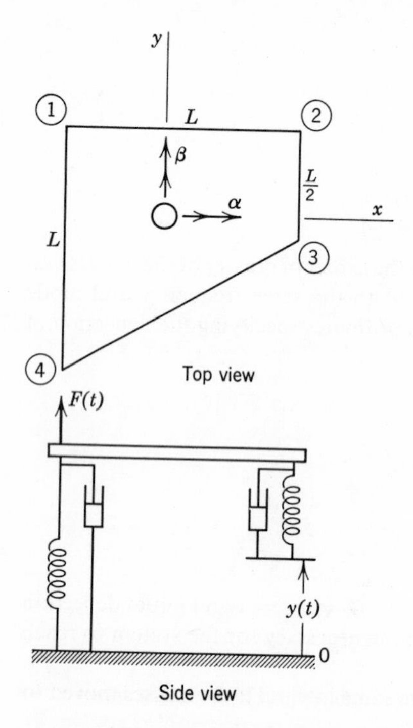

Fig. P7-9

7.10 What dissipation function should be used in Problem 7.5,
(a) If there is a viscous damper between the two masses?
(b) If the two masses rest on a surface and the coefficient of friction remains constant for all configurations of the system?

7.11 (a) Define a set of principal coordinates in terms of the coordinates of Problem 7.5.
(b) Determine requirements for adding dampers to this system so that the definition of principal coordinates will not be affected.
(c) Write differential equations showing the coupling of the generalized coordinates of (a) if another mass, m, is rigidly attached to m_2.

7.12 (a) For systems having damping and external loads show that the Hamilton equations are

$$\frac{\partial H}{\partial p_i} = \frac{\partial q_i}{\partial t}$$

$$\frac{\partial H}{\partial q_i} = -\frac{dp_i}{dt} - \frac{\partial \mathscr{F}_d}{\partial \dot{q}_i} + Q_i$$

where $\mathscr{F}_d$ = dissipation function and Q_i is defined by Equation 7-41.

(b) By matrix algebra show that $2T = \sum_i p_i \dot{q}_i$ as indicated in the text in connection with Equation 7-53.

Chapter 8

8.1 (a) Determine flexibility and stiffness matrices (Fig. P8-1).

(b) Would it be satisfactory to normalize modes on the deflection of the center mass? Explain.

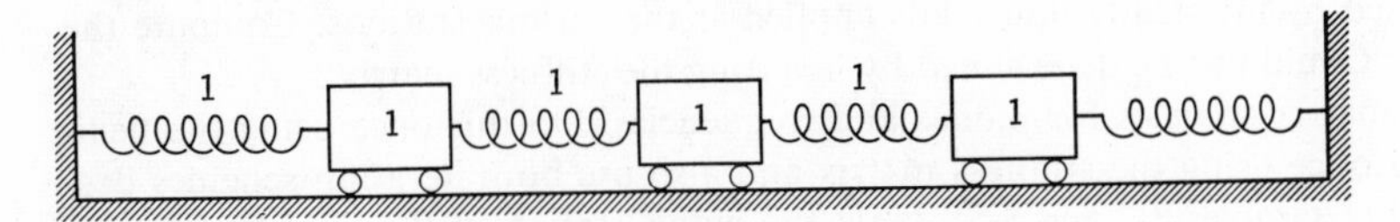

Fig. P8-1

8.2 Determine stiffness, flexibility, and inertia matrices for Problem 7.8, letting the damping coefficients be zero. Assume $y = 0$.

Determine normal modes and frequencies if $m_1 = m_2 = 1.0$ and $k_1 = k_2 = k_3 = k_4 = 1.0$ (in consistent units) and $c_1 = c_2 = 0$. Explain the result.

8.3 In Problem 7.9 if the mass of the plate is 1 slug, $L = 1$ ft, the four springs each have spring constants of 1 lb/ft, the dampers are zero, and $y = 0$, determine by matrix methods the first mode frequency and description.

8.4 A point mass is held in space by a set of five weightless extension springs. The equilibrium position of the mass is the origin, and the spring constants and position of the opposite ends of the springs are shown in Table P8-4. Determine the flexibility and stiffness matrices and the lowest natural frequency and mode.

Table P8–4

Spring	Spring Constant	Location of Fixed End of Spring		
		x direction	y direction	z direction
1	$1.0k$	$1.0L$	$1.0L$	$1.0L$
2	$2.0k$	$1.0L$	$-1.0L$	$2.0L$
3	$1.0k$	$-1.0L$	$-1.0L$	$1.0L$
4	$0.5k$	$-1.0L$	$2.0L$	$1.0L$
5	$2.0k$	$0.0L$	$1.0L$	$-1.0L$

8.5 Determine a stiffness and inertia matrix for the transmission and shafting system of Fig. P8-5. Assume the gears, I_2, I_3, I_4 are solid disks.

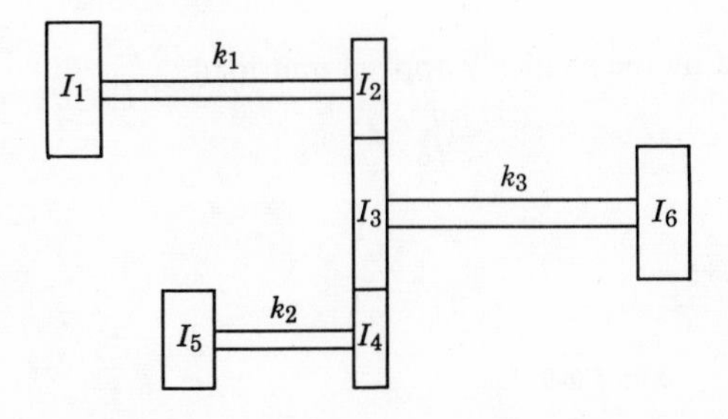

Fig. P8-5

8.6 Several interesting variations of the three-mass analysis discussed in Chapter 8 are illustrated by the free system depicted in Fig. P8-6. For this system, do the following.

(a) Set up the differential equations of motion.

(b) Formulate matrix equation and identify inertia and stiffness matrices.

(c) Verify stiffness matrix by direct computation.

(d) Using numerical values, $k_1 = k_2 = m_1 = m_2 = m_3 = 1$, define a flexibility matrix using deflections from the position in space where the masses would be located if the system were a rigid system, subject to the stipulation that the center of gravity of the flexible system be located at the same point as the center of gravity of the rigid system under the constant acceleration caused by the steady unit loads applied at the various stations. Compute the flexibility matrix. Could this be determined by inverting the stiffness matrix?

(e) Perform a matrix analysis for modes and frequencies. Do this once using the flexibility matrix and once using the stiffness matrix and also use both iteration schemes described in the text (Examples 8-2 and 8-5). Note the manifestation of the rigid-body mode in these analyses.

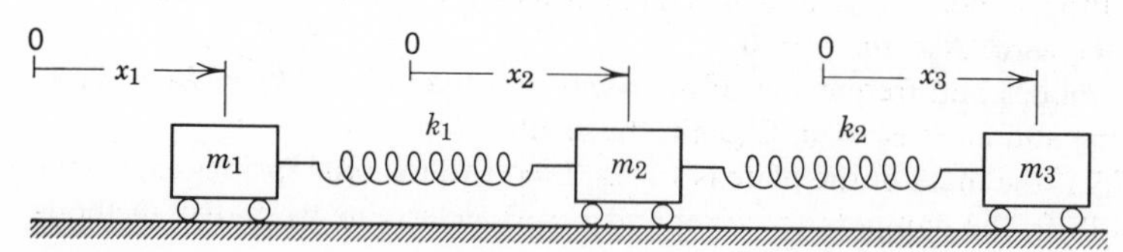

Fig. P8-6

8.7 Investigate the system of Fig. P8-7 in the same manner as suggested for Problem 8.6. This sketch represents a rigid bar of constant cross section supporting a mass at each end by means of a flexible attachment, the whole assembly free to move in space. For simplification of numerical computations, use unit values for spring constants, masses, and moment of inertia of the bar.

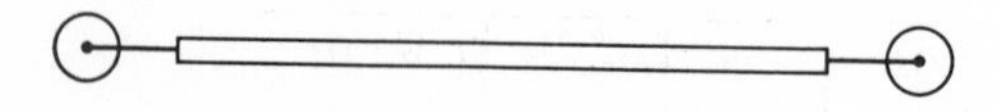

Fig. P8-7

8.8 Write differential equations of motion for natural vibration of the system of Example 8-7 in terms of the generalized coordinates used in that example.

(a) Make the same assumptions as the example, neglecting damper coupling.

(b) Do not neglect coupling between the generalized coordinates.

8.9 (a) Define normal modes and generalized coordinates to represent them for the system illustrated in Fig. P8-9.

(b) How much of each coordinate is excited by the suddenly applied unit load?

(c) Where is each mass at $t = 1$?

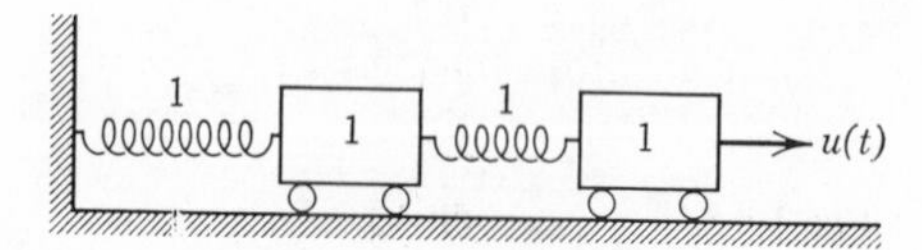

Fig. P8-9

8.10 For Example 8-5, with normalization on the third coordinate.

(a) What is the generalized mass in the sěcond mode?

(b) If a force of 1 lb is applied on the first mass in the positive x direction and a 1-lb force is applied on the second mass in the negative x direction, and then released, what will be the relative magnitudes of the three normal modes?

8.11 For Example 8-5, with normalized modes of

$$\begin{Bmatrix} 0.395 \\ 0.759 \\ 1.000 \end{Bmatrix} \quad \begin{Bmatrix} -1.421 \\ -1.607 \\ 1.000 \end{Bmatrix} \quad \begin{Bmatrix} 16.00 \\ -6.15 \\ 1.000 \end{Bmatrix}$$

at frequencies of 0.284, 0.932, 1.542 rad/sec respectively, suppose an oscillatory force of $3.0 \sin 0.5t$ is applied to the center mass. Determine amplitude and frequency of oscillation of the three masses after a long time by use of the generalized coordinate concept. (Assume slight structural damping will damp out the transients.)

8.12 Figure P8-12 represents an L-shaped structure whose plane is horizontal. One end of the L is rigidly attached to a wall. The other supports a mass suspended by a spring. Beam A is a solid, round aluminium rod, 1 in. in diameter and 50 in. long. Neglect its weight but not its flexibility. Beam B is a very rigid bar 40 in. long weighing 30 lb. The suspended mass weighs 10 lb and is attached by a spring having spring constant of 20 lb per inch.

(a) Determine stiffness and flexibility matrices by direct computation and check if they are inverses of each other.

(b) Determine normal modes and frequencies.

(c) The mass is pulled down 1 in. and released from rest. Determine how much of each mode is excited (magnitude of the corresponding generalized coordinates).

(d) If a sinusoidal force of 1 lb is applied on the mass at a frequency of 27.7 rad/sec, what is the steady-state amplitude of the first mode generalized coordinate?

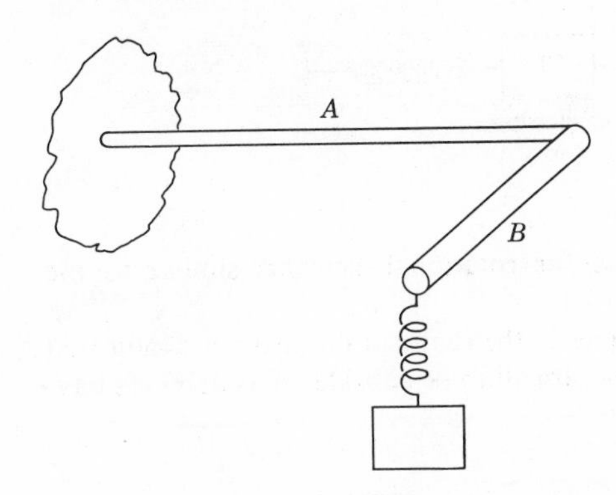

Fig. P8-12

8.13 Example 8-4 specifies a matrix equation which describes the same physical system as Fig. 8-1 with numerical values of $m_1 = 1$, $m_2 = 2$, $m_3 = 3$, $k_1 = k_2 = k_3 = 1$, but the coordinates are generalized coordinates which do not represent distances in Fig. 8-1. Are these coordinates principal coordinates? Using appropriate matrix relationships of Section 8.7 show how to obtain a matrix equation relating these generalized coordinates to the ordinary coordinates of Fig. 8-1.

8.14 Write a set of equations in terms of the Laplace transform variable, s, for Problem 8.13. Determine the characteristic equation, solve for the frequencies, and obtain normal modes in terms of these generalized coordinates.

8.15 Define principal coordinates for the results of Problem 8.14, verify the appropriate matrix orthogonality relationships of Section 8.7, and determine the generalized mass and spring constant for the defined principal coordinates.

Chapter 9

9.1 Determine factors of the following polynomials.

(a) $s^3 + s^2 - 2$

(b) $s^4 + 6s^3 + 18s^2 + 30s + 65$

(c) $s^5 + s^4 - 7s^3 - s^2 + 16s + 30$

(d) $s^6 + 10s^5 + 47s^4 + 126s^3 + 202s^2 + 184s + 80$

Answer: $(s^2 + 2s + 2)(s^2 + 4s + 5)(s^2 + 4s + 8)$.

9.2 Verify that the system represented by the following set of equations has the same characteristic equation as Problem 9.1(d). Determine relationships between the variables for one of the natural modes.

$$\begin{bmatrix} (3s^2 + 10s + 15) & -(2s + 3) & -(2s + 6) \\ -(2s + 3) & (2s^2 + 6s + 7) & (s^2 + 2s + 2) \\ -(2s + 6) & (s^2 + 2s + 2) & (2s^2 + 6s + 10) \end{bmatrix} \begin{Bmatrix} x_1 \\ x_2 \\ x_3 \end{Bmatrix} = \begin{Bmatrix} 0 \\ 0 \\ 0 \end{Bmatrix}$$

Chapter 10

10.1 (a) Determine transfer functions X_1/F, X_3/X_1, X_3/X_2, (Fig. P10-1) using the methods of Section 10.2. The numerical values of the masses are 1, 2, and 3 units, respectively.

(b) Compute and plot the frequency response for harmonic forcing functions.

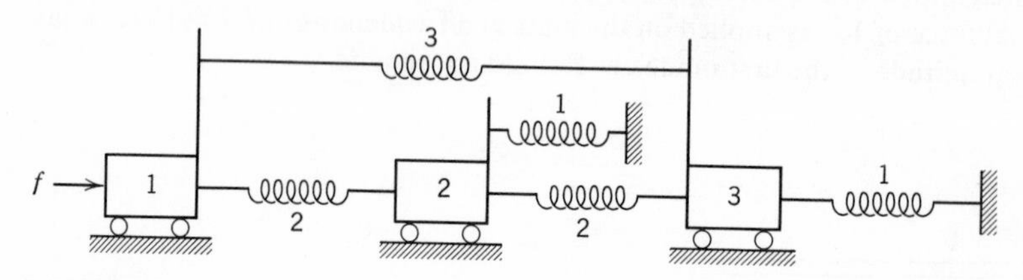

Fig. P10-1

10.2 (a) Determine mobility and impedance for rotational elements similar to the translational elements of Table 10-1.

(b) Determine transfer functions relating torques in the shafts of the gear train indicated in Fig. P10.2 to the input torque, Q. The bearings are all to be considered as dampers having the same coefficient.

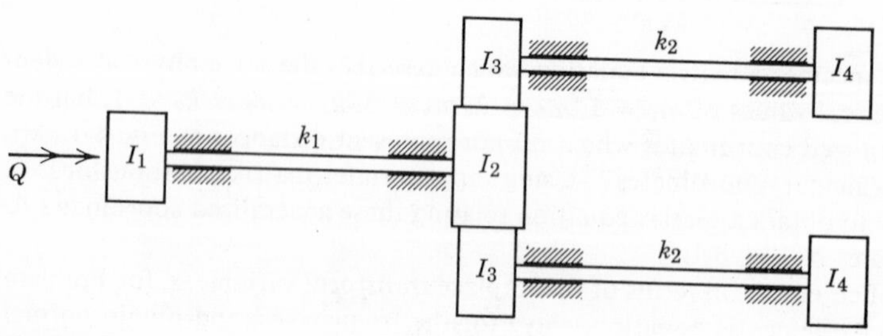

Fig. P10-2

10.3 Figure P10-3 represents a rigid bar with freedom to move in both the angular and vertical directions. Devise a scheme for determining the transfer function relating the force, f, and displacement, y, making use of impedance and mobility concepts, and check results with the Lagrange equation.

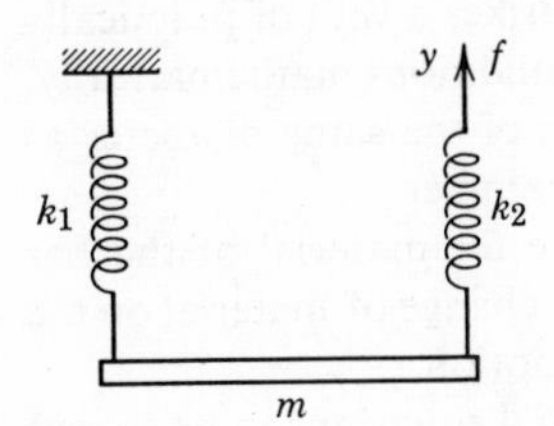

Fig. P10-3

10.4 Repeat Problem 10.3 for the system indicated in Fig. P10-4.

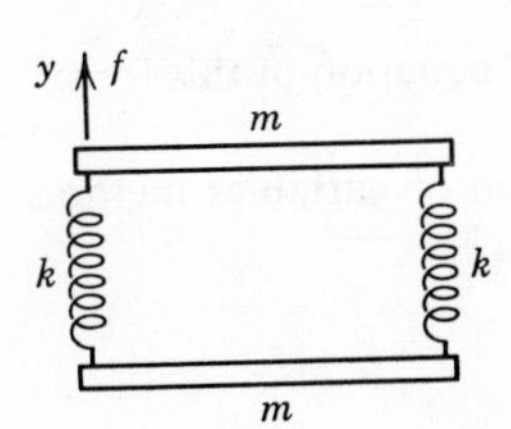

Fig. P10-4

10.5 Compute and plot the response for the system of Problem 10.4, if the input is a sinusoidal function, for (a) force input, and (b) displacement input.

Chapter 11

11.1 Derive the partial differential equation for the vibration of a drumhead (or stretched membrane), assuming zero damping. The membrane is assumed to have equal internal tension forces in all directions.

11.2 Repeat Problem 11.1, deriving the partial differential equation by minimizing the Lagrangian.

11.3 A semi-infinite string stretched initially into the shape shown in Fig. P11-3 is released from rest. The velocity of a wave in the string is 2 units per second. What is the displacement of the string at:

(a) $x = 20$, $t = 5$?

(b) $x = 20$, $t = 2.5$?

(c) $x = 15$, $t = 2.5$?

(d) $x = 20$, $t = 20$?

(e) $x = 40$, $t = 5$ if the sketch is a description of the initial velocity rather than the initial displacement?

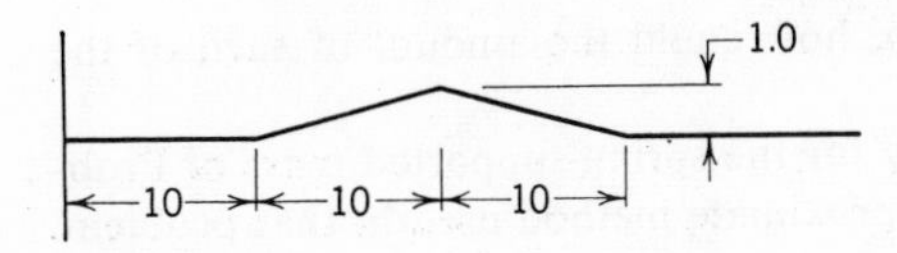

Fig. P11-3

11.4 Determine the form of a solution similar to the D'Alembert solution for the partial differential equation of Problem 11.1.

11.5 Derive Equations 11-26 and 11-27.

11.6 A longitudinal wave traveling in a bar of steel reaches a free end. What is the nature of the reflected wave?

11.7 A longitudinal wave traveling in an elastic medium (a) strikes a wall of practically unyielding material, or (b) reaches a free surface. Describe these conditions mathematically.

11.8 A steel hammer head strikes one end of a free steel rod of the same diameter as the hammer. Describe the resulting motion of the rod and of the hammer.

11.9 A torsion wave in a circular bar reaches a point where the material of the bar changes to one having greater density. Describe the effect of this change of material on the wave. Describe similar effects for lateral and longitudinal wave motion.

11.10 By separation of variables, determine ordinary differential equations to be solved if

$$\frac{\partial^2 y}{\partial t^2} + c\frac{\partial y}{\partial t} = a^2\frac{\partial^2 y}{\partial x^2}$$

What kind of a physical problem could lead to a partial differential equation of this form? What would be the nature of the solution?

11.11 For which of the following equations does the separation of variables method fail?

(a) $\dfrac{\partial^3 u}{\partial x^2 \partial y} + u = 0$

(b) $\dfrac{\partial^2 u}{\partial x^2} + \dfrac{\partial u}{\partial x} + \dfrac{\partial u}{\partial y} = 0$

(c) $\dfrac{\partial^2 u}{\partial x^2} + \dfrac{\partial^2 u}{\partial y^2} + \dfrac{\partial^2 u}{\partial z^2} = 0$

(d) $xy\dfrac{\partial^2 u}{\partial x^2} + \dfrac{\partial^2 u}{\partial y^2} = 0$

(e) $\dfrac{\partial^4 u}{\partial x^4} + \dfrac{\partial^4 u}{\partial x^2\,\partial y^2} + \dfrac{\partial^4 u}{\partial y^4} = 0$

11.12 (a) A round, uniform shaft adequately supported against lateral deflection by bearings is fixed at one end and only partially fixed at the other end, where a torsional deflection is opposed by a flexible constraint. Determine the frequency equation and the equation describing the normal modes.

(b) Repeat (a) if the end opposite the fixed end is attached to a mass instead of a flexible constraint.

11.13 It is known that the normal *modes* resulting from the computations of Problem 11.12 are orthogonal. That is, inertia forces generated by acceleration of all masses vibrating in one of the modes do not excite other modes (the generalized force corresponding to these inertia forces is zero in the other modes).

(a) Are the functions which describe the shaft deflection in the various normal modes orthogonal *functions* in the sense that $\int_0^L X_n X_m \, dx = 0$ if $n \neq m$? [Answer for both (a) and (b) of Problem 11.12.]

(b) If an initial deflection pattern were known, how could the amount of each of the various modes be computed?

11.14 Determine the lowest natural frequency for the spring-supported mass of Problem 7.1(a) and compare with the result of the approximate method used in that problem.

11.15 Using the more exact methods of Chapter 11, check the results of Problem 5.17 to see if the approximate analysis used was sufficiently accurate.

11.16 Show that the D'Alembert solution of the wave equation applied to a string stretched between fixed points can be converted to the Fourier series statement of the solution which results from the separation of variables technique.

11.17 The partial differential equation for one-dimensional heat conduction in a homogeneous medium is $\partial^2 u/\partial x^2 = a^2(\partial u/\partial t)$ where $a^2 = c\gamma/k$ and

c = specific heat
γ = weight density
k = conductivity coefficient
u = temperature

If it is assumed that the temperature at a point under ground obeys this equation in response to temperature variations at the surface, determine an expression for the steady-state temperature variation at a point under the ground when the surface temperature varies according to $u_0 \sin \omega t$.

(a) Use separation of variables. (*Hint.* The common constant may not be real.)

(b) Solve by using an assumed solution similar to Equation 11-10 except that the functions of x and t can be assumed to be of the form e^{Ax+Bt}.

11.18 (a) Solve Problem 11.17 by use of the Laplace transform. Transform with respect to t, solve the differential equation, obtain the inverse transform and check the results of Problem 11.17.

(b) Repeat (a) but transform with respect to x.

11.19 Using the Rayleigh method obtain an approximate first mode natural frequency for a constant cross-section cantilever beam rotating about its base (similar to a propeller blade). Assume parabolic mode shape.

11.20 A beam with one end supported flexibly is hinged at the other end, but a mass m with radius of gyration, ρ, is attached there. What is the frequency equation?

11.21 Which of the following beams would have mode shapes described by functions which are not orthogonal functions?

(a) Fixed-free.
(b) Fixed-spring supported.
(c) Each end spring supported.
(d) Free ends but depth is not constant along the beam.
(e) Beam of Problem 11.20.

11.22 A hinged-hinged beam is displaced into the initial shape, $0.01x(L - x)$, and released from rest. Which modes of vibration would be excited?

11.23 For a beam of uniform cross section, determine the generalized force in the second mode of "inertia forces" in the first mode. What property does the result illustrate? How could this be used to determine the coefficients of a series used to describe an arbitrary deflection pattern in terms of normal mode functions when the mode functions are not orthogonal functions?

Chapter 12

12.1 Suppose a concentrated mass is attached at the free end of a cantilever beam off the centerline of the beam a distance, z, with a rigid weightless connection. Use the deflection of this mass as one coordinate. Let the beam be of constant cross section and partitioned as in Example 12-2, and consider that the masses of the beam are point masses concentrated at the appropriate stations.

Specify a flexibility and inertia matrix for this system, from which modes and frequencies could be determined.

12.2 Determine the flexbility matrix, inertia matrix, and first mode frequency and description for a cantilever having a tapered cross section. Let the cross section have similar geometric shape along the beam but taper linearly from the root to the tip so that the tip dimensions are one half of the root dimensions. Segment the beam as in Example 12-1 and compare the results with that example.

12.3 Determine the flexibility matrix for a constant cross section beam having a spring support at each end, using a numerical procedure and the segmentation of Example 12-2. Let the spring supports have spring constants selected so that the first bending frequency of a simply supported beam would be the same as the lowest frequency of the spring supported beam considered completely rigid.

Determine the first mode frequency and description by the method of separation of variables and see if the solution satisfies the matrix equation representing the numerical solution.

12.4 Rework Example 12-2 for a beam fixed at each end. *Hint*. Show that a rigid support to rotation requires substitution in the appropriate position in [λ] the column

$$\begin{Bmatrix} 0 \\ -\epsilon_{23} \\ -\epsilon_{33} \\ \cdots \\ -\epsilon_{n3} \\ -1 \\ -\phi_{23} \\ -\phi_{33} \\ \cdots \\ -\phi_{n3} \end{Bmatrix}$$

12.5 Determine the flexibility matrix for a free beam whose dimensions taper linearly from a maximum at the center to one half of these at each end. Use the same segmentation as Example 12.2 and 12.3.

12.6 Develop equations similar to Equations 12-18 and 12-19 for a beam having only one support.

(a) The support is flexible to translation, but allows complete rotational freedom.
(b) The flexible support of (a) becomes rigid to translation.
(c) The support is flexible to rotation, but allows complete translational freedom.
(d) The flexible support of (c) becomes rigid to rotation.

12.7 Rework Example 12-4 for a beam fixed at each end and check with results of Problem 12.4.

12.8 What is likely to be wrong with an attempt to determine the flexibility matrix of a free beam by inverting a suitable stiffness matrix?

12.9 Determine by numerical means the natural modes and frequencies in bending of a semicircular cantilever beam having constant cross section (Fig. P12-9).

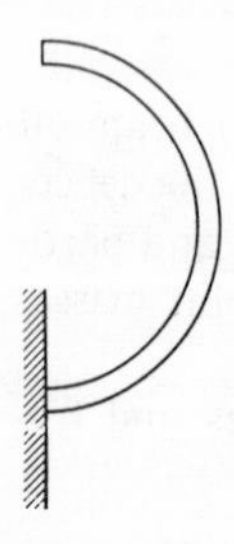

Fig. P12-9

Chapter 13

13.1 Derive Equations 13-5.

13.2 (a) Derive Simpson's rule for integration of a function over a range of the independent variable by obtaining the integral of a quadratic which fits at three points. Simpson's rule states that if the range of the independent variable is divided into an even number $(n - 1)$ of equal increments, Δx, the integral of the function, $f(x)$, is given by

$$I = \frac{\Delta x}{3}(f_1 + 4f_2 + 2f_3 + 4f_4 + \cdots + 2f_{n-2} + 4f_{n-1} + f_n)$$

(b) Modify (a) so that the integral is computed from a quadratic equation matching the tabular function at three successive values of x, not necessarily evenly spaced. The integral of the function between two successive values of x can be taken as the average of the integral when that interval is the left interval and when it is the right interval (The integral between x_4 and x_5 is the average of the integral when the quadratic fits at Stations 3, 4, and 5 and when it fits at Stations 4, 5, and 6 in Fig. P13-2.)

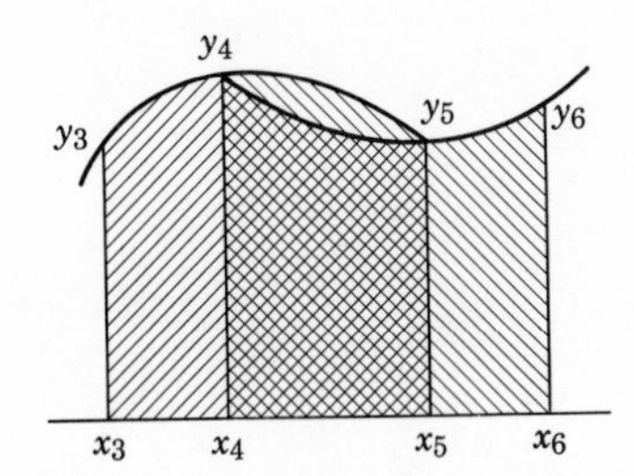

Fig. P13-2

13.3 Compute one element of a flexibility matrix for a circular shaft under torsion by using Equations 13-4. The shaft is fixed at each end and the diameter tapers linearly between the two ends, the diameter at one end being twice that at the other end. Develop the inertia matrix to be used with the proposed flexibility matrix.

13.4 Compute the deflection at the end of a constant cross section cantilever beam caused by a load at the end. Use Equations 13-6 and six stations along the beam. Compare the computed value using this numerical method with the exact value and explain the result.

13.5 Compute one element of a flexibility matrix for a beam of constant cross section supported by a distributed spring. Compare with an exact computation.

13.6 Set up a method for solving the wave equation numerically, using the method of Section 13.4, for a string stretched between two points.

13.7 Determine the first mode and frequency for a square vibrating membrane under uniform tension.

(a) Use the classical technique.

(b) Use a numerical method.

13.8 Determine the first mode and frequency for a circular membrane under uniform tension.

(a) Use classical technique with cylindrical coordinates.

(b) Use a numerical method with cylindrical coordinates.

(c) Use a numerical method with Cartesian coordinates.

13.9 In Example 13-2 the deflection at the center of a square plate having simply supported edges was computed using a numerical method. Rework this problem treating the square plate as a diamond-shaped plate, selecting lattice points running parallel with the diagonals.

13.10 Determine a flexibility matrix and inertia matrix which could be used to determine the natural modes and frequencies of vibration of a thin homogeneous rectangular flat plate fixed on one edge and free on the others. The thickness tapers linearly from a constant value along the fixed side to some constant fraction of this along the opposite side. If a digital computer is available, determine several modes and frequencies for a square plate if this fixed fraction is $\frac{1}{2}$. (See programs of Reference 1.)

13.11 Derive the partial differential equation governing the deflection of a rectangular membrane under pressure by use of variational calculus. Set up a method for solving this equation numerically.

13.12 Develop a stiffness matrix for the three-dimensional structure shown in Fig. P13-12. The points A, B, C, and D can deflect in three dimensional space in response to loads at these points. The points E, F, G, and H are connected to a wall. Assume all joints are pinned and only energy of tension and compression needs to be considered. The members of the truss all have the same cross section and all except the diagonal members have the same length.

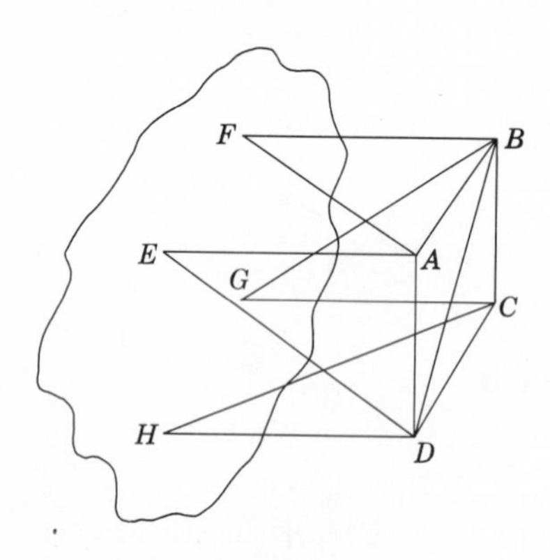

Fig. P13-12

13.13 Show how to obtain the inverse of a matrix using the method of Section 13.7 provided that the matrix is of suitable form.

Chapter 14

14.1 Describe an alternate procedure for Problem 12.1, using generalized coordinates and forces, where the generalized coordinates are the beam mode shapes without the attached mass.

14.2 Consider the free beam of Section 14.1 and Table 14-1. Let a concentrated mass, M, be fastened to the beam at the center station. Assume that bending of this modified beam in a natural mode of vibration may be represented by generalized coordinates which define the bending of the original beam in its various natural modes and then assume for this problem (in order to save work and time) that only the first of these will be used. Use any additional coordinates which seem appropriate.

(a) Determine the first natural frequency of this modified beam, and note if the result seems reasonable if the supported mass is large or small relative to the beam mass.

(b) Repeat using two significant bending modes instead of only one.

14.3 Consider a beam simply supported at each end. A load is suddenly applied at the center. Determine the amount of vibration which is induced in Modes 1, 2, and 3.

14.4 Indicate how to determine natural modes and frequencies of a system consisting of a simply supported beam and a mass suspended from the beam by a spring. Use generalized coordinates which specify beam deflection in several bending modes.

14.5 Using the information of Table 14-1, determine the first mode frequency of a free beam having a mass equal to the beam mass suspended by a spring from Station 6. Let the natural frequency of the spring-suspended mass (if the spring were attached to a rigid support instead of the beam) be the same as the first mode of the free beam without the suspended weight. Use only two bending modes to describe the beam bending.

14.6 (a) Calculate the lowest natural frequency of a free steel beam having circular cross section if one half of the beam has a diameter which is twice that of the other half, as indicated in Fig. P14-6, using numerical means.

(b) Check the above results by solving this problem using generalized coordinates representing the first two cantilever bending modes of each beam separately. Why should the cantilever modes be used rather than free beam modes?

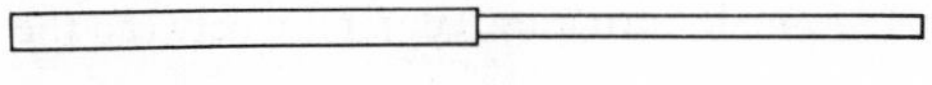

Fig. P14-6

14.7 Consider a long, constant cross section cantilever beam oriented in the direction of the gravity field (vertical). Determine the natural frequency and mode descriptions for small deflections from the vertical by the following methods.

(a) Separation of variables.

(b) Direct computation by numerical means.

(c) Use of generalized coordinates which describe beam modes without gravity to determine new modes and frequencies which include the effect of gravity.

14.8 In Example 14.3 it was assumed that the thrust would have a negligible effect on body bending modes. Demonstrate that this is a valid assumption for the numerical parameters used. If the effect were not negligible, describe a modification which would account for it.

14.9 Investigate the following effect for Example 14.3. Suppose the corrective control force is caused by swivelling the thrust vector relative to the local missile body axis. What changes in the equations of motion result? Then if a computer is available determine if there is a significant change in stability.

Chapter 15

15.1 A spring-damper system is subjected to a force having the history shown (Fig. P15-1).

Determine the displacement by use of the convolution theorem, for $0 < t < 1$ and for $t > 1$.

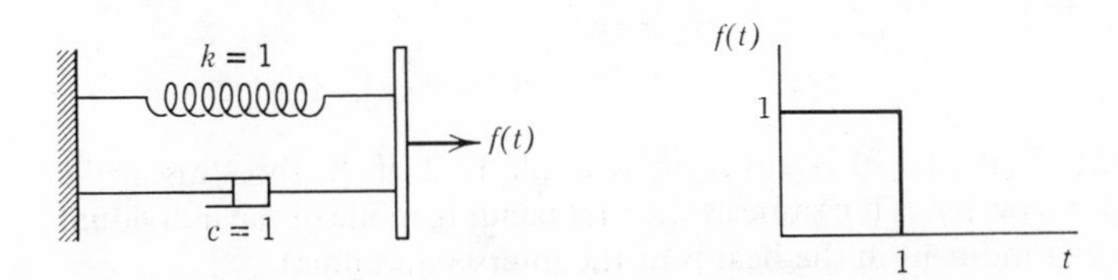

Fig. P15-1

15.2 The sketch of Fig. P15-2 represents a simplified version of a problem which could arise in longitudinal vibration of a missile whose major masses are connected by structure which cannot be assumed rigid. For convenience of numerical computation, let the masses and springs have unit values as in Problem 8.6. Let the force (rocket thrust) history be approximated by a ramp to a final constant value. Determine the maximum load in the connecting structure and investigate the effect of ramp time on this load. Use generalized coordinates which represent the normal modes.

Fig. P15-2

15.3 For Problem 15.2 investigate the effect of small (structural) damping between the masses.

15.4 Assume that a relationship between a forcing function and a coordinate is described by the following transfer function.

$$\frac{X}{F} = \frac{(s+1)^3(s+4)(s^2+s+2)}{(s+2)^3(s^2+s+1)^2}$$

Use the general method described by Equations A1-19 to A1-28 to determine the response to unit impulse. Then use the general method described by Equations 15-6 to 15-16 to obtain the value of the coordinate at $t = 2$ if the forcing function is described by the graph of Fig. P15-4. Check the result with a direct computation.

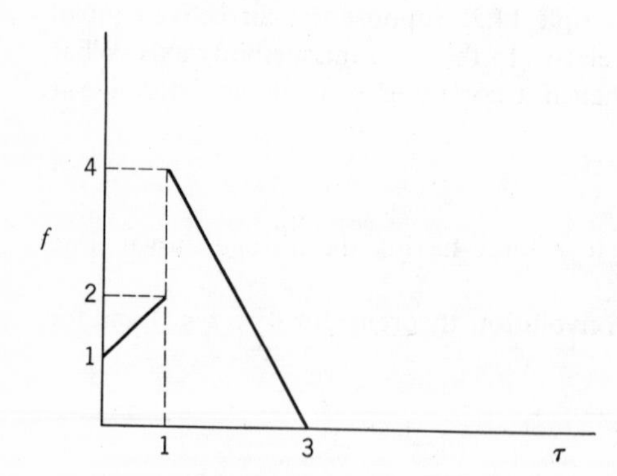

Fig. P15-4

15.5 A force is applied to Station 7 of Beam A of Example 14-2. If the force history is one cycle of a sine curve whose period is the same as the first bending mode of the individual beams, determine the bending moment in the beams at the intersection point.

15.6 Consider a very tall building assuming constant EI and mass distribution (Fig. P15-6). Assume that an earthquake causes the base of the building to move in the horizontal direction with the acceleration indicated in the sketch. What magnitude of the generalized coordinates of the first and second bending modes is excited, and what generalized force in these modes is required if these are the only modes entering the picture? In what way would the analysis be different if the assumption of constant EI and mass distribution were not made?

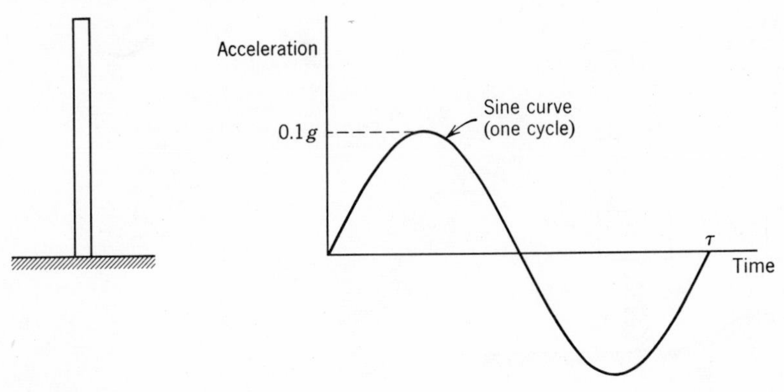

Fig. P15-6

15.7 If the missile of Example 14-3 encounters a 50 ft per second transverse gust (sharp edged), what is the maximum bending moment induced in the beam body?

15.8 A 4 × 6 ft glass window pane $\frac{1}{8}$ in. thick is hit by a "sonic boom" having the assumed pressure-time relationship shown in Fig. P15-8. Will the window break? Assume breaking stress and modulus of elasticity for glass are 3000 and 10^6 psi respectively, specific gravity 2.5.

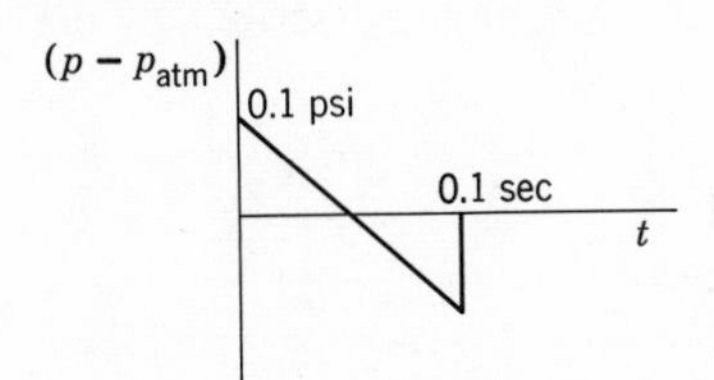

Fig. P15-8

15.9 Consider a beam subjected to a transverse load which moves along the beam at a constant velocity. If the beam were of constant cross section, it would be possible to attack the problem using Laplace transforms. However, if the beam were of arbitrary cross section, numerical methods would be needed. Devise a numerical method of analysis based on generalized coordinates for the beam bending modes which would be applicable to any beam and then apply it to the constant area, simply supported beam of Example 12-2.

15.10 Figure P15-10 represents a simplified form of an aircraft bicycle landing gear problem. The suspended masses represent wheels, the lower springs the tire flexibility. Assume that in taxiing the aircraft encounters a bump which can be represented by the expression

$$\frac{h}{2}\left(1 - \cos \frac{2\pi x}{L}\right)$$

A time history of the bending moment at several points along the beam is desired. To alleviate some of the numerical work, assume the physical data of Example 14-3 wherever needed. Assume the gear is attached at Stations 2 and 8 and the mass of each is 15 slugs. Assume that the aircraft taxies at 100 ft/sec, and let the bump dimensions be $h = 6$ in., $L = 25$ ft. Assume all springs and dampers linear and that two bending modes adequately represent the beam bending. Neglect aerodynamic loads. Assume that the spring rates are 20,000 lb/ft and 5000 lb/ft respectively for the lower and upper springs and that the damping coefficients are 300 lb per ft/sec.

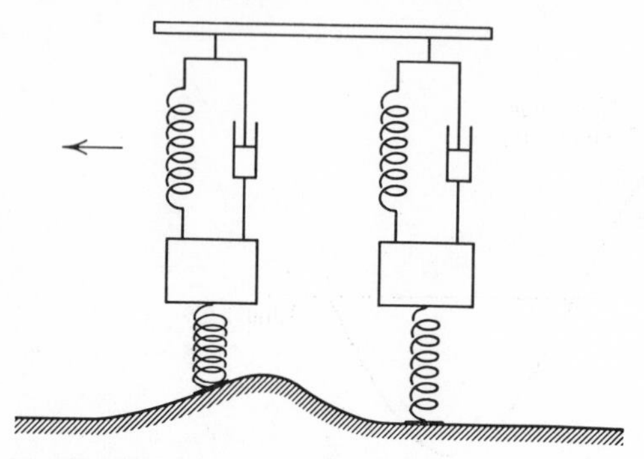

Fig. P15-10

Chapter 16

16.1 (a) Check several points on Fig. 16-3.

(b) Could Fig. 16-3 be developed from Equation 16-1 by appropriately combining the response to two shocks of the form shown in Fig. 16-1, where

$$\frac{T_a}{T} = 1, \quad \frac{T_b}{T} = 0, \quad \frac{T_c}{T} = 0$$

for one of the shocks and

$$\frac{T_a}{T} = 0, \quad \frac{T_b}{T} = 0, \quad \frac{T_c}{T} = 1$$

for the other shock?

(c) Could Fig. 16-4 be developed from two other figures (one of which could be Fig. 16-8) for which the parameters are as specified in (b)? Why?

16.2 If Fig. P16-2 represents the acceleration, $\ddot{y}$, of Fig. 16-1 (but without damper), obtain a point on the shock spectrum for this shock.

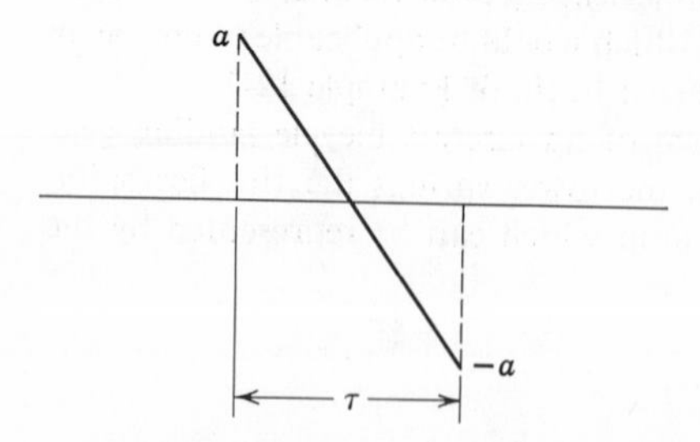

Fig. P16-2

16.3 (a) Derive the following equations for acceleration and rate of change of acceleration for the system of Fig. 16-1a when the input acceleration, a_y, is the linear function specified below. Then explain how to use these equations to compute the shock spectrum for an input shock having a general description rather than the specific shock of Fig. 16-16.

What is the advantage of this computation over the convolution integral? Can you think of a type of problem for which the convolution integral is more convenient?

$$a_x = a_{y_0} + \dot{a}_{y_0}t + e^{-\zeta\beta t}\left[(a_{x_0} - a_{y_0}) \cos \beta\sqrt{1 - \zeta^2}\, t + \frac{\zeta\beta(a_{x_0} - a_{y_0}) + \dot{a}_{x_0} - \dot{a}_{y_0}}{\beta\sqrt{1 - \zeta^2}} \sin \beta\sqrt{1 - \zeta^2}\, t\right]$$

$$\dot{a}_x = \dot{a}_{y_0} + e^{-\zeta\beta t}\left[(\dot{a}_{x_0} - \dot{a}_{y_0}) \cos \beta\sqrt{1 - \zeta^2}\, t - \frac{\beta(a_{x_0} - a_{y_0}) + \zeta(\dot{a}_{x_0} - \dot{a}_{y_0})}{\sqrt{1 - \zeta^2}} \sin \beta\sqrt{1 - \zeta^2}\, t\right]$$

where

a_x = acceleration of the mass

$a_y = a_{y_0} + \dot{a}_{y_0}t$ = acceleration of the platform

a_{y_0} = initial acceleration of the platform

$\dot{a}_{y_0}$ = rate of change of platform acceleration, a constant

a_{x_0} = initial acceleration of the mass

$\dot{a}_{x_0}$ = initial rate of change of mass acceleration

(b) Check a point on Fig. 16-3 using these equations.

16.4 Assume that a piece of equipment is expected to be able to withstand shocks whose acceleration history is one half of a sine curve, but that the only shock testing apparatus available generates "terminal saw tooth" shocks. Determine suitable parameters for reasonable simulation of the expected shocks on the testing apparatus.

Chapter 17

17.1 Verify Equations 17-5 and 17-6 and also that the imaginary part of the inverse is identically zero.

17.2 By reference to Example 17-1 determine the value of the definite integral

$$\int_0^\infty \frac{1 - \cos \omega}{\omega^2}\, d\omega$$

17.3 (a) Compute and plot the Fourier transform of the function shown in Fig. P16-2.

(b) If Fig. P16-2 represents an acceleration, $\ddot{y}$ of Fig. 16-1 (but without damper), comment on possible difficulties to be expected in computing the response acceleration, $\ddot{x}$ numerically, using the Fourier inverse transform. Compute a point on the response curve this way if possible and check the results of Problem 16.2.

17.4 Suppose an infinitely long beam is loaded with a constant static distributed load for $-a < x < +a$ and zero loading outside this interval (Fig. P17-4). The beam rests on a flexible foundation, having spring constant k lb/in./in.

(a) Using Fourier transforms derive an expression for the moment at any point in the beam. Using this, determine the moment in the beam at the origin if a concentrated force is applied there.

(b) How could this analysis be modified to account for loading which varies sinusoidally with time?

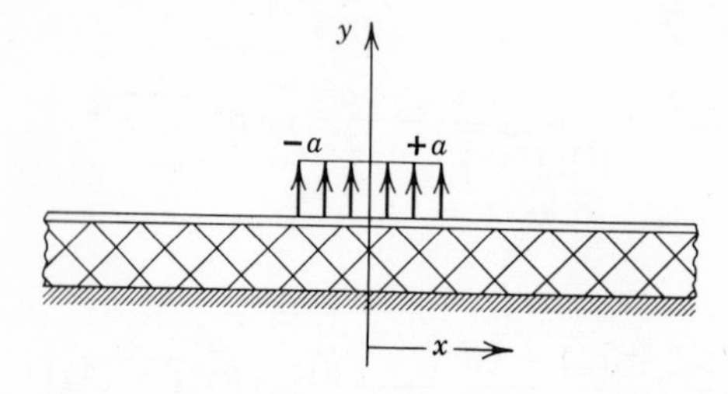

Fig. P17-4

17.5 Repeat Problem 15.1 using the Fourier transform. (*Hint.* The final definite integral may be evaluated by an application of complex variable residue theory.)

17.6 Integrate the function

$$\frac{2}{\pi}\int_{\omega=0}^{\infty}\frac{a}{\omega^2 T_a}(1 - \cos T_a\omega)\cos t\omega\,d\omega$$

obtained in Example 17-1 in closed form and show that the result is indeed the original pulse correctly defined in every region. (See the hint for Problem 17.5.)

17.7 Solve Problem 11.17 using an appropriate Fourier transform.

Answers to Problems

1.1 (a) $x = x_0$

(b) $x = x_0 + \ddot{x}_0\dfrac{m}{c}(1 - e^{-ct/m})$

1.2 (a) $\dddot{x} + \dfrac{k}{c}\ddot{x} + \dfrac{k}{m}\dot{x} = \dfrac{1}{m}\dot{f} + \dfrac{k}{mc}f$

(e) $\ddot{x} + \dfrac{c}{m}\dot{x} = \dfrac{c}{m}\dot{y}$

(h) $\dot{x} + \dfrac{k}{c}x = f$

1.3 (a) $x = x_0 + 2\zeta\dot{x}_0/\beta + \ddot{x}_0/\beta^2$

$$+ e^{-\zeta\beta t}\left[-\frac{1}{\beta}\left(2\zeta\beta\dot{x}_0 + \frac{\ddot{x}_0}{\beta}\right)\cos\beta\sqrt{1-\zeta^2}\,t + \left(\frac{1-2\zeta^2}{\beta\sqrt{1-\zeta^2}}\dot{x}_0 - \frac{\zeta\ddot{x}_0}{\beta^2\sqrt{1-\zeta^2}}\right)\sin\beta\sqrt{1-\zeta^2}\,t\right]$$

$$\beta = \sqrt{\frac{k}{m}}, \qquad \zeta = \frac{k}{2c\beta}$$

(d) With $y = 0$, end of spring restrained, see Equation 1–8. With end of spring unrestrained, see Problem 1.1*b*.

(h) $x = x_0 e^{-kt/c}$

2.4 0.805 lb/ft.

2.6 $\mu = \dfrac{x_0\beta^2}{4g}(1 - e^{-2\pi\zeta/\sqrt{1-\zeta^2}})$

or approximately

$$\zeta = -\frac{1}{2\pi}\ln\left(1 - \frac{4\mu g}{\beta^2 x_0}\right)$$

3.3 $\zeta \doteq 0.25$.

3.4 (a) No difference unless the natural frequency is lowered by increasing the mass. Then this would be better.

(b) Same as (*a*).

3.5 Same as 3.4.

3.8 $\zeta \doteq 0.64$.

3.9 (a) The relationship between energies dissipated is

$$\frac{4\mu g f_0}{\beta^2}\sqrt{\left[\frac{(\beta/\omega)^2}{1-(\beta/\omega)^2}\right]^2-\left[\frac{\beta}{\omega}\left(\frac{m\mu g}{f_0}\right)\frac{\sin\pi\beta/\omega}{1+\cos\pi\beta/\omega}\right]^2}$$

$$=\frac{2\pi\zeta f_0^2}{k}\frac{(\omega/\beta)}{[1-(\omega/\beta)^2]^2+(2\zeta\omega/\beta)^2}$$

3.13 76.9°F, 23.2 minutes.

3.15 (a) If $f = f_0 \sin \omega t$

$$x = \frac{f_0}{k} A \sin(\omega t + \phi)$$

$$A \frac{\sqrt{(\omega/\beta)^2[1-(\omega/\beta)^2-(2\zeta)^2]^2+(2\zeta)^2}}{(\omega/\beta)\{[1-(\omega/\beta)^2]^2+(2\zeta\omega/\beta)^2\}}$$

$$\phi = \tan^{-1}\frac{-2\zeta}{(\omega/\beta)[1-(\omega/\beta)^2-(2\zeta)^2]}$$

4.2 $\beta = \dfrac{6.6}{T}$ (based on the exponential term alone).

4.5 $t_m = \pi/\beta\sqrt{1-\zeta^2} \qquad r = 1 + e^{-\pi\zeta/\sqrt{1-\zeta^2}}$

5.1 $k = pA\gamma/L$ for adiabatic process ($p \sim$ absolute pressure).

5.5 For equal frequencies the length of the rod must be $\sqrt{3}$ times the distance between the springs. The system is a two-degree system, but because of the symmetry the translational and rotational modes are uncoupled and each mode can be analyzed as if it were a single-degree system.

5.9 $\beta = \omega$, where β = natural frequency for small angular displacements. The bar rotates in a flat plane tilted from the shaft axis if initially displaced from the perpendicular plane.

5.11 1.8 rad/sec.

5.16 153 lb/in.

5.19 $\theta = \theta_0 \cosh \beta t + \dfrac{\dot{\theta}_0}{\beta} \sinh \beta t$

$\beta = 3Tl/mL(l + L)$

T = spring tension at neutral point
L = length of bar
l = distance between hinge and point of spring attachment

6.4 3.4 sec.

6.7 $x_2 = f_1(1 - 1.05 \cos 0.690t + 0.05 \cos 3.25t)$.
$x_2 = f_2(1.2 - 1.16 \cos 0.690t - 0.04 \cos 3.25t)$.

6.9 Assume mass of bar concentrated on its centerline. Then there are five normal modes and frequencies. One of these is uncoupled, right and left in the figure. The other four are coupled in pairs, the pairs not coupled to each other. If k is a distributed spring constant (shear for one pair, tension-compression for the other), (lbs/in.)/in., then the frequencies for the coupled modes are

$$\beta = 0.259\sqrt{kl/m}$$

$$\beta = 0.968\sqrt{kl/m}$$

7.1 (a) Increase mass by one third of the spring mass.
(b) Increase first mass as in (a) and the second mass by $\frac{1}{3}$ of the second spring mass multiplied by the factor $\left(1 - \frac{x_1}{x_2}\right)^2$ where x_1/x_2 is the coordinate ratio in the normal mode.

7.7 $Q_1 = f_1 + f_2$
$Q_2 = -m_2 f_1/(m_1 + m_2) + m_1 f_2/(m_1 + m_2)$

7.10 (a) $\mathscr{F}_d = \frac{1}{2} c \dot{q}_2^2$
(b) $\mathscr{F}_d = \mu m g \dot{q}_2, \quad \dot{q}_2 > 0$
$\mathscr{F}_d = -\mu m g \dot{q}_2, \quad \dot{q}_2 < 0$

8.1 (a)

$$[K] = \begin{bmatrix} 2 & -1 & 0 \\ -1 & 2 & -1 \\ 0 & -1 & 2 \end{bmatrix} \qquad [\delta] = \frac{1}{4}\begin{bmatrix} 3 & 2 & 1 \\ 2 & 1 & 2 \\ 1 & 2 & 3 \end{bmatrix}$$

(b) No, since the deflection of the center mass is zero in one of the modes.

8.4

$$[K] = \frac{k}{12}\begin{bmatrix} 13 & 2 & 7 \\ 2 & 28 & -18 \\ 7 & -18 & 37 \end{bmatrix}$$

8.6 (c)

$$[\delta] = \frac{1}{9}\begin{bmatrix} 5 & 1 & -4 \\ -1 & 2 & -1 \\ -4 & -1 & 5 \end{bmatrix}$$

8.9 (a) If y_1 and y_2 are principal coordinates

$$\partial x_1/\partial y_1 = 0.618 \qquad \partial x_1/\partial y_2 = -1.613$$
$$\partial x_2/\partial y_1 = 1.000 \qquad \partial x_2/\partial y_2 = 1.000$$

(b) Amplitude of vibratory components of motion

$$y_1 = 1.900 \qquad y_2 = 0.106$$

(c) $x_1 = 0.04 \qquad x_2 = 0.46$

8.12 If x_1 = deflection of center of gravity of bar
x_2 = angular deflection of bar
x_3 = deflection of mass

and normalization is such that $x_3 = 1$

(a)

$$[K] = 100\begin{bmatrix} 3.82 & 1.64 & -2.40 \\ 1.64 & 16.90 & -4.00 \\ -2.40 & -4.00 & 2.40 \end{bmatrix}$$

(b)

$$\begin{Bmatrix} 0.616 \\ 0.181 \\ 1.000 \end{Bmatrix} \quad \begin{Bmatrix} -0.938 \\ 0.470 \\ 1.000 \end{Bmatrix} \quad \begin{Bmatrix} -1.096 \\ -6.98 \\ 1.000 \end{Bmatrix} \qquad 8.00,\ 30.0,\ 58.0 \text{ rad/sec}$$

(c)

$$\{y\} = \begin{Bmatrix} 0.0798 \\ 0.0034 \\ 0.0001 \end{Bmatrix}$$

(d) 0.00252

10.1 (a) $\dfrac{x_1}{F} = \dfrac{6s^4 + 27s^2 + 26}{6s^6 + 57s^4 + 131s^2 + 37}$

10.3 $\dfrac{Y}{F} = \dfrac{m^2 s^4 + 4k_2(k_1 + k_2)ms^2 + 12k_1k_2}{s^2(m^2s^2 + 4k_1k_2m)}$

11.1 $\frac{\partial^2 w}{\partial t^2} = \frac{T}{m}\left(\frac{\partial^2 w}{\partial x^2} + \frac{\partial^2 w}{\partial y^2}\right)$

$T \sim$ tension per unit length of membrane
$m \sim$ mass per unit area of membrane
$w \sim$ transverse deflection at x, y

11.3 (a) 0 (b) 0.5 (c) 0.5 (d) -0.5 (e) 0

11.11 (e) Fails.

11.14 Frequency equation

$$\theta \tan \theta = m_s/m$$

where $\theta = \lambda/\sqrt{k/m_s}$ and λ is the natural frequency. The approximation of 7.1(a) will give the correct frequency for $m_s/m \doteq 0.3$. If the mass is increased by

$$\frac{m_s}{2}\left(\frac{1}{\sin^2 \theta} - \frac{1}{\theta \tan \theta}\right)$$

the frequency will then be correct.

11.17 $u = u_0 e^{-a\sqrt{\omega/2}x} \sin(\omega t - a\sqrt{\omega/2}\, x)$

11.20 Frequency determined from

$$\lambda = z^2 a/L^2$$

where $a^2 = EI/A\delta$, $\delta \sim$ mass density and z determined from

$$\begin{vmatrix} -1 & 0 & 1 & 0 \\ 1 & -Hz^3 & 1 & Hz^3 \\ \sin z & -\cos z & \sinh z & \cosh z \\ (-Gz^3 \sin z + \cos z) & (Gz^3 \cos z + \sin z) & (Gz^3 \sinh z - \cosh z) & (Gz^3 \cosh z - \sinh z) \end{vmatrix} = 0$$

$$G = mp^2a^2/EIL^3 \qquad H = EI/kL^3$$

12.1

$$[\delta] = \frac{L^3}{1296EI}\begin{bmatrix} 2 & 8 & 14 & 17 \\ 8 & 54 & 108 & 135 \\ 14 & 108 & 250 & 325 \\ 17 & 135 & 325 & \left(432 + \frac{1296z^2EI}{L^2GJ}\right) \end{bmatrix}$$

$$[M] = m_b \begin{bmatrix} \frac{1}{3} & 0 & 0 & 0 \\ 0 & \frac{1}{3} & 0 & 0 \\ 0 & 0 & \frac{1}{3} & 0 \\ 0 & 0 & 0 & \frac{m}{m_b} \end{bmatrix}$$

12.4 Replace the 6th and 10th columns of $[\lambda]$ with, respectively,

$$\begin{matrix} 0 & 0 \\ 0 & 18L^2/1296EI \\ 0 & 162L^2/1296EI \\ 0 & 450L^2/1296EI \\ 0 & 648L^2/1296EI \\ -1 & -1 \\ 0 & 216L/1296EI \\ 0 & 648L/1296EI \\ 0 & 1080L/1296EI \\ 0 & 1296L/1296EI \end{matrix}$$

12.7 Columns 1 and 5 of $[K]$ have already been modified as required. Change columns 6 and 10 to, respectively,

$$\begin{matrix} 0 & 0 \\ 0 & 0 \\ 0 & 0 \\ 0 & 0 \\ 0 & 0 \\ -1 & 0 \\ 0 & 0 \\ 0 & 0 \\ 0 & 0 \\ 0 & -1 \end{matrix}$$

13.4 $\delta_{66} = L^3/3EI$, the exact value. This happens because the assumed polynomial from which Equations 13-6 were derived is of the same form as the exact solution.

13.11 $U = V - W = \int_0^b \int_0^a [\frac{1}{2}T(w_x^2 + w_y^2) - pw]\, dx\, dy$

where $\dfrac{\partial^2 w}{\partial x^2} + \dfrac{\partial^2 w}{\partial y^2} = -\dfrac{p}{T}$

$p \sim$ pressure
$T \sim$ tension per unit length of membrane

13.13 If the conditions for convergence of the Gauss-Seidel iteration scheme are satisfied, successive columns of the inverse matrix can be obtained by solving the set of simultaneous equations with unity appearing on the right side in order of rows. For instance, if $[B] = [A]^{-1}$ and $[A]$ is known, solution of the set of equations represented

by $[A]\begin{Bmatrix} x_1 \\ x_2 \\ \vdots \end{Bmatrix} = \begin{Bmatrix} 1 \\ 0 \\ \vdots \end{Bmatrix}$ for the x's will result in the first column of $[B]$.

14.2 (a) $\omega_n = \dfrac{\beta_1 \sqrt{m_b/m}}{\sqrt{2.55 + m_b/m}}$

This reduces to the correct value for either $m_b/m \to 0$ or ∞.

(b) $\omega_n^2 = \dfrac{B \pm \sqrt{B^2 - 4AC}}{2A}$

$$A = 4.74 + m_b/m$$
$$B = \beta_1^2(3.19 + m_b/m) + \beta_3^2(2.55 + m_b/m)$$
$$C = \beta_1^2\beta_3^2(1 + m_b/m)$$

14.5 $0.807\beta_1$

15.1 $g(t) = \dfrac{1}{c}e^{-kt/c}$ leads to

$$x = \frac{1}{k}(1 - e^{-kt/c}), \quad t < 1$$
$$= \frac{1}{k}(e^{-k(t-1)/c} - e^{-kt/c}), \quad t > 1$$

15.5 If the two lowest modes of the combination structure are used, the moment at the attachment is

$$M = (-0.261 \sin \beta_1 t + 0.153 \sin \beta_2 t + 0.0275\beta_2 t \cos \beta_2 t) fL, \quad \beta_2 t < 2\pi$$
$$M = [-0.246 \sin \beta_1 t + 0.246 \sin (\beta_1 t - 4.33) + 0.1725\beta_2 \cos \beta_2 t] fL, \quad \beta_2 t > 2\pi$$

where

$$\beta_1 = 15.95\sqrt{EI/mL^3}$$

$$\beta_2 = 23.11\sqrt{EI/mL^3}$$

15.8 Approximate the first mode with $w = w_0 \sin \pi x/a \sin \pi y/a$ and neglect higher modes. With these assumptions, maximum stress = 2600 psi at $t = 0.0846$ sec, and the window should not break if there are no stress raisers. However, the higher modes could affect this conclusion.

17.4 (a) $M = -\dfrac{2w}{\pi}\displaystyle\int_0^\infty \frac{\omega \sin a\omega \cos x\omega}{\omega^4 + k/EI}\, d\omega$

$$M = \frac{-f}{2\sqrt{2}(k/EI)^{1/4}}$$

Index